INSTRUCTOR
RESOURCE MANUAL

Linda S. Brunauer
Santa Clara University

•

Elzbieta Cook
Louisiana State University

TWELFTH EDITION

CHEMISTRY
THE CENTRAL SCIENCE

BROWN LeMAY BURSTEN MURPHY WOODWARD

Prentice Hall

Boston Columbus Indianapolis New York San Francisco Upper Saddle River
Amsterdam Cape Town Dubai London Madrid Milan Munich Paris Montréal Toronto
Delhi Mexico City São Paulo Sydney Hong Kong Seoul Singapore Taipei Tokyo

Editor in Chief, Chemistry: Adam Jaworski
Acquisitions Editor: Terry Haugen
Marketing Manager: Erin Gardner
Senior Project Editor: Jennifer Hart
Editorial Assistant: Catherine Martinez
Marketing Assistant: Nicola Houston
Managing Editor, Chemistry and Geosciences: Gina M. Cheselka
Project Manager, Science: Ed Thomas
Operations Specialist: Maura Zaldivar
Supplement Cover Designer: Paul Gourhan
Cover Credit: Graphene by Dr. Jannik C. Meyer of the University of Ulm, Germany

Prentice Hall
is an imprint of

www.pearsonhighered.com

Chapter 1	Introduction: Matter and Measurement	1
Chapter 2	Atoms, Molecules, and Ions	14
Chapter 3	Stoichiometry: Calculations with Chemical Formulas and Equations	30
Chapter 4	Reactions in Aqueous Solution	44
Chapter 5	Thermochemistry	59
Chapter 6	Electronic Structures of Atoms	72
Chapter 7	Periodic Properties of the Elements	87
Chapter 8	Basic Concepts of Chemical Bonding	102
Chapter 9	Molecular Geometry and Bonding Theories	117
Chapter 10	Gases	133
Chapter 11	Liquids and Intermolecular Forces	146
Chapter 12	Solids and Modern Materials	161
Chapter 13	Properties of Solutions	178
Chapter 14	Chemical Kinetics	196
Chapter 15	Chemical Equilibrium	216
Chapter 16	Acid-Base Equilibria	229
Chapter 17	Additional Aspects of Aqueous Equilibria	245
Chapter 18	Chemistry of the Environment	261
Chapter 19	Chemical Thermodynamics	274
Chapter 20	Electrochemistry	287
Chapter 21	Nuclear Chemistry	301
Chapter 22	Chemistry of the Nonmetals	314
Chapter 23	Transition Metals and Coordination Compounds	333
Chapter 24	The Chemistry of Life: Organic and Biological Chemistry	348

Chapter 1. Introduction: Matter and Measurement

Media Resources

Figures and Tables in Transparency Pack:	**Section:**
Figure 1.5 Molecular Comparison of Elements, Compounds, and Mixtures	1.2 Classifications of Matter
Figure 1.7 Electrolysis of Water	1.2 Classifications of Matter
Figure 1.9 Classification of Matter	1.2 Classifications of Matter
Figure 1.10 A Chemical Reaction	1.3 Properties of Matter
Figure 1.16 The Scientific Method	1.3 Properties of Matter
Table 1.5 Prefixes Used in the Metric System and with SI Units	1.4 Units of Measurement
Figure 1.18 Volume Relationships	1.4 Units of Measurement

Animations:	**Section:**
Electrolysis of Water	1.2 Classifications of Matter
Changes of State	1.3 Properties of Matter

Movies:	**Section:**
Sodium and Potassium in Water	1.3 Properties of Matter
Mixtures and Compounds	1.3 Properties of Matter
Paper Chromatography of Ink	1.3 Properties of Matter

Activities:	**Section:**
Phases of Water	1.2 Classifications of Matter
Phases of the Elements	1.2 Classifications of Matter
Classification of Matter	1.2 Classifications of Matter
Temperature	1.4 Units of Measurement
Uncertainty in Measurement	1.5 Uncertainty in Measurement
Significant Figures	1.5 Uncertainty in Measurement

3-D Models:	**Section:**
Oxygen	1.1 The Study of Chemistry
Water	1.1 The Study of Chemistry
Hydrogen	1.1 The Study of Chemistry
Ethanol	1.1 The Study of Chemistry
Ethylene Glycol	1.1 The Study of Chemistry
Aspirin	1.1 The Study of Chemistry

Other Resources

Further Readings: **Section:**

Chemistry in the Real World   1.1 The Study of Chemistry
Chemicals in Everyday Life   1.1 The Study of Chemistry
What's the Use?   1.2 Classifications of Matter
It's Elementary   1.2 Classifications of Matter
Element Zoo   1.2 Classifications of Matter
Important Elements   1.2 Classifications of Matter
Origin of the Names of Chemical Elements   1.2 Classifications of Matter
Connecting Element names with the Names of   1.2 Classifications of Matter
    U.S. Towns
The Inquiry Wheel, an Alternative to the Scientific   1.3 Properties of Matter
    Method: A View of the Science Education
    Research Literature
Why Does Popcorn Pop?   1.3 Properties of Matter
Using History to Teach The Scientific Method: The   1.3 Properties of Matter
    Role of Errors
Having Fun with the Metric System   1.4 Units of Measurement
Method for Separating or Identifying Plastics   1.4 Units of Measurement
Error, Precision, and Uncertainty   1.5 Uncertainty in Measurement
Precision and Accuracy in Measurements: A Tale   1.5 Uncertainty in Measurement
    of Four Graduated Cylinders
A Simple but Effective Demonstration for   1.5 Uncertainty in Measurement
    Illustrating Significant Figure Rules When
    Making Measurements and Doing Calculations
A Joke Based on Significant Figures   1.5 Uncertainty in Measurement
Significant Figures   1.5 Uncertainty in Measurement
Significant Figures: A Classroom Demonstration   1.5 Uncertainty in Measurement
Expanded Dimensional Analysis: A Blending of   1.6 Dimensional Analysis
    English and Math
Appalachian Trail Problems   1.6 Dimensional Analysis

Live Demonstrations: **Section:**

The First Demonstration: Proof that Air Is a   1.1 The Study of Chemistry
    Substance
Science Demonstrations, Experiments, and   1.1 The Study of Chemistry
    Resources. A Reference List for Elementary
    through College Teachers Emphasizing
    Chemistry with Some Physics and Life
    Science
Ira Remsen's Investigation of Nitric Acid   1.3 Properties of Matter
An Experiment to Demonstrate the Application   1.3. Properties of Matter
    of the Scientific Method
A Simple Demonstration for Introducing the Metric   1.4 Units of Measurement
    System to Introductory Chemistry Classes
Sugar in a Can of Soft Drink: A Density Exercise   1.4 Units of Measurement
The Mysterious Sunken Ice Cube   1.4 Units of Measurement
Densities and Miscibilities of Liquids and Liquid   1.4 Units of Measurement
    Mixtures

Chapter 1. Introduction: Matter and Measurement

Common Student Misconceptions
- Students often confuse mass and weight.
- Students have difficulty with algebraic manipulation. Conversion of temperatures between Celsius and Fahrenheit scales is particularly problematic.
- Students tend to equate density with mass.
- Students often either are unfamiliar with the prefixes used in the metric system or cannot use them properly (e.g. $1 \text{ pm} = 1 \times 10^{-12} \text{ m} \rightarrow 1 \text{ m} = 1 \times 10^{12} \text{ pm}$).
- Students often use precision and accuracy interchangeably.
- Students often do not appreciate that in chemistry, measurement yields numbers determined with certain precision and in certain units; both depend on the type of the measuring device.
- Students often cannot find exact numbers in calculations.
- Students confuse significant figures and decimal places in arithmetic manipulations.
- Students often either round off too soon in calculations or they report the result to as many figures as their calculators produce.
- Some students do not understand the use of a conversion factor of exactly one.
- In dimensional analysis problems students do not see that a physical quantity is a multiplication of value and units. Therefore, they do not perform algebraic operations on both the number and units.

Teaching Tips
- Many students have problems using dimensional analysis ("from physics") in chemistry. This text bases the whole of stoichiometry on dimensional analysis: students should be encouraged to embrace the concept as soon as possible.
- Emphasize the importance of quickly mastering the use of common metric prefixes and scientific notation.
- Conversion involving commonly encountered metric prefixes need frequent reinforcement; for example, $10^6 \text{ μg} = 10^3 \text{ mg} = 1 \text{ g} = 10^{-3} \text{ kg}$

Lecture Outline

1.1 The Study of Chemistry
- Chemistry:
  - is the study of properties of materials and changes that they undergo.
  - can be applied to all aspects of life (e.g., development of pharmaceuticals, leaf color change in fall, etc.).

The Atomic and Molecular Perspective of Chemistry[1,2,3,4,5,6,7]
Chemistry involves the study of the properties and the behavior of matter.

---

[1] "The First Demonstration: Proof that Air Is a Substance" from Live Demonstrations
[2] "Oxygen" 3-D Model from Instructor's Resource CD/DVD
[3] "Water" 3-D Model from Instructor's Resource CD/DVD
[4] "Hydrogen" 3-D Model from Instructor's Resource CD/DVD
[5] "Ethanol" 3-D Model from Instructor's Resource CD/DVD
[6] "Ethylene Glycol" 3-D Model from Instructor's Resource CD/DVD
[7] "Aspirin" 3-D Model from Instructor's Resource CD/DVD

- **Matter:**
  - is the physical material of the universe.
  - has mass.
  - occupies space.
  - A **property** is any characteristic that allows us to recognize a particular type of matter and to distinguish it from other types of matter.
  - About 100 **elements** constitute all matter.
- **Elements:**
  - are made up of unique **atoms**, the building blocks of matter.
  - Names of the elements are derived from a wide variety of sources (e.g., Latin or Greek, mythological characters, names of people or places).
- **Molecules:**
  - are combinations of atoms held together in specific shapes.
  - *Macroscopic* (observable) properties of matter relate to *submicroscopic* realms of atoms.
  - Properties relate to composition (types of atoms present) and structure (arrangement of atoms) present.

Why Study Chemistry?[8,9,10]

We study chemistry because:
- it has a considerable impact on society (health care, food, clothing, conservation of natural resources, environmental issues, etc.).
- it is part of your curriculum! Chemistry serves biology, engineering, agriculture, geology, physics, etc.. **Chemistry is the *central science*.**

1.2 Classifications of Matter

- Matter is classified by *state* (solid, liquid, or gas) or by *composition* (element, compound or mixture).

States of Matter[11]

- Solids, liquids and gases are the three forms of matter called the **states of matter**.
- Properties described on the macroscopic level:
  - **gas** (vapor): no fixed volume or shape, conforms to shape of container, compressible.
  - **liquid:** volume independent of container, no fixed shape, incompressible.
  - **solid:** volume and shape independent of container, rigid, incompressible.
- Properties described on the molecular level:
  - **gas:** molecules far apart, move at high speeds, collide often.
  - **liquid:** molecules closer than gas, move rapidly but can slide over each other.
  - **solid:** molecules packed closely in definite arrangements.

Pure Substances[12]

- **Pure substances:**
  - are matter with distinct properties and fixed composition..
  - are **elements** (cannot be decomposed into simpler substances; i.e. only one kind of atom) or **compounds** (consist of two or more elements).

---

[8] "Chemistry in the Real World" from Further Readings
[9] "Science Demonstrations, Experiments, and Resources. A Reference List for Elementary through College Teachers Emphasizing Chemistry with Some Physics and Life Science" from Live Demonstrations
[10] "Chemicals in Everyday Life" from Further Readings
[11] "Phases of Water" Activity from Instructor's Resource CD/DVD
[12] Figure 1.5 from Transparency Pack

- **Mixtures**:
  - are a combination of two or more pure substances.
  - Each substance retains its own identity.

Elements[13,14,15,16,17,18,19,20,21]

- There are 117 known elements.
- They vary in abundance.
  - Oxygen, silicon, aluminum, iron, and calcium make up over 90% of the Earth's crust (including oceans and atmosphere).
  - Oxygen, carbon, and hydrogen make up over 90% of mass of the human body.
- Each is given a unique name and is abbreviated by a chemical *symbol*.
- They are organized in the *periodic table*.
- Each is given a one- or two-letter symbol derived from its name.

Compounds[22,23]

- **Compounds** are combinations of elements.
  Example: The compound H_2O is a combination of elements H and O.
- The opposite of compound formation is decomposition.
- Compounds have different properties than their component elements (e.g., water is liquid, hydrogen and oxygen are both gases at the same temperature and pressure).
- **Law of Constant Composition or the Law of Constant (Definite) Proportions** (Proust): A compound always consists of the same combination of elements (e.g., water is always 11% H and 89% O).

Mixtures[24,25,26]

- A **mixture** is a combination of two or more pure substances.
  - Each substance retains its own identity, each substance is a *component* of the mixture.
  - Mixtures have variable composition.
  - *Heterogeneous* mixtures do not have uniform composition, properties and appearance, e.g., sand.
  - *Homogeneous* mixtures are uniform throughout, e.g., clean air or vinegar; they are **solutions**.

FORWARD REFERENCES

- States of matter will be essential in properly writing chemical reaction equations, including net ionic equations, in Chapter 4, as well as equilibrium constant expressions in Chapters 15, 19, and 20.
- Solutions will be further discussed in Chapters 4 and 13.
- Mixtures of gases will be discussed in Chapter 10.

---

[13] "What's the Use?" from Further Readings
[14] "Phases of the Elements" Activity from Instructor's Resource CD/DVD
[15] "It's Elementary" from Further Readings
[16] "Element ZOO" from Further Readings
[17] "Important Elements" from Further Readings
[18] "Origin of the Names of Chemical Elements" from Further Readings
[19] "Connecting Element names with the Names of U.S. Towns" from Further Readings
[20] "Elementary My Dear Watson" from Further Readings
[21] "Elementary Riddles" from Further Readings
[22] "Electrolysis of Water" Animation from Instructor's Resource CD/DVD
[23] Figure 1.7 from Transparency Pack
[24] Figure 1.9 from Transparency Pack
[25] "Classification of Matter" Activity from Instructor's Resource CD/DVD
[26] "Classifying Matter: A Physical Model Using Paper Clips" from Further Readings

1.3 Properties of Matter

- Each substance has a unique set of physical and chemical properties.
  - **Physical properties** are measured without changing the substance (e.g., color, density, odor, melting point, etc.).
  - **Chemical properties** describe how substances react or change to form different substances (e.g., hydrogen burns in oxygen).
  - Properties may be categorized as intensive or extensive.
    - **Intensive properties** do not depend on the amount of substance present (e.g., temperature, melting point etc.).
    - **Extensive properties** depend on the quantity of substance present (e.g., mass, volume etc.).
    - Intensive properties give an idea of the composition of a substance whereas extensive properties give an indication of the quantity of substance present.

Physical and Chemical Changes[27,28,29,30]

- **Physical change**: substance changes physical appearance without altering its identity (e.g., **changes of state**).
- **Chemical change** (or **chemical reaction**): substance transforms into a chemically different substances (i.e. identity changes, e.g., reaction of hydrogen and oxygen gases to produce water).

Separation of Mixtures[31,32,33,34]

- Key: separation techniques exploit differences in properties of the *components*.
  - Filtration: remove solid from liquid.
  - Distillation: boil off one or more components of the mixture.
  - Chromatography: exploits differing abilities of substances to adhere to the surfaces of solids..

The Scientific Method[35,36,37,38,39]

- **The scientific method** provides guidelines for the practice of science.
  - Collect data (observe, experiment, etc.).
  - Look for patterns, try to explain them and develop a **hypothesis** *or tentative explanation*.
  - Test hypothesis, then refine it.
  - Bring all information together into a **scientific law** (*concise statement or equation that summarizes tested hypotheses*).
  - Bring hypotheses and laws together into a theory. A **theory** should explain general principles.

1.4 Units of Measurement

- Many properties of matter are quantitative, i.e., associated with numbers.

---

[27] "Changes of State" Animation from Instructor's Resource CD/DVD

[28] Figure 1.10 from Transparency Pack

[29] "Ira Remsen's Investigation of Nitric Acid" from Live Demonstrations

[30] "Sodium and Potassium in Water" Movie from Instructor's Resource CD/DVD

[31] "Mixtures and Compounds" Movie from Instructor's Resource CD/DVD

[32] Figure 1.16 from Transparency Pack

[33] "Paper Chromatography of Ink" Movie from Instructor's Resource CD/DVD

[34] "T-Shirt Chromatography: A Chromatogram You Can Wear" from Further Readings

[35] "The Inquiry Wheel, an Alternative to the Scientific Method: A View of the Science Education Research Literature" from Further Readings

[36] "An Experiment to Demonstrate the Application of the Scientific Method" from Live Demonstrations

[37] "Why Does Popcorn Pop? An Introduction to the Scientific Method" from Further Readings

[38] "Mentos and the Scientific Method: A Sweet Combination" from Further Readings

[39] "Using History to Teach the Scientific Method: The Role of Errors" from Further Readings

- A measured quantity must have BOTH a number and a unit.
- The units most often used for scientific measurement are those of the **metric system**.

SI Units[40,41,42]

- 1960: All scientific units use Système International d'Unités (SI Units).
- There are seven base units.
- Prefixes are used to indicate smaller and larger units obtained by decimal fractions or multiples of the base units.

Length and Mass

- SI base unit of length = meter (1 m = 1.0936 yards).
- SI base unit of mass (not weight) = kilogram (1 kg = 2.2 pounds).
  - **Mass** is a measure of the amount of material in an object.

Temperature[43]

- *Temperature* is the measure of the hotness or coldness of an object.
  - Physical property that determines the direction of heat flow.
  - Heat flows spontaneously from a substance of higher temperature to one at lower temperature.
- Scientific studies use Celsius and Kelvin scales.
- **Celsius scale**: water freezes at 0 °C and boils at 100 °C (sea level).
- **Kelvin scale** (SI Unit):
  - Water freezes at 273.15 K and boils at 373.15 K (sea level).
  - is based on properties of gases.
  - Zero is lowest possible temperature (*absolute zero*).
  - 0 K = –273.15 °C.
- Fahrenheit (not used in science):
  - Water freezes at 32 °F and boils at 212 °F (sea level).
  - Conversions:

$$°F = (9/5)°C + 32 \qquad °C = (5/9)(°F - 32)$$

$$°C = K - 273.15 \qquad K = °C + 273.15$$

Derived SI Units

- These are formed from the seven base units.
- Example: velocity is distance traveled per unit time, so units of velocity are units of distance (m) divided by units of time (s): m/s.

Volume[44]

- Units of *volume* = (units of length)^3 = m^3.
- This unit is unrealistically large, so we use more reasonable units:
  - cm^3 (also known as mL (*milliliter*) or cc (*cubic centimeters*))
  - dm^3 (also known as *liters*, L).

- **Important: the liter is not an SI unit.**

---

[40] "A Simple Demonstration for Introducing the Metric System to Introductory Chemistry Classes" from Live Demonstrations
[41] "Having Fun with the Metric System" from Further Readings
[42] Table 1.5 from Transparency Pack
[43] "Temperature" Activity from Instructor's Resource CD/DVD
[44] Figure 1.18 from Transparency Pack

Density[45,46,47,48,49,50,51]

- **Density** is defined as mass divided by volume.
- Units: g/cm^3 or g/mL (for solids and liquids); g/L (often used for gases).
- Was originally based on mass (the density was defined as the mass of 1.00 mL of pure water at 25˚C).

FORWARD REFERENCES

- Prefixes (Table 1.5) will be heavily used in future chapters: kJ (Chapters: 5-8, 14, 19-21); nm, pm and MHz (Chapter 6).
- Density will be a quantity commonly used in Chapter 10 (for gases), Chapter 11 (to compare liquid and solid water), Chapter 13 (for solutions).
- Conversions of temperature units will be commonplace in Chapters 5, 14-20.

1.5 Uncertainty in Measurement[52,53,54,55]

- There are two types of numbers:
  - *exact numbers* (known as counting or defined).
  - *inexact numbers* (derived from measurement).

Precision and Accuracy

- **Precision**: how well measured quantities agree with each other.
- **Accuracy**: how well measured quantities agree with the "true value".
- Figure 1.23 is very helpful in making this distinction.

Significant Figures[56,57,58,59,60,61,62]

- All measurements have some degree of *uncertainty* or *error* associated with them.
- In a measurement it is useful to indicate the exactness of the measurement. This exactness is reflected in the number of **significant figures**.
- Guidelines for determining the number of significant figures in a measured quantity are:
  - The number of significant figures is the number of digits known with certainty plus one uncertain digit. (Example: 2.2405 g means we are sure the mass is 2.240 g but we are uncertain about the nearest 0.0001 g.)

---

[45] "Sugar in a Can of Soft Drink: A Density Exercise" from Live Demonstrations
[46] "The Mysterious Sunken Ice Cube" from Live Demonstrations
[47] "Method for Separating or Identifying Plastics" from Further Readings
[48] "Densities and Miscibilities of Liquids and Liquid Mixtures" from Live Demonstrations
[49] "The Concept of Density" from Further Readings
[50] "Bowling for Density!" from Live Demonstrations
[51] "Whatever Floats (or Sinks)" from Live Demonstrations
[52] "Uncertainty in Measurement" Activity from Instructor's Resource CD/DVD
[53] "Meter Sticks in the Demonstration of Error Measurement" from Further Readings
[54] "Basic Principles of Scale Reading" from Further Readings
[55] "Measuring with a Purpose. Involving Students in the Learning Process" from Further Readings
[56] "Error, Precision, and Uncertainty" from Further Readings
[57] "Precision and Accuracy in Measurements: A Tale of Four Graduated Cylinders" from Further Readings
[58] "A Simple but Effective Demonstration for Illustrating Significant Figure Rules When Making Measurements and Doing Calculations" from Further Readings
[59] "Significant Figures" Activity from Instructor's Resource CD/DVD
[60] "A Joke Based on Significant Figures" from Further Readings
[61] "Significant Figures" from Further Readings
[62] "Significant Figures: A Classroom Demonstration" from Further Readings

- Final calculations are only as significant as the least significant measurement.
- Rules:
    1. Nonzero numbers and zeros between nonzero numbers (ie. imbedded zeros) are always significant.
    2. Zeros before the first nonzero digit (ie. leading zeros) are not significant. (Example: 0.0026 has two significant figures.)
    3. Zeros at the end of the number after a decimal point are significant.
    4. Zeros at the end of a number before a decimal point are ambiguous (e.g., 10,300 g). Exponential notation, such as scientific notation, eliminates this ambiguity.
- Method:
    1. Write the number in scientific notation.
    2. The number of digits remaining is the number of significant figures.
    3. Examples:
        2.50×10^2 cm has 3 significant figures as written.
        1.03×10^4 g has 3 significant figures.
        1.030×10^4 g has 4 significant figures.
        1.0300×10^4 g has 5 significant figures.

Significant Figures in Calculations

- In calculations, the least certain measurement limits the certainty of the calculated result
    - The answer is reported with only 1 uncertain digit.
- Guidelines for keeping track of significant figures:
    - Addition and Subtraction:
    - Report to the least number of decimal places
      (e.g., 20.4 g – 1.322 g = 19.1 g).
    - Multiplication and Division:
    - Report to the least number of significant figures
      (e.g., 6.221 cm $\times$ 5.2 cm = 32 cm^2).
- In multiple step calculations always retain an extra significant figure until the end to prevent rounding errors.

FORWARD REFERENCES

- Working in scientific notation will be required in Chapters: 6 (wavelength, frequency, energy of levels), 14 (rate constant), 15 (equilibrium constant calculations), 16 and 17 (acid or base ionization constants, concentrations), 19 ($\Delta G°$ vs K calculations), 20 ($\Delta G°$ vs K vs $E°$ calculations).
- Rules for significant figures will appear whenever calculations are to be performed; rules for significant figures in calculations with logarithms will be needed in Chapters 14, 16, 17, 19, and 20.

1.6 Dimensional Analysis[63,64]

- **Dimensional analysis** is a method of calculation utilizing a knowledge of units.
- Given units can be multiplied and divided to give the desired units.
- Conversion factors are used to manipulate units:
    - desired unit = given unit $\times$ (conversion factor)
- The **conversion factors** are simple ratios:
    - conversion factor = (desired unit) / (given unit)
        - These are fractions whose numerator and denominator are the same quantity expressed in different units.
        - Multiplication by a conversion factor is equivalent to multiplying by a factor of 1.

---

[63] "Expanded Dimensional Analysis: A Blending of English and Math" from Further Readings
[64] "Appalachian Trail Problems" from Further Readings

Using Two or More Conversion Factors

- We often need to use more than one conversion factor in order to complete a problem.
- When identical units are found in the numerator and denominator of a conversion, they will cancel. The final answer MUST have the correct units.
- For example:
  - Suppose that we want to convert length in meters to length in inches. We could do this conversion with the following conversion factors:
    - 1 meter = 100 centimeters and 1 inch = 2.54 centimeters
- The calculation would involve both conversion factors; the units of the final answer will be inches:
  - (# meters) (100 centimeters / 1 meter) (1 inch / 2.54 centimeters) = # inches

Conversions Involving Volume

- We often will encounter conversions from one measure to a different measure.
- For example:
  - Suppose that we wish to know the mass in grams of 2.00 cubic inches of gold given that the density of the gold is 19.3 g/cm^3.
  - We could do this conversion with the following conversion factors:
$$2.54 \text{ cm} = 1 \text{ inch and } 1 \text{ cm}^3 = 19.3 \text{ g gold}$$
  - The calculation would involve both of these factors:
$$(2.00 \text{ in.}^3) (2.54 \text{ cm / in.})^3 (19.3 \text{ g gold } / 1 \text{ cm}^3) = 633 \text{ g gold}$$
  - Note that the calculation will NOT be correct unless the centimeter to inch conversion factor is cubed!! Both the units AND the number must be cubed.

Summary of Dimensional Analysis

- In dimensional analysis always ask three questions:
  1. What data are we given?
  2. What quantity do we need?
  3. What conversion factors are available to take us from what we are given to what we need?

FORWARD REFERENCES

- Solving problems using dimensional analysis can be found virtually in each chapter.

Further Readings:

1. Martin B. Jones and Christina R. Miller, "Chemistry in the Real World," *J. Chem. Educ.*, Vol. 78, **2001**, 484–487.

2. Raymond B. Seymour, "Chemicals in Everyday Life," *J. Chem. Educ.*, Vol. 64, **1987**, 63–68.

3. Each of the "What's the Use?" articles, written by Alton Banks, focuses on the uses of a specific element. See *J. Chem. Educ.*, Vols. 66 (**1989**), 67 (**1990**), 68 (**1991**) and 69 (**1992**).

4. Milton J. Wieder, "It's Elementary," *J. Chem. Educ.*, Vol. 78, **2001**, 468–469.

5. Terry L. Helser, "Element ZOO", *J. Chem. Educ.*, Vol. 80, **2003**, 409–410.

6. P. G. Nelson, "Important Elements," *J. Chem. Educ.*, Vol. 68, **1991**, 732–737.

7. Vivi Ringes, "Origin of the Names of Chemical Elements," *J. Chem. Educ.*, Vol. 66, **1989**, 731–738.

8. Nicholas C. Thomas, "Connecting Element names with the Names of U.S. Towns," *J. Chem. Educ.*, Vol. 86, **2009**, 181-184. A sampling of towns in the US with names based on chemical elements.

9. Terry L. Helser, "Elementary My Dear Watson," *J. Chem. Educ.*, Vol. 66, **1989**, 980. Puzzles involving element names and symbols.

10. Doris Eckey, "Elementary Riddles", *J. Chem. Educ.*, Vol. 71, **1994**, 1051. A series of riddles involving the names of the elements.

11. Bob Blake, Lynn Hogue, and Jerry L. Sarquis, "Classifying Matter: A Physical Model Using Paper Clips," *J. Chem. Educ.*, Vol. 83, **2006**, 1317–1318.

12. Jeanne M. Buccigros, "T-Shirt Chromatography: A Chromatogram You Can Wear," *J. Chem. Educ.*, Vol. 69, **1992**, 977–978.

13. Frederick C. Sauls, "Why Does Popcorn Pop? An Introduction to the Scientific Method," *J. Chem. Educ.*, Vol. 86, **1991**, 415–416.

14. Carmen J. Guinta, "Using History to Teach Scientific Method: The Case of Argon," *J. Chem. Educ.*, Vol. 75, **1998**, 1322–1325. The scientific method is introduced using a case-study approach involving the discovery of argon.

15. Jack F. Eichler, Heather Patrick, Brenda Harmon and Janet Coonce, "Mentos and the Scientific Method: A Sweet Combination," *J. Chem. Educ.*, Vol. 84, **2007**, 1120–1123.

16. William R. Robinson, "The Inquiry Wheel, an Alternative to the Scientific Method: A View of the Science Education Research Literature," *J. Chem. Educ.*, Vol. 81, **2004**, 791–792.

17. Mark L. Campbell, "Having Fun with the Metric System," *J. Chem. Educ.*, Vol. 68, **1991**, 1043. A word game.

18. Kenneth E. Kolb and Doris K. Kolb, "Method for Separating or Identifying Plastics," *J. Chem. Educ.*, Vol. 68, **1991**, 348. A demonstration of the concept of density.

19. Stephen J. Hawkes, "The Concept of Density," *J. Chem. Educ.*, Vol. 81, **2004**, 14–15.

20. Robert Suder, "Meter Sticks in the Demonstration of Error Measurements," *J. Chem. Educ.*, Vol. 66, **1989**, 437.

21. Gavin D. Peckhan, "Basic Principles of Scale Reading," *J. Chem. Educ.*, Vol. 71, **1994**, 423–424.

22. Patricia A. Metz and Jeffrey R. Pribyl, "Measuring with a Purpose. Involving Students in the Learning Process," *J. Chem. Educ.*, Vol. 72, **1995**, 130–132.

23. Richard S. Treptow, "Precision and Accuracy in Measurements: a Tale of Four Graduated Cylinders," *J. Chem. Educ.*, Vol. 75, **1998**, 992–995.

24. Charles J. Guare, "Error, Precision, and Uncertainty," *J. Chem. Educ.*, Vol. 68, **1991**, 649–652.

25. Kenton B. Abel and William M. Hemmerlin, "Significant Figures," *J. Chem. Educ.*, Vol. 67, **1990**, 213.

26. H. Graden Kirksey and Paul Krause, "Significant Figures: A Classroom Demonstration," *J. Chem. Educ.*, Vol. 69, **1992**, 497–498.

27. Ben Ruekberg, "A Joke Based on Significant Figures," *J. Chem. Educ.*, Vol. 71, **1994**, 306.

28. Arden P. Zipp, "A Simple but Effective Demonstration for Illustrating Significant Figure Rules When Making Measurements and Doing Calculations," *J. Chem. Educ.*, Vol. 69, **1992**, 291.

29. Ronald DeLorenzo, "Expanded Dimensional Analysis: A Blending of English and Math," *J. Chem. Educ.*, Vol. 71, **1994**, 789–791.

30. Brian N. Akers, "Appalachian Trail Problems," *J. Chem. Educ.*, Vol. 75, **1998**, 1571–1572. This short article provides some unit analysis problems.

31. W. Kirk Stephenson, "The Box-and-Dot Method: A Simple Strategy for Counting Significant Figures," *J. Chem. Educ.*, Vol. 86, **2009**, 933-935.

Live Demonstrations:

1. David A. Katz, "Science Demonstrations, Experiments, and Resources. A Reference List for Elementary through College Teachers Emphasizing Chemistry with Some Physics and Life Science," *J. Chem. Educ.*, Vol. 68, **1991**, 235–244. An extensive listing of various demonstrations, experiments and resources for the science educator.

2. Lee R. Summerlin, Christie L. Borgford, and Julie B. Ealy, "Ira Remsen's Investigation of Nitric Acid," *Chemical Demonstrations. A Sourcebook for Teachers*, Volume 2 (Washington: American Chemical Society, **1988**), pp. 4–5.

3. Irving R Tannenbaum, "An Experiment to Demonstrate the Application of the Scientific Method," *J. Chem. Educ.*, Vol. 66, **1989**, 597. A simple experiment to heat water to boiling.

4. David A. Franz and David Speckhard, "Densities and Miscibilities of Liquids and Liquid Mixtures," *J. Chem. Educ.*, Vol. 68, **1991**, 594. Demonstrations involving densities and miscibility of liquids.

5. Lee. R. Summerlin, Christie L. Borgford, and Julie B. Ealy, "The First Demonstration: Proof That Air Is a Substance," *Chemical Demonstrations, A Sourcebook for Teachers*, Volume 2 (Washington: American Chemical Society, **1988**), p. 3.

6. Clarke W. Earley, "A Simple Demonstration for Introducing the Metric System to Introductory Chemistry Classes," *J. Chem. Educ.*, Vol. 76, **1999**, 1215–1216.

7. Lee. R. Summerlin, Christie L. Borgford, and Julie B. Ealy, "Sugar in a Can of Soft Drink: A Density Exercise," *Chemical Demonstrations, A Sourcebook for Teachers*, Volume 2 (Washington: American Chemical Society, 1988), p. 126–127.

8. Lee. R. Summerlin, Christie L. Borgford, and Julie B. Ealy, "The Mysterious Sunken Ice Cube," *Chemical Demonstrations, A Sourcebook for Teachers*, Volume 2 (Washington: American Chemical Society, 1988), p. 15–16.

9. Kathleen Holley, Diana Mason, and Kirk Hunte, "Bowling for Density!", *J. Chem. Educ.*, Vol. 81, **2004**, 1312A.

10. Michael J. Sanger, "Whatever Floats (or Sinks) Your Can," *J. Chem. Educ.*, Vol. 83, **2006**, 1632A.

11. Michael Davis and Charles Henry, "The Sweeter Side of Density," *J. Chem. Educ.*, Vol. 85, **2008**, 1088A-1088B.

Chapter 2. Atoms, Molecules, and Ions

Media Resources

Figures and Tables in Transparency Pack: **Section:**

Figure 2.4 Cathode-ray Tube with Perpendicular Magnetic and Electric Fields — 2.2 The Discovery of Atomic Structure

Figure 2.5 Millikan's Oil-drop Experiment — 2.2 The Discovery of Atomic Structure

Figure 2.8 The Behavior of Alpha (α), Beta (β), and Gamma (γ) Rays in an Electric Field — 2.2 The Discovery of Atomic Structure

Figure 2.10 Rutherford's α-scattering Experiment — 2.2 The Discovery of Atomic Structure

Figure 2.12 The Structure of the Atom — 2.3 The Modern View of Atomic Structure

Figure 2.13 A Mass Spectrometer — 2.4 Atomic Weights

Figure 2.15 Periodic Table of the Elements — 2.5 The Periodic Table

Figure 2.20 Predictable Charges of Some Common Ions — 2.7 Ions and Ionic Compounds

Figure 2.21 Formation of an Ionic Compound — 2.7 Ions and Ionic Compounds

Figure 2.22 Elements Essential to Life — 2.7 Ions and Ionic Compounds

Figure 2.24 Procedure for Naming Anions — 2.8 Naming Inorganic Compounds

Figure 2.26 How Anion Names and Acid Names Relate — 2.8 Naming Inorganic Compounds

Animations: **Section:**

Multiple Proportions — 2.1 The Atomic Theory of Matter

Millikan Oil Drop Experiment — 2.2 The Discovery of Atomic Structure

Separation of Alpha, Beta, and Gamma Rays — 2.2 The Discovery of Atomic Structure

Rutherford Experiment: Nuclear Atom — 2.2 The Discovery of Atomic Structure

Activities: **Section:**

Law of Multiple Proportions — 2.1 The Atomic Theory of Matter

Isotopes of Hydrogen — 2.3 The Modern View of Atomic Structure

Coulomb's Law — 2.3 The Modern View of Atomic Structure

Mass Spectrometer — 2.4 Atomic Weights

Periodic Table — 2.5 The Periodic Table

Representations of Methane — 2.6 Molecules and Molecular Compounds

Naming Cations — 2.8 Naming Inorganic Compounds

Naming Anions — 2.8 Naming Inorganic Compounds

Polyatomic Ions — 2.8 Naming Inorganic Compounds

Ionic Compounds — 2.8 Naming Inorganic Compounds

3-D Models: **Section:**

Hydrogen — 2.6 Molecules and Molecular Compounds

Oxygen — 2.6 Molecules and Molecular Compounds

Chlorine — 2.6 Molecules and Molecular Compounds

Water — 2.6 Molecules and Molecular Compounds

Hydrogen Peroxide — 2.6 Molecules and Molecular Compounds

Carbon Dioxide — 2.6 Molecules and Molecular Compounds

Carbon Monoxide — 2.6 Molecules and Molecular Compounds

Sulfur Trioxide — 2.6 Molecules and Molecular Compounds

Nitrogen Dioxide	2.6 Molecules and Molecular Compounds
Iodine Pentafluoride	2.6 Molecules and Molecular Compounds
Sodium Chloride (1 × 1 Unit Cell)	2.7 Ions and Ionic Compounds
Nitrite Ion	2.8 Naming Inorganic Compounds
Acetone	2.9 Some Simple Organic Compounds
Hydroxylamine	2.9 Some Simple Organic Compounds
Chloromethane	2.9 Some Simple Organic Compounds
Ethylene	2.9 Some Simple Organic Compounds
Methane	2.9 Some Simple Organic Compounds
Propane	2.9 Some Simple Organic Compounds
Methanol	2.9 Some Simple Organic Compounds
Ethanol	2.9 Some Simple Organic Compounds
1-Propanol	2.9 Some Simple Organic Compounds
2-Propanol	2.9 Some Simple Organic Compounds
Bromoethane	2.9 Some Simple Organic Compounds
Dimethylamine	2.9 Some Simple Organic Compounds
Methylene Chloride	2.9 Some Simple Organic Compounds

Other Resources

Further Readings:	**Section:**
Analogical Demonstration	2.1 The Atomic Theory of Matter
A Millikan Oil Drop Analogy	2.2 The Discovery of Atomic Structure
Marie Curie's Doctoral Thesis: Prelude to a Nobel Prize	2.2 The Discovery of Atomic Structure
Bowling Balls and Beads: A Concrete Analogy to the Rutherford Experiment	2.2 The Discovery of Atomic Structure
The Curie-Becquerel Story	2.2 The Discovery of Atomic Structure
The Discovery of the Electron, Proton, and Neutron	2.3 The Modern View of Atomic Structure
Isotope Separation	2.3 The Modern View of Atomic Structure
Relative Atomic Mass and the Mole: A Concrete Analogy to Help Students Understand These Abstract Concepts	2.4 Atomic Weights
Revising Molar Mass, Atomic Mass, and Mass Number: Organizing, Integrating, and Sequencing Fundamental Chemical Concepts	2.4 Atomic Weights
Using Monetary Analogies to Teach Average Atomic Mass	2.4 Atomic Weights
Pictorial Analogies IV: Relative Atomic Weights	2.4 Atomic Weights
Mass Spectrometry for the Masses	2.4 Atomic Weights
Periodic Tables of Elemental Abundance	2.5 The Periodic Table
A Second Note on the Term 'Chalcogen'	2.5 The Periodic Table
The Proper Place for Hydrogen in the Periodic Table	2.5 The Periodic Table
The Periodic Table: Key to Past 'Elemental' Discoveries—A New Role in the Future?	2.5 The Periodic Table
Teaching Inorganic Nomenclature: A Systematic Approach	2.8 Naming Inorganic Compounds

Nomenclature Made Practical: Student Discovery
    of the Nomenclature

Flow Chart for Naming Inorganic Compounds

Using Games to Teach Chemistry: An Annotated
    Bibiography

A Mnemonic for Oxy-Anions

2.8 Naming Inorganic Compounds

2.8 Naming Inorganic Compounds
2.8 Naming Inorganic Compounds

2.8 Naming Inorganic Compounds

Live Demonstrations:

Turning Plastic into Gold: An Analogy to
    Demonstrate Rutherford Gold Foil Experiment

Dramatizing Isotopes: Deuterated Ice Cubes Sink

Section:

2.2 The Discovery of Atomic Structure

2.3 The Modern View of Atomic Structure

Chapter 2. Atoms, Molecules, and Ions

Common Student Misconceptions

- Students have problems with the concept of amu.
- Beginning students often do not see the difference between empirical and molecular formulas.
- Students think that polyatomic ions can easily dissociate into smaller ions.
- Students often fail to recognize the importance of the periodic table as a tool for organizing and remembering chemical facts.
- Students often cannot relate the charges on common monoatomic ions to their position in the periodic table.
- Students often do not realize that an ionic compound *can* consist of nonmetals only, e.g., $(NH_4)_2SO_4$.
- Students often confuse the guidelines for naming ionic compounds with those for naming binary molecular compounds.
- Students routinely underestimate the importance of this chapter.

Teaching Tips

- It is critical that students learn the names and formulas of common and polyatomic ions as soon as possible. They sometimes need to be told that this information will be used throughout their careers as chemists (even if that career is only one semester).
- Remind students that *families* or *groups* are the columns in the periodic table; *periods* are the rows.
- Emphasize to students that the subscripts in the molecular formula of a substance are always an integral multiple of the subscripts in the empirical formula of that substance.

Lecture Outline

2.1 The Atomic Theory of Matter[1,2,3]

- Greek Philosophers: Can matter be subdivided into fundamental particles?
- Democritus (460–370 BC): All matter can be divided into indivisible *atomos*.
- Dalton: proposed atomic theory with the following postulates:
  - Elements are composed of atoms.
  - All atoms of an element are identical.
  - In chemical reactions atoms are not changed into different types of atoms. Atoms are neither created nor destroyed.
  - Compounds are formed when atoms of elements combine.
- **Atoms** are the building blocks of matter.
- *Law of constant composition*: The relative kinds and numbers of atoms are constant for a given compound.
- *Law of conservation of mass (matter)*: During a chemical reaction, the total mass before the reaction is equal to the total mass after the reaction.
  - Conservation means something can neither be created nor destroyed. Here, it applies to matter (mass). Later we will apply it to energy (Chapter 5).
- *Law of multiple proportions*: If two elements, A and B, combine to form more than one compound, then the mass of B, which combines with the mass of A, is a ratio of small whole numbers.
- Dalton's theory *predicted* the law of multiple proportions.

---

[1] "Analogical Demonstration" from Further Readings
[2] "Law of Multiple Proportions" Activity from Instructor's Resource CD/DVD
[3] "Multiple Proportions" Animation from Instructor's Resource CD/DVD

FUTURE REFERENCES
- The law of conservation of mass (matter) falls under the First Law of Thermodynamics discussed in Chapter 5.

2.2 The Discovery of Atomic Structure
- By 1850 scientists knew that atoms consisted of charged particles.
- **Subatomic particles** are those particles that make up the atom.
- Recall the law of electrostatic attraction: like charges repel and opposite charges attract.

Cathode Rays and Electrons[4,5,6,7,8]
- Cathode rays were first discovered in the mid-1800s from studies of electrical discharge through partially evacuated tubes (cathode-ray tubes, or CRTs).
  - Computer terminals were once popularly referred to as CRTs (cathode-ray tubes).
  - Cathode rays = radiation produced when high voltage is applied across the tube.
- The voltage causes negative particles to move from the negative electrode (cathode) to the positive electrode (anode).
- The path of the electrons can be altered by the presence of a magnetic field.
- Consider cathode rays leaving the positive electrode through a small hole.
  - If they interact with a magnetic field perpendicular to an applied electric field, then the cathode rays can be deflected by different amounts.
  - The amount of deflection of the cathode rays depends on the applied magnetic and electric fields.
  - In turn, the amount of deflection also depends on the charge-to-mass ratio of the electron.
  - In 1897 Thomson determined the charge-to-mass ratio of an electron.
    - Charge-to-mass ratio: 1.76×10^8 C/g.
    - C is a symbol for coulomb.
      - It is the SI unit for electric charge.
- Millikan Oil-Drop Experiment (1909)
  - Goal: find the charge on the electron to determine its mass.
  - Oil drops are sprayed above a positively charged plate containing a small hole.
  - As the oil drops fall through the hole they acquire a negative charge.
  - Gravity forces the drops downward. The applied electric field forces the drops upward.
  - When a drop is perfectly balanced, then the weight of the drop is equal to the electrostatic force of attraction between the drop and the positive plate.
  - Millikan carried out the above experiment and determined the charges on the oil drops to be multiples of 1.60×10^{-19} C.
  - He concluded the charge on the electron must be 1.60×10^{-19} C.
- Knowing the charge-to-mass ratio of the electron, we can calculate the mass of the electron:

$$\text{Mass} = \frac{1.60 \times 10^{-19}\,\text{C}}{1.76 \times 10^8\,\text{C/g}} = 9.10 \times 10^{-28}\,\text{g}$$

Radioactivity[9]
- **Radioactivity** is the spontaneous emission of radiation.
- Consider the following experiment:

---

[4] Figure 2.4 from Transparency Pack
[5] "A Millikan Oil Drop Analogy" from Further Readings
[6] "Millikan Oil Drop Experiment" Animation from Instructor's Resource CD/DVD
[7] "Marie Curie's Doctoral Thesis: Prelude to a Nobel Prize" from Further Readings
[8] Figure 2.5 from Transparency Pack
[9] "The Curie-Becquerel Story" from Further Readings

- A radioactive substance is placed in a lead shield containing a small hole so that a beam of radiation is emitted from the shield.
- The radiation is passed between two electrically charged plates and detected.
- Three spots are observed on the detector:
  1. a spot deflected in the direction of the positive plate,
  2. a spot that is not affected by the electric field, and
  3. a spot deflected in the direction of the negative plate.
- A large deflection towards the positive plate corresponds to radiation that is negatively charged and of low mass. This is called β-radiation (consists of electrons).
  - No deflection corresponds to neutral radiation. This is called γ-radiation (similar to X-rays).
- A small deflection toward the negatively charged plate corresponds to high mass, positively charged radiation. This is called α-radiation (positively charged core of a helium atom).
  - X-rays and γ radiation are true electromagnetic radiation, whereas α- and β-radiation are actually streams of particles–helium nuclei and electrons, respectively.

The Nuclear Atom[10,11,12,13,14,15]

- The plum pudding model is an early picture of the atom.
- The Thomson model pictures the atom as a sphere with small electrons embedded in a positively charged mass.
- Rutherford carried out the following "gold foil" experiment:
  - A source of α-particles was placed at the mouth of a circular detector.
  - The α-particles were shot through a piece of gold foil.
  - Both the gold nucleus and the α-particle were positively charged, so they repelled each other.
  - Most of the α-particles went straight through the foil without deflection.
  - If the Thomson model of the atom was correct, then Rutherford's result was impossible.
- Rutherford modified Thomson's model as follows:
  - Assume the atom is spherical, but the positive charge must be located at the center with a diffuse negative charge surrounding it.
  - In order for the majority of α-particles that pass through a piece of foil to be undeflected, the majority of the atom must consist of a low mass, diffuse negative charge -- the electron.
  - To account for the small number of large deflections of the α-particles, the center, or **nucleus,** of the atom must consist of a dense positive charge.

FUTURE REFERENCES
- Radioactivity will be further discussed in Chapter 21.

2.3 The Modern View of Atomic Structure[16,17,18]

- The atom consists of positive, negative and neutral entities (**protons, electrons** and **neutrons**).
- Protons and neutrons are located in the nucleus of the atom, which is small. Most of the mass of the atom is due to the nucleus.
- Electrons are located outside of the nucleus. Most of the volume of the atom is due to electrons.

---

[10] Figure 2.8 from Transparency Pack
[11] "Separation of Alpha, Beta, and Gamma Rays" Animation from Instructor's Resource CD/DVD
[12] "Bowling Balls and Beads: A Concrete Analogy to the Rutherford Experiment" from Further Readings
[13] "Rutherford Experiment: Nuclear Atom" Animation from Instructor's Resource CD/DVD
[14] Figure 2.10 from Transparency Pack
[15] "Turning Plastic into Gold" from Live Demonstrations
[16] "The Discovery of the Electron, Proton, and Neutron" from Further Readings
[17] Figure 2.12 from Transparency Pack
[18] "Coulomb's Law" Activity from Instructor's Resource CD/DVD

- The quantity 1.602×10^{-19} C is called the **electronic charge**.
    - The charge on an electron is -1.602×10^{-19} C; the charge on a proton is $+1.602 \times 10^{-19}$ C; neutrons are uncharged.
    - Atoms have an equal number of protons and electrons thus they have no net electrical charge.
- Masses are so small that we define the **atomic mass unit**, amu.
    - 1 amu = 1.66054×10^{-24} g.
    - The mass of a proton is 1.0073 amu, a neutron is 1.0087 amu, and an electron is 5.486×10^{-4} amu.
- The **angstrom** is a convenient non-SI unit of length used to denote atomic dimensions.
    - Because most atoms have radii around 1×10^{-10} m, we define 1 Å = 1×10^{-10} m.

Atomic Numbers, Mass Numbers, and Isotopes[19,20,21,22]

- **Atomic number** (Z) = number of protons in the nucleus.
- **Mass number** (A) = total number of nucleons in the nucleus (i.e., protons and neutrons).

- By convention, for element X, we write $_Z^A X$.
    - Thus, isotopes have the same Z but different A.
        - There can be a variable number of neutrons for the same number of protons. Isotopes have the same number of protons but different numbers of neutrons.
- All atoms of a specific element have the same number of protons.
    - **Isotopes** of a specific element differ in the number of neutrons.

FUTURE REFERENCES
- The concept of an isotope (specifically ^{12}C) will be useful when defining the mole in Chapter 3.
- Because the atomic number signifies the number of electrons in an atom, it will be commonly used to write electron configurations of atoms (Chapter 6), draw Lewis structures (Chapter 8), and understand molecular orbitals (Chapter 9).
- Radioactive decay will be further discussed in Chapter 14 as an example of first order kinetics.
- Atomic structure ideas developed in section 2.3 will be applied to the understanding of nuclear reactions in Chapter 21.

2.4 Atomic Weights

The Atomic Mass Scale[23,24]
- Consider 100 g of water:
    - Upon decomposition 11.1 g of hydrogen and 88.9 g of oxygen are produced.
    - The mass ratio of O to H in water is 88.9/11.1 = 8.
    - Therefore, the mass of O is $2 \times 8 = 16$ times the mass of H.
    - If H has a mass of 1, then O has a *relative mass* of 16.
    - We can measure atomic masses using a mass spectrometer.
    - We know ^{1}H has a mass of 1.6735×10^{-24} g and ^{16}O has a mass of 2.6560×10^{-23} g.

[19] "Isotope Separation" from Further Readings
[20] "Dramatizing Isotopes: Deuterated Ice Cubes Sink" from Live Demonstrations
[21] "Element Symbology" Activity from Instructor's Resource CD/DVD
[22] "Isotopes of Hydrogen" Activity from Instructor's Resource CD/DVD
[23] "Revisiting Molar Mass, Atomic Mass, and Mass Number: Organizing, Integrating, and Sequencing Fundamental Chemical Concepts" from Further Readings
[24] "Relative Atomic Mass and the Mole: A Concrete Analogy to Help Students Understand These Abstract Concepts" from Further Readings

- *Atomic mass units* (amu) are convenient units to use when dealing with extremely small masses of individual atoms.
- $1\ \text{amu} = 1.66054 \times 10^{-24}\ \text{g}$ and $1\ \text{g} = 6.02214 \times 10^{23}\ \text{amu}$
- By definition, the mass of ^{12}C is exactly 12 amu.

Average Atomic Masses[25,26]

- We average the masses of isotopes to give average atomic masses.
- Naturally occurring C consists of 98.93% ^{12}C (12 amu) and 1.07% ^{13}C (13.00335 amu).
- The average mass of C is:
  - $(0.9893)(12\ \text{amu}) + (0.0107)(13.00335\ \text{amu}) = 12.01\ \text{amu}$.
- **Atomic weight** (AW) is also known as *average atomic mass* (atomic weight).
- *Atomic weights* are listed on the periodic table.

The Mass Spectrometer[27,28]

- A **mass spectrometer** is an instrument that allows for direct and accurate determination of atomic (and molecular) weights.
- The sample is charged as soon as it enters the spectrometer.
- The charged sample is accelerated using an applied voltage.
- The ions are then passed into an evacuated tube and through a magnetic field.
- The magnetic field causes the ions to be deflected by different amounts depending on their mass.
- The ions are then detected.
  - A graph of signal intensity vs. mass of the ion is called a *mass spectrum*.

FUTURE REFERENCES

- Being able to locate atomic weights on the periodic table will be crucial in calculating molar masses in Chapter 3 and beyond.

2.5 The Periodic Table[29,30,31,32,33,34]

- The **periodic table** is used to organize the elements in a meaningful way.
- As a consequence of this organization, there are periodic properties associated with the periodic table.
- Rows in the periodic table are called **periods**.
- Columns in the periodic table are called **groups**.
  - Several numbering conventions are used (i.e., groups may be numbered from 1 to 18, or from 1A to 8A and 1B to 8B).
- Some of the groups in the periodic table are given special names.
  - These names indicate the similarities between group members.
  - Examples:
    - Group 1A: alkali metals
    - Group 2A: alkaline earth metals
    - Group 7A: halogens

[25] "Using Monetary Analogies to Teach Average Atomic Mass" from Further Readings
[26] "Pictorial Analogies IV: Relative Atomic Weights" from Further Readings
[27] "Mass Spectrometer" Activity from Instructor's Resource CD/DVD
[28] "Mass Spectrometry for the Masses" from Further Readings
[29] "Periodic Tables of Elemental Abundance" from Further Readings
[30] Figure 2.15 from Transparency Pack
[31] "Periodic Table" Activity from Instructor's Resource CD/DVD
[32] "A Second Note on the Term 'Chalcogen'" from Further Readings
[33] "The Proper Place for Hydrogen in the Periodic Table" from Further Readings
[34] "The Periodic Table: Key to Past 'Elemental' Discoveries—A New Role in the Future?" from Further Readings

- Group 8A: noble gases
- **Metallic elements**, or **metals**, are located on the left-hand side of the periodic table (most of the elements are metals).
  - Metals tend to be malleable, ductile, and lustrous and are good thermal and electrical conductors.
- **Nonmetallic elements**, or **nonmetals**, are located in the top right-hand side of the periodic table.
  - Nonmetals tend to be brittle as solids, dull in appearance, and do not conduct heat or electricity well.
- Elements with properties similar to both metals and nonmetals are called **metalloids** and are located at the interface between the metals and nonmetals.
  - These include the elements B, Si, Ge, As, Sb, and Te.

FORWARD REFERENCES
- Additional information that can be associated with the unique location of an element in the periodic table will be covered in Chapter 6 (electron configurations), Chapter 7 (periodic properties), Chapter 8 (tendency to form ionic or covalent bonds), and Chapter 16 (relative acid strength).

2.6 Molecules and Molecular Compounds

- A **molecule** consists of two or more atoms bound tightly together.

Molecules and Chemical Formulas

- Each molecule has a **chemical formula**.
- The chemical formula indicates
  1. which atoms are found in the molecule, and
  2. in what proportion they are found.
- A molecule made up of two atoms is called a **diatomic molecule**.
  - Different forms of an element, which have different chemical formulas, are known as allotropes.
  - Allotropes differ in their chemical and physical properties.
    - Examples: ozone (O_3) and "normal" oxygen (O_2)
- Compounds composed of molecules are **molecular compounds**.
  - These contain at least two types of atoms.
  - Most molecular substances contain only nonmetals.

Molecular and Empirical Formulas[35,36,37,38,39,40,41,42,43,44,45]

- **Molecular formulas**
  - These formulas give the actual numbers and types of atoms in a molecule.
  - Examples: H_2O, CO_2, CO, CH_4, H_2O_2, O_2, O_3, and C_2H_4.
- **Empirical formulas**
  - These formulas give the relative numbers and types of atoms in a molecule (they give the lowest whole-number ratio of atoms in a molecule).

[35] "Representations of Methane" Activity from Instructor's Resource CD/DVD
[36] "Hydrogen" 3-D Model from Instructor's Resource CD/DVD
[37] "Oxygen" 3-D Model from Instructor's Resource CD/DVD
[38] "Water" 3-D Model from Instructor's Resource CD/DVD
[39] "Hydrogen Peroxide" 3-D Model from Instructor's Resource CD/DVD
[40] "Carbon Dioxide" 3-D Model from Instructor's Resource CD/DVD
[41] "Carbon Monoxide" 3-D Model from Instructor's Resource CD/DVD
[42] "Iodine Pentafluoride" 3-D Model from Instructor's Resource CD/DVD
[43] "Chlorine" 3-D Model from Instructor's Resource CD/DVD
[44] "Sulfur Trioxide" 3-D Model from Instructor's Resource CD/DVD
[45] "Nitrogen Dioxide" 3-D Model from Instructor's Resource CD/DVD

- Examples: H_2O, CO_2, CO, CH_4, HO, CH_2.

Picturing Molecules

- Molecules occupy three-dimensional space.
- However, we often represent them in two dimensions.
- The **structural formula** gives the connectivity between individual atoms in the molecule.
- The structural formula may or may not be used to show the three-dimensional shape of the molecule.
- If the structural formula does show the shape of the molecule, then either a perspective drawing, a ball-and-stick model, or a space-filling model is used.
  - *Perspective drawings* use dashed lines and wedges to represent bonds receding and emerging from the plane of the paper.
  - *Ball-and-stick models* show atoms as contracted spheres and the bonds as sticks.
    - The angles in the ball-and-stick model are accurate.
  - *Space-filling models* give an accurate representation of the 3-D shape of the molecule.

FORWARD REFERENCES

- More detailed discussion of bonding in molecules and molecular shapes will take place in Chapters 8 and 9, respectively.

2.7 Ions and Ionic Compounds

- If electrons are added to or removed from a neutral atom, an **ion** is formed.
- When an atom or molecule loses electrons it becomes positively charged.
  - Positively charged ions are called **cations**.
- When an atom or molecule gains electrons it becomes negatively charged.
  - Negatively charged ions are called **anions**.
- In general, metal atoms tend to lose electrons and nonmetal atoms tend to gain electrons.
- When molecules lose electrons, **polyatomic ions** are formed (e.g., SO_4^{2-}, NH_4^+).

Predicting Ionic Charges[46]

- An atom or molecule can lose more than one electron.
- Many atoms gain or lose enough electrons to have the same number of electrons as the nearest noble gas (group 8A).
- The number of electrons an atom loses is related to its position on the periodic table.
- Anions can also be viewed as particles originating from acids, and therefore, having negative charges equal to the number of (acidic) hydrogen atoms in molecules of those acids (e.g. HNO_3 has 1 H atom, hence NO_3^- has a charge of −1).

Ionic Compounds[47,48]

- A great deal of chemistry involves the transfer of electrons between species.
- Example:
  - To form NaCl, the neutral sodium atom, Na, must lose an electron to become a cation: Na^+.
  - The electron cannot be lost entirely, so it is transferred to a chlorine atom, Cl, which then becomes an anion: Cl^-.
  - The Na^+ and Cl^- ions are attracted to form an ionic NaCl lattice, which crystallizes.
- NaCl is an example of an **ionic compound** consisting of positively charged cations and negatively charged anions.
  - Important: note that there are no easily identified NaCl molecules in the ionic lattice. Therefore, we cannot use molecular formulas to describe ionic substances.

---

[46] Figure 2.20 from Transparency Pack
[47] Figure 2.21 from Transparency Pack
[48] "Sodium Chloride (1 × 1 Unit Cell)" 3-D Model from Instructor's Resource CD/DVD

- In general, ionic compounds are combinations of metals and nonmetals, whereas molecular compounds are composed of nonmetals only.
  - There are exceptions; notably $(NH_4)_2SO_4$ and other ammonium salts are ionic.
- Writing empirical formulas for ionic compounds:
  - You need to know the ions of which it is composed.
  - The formula must reflect the electrical neutrality of the compound.
  - You must combine cations and anions in a ratio so that the total positive charge is equal to the total negative charge.
  - Example: Consider the formation of Mg_3N_2:
    - Mg loses two electrons to become Mg^{2+}
    - Nitrogen gains three electrons to become N^{3-}.
    - For a neutral species, the number of electrons lost and gained must be equal.
    - However, Mg can only lose electrons in twos and N can only accept electrons in threes.
    - Therefore, Mg needs to lose six electrons (2×3) and N gains those six electrons (3×2).
    - That is, 3Mg atoms need to form $3Mg^{2+}$ ions (total 3×2 positive charges) and 2N atoms need to form $2N^{3-}$ ions (total 2×3 negative charges).
    - Therefore, the formula is Mg_3N_2.

Chemistry and Life: Elements Required by Living Organisms[49]

- Of the known elements, only about 29 are required for life.
- Water accounts for at least 70% of the mass of most cells.
- More than 97% of the mass of most organisms comprises just six elements (O, C, H, N, P and S).
- Carbon is the most common element in the solid components of cells.
- The most important elements for life are H, C, N, O, P and S (red).
- The next most important ions are Na^+, Mg^{2+}, K^+, Ca^{2+}, and Cl^- (blue).
- The other required 18 elements are only needed in trace amounts (green); they are *trace elements*.

FORWARD REFERENCES

- Formulas (including correct charges) of ions will be important in writing metathesis and net ionic equations in Chapter 4 (sections 4.2-4.3).
- Periodic trends in ionization energy (in gas phase) as well as ionic radii (in crystals) will be covered in Chapter 7.
- The nature of bonding between ions and charges of most monoatomic ions will be rationalized in terms of electron configurations in Chapter 8 (section 8.2).
- Common types of ionic structures will be discussed in Chapter 11.
- Qualitatively, solubility of ionic solids will be covered in Chapter 4 (section 4.2) and quantitatively in Chapter 17 (section 17.4).
- The faith of ionic solids when dissolved in water will be briefly discussed in Chapter 4 (section 4.1) and elaborated on in Chapter 13 (section 13.1); ion-dipole forces will be explained in Chapter 11 (section 11.2).
- The loss of electrons to form monoatomic metal cations (oxidation) and the gain of electrons to form monoatomic nonmetal anions (reduction) will be further discussed in Chapter 4 (section 4.4).
- Atoms of the same element appearing in several different ions (as well as molecules), and hence, having different oxidation numbers will be the basis of redox reactions in Chapter 20.
- The role of metal cations in the formation of metal complexes will be discussed in Chapter 23.

---

[49] Figure 2.22 from Transparency Pack

2.8 Naming Inorganic Compounds[50,51,52,53]

- **Chemical nomenclature** is the naming of substances.
- Common names are traditional names for substances (e.g., water, ammonia).
- Systematic names are based on a systematic set of rules.
    - Divided into organic compounds (those containing C, usually in combination with H, O, N, or S) and inorganic compounds (all other compounds).

Names and Formulas of Ionic Compounds[54,55]

1. Positive Ions (Cations)

- Cations formed from a metal have the same name as the metal.
    - Example: Na^+ = sodium ion.
    - Ions formed from a single atom are called *monoatomic ions*.
- Many transition metals exhibit variable charge.
    - If the metal can form more than one cation, then the charge is indicated in parentheses in the name.
        - Examples: Cu^+ = copper(I) ion; Cu^{2+} = copper(II) ion.
    - An alternative nomenclature method uses the endings **-ous** and **-ic** to represent the lower and higher charged ions, respectively.
        - Examples: Cu^+ = cuprous ion; Cu^{2+} = cupric ion.
- Cations formed from nonmetals end in **-ium**.
    - Examples: NH_4^+ = ammonium ion; H_3O^+ = hydronium ion.

2. Negative Ions (Anions)[56,57,58,59]

- Monatomic anions (with only one atom) use the ending **-ide**.
    - Example: Cl^- is the chloride ion.
- Some polyatomic anions also use the -ide ending:
    - Examples: hydroxide, cyanide, and peroxide ions.
- Polyatomic anions (with many atoms) containing oxygen are called **oxyanions**.
    - Their names end in **-ate** or **-ite**. (The one with more oxygen is called **-ate**.)
    - Examples: NO_3^- is nit**rate**; NO_2^- is nit**rite**.
- Polyatomic anions containing oxygen with more than two members in the series are named as follows (in order of **decreasing oxygen**):

per-....-ate	example:	ClO_4^-	**perchlorate**
-ate		ClO_3^-	chlorate
-ite		ClO_2^-	chlorite
hypo-....-ite		ClO^-	**hypo**chlorite

- Polyatomic anions containing oxygen with additional hydrogens are named by adding hydrogen or bi- (one H), dihydrogen (two H) etc., to the name as follows:
    - CO_3^{2-} is the carbon**ate** anion.

---

[50] "Teaching Inorganic Nomenclature: A Systematic Approach" from Further Readings

[51] "Nomenclature Made Practical; Student Discovery of the Nomenclature Rules" from Further Readings

[52] "Flow Chart for Naming Inorganic Compounds" from Further Readings

[53] "Using Games to Teach Chemistry: An Annotated Bibliography" from Further Readings

[54] "Naming Cations" Activity from Instructor's Resource CD/DVD

[55] "Naming Anions" Activity from Instructor's Resource CD/DVD

[56] "Polyatomic Ions" Activity from Instructor's Resource CD/DVD

[57] "A Mnemonic for Oxy-Anions" from Further Readings

[58] Figure 2.24 from Transparency Pack

[59] "Nitrite Ion" 3-D Model from Instructor's Resource CD/DVD

- HCO_3^- is the hydrogen carbonate (or **bicarbonate**) anion.
- PO_4^{3-} is the phosphate ion.
- $H_2PO_4^-$ is the **dihydrogen** phosphate anion.

3. Ionic Compounds[60]
- These are named by the cation then the anion.
- Examples:
  - $CaCl_2$ = calcium chloride
  - $(NH_4)_3PO_4$ = ammonium phosphate
  - $KClO_4$ = potassium perchlorate

Names and Formulas of Acids[61]
- Acids are substances that yield hydrogen ions when dissolved in water (Arrhenius definition).
  - The names of acids are related to the names of anions:
    - **-ide** becomes **hydro-**....**-ic** acid;   example: HCl   **hydro**chlor**ic** acid
    - **-ate** becomes **-ic** acid; $HClO_4$ perchlor**ic** acid
    - **-ite** becomes **-ous** acid.   HClO   hypochlor**ous** acid

Names and Formulas of Binary Molecular Compounds
- *Binary* molecular compounds have two elements.
- The most metallic element (i.e., the one to the farthest left on the periodic table) is usually written first. The exception is NH_3.
- If both elements are in the same group, the lower one is written first.
- Greek prefixes are used to indicate the number of atoms (e.g., mono, di, tri).
  - The prefix mono is never used with the first element (i.e., carbon monoxide, CO).
- Examples:
  - Cl_2O is **di**chlorine *mon*oxide.
  - N_2O_4 is **di**nitrogen *tetr*oxide.
  - NF_3 is nitrogen *tri*fluoride.
  - P_4S_{10} is **tetra**phosphorus *deca*sulfide.

FORWARD REFERENCES
- Nomenclature will be required throughout the textbook.
- Acids will be mentioned again in Chapter 4 and further discussed in Chapters 16 and 17.

2.9 Some Simple Organic Compounds[62,63,64,65]
- **Organic chemistry** is the study of carbon-containing compounds.
  - *Organic compounds* are those that contain carbon and hydrogen, often in combination with other elements.

Alkanes[66,67]
- Compounds containing only carbon and hydrogen are called **hydrocarbons**.
- In **alkanes** each carbon atom is bonded to four other atoms.

---

[60] "Ionic Compounds" Activity from Instructor's Resource CD/DVD
[61] Figure 2.26 from Transparency Pack
[62] "Acetone" 3-D Model from Instructor's Resource CD/DVD
[63] "Dimethylamine" 3-D Model from Instructor's Resource CD/DVD
[64] "Hydroxylamine" 3-D Model from Instructor's Resource CD/DVD
[65] "Ethylene" 3-D Model from Instructor's Resource CD/DVD
[66] "Methane" 3-D Model from Instructor's Resource CD/DVD
[67] "Propane" 3-D Model from Instructor's Resource CD/DVD

- The names of alkanes end in *-ane*.
  - Examples: methane, ethane, propane, butane.

Some Derivatives of Alkanes[68,69,70,71,72,73,74]

- When *functional groups*, specific groups of atoms, are used to replace hydrogen atoms on alkanes, new classes of organic compounds are obtained.
  - **Alcohols** are obtained by replacing a hydrogen atom of an alkane with an –OH group.
  - Alcohol names derive from the name of the alkane and have an *-ol* ending.
    - Examples: methane becomes methanol; ethane becomes ethanol.
  - Carbon atoms often form compounds with long chains of carbon atoms.
    - Properties of alkanes and derivatives change with changes in chain length.
    - *Polyethylene*, a material used to make many plastic products, is an alkane with thousands of carbons.
    - This is an example of a *polymer*.
- Carbon may form *multiple bonds* to itself or other atoms.

FORWARD REFERENCES

- Simple organic compounds will be used throughout the textbook to illustrate: weak acid behavior (e.g., acetic acid in Chapters 16 and 17), weak base behavior (e.g., amines in Chapters 16 and 17), resonance (e.g., benzene in Chapter 9), molecular polarity (e.g., CH_3Cl vs. CCl_4 in Chapter 9), solubility of organic compounds in water or organic solvents (e.g., pentane in Chapter 13), to mention just a few.
- Non-polar organic compounds will be mentioned again when discussing London dispersion forces in Chapter 11.
- This section introduces organic chemistry, which will be elaborated on in Chapter 24.

---

[68] "Methanol" 3-D Model from Instructor's Resource CD/DVD

[69] "Ethanol" 3-D Model from Instructor's Resource CD/DVD

[70] "1-Propanol" 3-D Model from Instructor's Resource CD/DVD

[71] "2-Propanol" 3-D Model from Instructor's Resource CD/DVD

[72] "Methylene Chloride (Dichloromethane)" 3-D Model from Instructor's Resource CD/DVD

[73] "Chloromethane" 3-D Model from Instructor's Resource CD/DVD

[74] "Bromoethane" 3-D Model from Instructor's Resource CD/DVD

Further Readings:

1. John J. Fortman, "Analogical Demonstration," *J. Chem. Educ.*, Vol. 69, **1992**, 323–324. This reference includes demonstrations of the concepts of the conservation of mass in chemical reactions, the Law of Multiple Proportions, etc.

2. Doris Eckey, "A Millikan Oil Drop Analogy," *J. Chem. Educ.*, Vol. 73, **1996**, 237–238.

3. Robert L. Wolke, "Marie Curie's Doctoral Thesis: Prelude to a Nobel Prize," *J. Chem. Educ.*, Vol. 65, **1988**, 561–573.

4. Mary V. Lorenz, "Bowling Balls and Beads: A Concrete Analogy to the Rutherford Experiment," *J. Chem. Educ.*, Vol. 65, **1988**, 1082.

5. Barrie M. Peake, "The Discovery of the Electron, Proton, and Neutron," *J. Chem. Educ.*, Vol. 66, **1989**, 738.

6. Harold F. Walton, "The Curie-Becquerel Story," *J. Chem. Educ.*, Vol. 69, **1992**, 10–15.

7. William Spindel and Takanobu Ishida, "Isotope Separation," *J. Chem. Educ.*, Vol. 68, **1991**, 312–318. An article describing methods used to isolate important isotopes.

8. Stephen DeMeo, "Revisiting Molar Mass, Atomic Mass, and Mass Number: Organizing, Integrating, and Sequencing Fundamental Chemical Concepts," *J. Chem. Educ.*, Vol. 83, **2006**, 617–620.

9. Josefina Arce de Sanabia, "Relative Atomic Mass and the Mole: A Concrete Analogy to Help Students Understand These Abstract Concepts," *J. Chem. Educ*, Vol. 70, **1993**, 233–234.

10. Arthur M. Last and Michael J. Webb, "Using Monetary Analogies to Teach Average Atomic Mass," *J. Chem. Educ.* Vol. 70, **1993**, 234–235.

11. John H. Fortman, "Pictorial Analogies IV: Relative Atomic Weights," *J. Chem. Educ.* Vol. 70, **1993**, 235–236.

12. Jared D. Persinger, Geoffrey C. Hoops, and Michael J. Samide, "Mass Spectrometry for the Masses," *J. Chem. Educ.,* Vol. 81, **2004**, 1169-1171.

13. Steven I. Dutch, "Periodic Tables of Elemental Abundance," *J. Chem. Educ.*, Vol. 76, **1999**, 356–358.

14. Werner Fischer, "A Second Note on the Term 'Chalcogen'," *J. Chem. Educ.*, Vol. 78, **2001**, 1333.

15. Marshall W. Cronyn, "The Proper Place for Hydrogen in the Periodic Table," *J. Chem. Educ.*, Vol. 80, **2003**, 947–950.

16. Darleane C. Hoffman, "The Periodic Table: Key to Past 'Elemental' Discoveries—A New Role in the Future?", *J. Chem. Educ.*, Vol. 86, **2009**, 1122–1128.

17. Gerhard Lind, "Teaching Inorganic Nomenclature: A Systematic Approach," *J. Chem. Educ.*, Vol. 69, **1992**, 613–614.

18. Michael C. Wirtz, Joan Kaufmann, and Gary Hawley, "Nomenclature Made Practical: Student Discovery of the Nomenclature Rules," *J. Chem. Educ.,* Vol. 83, **2006**, 595–598.

19. Steven J. Hawkes, "A Mnemonic for Oxy-Anions," *J. Chem. Educ.*, Vol. 67, **1990**, 149.

20. David Robson, "Flow Chart for Naming Inorganic Compounds," *J. Chem. Educ.*, Vol. 60, **1983**, 131–132.

21. Jeanne V. Russell, "Using Games to Teach Chemistry. An Annotated Bibliography," *J. Chem. Educ.*, Vol. 76, **1999**, 481–484. This is the first article in a special issue that contains many articles describing games and puzzles that may be used to teach chemistry.

Live Demonstrations:

1. Arthur B. Ellis, Edward A Adler, and Frederick H. Juergens, "Dramatizing Isotopes: Deuterated Ice Cubes Sink," *J. Chem. Educ.*, Vol. 67, **1990**, 159–160. Differences in density of $H_2O(l)$ and $D_2O(s)$ are used to demonstrate the effects of isotopic substitution.

2. Robert B. Gregory and Ed Vitz, "Turning Plastic into Gold: An Analogy To Demonstrate the Rutherford Gold Foil Experiment," *J. Chem. Educ.,* Vol 84, **2007**, 626–628.

Chapter 3. Stoichiometry: Calculations with Chemical Formulas and Equations

Media Resources

Figures and Tables in Transparency Pack:	**Section:**
Figure 3.3 The Difference Between Changing Subscripts and Changing Coefficients in Chemical Equations	3.1 Chemical Equations
Figure 3.4 Methane Reacts with Oxygen in a Bunsen Burner	3.1 Chemical Equations
Figure 3.5 Balanced Chemical Equation for the Combustion of CH_4	3.1 Chemical Equations
Figure 3.6 Combustion of Magnesium Metal in Air, a Combination Reaction	3.2 Some Simple Patterns of Chemical Reactivity
Figure 3.8 Comparing the Mass of 1 Molecule H_2O and 1 Mol H_2O	3.4 Avogadro's Number and the Mole
Figure 3.12 Procedure for Interconverting Mass and Number of Formula Units	3.4 Avogadro's Number and the Mole
Figure 3.13 Procedure for Calculating an Empirical Formula from Percentage Composition	3.5 Empirical Formulas from Analyses
Figure 3.16 Procedure for Calculating Amounts of Reactants or Products Formed in a Reaction	3.6 Quantitative Information from Balanced Equations
Figure 3.17 Limiting Reactant	3.7 Limiting Reactants

Animations:	**Section:**
Air Bags	3.2 Some Simple Patterns of Chemical Reactivity
Limiting Reagent	3.7 Limiting Reactants

Movies:	**Section:**
Formation of Water	3.1 Chemical Equations
Sodium and Potassium in Water	3.1 Chemical Equations
Reactions with Oxygen	3.2 Some Simple Patterns of Chemical Reactivity
Nitrogen Triiodide	3.2 Some Simple Patterns of Chemical Reactivity
Formation of Aluminum Bromide	3.2 Some Simple Patterns of Chemical Reactivity

Activities:	**Section:**
Reading a Chemical Equation	3.1 Chemical Equations
Reading a Balanced Chemical Equation	3.1 Chemical Equations
Counting Atoms	3.1 Chemical Equations
Balancing Equations	3.1 Chemical Equations
Molecular Weight and Weight Percent	3.3 Formula Weights
Empirical Formula Determination: C_8H_6O	3.5 Empirical Formulas from Analyses
Stoichiometry Calculation	3.6 Quantitative Information from Balanced Equations
Limiting Reagents	3.7 Limiting Reactants

3-D Models:	Section:
Water	3.5 Empirical Formulas from Analyses
Hydrogen Peroxide	3.5 Empirical Formulas from Analyses
Sucrose	3.5 Empirical Formulas from Analyses
Oxygen	3.5 Empirical Formulas from Analyses
Methane	3.5 Empirical Formulas from Analyses
Carbon Dioxide	3.5 Empirical Formulas from Analyses
Glycine (molecular form)	3.5 Empirical Formulas from Analyses
Methanol	3.5 Empirical Formulas from Analyses
Ethane	3.5 Empirical Formulas from Analyses

Other Resources

Further Readings:	Section:
More Chemistry in a Soda Bottle: A Conservation of Mass Activity	3.1 Chemical Equations
Chemical Wastes and the Law of Conservation of Matter	3.1 Chemical Equations
Antoine Lavoisier and the Conservation of Matter	3.1 Chemical Equations
The Fruit Basket Analogy	3.1 Chemical Equations
Balancing Chemical Equations by Inspection	3.1 Chemical Equations
A New Inspection Method for Balancing Redox Equations	3.1 Chemical Equations
On Balancing Chemical Equations: Past and Present (A Critical Review and Annotated Bibliography)	3.1 Chemical Equations
How to Say How Much: Amounts and Stoichiometry	3.1 Chemical Equations
Lime	3.2 Some Simple Patterns of Chemical Reactivity
Gram Formula Weights and Fruit Salad	3.3 Formula Weights
Percentage Composition and Empirical Formula–A New View	3.3 Formula Weights
Mole, Mole per Liter, and Molar. A Primer on SI and Related Units for Chemistry Students	3.3 Formula Weights
Using Monetary Analogies to Teach Average Atomic Mass	3.4 Avogadro's Number and the Mole
Pictorial Analogies IV: Relative Atomic Weights	3.4 Avogadro's Number and the Mole
Relative Atomic Mass and the Mole: A Concrete Analogy to Help Students These Abstract Concepts	3.4 Avogadro's Number and the Mole
Moles, Pennies, and Nickels	3.4 Avogadro's Number and the Mole
A Mole Mnemonic	3.4 Avogadro's Number and the Mole
Analogies that Indicate the Size of Atoms and Molecules and the Magnitude of Avogadro's Number	3.4 Avogadro's Number and the Mole
Developing an Intuitive Approach to Moles	3.4 Avogadro's Number and the Mole
The Mole, the Periodic Table, and Quantum Numbers: An Introductory Trio	3.4 Avogadro's Number and the Mole
The Size of a Mole	3.4 Avogadro's Number and the Mole
What's a Mole For?	3.4 Avogadro's Number and the Mole
The Mole Concept: Developing an Instrument	3.4 Avogadro's Number and the Mole

to Assess Conceptual Understanding

A Mole of M&M's — 3.4 Avogadro's Number and the Mole

How to Visualize Avogadro's Number — 3.4 Avogadro's Number and the Mole

Demonstrations of the Enormity of Avogadro's Number — 3.4 Avogadro's Number and the Mole

For Mole Problems, Call Avogadro: 602-1023 — 3.4 Avogadro's Number and the Mole

A Known-to-Unknown Approach to Teach About Empirical and Molecular Formulas — 3.5 Empirical Formulas from Analyses

Making Assumptions Explicit: How the Law of Conservation of Matter Can Explain Empirical Formula Problems — 3.5 Empirical Formulas from Analyses

A Simple Rhyme for a Simple Formula — 3.5 Empirical Formulas from Analyses

How Many Digits Should We Use in Formula or Molar Mass Calculation — 3.6 Quantitative Information from Balanced Equations

Amounts Tables as a Diagnostic Tool for Flawed Stoichiometric Reasoning — 3.6 Quantitative Information from Balanced Equations

Stoogiometry: A Cognitive Approach to Teaching Stoichiometry — 3.6 Quantitative Information from Balanced Equations

Teaching Stoichiometry: A Two-Cycle Approach — 3.6 Quantitative Information from Balanced Equations

A Recipe for Teaching Stoichiometry — 3.6 Quantitative Information from Balanced Equations

Pictorial Analogies XII: Stoichiometric Calculations — 3.6 Quantitative Information from Balanced Equations

Learning Stoichiometry with Hamburger Sandwiches — 3.7 Limiting Reactants

Limiting and Excess Reagents, Theoretical Yield — 3.7 Limiting Reactants

Limiting Reactant: An Alternative Analogy — 3.7 Limiting Reactants

Limiting Reagent Problems Made Simple for Students — 3.7 Limiting Reactants

Coffee, Coins, and Limiting Reagents — 3.7 Limiting Reactants

Electron Results and Reaction Yields — 3.7 Limiting Reactants

Live Demonstrations: — **Section:**

Measuring Avogadro's Number on the Overhead Projector — 3.4 Avogadro's Number and the Mole

Demonstrations for Nonscience Majors: Using Common Objects to Illustrate Abstract Concepts — 3.4 Avogadro's Number and the Mole

Copper Sulfate: Blue to White — 3.5 Empirical Formulas from Analyses

Combustion of Hydrocarbons: A Stoichiometry Demonstration — 3.5 Empirical Formulas from Analyses

Interactive Demonstrations for Mole Ratios and Limiting Reagents — 3.7 Limiting Reactants

A Dramatic Classroom Demonstration of Limiting Reagent Using the Vinegar and Sodium Hydrogen Carbonate Reaction," — 3.7 Limiting Reactants

Chapter 3. Stoichiometry: Calculations with Chemical Formulas and Equations

Common Student Misconceptions

- Students confuse the subscripts in a chemical formula with the coefficients in front of the formula in a balanced reaction equation.
- Students have difficulties grasping the meaning of a mole as a "collective"; a mole of a substance contains a fixed number (6.022×10^{23}) of "building blocks" (atoms for most elements, molecules for molecular substances, formula units for ionic substances) in the same fashion as a dozen means 12 (eggs, people, items, etc.).
- Students often do not understand that mass of 1 mole of substance X can be significantly different from the mass of substance Y.
- Some students cannot distinguish between the number of moles actually manipulated in the laboratory versus the number of moles required by stoichiometry.
- Students do not appreciate that the coefficients in an empirical formula are not exact whole numbers because of experimental or round-off errors. In general, students have problems with the existence of experimental error.
- Students do not understand the difference between the amount of material present in the laboratory (or given in the problem) and the number of moles required by stoichiometry.
- Students do not understand that the reagent that gives the smallest amount of product is the limiting reactant.
- Students are often quite happy with a percent yield in excess of 100%.

Teaching Tips

- Students who have good high school backgrounds find this chapter quite easy. Others find this chapter extremely difficult. Very few students have heard the term *stoichiometry* and can be intimidated by the language of chemistry.
- Balancing equations requires some trial and error. Algorithm-loving students find this uncomfortable. It helps to make some "errors" on purpose when teaching how to balance reaction equations and show some common "tricks" of how to recover from those errors.
- The concept of limiting reactants is one of the most difficult for beginning students. Students need a lot of numerical practice here. The use of analogies is often quite helpful.
- Atomic weights may be obtained with many significant figures. Advise students to use a sufficient number of significant figures such that the number of significant figures in the answer to any calculation is not limited by the number of significant figures in the formula weights they use.

Lecture Outline

3.1 Chemical Equations[1,2,3,4,5]

- The quantitative nature of chemical formulas and reactions is called **stoichiometry**.
- Lavoisier observed that mass is conserved in a chemical reaction.
  - This observation is known as the law of conservation of mass.

---

[1] "More Chemistry in a Soda Bottle: A Conservation of Mass Activity" from Further Readings
[2] "Antoine Lavoisier and The Conservation of Matter" from Further Readings
[3] "Chemical Wastes and the Law of Conservation of Matter" from Further Readings
[4] "Formation of Water" Movie from Instructor's Resource CD/DVD
[5] Figure 3.3 from Transparency Pack

- **Chemical equations** give a description of a chemical reaction.
- There are two parts to any equation:
    - **reactants** (written to the left of the arrow) and
    - **products** (written to the right of the arrow):
$$2H_2 + O_2 \rightarrow 2H_2O$$
- There are two sets of numbers in a chemical equation:
    - numbers in front of the chemical formulas (called stoichiometric *coefficients*) and
    - numbers in the formulas (they appear as subscripts).
- Stoichiometric coefficients give the *ratio* in which the reactants and products exist.
- The subscripts give the ratio in which the atoms are found in the molecule.
    - Example:
        - H_2O means there are <u>two H atoms</u> for each one molecule of water.
        - $2H_2O$ means that there are <u>two water molecules</u> present.
- Note: in $2H_2O$ there are *four* hydrogen atoms present (two for each water molecule).

Balancing Equations[6,7,8,9,10,11,12,13,14,15,16,17]

- Matter cannot be lost in any chemical reaction.
    - Therefore, the products of a chemical reaction have to account for all the atoms present in the reactants–we must *balance* the chemical equation.
    - When balancing a chemical equation we adjust the stoichiometric coefficients in front of chemical formulas.
        - Subscripts in a formula are *never* changed when balancing an equation.
        - Example: the reaction of methane with oxygen:
$$CH_4 + O_2 \rightarrow CO_2 + H_2O$$
        - Counting *atoms* in the reactants yields:
            - 1 C;
            - 4 H; and
            - 2 O.
        - In the products we see:
            - 1 C;
            - 2 H; and
            - 3 O.
        - It appears as though H has been lost and O has been created.
        - To balance the equation, we adjust the stoichiometric coefficients:
$$CH_4 + 2O_2 \rightarrow CO_2 + 2H_2O$$

---

[6] "Reading a Chemical Equation" Activity from Instructor's Resource CD/DVD
[7] Figure 3.4 from Transparency Pack
[8] "Balancing Chemical Equations by Inspection" from Further Readings
[9] "The Fruit Basket Analogy" from Further Readings
[10] "A New Inspection Method for Balancing Redox Equations" from Further Readings
[11] "On Balancing Chemical Equations: Past and Present (A Critical Review and Annotated Bibliography)" from Further Readings
[12] "Reading A Balanced Chemical Equation" Activity from Instructor's Resource CD/DVD
[13] "How to Say How Much: Amounts and Stoichiometry" from Further Readings
[14] Figure 3.5 from Transparency Pack
[15] "Counting Atoms" Activity from Instructor's Resource CD/DVD
[16] "Balancing Equations" Activity from Instructor's Resource CD/DVD
[17] "Sodium and Potassium in Water" Movie from Instructor's Resource CD/DVD

Indicating the States of Reactants and Products

- The physical state of each reactant and product may be added to the equation:

$$CH_4(g) + 2O_2(g) \rightarrow CO_2(g) + 2H_2O(g)$$

- Reaction conditions occasionally appear above or below the reaction arrow (e.g., "Δ" is often used to indicate the addition of heat).

FORWARD REFERENCES

- Stoichiometric coefficients will be used to determine molar ratios (stoichiometric factors) in stoichiometric questions later in Chapter 3 as well as in Chapter 4 (section 4.6 on solution stoichiometry), Chapter 5 (stoichiometry of heat and Hess's Law), Chapter 10 (stoichiometry of gaseous reactions), Chapter 20 (section 20.9 on electrolysis).
- Stoichiometric coefficients will appear as powers to which concentrations and pressures are raised when writing equilibrium constant expressions of reversible reactions in Chapters 15-17, 19-20, and when writing rate law equations for elementary steps in Chapter 14.

3.2 Some Simple Patterns of Chemical Reactivity

Combination and Decomposition Reactions[18,19,20,21,22,23]

- In **combination reactions** two or more substances react to form one product.
- Combination reactions have more reactants than products.
    - Consider the reaction:

$$2Mg(s) + O_2(g) \rightarrow 2MgO(s)$$

    - Since there are fewer products than reactants, the Mg has combined with O_2 to form MgO.
    - Note that the structure of the reactants has changed.
    - Mg consists of closely packed atoms and O_2 consists of dispersed molecules.
    - MgO consists of a lattice of Mg^{2+} and O^{2-} ions.
- In **decomposition reactions** one substance undergoes a reaction to produce two or more other substances.
- Decomposition reactions have more products than reactants.
    - Consider the reaction that occurs in an automobile air bag:

$$2NaN_3(s) \rightarrow 2Na(s) + 3N_2(g)$$

    - Since there are more products than reactants, the sodium azide has decomposed into sodium metal and nitrogen gas.

Combustion Reactions

- **Combustion reactions** are rapid reactions that produce a flame.
    - Most combustion reactions involve the reaction of $O_2(g)$ from air.
    - Example: combustion of a hydrocarbon (propane) to produce carbon dioxide and water.

$$C_3H_8(g) + 5O_2(g) \rightarrow 3CO_2(g) + 4H_2O(l)$$

FORWARD REFERENCES

- Combustion reactions will be mentioned in Chapter 5 (as exothermic reactions involving fuels) and further discussed in Chapter 24 (as oxidation of organic compounds).
- Additional specific/important types of reactions will be introduced throughout the textbook.

---

[18] "Lime" from Further Readings
[19] Figure 3.6 from Transparency Pack
[20] "Reactions with Oxygen" Movie from Instructor's Resource CD/DVD
[21] "Air Bags" Animation from Instructor's Resource CD/DVD
[22] "Nitrogen Triiodide" Movie from Instructor's Resource CD/DVD
[23] "Formation of Aluminum Bromide" Movie from Instructor's Resource CD/DVD

3.3 Formula Weights

Formula and Molecular Weights[24]

- **Formula weight** (FW) is the sum of atomic weights for the atoms shown in the chemical formula.
  - Example: FW (H_2SO_4)
    - $= 2AW(H) + AW(S) + 4AW(O)$
    - $= 2(1.0 \text{ amu}) + 32.1 \text{ amu} + 4(16.0 \text{ amu}) = 98.1 \text{ amu}.$
- **Molecular weight** (MW) is the sum of the atomic weights of the atoms in a molecule as shown in the molecular formula.
  - Example: MW ($C_6H_{12}O_6$)
    - $= 6(12.0 \text{ amu}) + 12 (1.0 \text{ amu}) + 6 (16.0 \text{ amu})$
    - $= 180.0 \text{ amu}.$
- Formula weight of the repeating unit (*formula unit)* is used for ionic substances.
  - Example: FW (NaCl)
    - $= 23.0 \text{ amu} + 35.5 \text{ amu}$
    - $= 58.5 \text{ amu}.$

Percentage Composition from Formulas[25,26]

- *Percentage composition* is obtained by dividing the mass contributed by each element (number of atoms times AW) by the formula weight of the compound and multiplying by 100.

$$\% \text{ element} = \frac{(\text{number of atoms of that element})(\text{atomic weight of element})(100)}{(\text{formula weight of compound})}$$

FORWARD REFERENCES
- The ability to calculate molecular and formula weights will be an essential skill in finding molar masses throughout the textbook.

3.4 Avogadro's Number and The Mole[27,28,29,30,31,32,33,34,35,36,37,38,39,40,41,42]

---

[24] "Gram Formula Weights and Fruit Salad" from Further Readings
[25] "Percentage Composition and Empirical Formula—A New View" from Further Readings
[26] "Molecular Weight and Weight Percent" Activity from Instructor's Resource CD/DVD
[27] "Mole, Mole per Liter, and Molar: A Primer on SI and Related Units for Chemistry Students" from Further Readings
[28] "Developing an Intuitive Approach to Moles" from Further Readings
[29] "The Mole, the Periodic Table, and Quantum Numbers: An Introductory Trio" from Further Readings
[30] "The Size of a Mole" from Further Readings
[31] "What's a Mole For?" from Further Readings
[32] "The Mole Concept: Developing an Instrument to Assess Conceptual Understanding" from Further Readings
[33] "A Mole of M&Ms" from Further Readings
[34] "How to Visualize Avogadro's Number" from Further Readings
[35] "Measuring Avogadro's Number on the Overhead Projector" from Live Demonstrations
[36] "Demonstrations for Nonscience Majors: Using Common Objects to Illustrate Abstract Concepts" from Live Demonstrations
[37] "Using Monetary Analogies to Teach Average Atomic Mass" from Further Readings
[38] "Pictorial Analogies IV: Relative Atomic Weights" from Further Readings
[39] "Relative Atomic Mass and the Mole: A Concrete Analogy to Help Students These Abstract Concepts" from Further Readings

- The **mole** (abbreviated "mol") is a convenient measure of chemical quantities.
- 1 mole of something = 6.0221421×10^{23} of that thing.
  - This number is called **Avogadro's number**.
  - Thus, 1 mole of carbon atoms = 6.0221421×10^{23} carbon atoms.
- Experimentally, 1 mole of ^{12}C has a mass of 12 g.

Molar Mass[43,44,45]

- The mass in grams of 1 mole of substance is said to be the **molar mass** of that substance. Molar mass has units of g/mol (also written $g \cdot mol^{-1}$).
- The mass of 1 mole of ^{12}C = 12 g. Exactly.
- The molar mass of a molecule is the sum of the molar masses of the atoms:
  - Example: The molar mass of N_2 = 2 × (molar mass of N).
- Molar masses for elements are found on the periodic table.
- The formula weight (in amu) is numerically equal to the molar mass (in g/mol).

Interconverting Masses and Moles

- Look at units:
  - Mass: g
  - Moles: mol
  - Molar mass: g/mol
- To convert between grams and moles, we use the molar mass.

Interconverting Masses and Numbers of Particles[46]

- Units:
  - Number of particles: 6.022×10^{23} mol^{-1} (Avogadro's number).
  - Note: g/mol × mol = g (i.e. molar mass × moles = mass), and
  - mol × mol^{-1} = a number (i.e. moles × Avogadro's number = molecules).
- To convert between moles and molecules we use Avogadro's number.

FORWARD REFERENCES

- It may be desirable to calculate molar masses with higher precision in later chapters.
- Avogadro number will be used to calculate the energy of 1 mole of photons in Chapter 6.
- Moles of electrons will be used in Chapter 7 (ionization energy or electron affinity), and in Chapter 20 to balance half-reactions and solve electrolysis problems.
- Bond dissociation energies (Chapter 8) and tabulated thermodynamic data (Appendix C) are mostly expressed per mole of bonds or substance.
- Moles will be used to calculate *molar* and *molal* concentrations (Chapters 4 and 11).
- Moles will be used in the Ideal Gas Law in Chapter 10.

---

[40] "Moles, Pennies, and Nickels" from Further Readings
[41] "A Mole Mnemonic" from Further Readings
[42] "Analogies to Indicate the Size of Atoms and Molecules and the Magnitude of Avogadro's Number" from Further Readings
[43] Figure 3.8 from Transparency Pack
[44] "Demonstrations of the Enormity of Avogadro's Number" from Further Readings
[45] "For Mole Problems, Call Avogadro: 602-1023" from Further Readings
[46] Figure 3.12 from Transparency Pack

3.5 Empirical Formulas from Analyses[47,48,49,50,51,52,53,54,55,56,57,58,59,60]

- Recall that the empirical formula gives the *relative* number of atoms of each element in the molecule.
- Finding empirical formula from mass percent data:
  - We start with the mass percent of elements (i.e. empirical data) and calculate a formula.
  - Assume we start with 100 g of sample.
  - The mass percent then translates as the number of grams of each element in 100 g of sample.
  - From these masses, the number of moles can be calculated (using the atomic weights from the periodic table).
  - The lowest whole-number ratio of moles is the empirical formula.
- Finding the empirical mass percent of elements from the empirical formula.
  - If we have the empirical formula, we know how many moles of each element is present in one mole of same.
  - Then we use molar masses (or atomic weights) to convert to grams of each element.
  - We divide the number of grams of each element by the number of grams of 1 mole of sample to get the fraction of each element in 1 mole of sample.
  - Multiply each fraction by 100 to convert to a percent.

Molecular Formulas from Empirical Formulas[61]

- The empirical formula (relative ratio of elements in the molecule) may not be the molecular formula (actual ratio of elements in the molecule).
- Example: ascorbic acid (vitamin C) has the empirical formula $C_3H_4O_3$.
  - The molecular formula is $C_6H_8O_6$.
  - To get the molecular formula from the empirical formula, we need to know the molecular weight, MW.
  - The ratio of molecular weight (MW) to formula weight (FW) of the empirical formula must be a whole number.

Combustion Analysis[62]

- Empirical formulas are routinely determined by combustion analysis.
- A sample containing C, H, and O is combusted in excess oxygen to produce CO_2 and H_2O.
- The amount of CO_2 gives the amount of C originally present in the sample.

[47] "Water" 3-D Model from Instructor's Resource CD/DVD
[48] "Hydrogen Peroxide" 3-D Model from Instructor's Resource CD/DVD
[49] "Sucrose" 3-D Model from Instructor's Resource CD/DVD
[50] "Oxygen" 3-D Model from Instructor's Resource CD/DVD
[51] "Methane" 3-D Model from Instructor's Resource CD/DVD
[52] "Carbon Dioxide" 3-D Model from Instructor's Resource CD/DVD
[53] "Glycine (molecular form)" 3-D Model from Instructor's Resource CD/DVD
[54] "Ethane" 3-D Model from Instructor's Resource CD/DVD
[55] "Methanol" 3-D Model from Instructor's Resource CD/DVD
[56] "A Known-to-Unknown Approach to Teach About Empirical and Molecular Formulas" from Further Readings
[57] "Making Assumptions Explicit: How the Law of Conservation of Matter Can Explain Empirical Formula Problems" from Further Readings
[58] "A Simple Rhyme for a Simple Formula" from Further Readings
[59] Figure 3.13 from Transparency Pack
[60] "Empirical Formula Determination: C_8H_6O" Activity from Instructor's Resource CD/DVD
[61] "Copper Sulfate: Blue to White" from Live Demonstrations
[62] "Combustion of Hydrocarbons: A Stoichiometry Demonstration" from Live Demonstrations

- The amount of H_2O gives the amount of H originally present in the sample.
  - Watch the stoichiometry: 1 mol H_2O contains 2 mol H.
- The amount of O originally present in the sample is given by the difference between the amount of sample and the amount of C and H accounted for.
- More complicated methods can be used to quantify the amounts of other elements present, but they rely on analogous methods.

3.6 Quantitative Information from Balanced Equations[63,64,65,66,67,68,69,70]

- The coefficients in a balanced chemical equation give the relative numbers of molecules (or formula units) involved in the reaction.
- The stoichiometric coefficients in the balanced equation may be interpreted as:
  - the relative numbers of molecules or formula units involved in the reaction or
  - the relative numbers of moles involved in the reaction.
- The molar quantities indicated by the coefficients in a balanced equation are called *stoichiometrically equivalent quantities*.
- Stoichiometric factors (or molar ratios) may be used to convert between quantities of reactants and products in a reaction.
- It is important to realize that the stoichiometric ratios are the ideal proportions in which reactants are needed to form products.
- A balanced reaction equation often provides more stoichiometric factors (or molar ratios) than needed to solve any particular stoichiometric problem. Often only one or two of them are relevant in a given problem.
- The number of grams of reactant cannot be *directly* related to the number of grams of product.
  - To get grams of product from grams of reactant:
    - convert grams of reactant to moles of reactant (use molar mass),
    - convert moles of one reactant to moles of other reactants and products (use the stoichiometric ratio from the balanced chemical equation),
    - convert moles back into grams for desired product (use molar mass).

FORWARD REFERENCES
- In Chapter 4 students will learn how to convert solution molarity and volume data into moles.
- In Chapter 10 students will learn how to use P, V and T information to find moles of gas.
- Stoichiometry of reactions will be further exploited when writing rate law expressions for elementary steps (Chapter 14) as well as equilibrium constant and reaction quotient expressions (Chapters 15, 16, 17, 19, and 20).
- Acid-base titrations mentioned in Chapter 4, and further discussed in Chapter 17, are practical applications of stoichiometry of acid-base neutralization reactions.

---

[63] "How Many Digits Should We Use in Formula or Molar Mass Calculation" from Further Readings
[64] "Amounts Tables as a Diagnostic Tool for Flawed Stoichiometric Reasoning" from Further Readings
[65] "Stoogiometry: A Cognitive Approach to Teaching Stoichiometry" from Further Readings
[66] "Teaching Stoichiometry: A Two-Cycle Approach" from Further Readings
[67] "Pictorial Analogies XII: Stoichiometric Calculations" from Further Readings
[68] Figure 3.16 from Transparency Pack
[69] "Stoichiometry Calculation" Activity from Instructor's Resource CD/DVD
[70] "A Recipe for Teaching Stoichiometry" from Further Readings

3.7 Limiting Reactants[71,72,73,74,75,76,77,78,79,80,81]

- It is not necessary to have all reactants present in stoichiometric amounts.
- Often, one or more reactants is present in excess.
- Therefore, at the end of reaction those reactants present in excess will still be in the reaction mixture.
- The one or more reactants which are completely consumed are called the **limiting reactants**.
  - Reactants present in excess are called *excess reactants*.
- Consider 10 H_2 molecules mixed with 7 O_2 molecules to form water.
  - The balanced chemical equation tells us that the stoichiometric ratio of H_2 to O_2 is 2 to 1:
$$2H_2(g) + O_2(g) \rightarrow 2H_2O(l)$$
  - This means that our 10 H_2 molecules require 5 O_2 molecules (2:1).
  - Since we have 7 O_2 molecules, our reaction is *limited* by the amount of H_2 we have (the O_2 is present in excess).
  - So, all 10 H_2 molecules can (and do) react with 5 of the O_2 molecules producing 10 H_2O molecules.
  - At the end of the reaction, 2 O_2 molecules remain unreacted.

Theoretical Yields

- The amount of product predicted from stoichiometry, taking into account limiting reactants, is called the **theoretical yield**.
  - This is often different from the *actual yield* – the amount of product actually obtained in the reaction.
- The **percent yield** relates the actual yield (amount of material recovered in the laboratory) to the theoretical yield:

$$\text{Percent yield} = \frac{\text{actual yield}}{\text{theoretical yield}} \times 100$$

FORWARD REFERENCES

- Buffering action calculations in Chapter 17 (section 17.2) and pH calculations in acid-base titrations (section 17.3) can be viewed as stoichiometric problems with a limiting reactant (added strong acid or base).

---

[71] "Learning Stoichiometry with Hamburger Sandwiches" from Further Readings
[72] "Limiting Reagent" Animation from Instructor's Resource CD/DVD
[73] "Limiting and Excess Reagents, Theoretical Yield" from Further Readings
[74] "Limiting Reagents" Activity from Instructor's Resource CD/DVD
[75] "Limiting Reactant: An Alternative Analogy" from Further Readings
[76] "Limiting Reagent Problems Made Simple for Students" from Further Readings
[77] "Election Results and Reaction Yields" from Further Readings
[78] Figure 3.17 from Transparency Pack
[79] "Interactive Demonstrations for the Mole Ratios and Limiting Reagents" from Live Demonstrations
[80] "Coffee, Coins, and Limiting Reagents" from Further Readings
[81] "A Dramatic Classroom Demonstration of Limiting Reagent Using the Vinegar and Sodium Hydrogen Carbonate Reaction" from Live Demonstrations

Further Readings:

1. Frederic L. Holmes, "Antoine Lavoisier and The Conservation of Matter," *Chemical and Engineering News*, **September 12, 1994**, 38–45.

2. John W. Hill, "Chemical Wastes and the Law of Conservation of Matter," *J. Chem. Educ.*, Vol. 58, **1981**, 996.

3. Daniel Q. Duffy, Stephanie A. Shaw, William D. Bare and Kenneth A. Goldsby, "More Chemistry in a Soda Bottle: A Conservation of Mass Activity," *J. Chem. Educ.*, Vol. 72, **1995**, 734–736.

4. William C. Herndon, "On Balancing Chemical Equations: Past and Present (A Critical Review and Annotated Bibliography)," *J. Chem. Educ.*, Vol. 74, **1997**, 1359–1362.

5. Zoltan Toth, "Balancing Chemical Equations by Inspection," *J. Chem. Educ.*, Vol. 74, **1997**, 1363–1364.

6. William Bleam, Jr., "The Fruit Basket Analogy," *J. Chem. Educ.*, Vol. 58, **1981**, 184. An analogy to help students master balancing equations.

7. Chunshi Guo, "A New Inspection Method for Balancing Redox Equations," *J. Chem. Educ.*, Vol. 74, **1997**, 1365–1366.

8. Kenneth W. Watkins, "Lime," J. *Chem. Educ.*, Vol. 60, **1983**, 60–63. An article on a some of the uses of quicklime (CaO) and hydrated lime (Ca(OH)$_2$).

9. Arthur M. Last and Michael J. Webb, "Using Monetary Analogies to Teach Average Atomic Mass," *J. Chem. Educ.*, Vol. 70, **1993**, 234–235.

10. John H. Fortman, "Pictorial Analogies IV: Relative Atomic Weights," *J. Chem. Educ.*, Vol. 70, **1993**, 235–236.

11. Josefina Arce de Sanabia, "Relative Atomic Mass and the Mole: A Concrete Analogy to Help Students Understand These Abstract Concepts," *J. Chem. Educ.*, Vol. 70, **1993**, 233–234.

12. George L. Gilbert, "Percentage Composition and Empirical Formula–A New View," *J. Chem. Educ.*, Vol. 75, **1998**, 851.

13. George Gorin, "Mole, Mole per Liter, and Molar. A Primer on SI and Related Units for Chemistry Students," *J. Chem. Educ.*, Vol. 80, **2003**, 103–104.

14. Dawn M. Wakeley and Hans de Grys, "Developing an Intuitive Approach to Moles," *J. Chem. Educ.*, Vol. 77, **2000**, 1007–1009.

15. Mali Yin and Raymond S. Ochs, "The Mole, the Periodic Table, and Quantum Numbers: An Introductory Trio," *J. Chem. Educ.*, Vol. 78, **2001**, 1345–1347.

16. Miriam Toloudis, "The Size of a Mole," *J. Chem. Educ.*, Vol. 73, **1996**, 348.

17. Sheryl Dominic, "What's a Mole For?" *J. Chem. Educ.*, Vol. 73, **1996**, 309.

18. Shanthi R. Krishnan and Ann C. Howe, "The Mole Concept: Developing An Instrument to Assess Conceptual Understanding," *J. Chem. Educ.*, Vol. 71, **1994**, 653–655.

19. R. Thomas Myers, "Moles, Pennies, and Nickels," *J. Chem. Educ.*, Vol. 66, **1989**, 249.

20. Bernard S. Brown, "A Mole Mnemonic," *J. Chem. Educ.*, Vol. 68, **1991**, 1039.

21. Carmela Merlo and Kathleen E. Turner, "A Mole of M&M's," *J. Chem. Educ.*, Vol. 70, **1993**, 453.

22. Henk van Lubeck, "How to Visualize Avogadro's Number," *J. Chem. Educ.*, Vol. 66, **1989**, 762.

23. Paul S. Poskozim, James W. Warrick, Permsook Tiempetpaisal and Joyce Albin Poskozim, "Analogies for Avogadro's Number," *J. Chem. Educ.*, Vol. 63, **1986**, 125–126.

24. Damon Diemente, "Demonstrations of the Enormity of Avogadro's Number," *J. Chem. Educ.*, Vol. 75, **1998**, 1565–1566.

25. R. E. Ulte, "For Mole Problems, Call Avogadro: 602-1023", *J. Chem. Educ.*, Vol. 79, **2002**, 1213.

26. M. Dale Alexander, Gordon J. Ewing, and Floyd T. Abbott, "Analogies that Indicate the Size of Atoms and Molecules and the Magnitude of Avogadro's Number," *J. Chem. Educ.*, Vol. 61, **1984**, 591.

27. Wayne L. Felty, "Gram Formula Weights and Fruit Salad," *J. Chem. Educ.*, Vol. 62, **1985**, 61.

28. P. K. Thamburaj, "A Known-to-Unknown Approach to Teach About Empirical and Molecular Formulas," *J. Chem. Educ.*, Vol. 78, **2001**, 915–916.

29. Stephen DeMeo, "Making Assumptions Explicit: How the Law of Conservation of Matter Can Explain Empirical Formula Problems," *J. Chem. Educ.*, Vol. 78, **2001**, 1050–1052.

30. Joel S. Thompson, "A Simple Rhyme for a Simple Formula," *J. Chem. Educ.*, Vol. 65, **1988**, 704. An easy way to remember the strategy for converting percentage composition to an empirical formula. "Percent to mass, Mass to mol, Divide by small, Multiply 'til whole".

31. Christer Svensson, "How Many Digits Should we Use in Formula or Molar Mass Calculation", *J. Chem. Educ.*, Vol. 81, **2004**, 827–829.

32. John Olmsted III, "Amounts Tables as a Diagnostic Tool for Flawed Stoichiometric Reasoning," *J. Chem. Educ.*, Vol. 76, **1999**, 52–54.

33. Carla R. Krieger, "Stoogiometry: A Cognitive Approach to Teaching Stoichiometry," *J. Chem. Educ.*, Vol. 74, **1997**, 306–309.

34. Richard L. Poole, "Teaching Stoichiometry: A Two-Cycle Approach," *J. Chem. Educ.*, Vol. 66, **1989**, 57.

35. Jean B. Umland, "A Recipe for Teaching Stoichiometry," *J. Chem. Educ.*, Vol. 61, **1984**, 1036–1037.

36. Addison Ault, "How to Say How Much: Amounts and Stoichiometry," *J. Chem. Educ.*, Vol. 78, **2001**, 1347–1348.

37. John J. Fortman, "Pictorial Analogies XII: Stoichiometric Calculations," *J. Chem. Educ.*, Vol. 71, **1994**, 571–572.

38. Liliana Haim, Eduardo Corton, Santiago Kocmur, and Lydia Galagovsky, "Learning Stoichiometry with Hamburger Sandwiches," *J. Chem. Educ.*, Vol. 80, **2003**, 1021–1022.

39. Ernest F. Silversmith, "Limiting and Excess Reagents, Theoretical Yield," *J. Chem. Educ.*, Vol. 62, **1985**, 61.

40. Zoltan Toth, "Limiting Reactant: An Alternative Analogy," *J. Chem. Educ.*, Vol. 76, **1999**, 934.

41. A. H. Kalantar, "Limiting Reagent Problems Made Simple for Students," *J. Chem. Educ.*, Vol. 62, **1985**, 106.

42. Dennis McMinn, "Coffee, Coins, and Limiting Reagents," *J. Chem. Educ.*, Vol. 61, **1984**, 591.

43. Romeu C. Rocha-Filho, "Electron Results and Reaction Yields," *J. Chem. Educ.*, Vol. 64, **1987**, 248.

Live Demonstrations:

1. Sally Solomon and Chinhyu Hur, "Measuring Avogadro's Number on the Overhead Projector," *J. Chem. Educ.*, Vol. 70, **1993**, 252–253. A monolayer of stearic acid on water is used to estimate Avogadro's number.

2. William Laurita, "Demonstrations for Nonscience Majors: Using Common Objects to Illustrate Abstract Concepts," *J. Chem. Educ.*, Vol. 67, **1990**, 60–61. This reference includes a demonstration of the measurement of Avogadro's number.

3. Lee. R. Summerlin,, Christie L. Borgford, and Julie B. Ealy, "Copper Sulfate: Blue to White," *Chemical Demonstrations, A Sourcebook for Teachers*, Volume 2 (Washington: American Chemical Society, **1988**), pp. 69–70. An exploration of color change associated with the dehydration of copper sulfate.

4. M. Dale Alexander and Wayne C. Woolsey, "Combustion of Hydrocarbons: A Stoichiometry Demonstration," *J. Chem. Educ.*, Vol. 70, **1993**, 327–328. The combustion of methane, propane, and butane are compared in this simple demonstration of stoichiometry.

5. Crystal Wood and Bryan Breyfogle, "Interactive Demonstrations for Mole Ratios and Limiting Reagents," *J. Chem. Educ.*, Vol. 83, **2006**, 741–748.

6. Romklao Artdej, Tienthong Thongpanchang, Stacy DeWees Hovede, "A Dramatic Classroom Demonstration of Limiting Reagent Using the Vinegar and Sodium Hydrogen Carbonate Reaction," *J. Chem. Educ.*, Vol. 85, **2008**, 1382-1384.

Chapter 4. Reactions in Aqueous Solution

Media Resources

Figures and Tables in Transparency Pack:	**Section:**
Figure 4.4 A Precipitation Reaction	4.2 Precipitation Reactions
Table 4.1 Solubility Guidelines for Common Ionic Compounds in Water	4.2 Precipitation Reactions
Table 4.5 Activity Series of Metals in Aqueous Solutions	4.4 Oxidation-Reduction Reactions
Figure 4.18 Procedures for Solving Stoichiometry Problems	4.6 Solution Stoichiometry and Chemical Analysis

Animations:	**Section:**
Electrolytes and Nonelectrolytes	4.1 General Properties of Aqueous Solutions
Dissolution of NaCl in Water	4.1 General Properties of Aqueous Solutions
Introduction to Aqueous Acids	4.3 Acids, Bases, and Neutralization Reactions
Introduction to Aqueous Bases	4.3 Acids, Bases, and Neutralization Reactions
Dissolution of $Mg(OH)_2$ by Acid	4.3 Acids, Bases, and Neutralization Reactions
Oxidation-Reduction Reactions: Part I	4.4 Oxidation-Reduction Reactions
Oxidation-Reduction Reactions: Part II	4.4 Oxidation-Reduction Reactions
Solution Formation from a Solid	4.5 Concentrations of Solutions
Dissolution of $KMnO_4$	4.5 Concentrations of Solutions
Solution Formation by Dilution	4.5 Concentrations of Solutions
Acid-Base Titration	4.6 Solution Stoichiometry and Chemical Analysis

Movies:	**Section:**
Strong and Weak Electrolytes	4.1 General Properties of Aqueous Solutions
Precipitation Reactions	4.2 Precipitation Reactions
Reduction of CuO	4.4 Oxidation-Reduction Reactions
Oxidation-Reduction Chemistry of Tin and Zinc	4.4 Oxidation-Reduction Reactions
Formation of Silver Crystals	4.4 Oxidation-Reduction Reactions

Activities:	**Section:**
Ionic Compounds	4.2 Precipitation Reactions
Writing a Net Ionic Equation	4.2 Precipitation Reactions
Oxidation Numbers I	4.4 Oxidation-Reduction Reactions
Oxidation Numbers II	4.4 Oxidation-Reduction Reactions
Precipitation, Redox, and Neutralization Reactions	4.4 Oxidation-Reduction Reactions
Acid-Base Titration	4.6 Solution Stoichiometry and Chemical Analysis

3-D Models:	**Section:**
Water	4.1 General Properties of Aqueous Solutions
Hydrogen Chloride	4.1 General Properties of Aqueous Solutions
Acetic Acid	4.1 General Properties of Aqueous Solutions
Ammonia	4.1 General Properties of Aqueous Solutions
Ammonium Ion	4.1 General Properties of Aqueous Solutions
Nitric Acid	4.1 General Properties of Aqueous Solutions

Ethanol
Formic Acid
Carbon Dioxide
Hydrogen Carbonate Ion
Hydroxide Ion

4.1 General Properties of Aqueous Solutions
4.1 General Properties of Aqueous Solutions
4.3 Acids, Bases, and Neutralization Reactions
4.3 Acids, Bases, and Neutralization Reactions
4.3 Acids, Bases, and Neutralization Reactions

Other Resources

Further Readings:

Solubility Rules: Three Suggestions for Improved Understanding

An Analogy for Solubility: Marbles and Magnets
Reinforcing Net Ionic Equation Writing
The Origin of the Term Base
Significance, Concentration Calculations, Weak and Strong Acids
Factors that Influence Relative Acid Strength in in Water: A Simple Model
When Is a Strong Electrolyte Strong?
Pictorial Analogies X: Solutions of Electrolytes
Oxidation and Reduction
Oxidation Numbers
Simple Method for Determination of Oxidation Numbers of Atoms in Compounds
What Makes Gold Such a Noble Metal?
A Cyclist's Guide to Ionic Concentration
Teaching Dilutions
On the Use of Intravenous Solutions to Teach Some Principles of Solution Chemistry
Acid-Base Indicators: A New Look at an Old Topic

Section:
4.2 Precipitation Reactions

4.2 Precipitation Reactions
4.2 Precipitation Reactions
4.3 Acids, Bases, and Neutralization Reactions
4.3 Acids, Bases, and Neutralization Reactions

4.3 Acids, Bases, and Neutralization Reactions

4.3 Acids, Bases, and Neutralization Reactions
4.3 Acids, Bases, and Neutralization Reactions
4.4 Oxidation-Reduction Reactions
4.4 Oxidation-Reduction Reactions
4.4 Oxidation-Reduction Reactions

4.5 Concentrations of Solutions
4.5 Concentrations of Solutions
4.5 Concentrations of Solutions
4.5 Concentrations of Solutions

4.6 Solution Stoichiometry and Chemical Analysis

Live Demonstrations:

Conductivity and Extent of Dissociation of Acids in Aqueous Solution
Name That Precipitate
Solubility of Some Silver Compounds
Alka Seltzer Poppers: an Interactive Exploration
Food Is Usually Acidic, Cleaners Are Usually Basic
A Hand-Held Reaction: Production of Ammonia Gas
Fizzing and Foaming: Reactions of Acids with Carbonates
Demonstrations with Red Cabbage Indicator
Determination of Neutralizing Capacity of Antacids
Milk of Magnesia versus Acid
Oxidation States of Manganese: Mn^{7+}, Mn^{6+}, Mn^{4+}, and Mn^{2+}
Producing Hydrogen Gas from Calcium Metal
Making Hydrogen Gas from an Acid and a Base
Activity Series for Some Metals
An Activity Series: Zinc, Copper, and Silver Half-Cells

Section:
4.1 General Properties of Aqueous Solutions

4.2 Precipitation Reactions
4.2 Precipitation Reactions
4.3 Acids, Bases, and Neutralization Reactions
4.3 Acids, Bases, and Neutralization Reactions
4.3 Acids, Bases, and Neutralization Reactions
4.3 Acids, Bases, and Neutralization Reactions

4.3 Acids, Bases, and Neutralization Reactions
4.3 Acids, Bases, and Neutralization Reactions
4.3 Acids, Bases, and Neutralization Reactions
4.4 Oxidation-Reduction Reactions

4.4 Oxidation-Reduction Reactions
4.4 Oxidation-Reduction Reactions
4.4 Oxidation-Reduction Reactions
4.4 Oxidation-Reduction Reactions

Floating Pennies
A Cool Drink! An Introduction to Concentrations
Colorful Acid-Base Indicators
Rainbow Colors with Mixed Acid-Base Indicators
Acid-Base Indicators Extracted from Plants
Teas as Natural Indicators

4.4 Oxidation-Reduction Reactions
4.5 Concentrations of Solutions
4.6 Solution Stoichiometry and Chemical Analysis
4.6 Solution Stoichiometry and Chemical Analysis
4.6 Solution Stoichiometry and Chemical Analysis
4.6 Solution Stoichiometry and Chemical Analysis

Chapter 4. Reactions in Aqueous Solution

Common Student Misconceptions

- Molarity is moles of solute per *liter of solution*, not per liter of solvent.
- Students sometimes use moles instead of molarity in $M_{initial}V_{initial} = M_{final}V_{final}$.
- Students often disregard rules for significant figures when calculating or using molarities.
- Students sometimes think that water is a good conductor.
- Students sometimes have a problem with the arbitrary difference between strong and weak electrolytes.
- Students often think that nonelectrolytes produce no ions in aqueous solution at all.
- Students sometimes cannot tell the difference between dissolution and dissociation.
- The symbols $\rightleftharpoons$ (equilibrium) and $\Leftrightarrow$ (resonance) are often confused.
- Students often do not see that the net ionic equation for the reaction between strong acids and strong bases is always $H^+(aq) + OH^-(aq) \rightleftharpoons H_2O(l)$.
- Students try to split polyatomic ions into smaller ions when they write net ionic equations.
- Students often think that a compound consisting of nonmetals only must be molecular (counter-example: $(NH_4)_2SO_4$ which is ionic!)
- Students do not realize that *insoluble* really means *poorly soluble*.
- Students do not appreciate the difference between equivalence point and end point.
- Students usually think that an oxidation necessarily involves a reaction with oxygen and/or addition of an atom of oxygen to the formula.
- Students often think that all atoms of the same element must have the same oxidation number and that this number is uniquely related to the atom's location in the periodic table.
- The equivalence point of a titration is the point where the stoichiometrically correct number of moles of each reactant is present. The end point of a titration is the point where the indicator changes. They are not the same although we choose an indicator that will change as close to the equivalence point as possible. As a consequence, students often equate the terms *equivalence point* and *end point*.

Teaching Tips

- Weaknesses in recollection of ionic nomenclature and the structure of common ions often make it difficult for students to write molecular, complete ionic, and net ionic equations for metathesis reactions. A brief review of ionic nomenclature is often useful prior to covering metathesis reactions.
- Writing the net ionic equation makes it easier for students to focus on the ions participating in a chemical reaction. It is important for students to remember that, although they do not appear in the net ionic equation, the spectator ions are still present in the solution.
- Students may be familiar with two good mnemonics for redox reactions: (1) LEO the lion says GER: *L*ose *e*lectrons *o*xidation, *g*ain *e*lectrons *r*eduction and (2) OIL RIG: *O*xidation *i*nvolves *l*oss of electrons, *r*eduction *i*nvolves *g*ain of electrons.

Lecture Outline

4.1 General Properties of Aqueous Solutions[1]

- A *solution* is a homogeneous mixture of two or more substances.
- A solution is made when one substance (the **solute**) is dissolved in another (the **solvent**).
- The solute is the substance that is present in the smallest amount.
- Solutions in which water is the solvent are called **aqueous solutions**.

Electrolytic Properties[2]

- All aqueous solutions can be classified in terms of whether or not they conduct electricity.
- If a substance forms ions in solution, then the substance is an **electrolyte** and the solution conducts electricity. An example is NaCl.
- If a substance does not form ions in solution, then the substance is a **nonelectrolyte** and the solution does not conduct electricity. Examples are sucrose and water.

Ionic Compounds in Water[3,4]

- When an ionic compound dissolves in water, the ions are said to *dissociate*.
    - This means that in solution, the solid no longer exists as a well-ordered arrangement of ions in contact with one another.
    - Instead, each ion is surrounded by several water molecules; it is called an *aqueous ion* denoted using the abbreviation "*aq*".
        - These ions are said to be **solvated**.
    - This tends to stabilize the ions in solution and prevent cations and anions from recombining.
    - The positive ions have the oxygen atoms of water pointing towards the ion; negative ions have the hydrogen atoms of water pointing towards the ion.
    - The transport of ions through the solution causes electric current to flow through the solution.

Molecular Compounds in Water[5,6]

- When a molecular compound (e.g. CH_3OH) dissolves in water, the solution usually consists of intact molecules dispersed homogeneously in the solution.
- Therefore, there is nothing in the solution to transport electric charge and the solution does not conduct electricity and most molecular compounds are nonelectrolytes.
- There are some important exceptions.
    - For example, $HCl(g)$ in water *ionizes* to form $H^+(aq)$ and $Cl^-(aq)$.

Strong and Weak Electrolytes[7,8,9,10,11]

- Compounds whose aqueous solutions conduct electricity well are called **strong electrolytes**.
    - These substances exist in solution mostly as ions.
        - Example: NaCl

---

[1] "Water" 3-D Model from Instructor's Resource CD/DVD
[2] "Electrolytes and Nonelectrolytes" Animation from Instructor's Resource CD/DVD
[3] "Dissolution of NaCl in Water" Animation from Instructor's Resource CD/DVD
[4] "Sodium Chloride (1 × 1 Unit Cell)" 3-D Model from Instructor's Resource CD/DVD
[5] "Hydrogen Chloride" 3-D Model from Instructor's Resource CD/DVD
[6] "Ethanol" 3-D Model from Instructor's Resource CD/DVD
[7] "Strong Electrolytes" Movie from Instructor's Resource CD/DVD
[8] "Conductivity and Extent of Dissociation of Acids in Aqueous Solution" from Live Demonstrations
[9] "Acetic Acid" 3-D Model from Instructor's Resource CD/DVD
[10] "Formic Acid" 3-D Model from Instructor's Resource CD/DVD
[11] "Nitric Acid" 3-D Model from Instructor's Resource CD/DVD

$$NaCl(aq) \rightarrow Na^+(aq) + Cl^-(aq)$$

- The single arrow indicates that the Na^+ and Cl^- ions have no tendency to recombine to form NaCl.
- In general, soluble ionic compounds are strong electrolytes.
- Other strong electrolytes include strong acids and soluble strong bases.
- Compounds whose aqueous solutions conduct electricity poorly are called **weak electrolytes.**
  - These substances exist as a mixture of ions and un-ionized molecules in solution.
    - The predominant form of the solute is the un-ionized molecule.
    - Example: acetic acid, $HC_2H_3O_2$
$$HC_2H_3O_2(aq) \leftrightarrows H^+(aq) + C_2H_3O_2^-(aq)$$
    - The half-arrows in both directions means that the reaction is significant in both directions.
    - It indicates that there is a balance between the forward and reverse reactions.
    - This balance produces a state of **chemical equilibrium**.

FORWARD REFERENCES:
  - Double arrows ($\leftrightarrows$) will be used in the chapter on chemical equilibria (Chapter 15) and beyond.
  - Strong and weak electrolytes will come up in chapters on acid-base and solubility equilibria (Chapters 16 and 17) as well as in electrochemistry (Chapter 20).
  - Equilibria involving *insoluble* or *poorly soluble* compounds and their ions will be discussed in more detail in Chapter 17 (section 4).
  - Dissolving of substances in solvents and properties of solutions will be discussed in Chapter 13.
  - Interactions between ions and molecules of a solvent (ion-dipole interactions) will be further discussed in Chapters 11 and 13.

4.2 Precipitation Reactions[12,13,14]

- Reactions that result in the formation of an insoluble product are known as **precipitation reactions**.
- A **precipitate** is an insoluble solid formed by a reaction in solution.
  - Example: $Pb(NO_3)_2(aq) + 2KI(aq) \rightarrow PbI_2(s) + 2KNO_3(aq)$

Solubility Guidelines for Ionic Compounds[15,16,17,18,19]

- The **solubility** of a substance at a particular temperature is the amount of that substance that can be dissolved in a given quantity of solvent at that temperature.
- A substance with a solubility of less than 0.01 mol/L is regarded as being *insoluble*.
- Experimental observations have led to empirical guidelines for predicting solubility.
- Solubility guidelines for common ionic compounds in water:
  - Compounds containing alkali metal ions or ammonium ions are soluble.
  - Compounds containing NO_3^- or $C_2H_3O_2^-$ are soluble.
  - Compounds containing Cl^-, Br^- or I^- are soluble.
    - Exceptions are the compounds of Ag^+, Hg_2^{2+}, and Pb^{2+}.
  - Compounds containing SO_4^{2-} are soluble.

---

[12] "Precipitation Reactions" Movie from Instructor's Resource CD/DVD
[13] Figure 4.4 from Transparency Pack
[14] "Name That Precipitate" from Live Demonstrations
[15] Table 4.1 from Transparency Pack
[16] "Ionic Compounds" Activity from Instructor's Resource CD/DVD
[17] "Solubility of Some Silver Compounds" from Live Demonstrations
[18] "Solubility Rules: Three Suggestions for Improved Understanding" from Further Readings
[19] "An Analogy for Solubility: Marbles and Magnets" from Further Readings

- • Exceptions are the compounds of Sr^{2+}, Ba^{2+}, Hg_2^{2+}, and Pb^{2+}.
- Compounds containing S^{2-} are insoluble.
  - • Exceptions are the compounds of NH_4^+, the alkali metal cations, and Ca^{2+}, Sr^{2+}, and Ba^{2+}.
- Compounds of CO_3^{2-} or PO_4^{3-} are insoluble.
  - • Exceptions are the compounds of NH_4^+ and the alkali metal cations.
- Compounds of OH^- are insoluble.
  - • Exceptions are the compounds of NH_4^+, the alkali metal cations, and Ca^{2+}, Sr^{2+}, and Ba^{2+}.

Exchange (Metathesis) Reactions

- **Exchange reactions**, or **metathesis reactions**, involve swapping ions in solution:
$$AX + BY \rightarrow AY + BX.$$
- Many precipitation and acid-base reactions exhibit this pattern.

Ionic Equations[20,21]

- Consider $2KI(aq) + Pb(NO_3)_2(aq) \rightarrow PbI_2(s) + 2KNO_3(aq)$.
- Both $KI(aq) + Pb(NO_3)_2(aq)$ are colorless solutions. When mixed, they form a bright yellow precipitate of PbI_2 and a solution of KNO_3.
- The final product of the reaction contains solid PbI_2, aqueous K^+, and aqueous NO_3^- ions.
- Sometimes we want to highlight the reaction between ions.
- The **molecular equation** lists all species in their complete chemical forms:
$$Pb(NO_3)_2(aq) + 2KI(aq) \rightarrow PbI_2(s) + 2KNO_3(aq)$$
- The **complete ionic equation** lists all strong soluble electrolytes in the reaction as ions:
$$Pb^{2+}(aq) + 2NO_3^-(aq) + 2K^+(aq) + 2I^-(aq) \rightarrow PbI_2(s) + 2K^+(aq) + 2NO_3^-(aq)$$
  - Only strong electrolytes dissolved in aqueous solution are written in ionic form.
  - Weak electrolytes and nonelectrolytes are written in their complete chemical form.
- The **net ionic equation** lists only those ions which are not common on both sides of the reaction:
$$Pb^{2+}(aq) + 2I^-(aq) \rightarrow PbI_2(s)$$
  - Note that **spectator ions**, ions that are present in the solution but play no direct role in the reaction, are omitted in the net ionic equation.
- A suitable procedure for writing net ionic equations is the following:
  - Write a balanced molecular equation for the reaction.
  - Rewrite the equation to show the ions that forming solution when each soluble strong electrolyte dissociates into its component ions.
    - Only strong electrolytes dissolved in aqueous solution are written in ionic form
  - Identify and cancel **spectator ions**.

FORWARD REFERENCES:
- • Net ionic equations will be frequently used in chapters dealing with acid-base reactions (Chapters 16 and 17) as well as in electrochemistry (Chapter 20, Appendix E)
- • Equilibria involving *insoluble* or *poorly soluble* compounds and their ions will be discussed in more detail in Chapter 17 (section 17.4).

4.3 Acids, Bases, and Neutralization Reactions

Acids

- **Acids** are substances that are able to ionize in aqueous solution to form H^+.
  - Ionization occurs when a neutral substance forms ions in solution.
    An example is $HC_2H_3O_2$ (acetic acid).
- Since H^+ is a naked proton, we refer to acids as *proton donors* and bases as *proton acceptors*.

---

[20] "Writing a Net Ionic Equation" Activity from Instructor's Resource CD/DVD
[21] "Reinforcing Net Ionic Equation Writing" from Further Readings

- Acids that ionize to form *one* H^+ ion are called *monoprotic* acids.
  - Common monoprotic acids include HCl, HNO_3 and $HC_2H_3O_2$.
- Acids that ionize to form *two* H^+ ions are called *diprotic acids*.
  - A common diprotic acid is H_2SO_4.

Bases[22,23,24,25]

- **Bases** are substances that accept or react with the H^+ ions.
- Hydroxide ions, OH^-, react with the H^+ ions to form water:
$$H^+(aq) + OH^-(aq) \rightarrow H_2O(l)$$
- Common bases are $NaOH$, KOH, and $Ca(OH)_2$.
- Compounds that do not contain OH^- ions can also be bases.
  - Proton transfer to NH_3 (a weak base) from water (a weak acid) is an example of an acid–base reaction.
  - Since there is a mixture of NH_3, H_2O, NH_4^+, and OH^- in solution, we write
$$NH_3(aq) + H_2O(l) \rightleftharpoons NH_4^+(aq) + OH^-(aq)$$

Strong and Weak Acids and Bases[26,27,28,29,30]

- **Strong acids** and **strong bases** are strong electrolytes.
  - They are completely ionized in solution.
  - Strong bases include: Group 1A metal hydroxides, $Ca(OH)_2$, $Ba(OH)_2$, and $Sr(OH)_2$.
  - Strong acids include: HCl, HBr, HI, $HClO_3$, $HClO_4$, H_2SO_4, and HNO_3.
  - We write the ionization of HCl as:
$$HCl \rightarrow H^+ + Cl^-$$
- **Weak acids** and **weak bases** are weak electrolytes.
  - They are partially ionized in aqueous solution.
  - $HF(aq)$ is a weak acid; most acids are weak acids.
  - We write the ionization of HF as:
$$HF \rightleftharpoons H^+ + F^-$$

Identifying Strong and Weak Electrolytes[31,32]

- Compounds can be classified as strong electrolytes, weak electrolytes, or nonelectrolytes by looking at their solubility.
- Strong electrolytes:
  - Soluble ionic compounds are strong electrolytes.
  - Molecular compounds that are strong acids are strong electrolytes.
- Weak electrolytes:
  - Weak acids and bases are weak electrolytes.
- Nonelectrolytes:

---

[22] "The Origin of the Term Base" from Further Readings
[23] "Hydroxide Ion" 3-D Model from Instructor's Resource CD/DVD
[24] "Ammonia" 3-D Model from Instructor's Resource CD/DVD
[25] "Ammonium Ion" 3-D Model from Instructor's Resource CD/DVD
[26] "Significance, Concentration Calculations, Weak and Strong Acids" from Further Readings
[27] "Introduction to Aqueous Acids" Animation from Instructor's Resource CD/DVD
[28] "Introduction to Aqueous Bases" Animation from Instructor's Resource CD/DVD
[29] "Factors that Influence Relative Acid Strength in Water: A Simple Model" from Further Readings
[30] "When Is a Strong Electrolyte Strong?" from Further Readings
[31] "Pictorial Analogies X: Solutions of Electrolytes" from Further Readings
[32] "Food Is Usually Acidic, Cleaners Are Usually Basic" from Live Demonstrations

- All other compounds, including water.

Neutralization Reactions and Salts[33,34,35,36,37]

- A **neutralization reaction** occurs when an acid and a base react:
  - $HCl(aq) + NaOH(aq) \rightarrow H_2O(l) + NaCl(aq)$
  - (acid) + (base) (water) + (salt)
- In general, an acid and a base react to form a **salt**.
- A salt is any ionic compound whose cation comes from a base and anion from an acid.
- The other product, H_2O, is a common non-electrolyte.
- A typical example of a neutralization reaction is the reaction between an acid and a metal hydroxide:
  - $Mg(OH)_2$ (milk of magnesia) is a suspension.
  - As HCl is added, the magnesium hydroxide dissolves, and a clear solution containing Mg^{2+} and Cl^- ions is formed.
  - Molecular equation:
    $$Mg(OH)_2(s) + 2HCl(aq) \rightarrow MgCl_2(aq) + 2H_2O(l)$$
  - Net ionic equation:
    $$Mg(OH)_2(s) + 2H^+(aq) \rightarrow Mg^{2+}(aq) + 2H_2O(l)$$
    - Note that the magnesium hydroxide is an insoluble solid; it appears in the net ionic equation.
    - Note that the ions exchange partners thus neutralization reactions between acids and metal hydroxides are metathesis reactions

Neutralization Reactions with Gas Formation[38,39,40,41]

- There are many bases besides OH^- that react with H^+ to form molecular compounds.
  - Reaction of sulfides with acid gives rise to $H_2S(g)$.
    - Sodium sulfide (Na_2S) reacts with HCl to form $H_2S(g)$:
    - Molecular equation:
      $$Na_2S(aq) + 2HCl(aq) \rightarrow H_2S(g) + 2NaCl(aq)$$
    - Net ionic equation:
      $$2H^+(aq) + S^{2-}(aq) \rightarrow H_2S(g)$$
  - Carbonates and hydrogen carbonates (or bicarbonates) will form $CO_2(g)$ when treated with an acid.
    - Sodium bicarbonate ($NaHCO_3$; baking soda) reacts with HCl to form bubbles of $CO_2(g)$:
    - Molecular equation:
      $$NaHCO_3(s) + HCl(aq) \rightarrow NaCl(aq) + H_2CO_3(aq) \rightarrow H_2O(l) + CO_2(g) + NaCl(aq)$$
    - Net ionic equation:
      $$H^+(aq) + HCO_3^-(aq) \rightarrow H_2O(l) + CO_2(g)$$

FORWARD REFERENCES:
- Strong acids and bases will be revisited in Chapter 16.
- Strong acids and bases will be used as titrants in acid-base titrations (Chapter 17)
- Equilibria involving weak acids and bases will be further discussed in Chapters 16 and 17.
- Environmental impact of weak acid equilibria will be discussed on Chapter 18.

---

[33] "A Hand-Held Reaction: Production of Ammonia Gas" from Live Demonstrations
[34] "Fizzing and Foaming: Reactions of Acids with Carbonates" from Live Demonstrations
[35] "Demonstrations with Red Cabbage Indicator" from Live Demonstrations
[36] "Dissolution of $Mg(OH)_2$ by Acid" Animation from Instructor's Resource CD/DVD
[37] "Alka Seltzer Poppers: An Interactive Exploration" from Live Demonstrations
[38] "Determination of Neutralizing Capacity of Antacids" from Live Demonstrations
[39] "Milk of Magnesia versus Acid" from Live Demonstrations
[40] "Carbon Dioxide" 3-D Model from Instructor's Resource CD/DVD
[41] "Hydrogen Carbonate Ion" 3-D Model from Instructor's Resource CD/DVD

4.4 Oxidation-Reduction Reactions

Oxidation and Reduction[42,43,44,45]

- **Oxidation-reduction**, or *redox*, reactions involve the transfer of electrons between reactants.
- When a substances loses electrons, it undergoes **oxidation**:
$$Ca(s) + 2H^+(aq) \rightarrow Ca^{2+}(aq) + H_2(g)$$
  - The neutral Ca has lost two electrons to $2H^+$ to become Ca^{2+}.
  - We say Ca has been oxidized to Ca^{2+}.
- When a substance gains electrons, it undergoes **reduction**:
$$2Ca(s) + O_2(g) \rightarrow 2CaO(s).$$
  - In this reaction the neutral O_2 has gained electrons from the Ca to become O^{2-} in CaO.
  - We say O_2 has been reduced to O^{2-}.
- In all redox reactions, one species is reduced at the same time as another is oxidized.

Oxidation Numbers[46,47,48,49,50]

- Electrons are not explicitly shown in chemical equations.
- **Oxidation numbers** (or *oxidation states*) help up keep track of electrons during chemical reactions.
- Oxidation numbers are assigned to atoms using specific rules.
  - For an atom in its *elemental form*, the oxidation number is always zero.
  - For any *monatomic ion*, the oxidation number equals the charge on the ion; positive for metals and negative for nonmetals.
  - The oxidation number of *oxygen* is usually –2.
    - The major exception is in peroxides (containing the O_2^{2-} ion).
  - The oxidation number of *hydrogen* is +1 when bonded to nonmetals and –1 when bonded to metals.
  - The oxidation number of *fluorine* is –1 in all compounds. The other *halogens* have an oxidation number of –1 in most binary compounds.
  - *The sum of the oxidation numbers* of all atoms in a neutral compound is zero.
  - The sum of the oxidation numbers in a polyatomic ion equals the charge of the ion.
- The oxidation of an element is evidenced by an increase in its oxidation number; reduction is accompanied by a decrease in an oxidation number.

Oxidation of Metals by Acids and Salts[51,52,53,54]

- The reaction of a metal with either an acid or a metal salt is called a **displacement reaction.**
- The general pattern is:
$$A + BX \rightarrow AX + B$$

---

[42] "Reduction of CuO" Movie from Instructor's Resource CD/DVD

[43] "Oxidation-Reduction Reactions: Part I" Animation from Instructor's Resource CD/DVD

[44] "Oxidation-Reduction Reactions: Part II" Animation from Instructor's Resource CD/DVD

[45] "Oxidation and Reduction" from Further Readings

[46] "Oxidation Numbers I" Activity from Instructor's Resource CD/DVD

[47] "Oxidation Numbers II" Activity from Instructor's Resource CD/DVD

[48] "Oxidation Numbers" from Further Readings

[49] "Oxidation States of Manganese: Mn^{7+}, Mn^{6+}, Mn^{4+}, and Mn^{2+}" from Live Demonstrations

[50] "Simple Method for Determination of Oxidation Numbers of Atoms in Compounds" from Further Readings

[51] "Oxidation-Reduction Chemistry of Tin and Zinc" Movie from Instructor's Resource CD/DVD

[52] "Producing Hydrogen Gas from Calcium Metal" from Live Demonstrations

[53] "Making Hydrogen Gas an Acid and a Base" from Live Demonstrations

[54] "Precipitation, Redox, and Neutralization Reactions" Activity from Instructor's Resource CD/DVD

- Example: It is common for metals to produce hydrogen gas when they react with acids. Consider the reaction between Mg and HCl:

$$Mg(s) + 2HCl(aq) \rightarrow MgCl_2(aq) + H_2(g)$$

- In the process the metal is oxidized and the H^+ is reduced.
- Example: It is possible for metals to be oxidized in the presence of a salt:

$$Fe(s) + Ni(NO_3)_2(aq) \rightarrow Fe(NO_3)_2(aq) + Ni(s)$$

- The net ionic equation shows the redox chemistry well:

$$Fe(s) + Ni^{2+}(aq) \rightarrow Fe^{2+}(aq) + Ni(s)$$

- In this reaction iron has been oxidized to Fe^{2+}, while the Ni^{2+} has been reduced to Ni.
- Always keep in mind that whenever one substance is oxidized, some other substance *must* be reduced.

The Activity Series[55,56,57,58,59]

- We can list metals in order of decreasing ease of oxidation.
  - This list is an **activity series**.
- The metals at the top of the activity series are called *active metals*.
- The metals at the bottom of the activity series are called *noble metals*.
- A metal in the activity series can only be oxidized by a metal ion below it.
- If we place Cu into a solution of Ag^+ ions, then Cu^{2+} ions can be formed because Cu is above Ag in the activity series:

$$Cu(s) + 2AgNO_3(aq) \rightarrow Cu(NO_3)_2(aq) + 2Ag(s)$$
or
$$Cu(s) + 2Ag^+(aq) \rightarrow Cu^{2+}(aq) + 2Ag(s)$$

FORWARD REFERENCES:

- Oxidation numbers will be frequently used in electrochemistry (Chapter 20, Appendix E).
- Balancing of redox reactions will be covered in Chapter 20.

4.5 Concentrations of Solutions[60,61]

- The term **concentration** is used to indicate the amount of solute dissolved in a given quantity of solvent or solution.

Molarity[62,63]

- Solutions can be prepared with different concentrations by adding different amounts of solute to solvent.
- The amount (moles) of solute per liter of solution is the **molarity** or molar concentration (symbol *M*) of the solution:

$$Molarity = \frac{moles\ solute}{liters\ of\ solution}$$

- By knowing the molarity of a quantity of liters of solution, we can easily calculate the number of moles (and, by using molar mass, the mass) of solute.

---

[55] "Activity Series for Some Metals" from Live Demonstrations
[56] "An Activity Series: Zinc, Copper, and Silver Half-Cells" from Live Demonstrations
[57] "Floating Pennies" from Live Demonstrations
[58] Table 4.5 from Transparency Pack
[59] "Formation of Silver Crystals" Movie from Instructor's Resource CD/DVD
[60] "What Makes Gold Such a Noble Metal?" from Further Readings
[61] "A Cool Drink! An Introduction to Concentrations" from Live Demonstrations
[62] "Solution Formation from a Solid" Animation from Instructor's Resource CD/DVD
[63] "Dissolution of $KMnO_4$" Animation from Instructor's Resource CD/DVD

- Consider weighed copper sulfate, $CuSO_4$ (39.9 g, 0.250 mol) placed in a 250. mL volumetric flask. A little water is added and the flask swirled to ensure the copper sulfate dissolves. When all the copper sulfate has dissolved, the flask is filled to the mark with water.
  - The molarity of the solution is 0.250 mol $CuSO_4$ / 0.250 L solution = 1.00 M.

Expressing the Concentration of an Electrolyte[64]

- When an ionic compound dissolves, the relative concentrations of the ions in the solution depend on the chemical formula of the compound.
  - Example: for a 1.0 M solution of NaCl:
    - The solution is 1.0 M in Na^+ ions and 1.0 M in Cl^- ions.
  - Example: for a 1.0 M solution of Na_2SO_4:
    - The solution is 2.0 M in Na^+ ions and 1.0 M in SO_4^{2-} ions.

Interconverting Molarity, Moles, and Volume

- The definition of molarity contains three quantities: molarity, moles of solute, and liters of solution.
  - If we know any two of these, we can calculate the third.
  - Dimensional analysis can be helpful in these calculations.

Dilution[65,66,67]

- A solution in concentrated form (*stock solution*) is mixed with solvent to obtain a solution of lower solute concentration.
  - This process is called **dilution**.
- An alternate way of making a solution is to take a solution of known molarity and dilute it with more solvent.
- Since the number of moles of solute remains the same in the concentrated and diluted forms of the solution, we can show:

$$M_{conc}V_{conc} = M_{dil}V_{dil}$$

- An alternate form of this equation is:

$$M_{initial}V_{initial} = M_{final}V_{final}$$

FORWARD REFERENCES:
- Molarity will be used throughout the course as the most common form of concentration.
- The concept of molarity is not limited to solutions; one can calculate molarity for gases and use them in K_c expressions in Chapter 15 and beyond.
- Molarity can be converted into other concentrations (molality, normality, ppm, etc.) as shown in Chapter 13; molarity will be used to calculate osmotic pressure (section 13.5).
- In some later chapters (14 and beyond) molarity will be also symbolized as [solute].
- Dilutions will come up in select acid-base equilibrium problems in Chapter 16 and in titrations (Chapter 17).

4.6 Solution Stoichiometry and Chemical Analysis[68]

- In approaching stoichiometry problems:
  - recognize that there are two different types of units:
    - laboratory units (the macroscopic units that we measure in lab) and
    - chemical units (the microscopic units that relate to moles).

---

[64] "A Cyclist's Guide to Ionic Concentration" from Further Readings
[65] "Solution Formation by Dilution" Animation from Instructor's Resource CD/DVD
[66] "Teaching Dilutions" from Further Readings
[67] "On the Use of Intravenous Solutions to Teach Some Principles of Solution Chemistry" from Further Readings
[68] Figure 4.18 from Transparency Pack

- Always convert the laboratory units into chemical units first.
  - Convert grams to moles using molar mass.
  - Convert volume or molarity into moles using M = mol/L.
- Use the stoichiometric coefficients to move between reactants and products.
  - ***This step requires the balanced chemical equation.***
- Convert the laboratory units back into the required units.
  - Convert moles to grams using molar mass.
  - Convert moles to molarity or volume using M = mol/L.

Titrations[69,70,71,72,73,74,75]

- A common way to determine the concentration of a solution is via **titration**.
- We determine the concentration of one substance by allowing it to undergo a specific chemical reaction, of known stoichiometry, with a substance with known concentration (**standard solution**).
- *Mono*protic acids and bases react with each other in a stoichiometric ratio of 1:1.
- Example: Suppose we know the molarity of an NaOH solution and we want to find the molarity of an HCl solution.
  - What do we know?
    - molarity of NaOH, volume of HCl
  - What do we want?
    - molarity of HCl
  - What do we do?
  - Take a known volume of the HCl solution (i.e., 20.00 mL) and measure the number of mL of 0.100 M NaOH solution required to react completely with the HCl solution.
  - The point at which stoichiometrically equivalent quantities of NaOH and HCl are brought together is known as the **equivalence point** of the titration.
    - The equivalence point is a theoretical concept that can be calculated "on paper" only.
  - In a titration we often use an acid-base **indicator** to allow us to determine when the equivalence point of the titration has been reached.
    - Acid-base indicators change color at the *end point* of the titration.
    - The indicator is chosen so that the end point corresponds to the equivalence point of the titration; the end point is determined experimentally.
  - What do we get?
    - We get the volume of NaOH. Since we already have the molarity of the NaOH, we can calculate moles of NaOH.
  - What is the next step?
    - We also know HCl + NaOH → NaCl + H_2O (note the 1:1 stoichiometric ratio between HCl and NaOH).
    - Therefore, we know moles of HCl.
  - Can we finish?
    - Knowing mol (HCl) and volume of HCl, we can calculate the molarity.

FORWARD REFERENCES:
  - Acid-base titrations will be discussed in detail in Chapter 17.

---

[69] "Acid-Base Titration" Animation from Instructor's Resource CD/DVD
[70] "Colorful Acid-Base Indicators" from Live Demonstrations
[71] "Acid-Base Titration" Activity from Instructor's Resource CD/DVD
[72] "Rainbow Colors with Mixed Acid-Base Indicators" from Live Demonstrations
[73] "Acid-Base Indicators Extracted from Plants" from Live Demonstrations
[74] "Acid-Base Indicators: A New Look at an Old Topic" from Further Readings
[75] "Teas as Natural Indicators" from Live Demonstrations

Further Readings:

1. Bob Blake, "Solubility Rules: Three Suggestions for Improved Understanding," *J. Chem. Educ.*, Vol. 80, **2003**, 1348–1349.

2. Richard A. Kjonaas, "An Analogy for Solubility: Marbles and Magnets," *J. Chem. Educ.*, Vol. 61, **1984**, 765.

3. Betty J. Wruck, "Reinforcing Net Ionic Equation Writing," *J. Chem. Educ.*, Vol. 73, **1996**, 149–150.

4. William B. Jensen, "The Origin of the Term "Base"," *J. Chem. Educ.*, Vol. 83, **2006**, 1130.

5. H. van Lubeck, "Significance, Concentration Calculations, Weak and Strong Acids," *J. Chem. Educ.*, Vol. 60, **1983**, 189.

6. Reading Michael J. Moran, "Factors that Influence Relative Acid Strength in Water: A Simple Model," *J. Chem. Educ.*, Vol. 83, **2006**, 800-803.

7. Albert Kowalak, "When Is a Strong Electrolyte Strong?" *J. Chem. Educ.*, Vol. 65, **1988**, 607.

8. John J. Fortman, "Pictorial Analogies X: Solutions of Electrolytes," *J. Chem. Educ.*, Vol. 71, **1994**, 27–28.

9. Gian Calzaferri, "Oxidation Numbers," *J. Chem. Educ.*, Vol. 76, **1999**, 362–363.

10. R. Lipkin, "What Makes Gold Such a Noble Metal?" *Science News*, July 22, **1995**, 62.

11. Arthur M. Last, "A Cyclist's Guide to Ionic Concentration," *J. Chem. Educ.*, Vol. 75, **1998**, 1433.

12. Lloyd J. McElroy, "Teaching Dilutions," *J. Chem. Educ.*, Vol. 73, **1996**, 765–766.

13. Irwin L. Shapiro, "On the Use of Intravenous Solutions to Teach Some Principles of Solution Chemistry," *J. Chem. Educ.*, Vol. 59, **1982**, 725.

14. Ara S. Kooser, Judith L. Jenkins, and Lawrence E. Welch, "Acid-Base Indicators: A New Look at an Old Topic," *J. Chem. Educ.*, Vol. 78, **2001**, 1504–1506.

15. Marten J. ten Hoor and Aletta Jacobs Scholengemeenschap, "Oxidation and Reduction," *J. Chem. Educ.*, Vol. 60, **1983**, 132. An analogy for remembering oxidation and reduction.

16. Joel M. Kauffman, "Simple Method for Determination of Oxidation Numbers of Atoms in Compounds," *J. Chem. Educ.*, Vol. 63, **1986**, 474–475.

Live Demonstrations:

1. Bassam Z. Shakhashiri, "Conductivity and Extent of Dissociation of Acids in Aqueous Solution," *Chemical Demonstrations: A Handbook for Teachers of Chemistry, Volume 3* (Madison: The University of Wisconsin Press, **1989**), pp. 140–145. Universal indicator and a conductivity probe are used to explore the relative acidity and conductivity of a series of aqueous acids.

2. A. M. Sarquis and L. M. Woodward, "Alka Seltzer Poppers: an Interactive Exploration," *J. Chem. Educ.*, Vol. 76, **1999**, 386–386. An interactive exercise involving the addition of water to Alka Seltzer®; this demonstration may be used to introduce a variety of concepts such as acid-base chemistry, kinetics, and solubility.

3. Lee R. Summerlin, Christie L. Borgford, and Julie B. Ealy, "Name That Precipitate," *Chemical Demonstrations, A Sourcebook for Teachers, Volume 2* (Washington: American Chemical Society, **1988**), pp. 121–123. Students explore a variety of ionic reactions that result in the formation of colored precipitates.

4. Lee. R. Summerlin, Christie L. Borgford, and Julie B. Ealy, "Solubility of Some Silver Compounds," *Chemical Demonstrations, A Sourcebook for Teachers, Volume 2* (Washington: American Chemical Society, **1988**), pp. 83–85. The solubility of a series of silver salts and complexes is explored in this colorful demonstration.

5. Bassam Z. Shakhashiri, "Food is Usually Acidic, Cleaners Are Usually Basic," *Chemical Demonstrations: A Handbook for Teachers of Chemistry, Volume 3* (Madison: The University of Wisconsin Press, **1989**), pp. 65–69. The pH of a variety of household chemicals is determined using indicators and pH meters.

6. Lee R. Summerlin, Christie L. Borgford, and Julie B. Ealy, "A Hand-Held Reaction: Production of Ammonia Gas," *Chemical Demonstrations, A Sourcebook for Teachers, Volume 2* Washington: American Chemical Society, **1988**), p. 38. An example of a reaction involving two solids (NH_4Cl and $Ca(OH)_2$) is demonstrated.

7. Bassam Z. Shakhashiri, "Fizzing and Foaming: Reactions of Acids with Carbonates," *Chemical Demonstrations: A Handbook for Teachers of Chemistry, Volume 3* (Madison: The University of Wisconsin Press, **1989**), pp. 96–99.

8. John J. Fortman and Katherine M. Stubbs, "Demonstrations with Red Cabbage Indicator," *J. Chem. Educ.*, Vol. 69, **1992**, 66–67. The acidic or basic nature of solutions of gases is investigated.

9. Bassam Z. Shakhashiri, "Determination of Neutralizing Capacity of Antacids", *Chemical Demonstrations: A Handbook for Teachers of Chemistry, Volume 3* (Madison: The University of Wisconsin Press, **1989**), pp. 162–166.

10. Lee. R. Summerlin, Christie L. Borgford, and Julie B. Ealy, "Milk of Magnesia versus Acid," *Chemical Demonstrations, A Sourcebook for Teachers, Volume 2* (Washington: American Chemical Society, **1988**), p. 173. An antacid, milk of magnesia, is mixed with acid in this demonstration.

11. Lee. R. Summerlin, and James. L. Ealy, Jr., "Oxidation States of Manganese: Mn^{7+}, Mn^{6+}, Mn^{4+}, and Mn^{2+}," *Chemical Demonstrations, A Sourcebook for Teachers, Volume 1* (Washington: American Chemical Society, **1988**), p.133–134 .

12. Lee. R. Summerlin, Christie L. Borgford, and Julie B. Ealy, " Producing Hydrogen Gas from Calcium Metal," *Chemical Demonstrations, A Sourcebook for Teachers, Volume 2* (Washington: American Chemical Society, **1988**), pp. 51–52.

13. Lee. R. Summerlin, and James. L. Ealy, Jr., "Activity Series for Some Metals," *Chemical Demonstrations, A Sourcebook for Teachers, Volume 1* (Washington: American Chemical Society, **1988**), p. 150. An overhead projector demonstration employing hydrogen gas formation.

14. Lee. R. Summerlin, Christie L. Borgford, and Julie B. Ealy, "Making Hydrogen Gas from an Acid and a Base," *Chemical Demonstrations, A Sourcebook for Teachers, Volume 2* (Washington: American Chemical Society, **1988**), pp. 33–34. Hydrogen gas is collected as a product of the reaction of aluminum with either HCl or NaOH.

15. Bassam Z. Shakhashiri, "An Activity Series: Zinc, Copper, and Silver Half Cells," *Chemical Demonstrations: A Handbook for Teachers of Chemistry, Volume 4* (Madison: The University of Wisconsin Press, **1992**), pp. 101–106.

16. Lee. R. Summerlin, Christie L. Borgford, and Julie B. Ealy, "Floating Pennies," *Chemical Demonstrations, A Sourcebook for Teachers, Volume 2* (Washington: American Chemical Society, **1988**), p. 63. The zinc core of copper-coated pennies reacts with acid to form pennies that float in this demonstration.

17. Mindy Bedrossian, "A Cool Drink! An Introduction to Concentrations," *J. Chem. Educ.*, Vol. 85, **2005**, 240A.

18. Bassam Z. Shakhashiri, "Colorful Acid-Base Indicators," *Chemical Demonstrations: A Handbook for Teachers of Chemistry, Volume 3* (Madison: The University of Wisconsin Press, **1989**), pp. 33–40.

19. Bassam Z. Shakhashiri, "Rainbow Colors with Mixed Acid-Base Indicators," *Chemical Demonstrations: A Handbook for Teachers of Chemistry, Volume 3* (Madison: The University of Wisconsin Press, **1989**), pp. 41–46.

20. Bassam Z. Shakhashiri, "Acid-Base Indicators Extracted from Plants," *Chemical Demonstrations: A Handbook for Teachers of Chemistry, Volume 3* (Madison: The University of Wisconsin Press, **1989**), pp. 50–57.

21. Dianne N. Epp, "Teas as Natural Indicators," *J. Chem. Educ.*, Vol. 70, **1993**, 326. Infusions from a series of herbal teas provide a source of natural pH indicators in this simple demonstration.

Chapter 5. Thermochemistry

Media Resources

Figures and Tables in Transparency Pack:	**Section:**
Figure 5.5 Changes in Internal Energy	5.2 The First Law of Thermodynamics
Figure 5.10 Internal Energy Is a State Function, but Heat and Work Are Not	5.2 The First Law of Thermodynamics
Figure 5.13 Pressure–Volume Work	5.3 Enthalpy
Figure 5.19 Bomb Calorimeter	5.5 Calorimetry
Figure 5.22 Enthalpy Diagram Illustrating Hess's Law	5.6 Hess's Law
Table 5.3 Standard Enthalpies of Formation, ΔH°_f, at 298 K	5.7 Enthalpies of Formation
Figure 5.23 Enthalpy Diagram for Propane Combustion	5.7 Enthalpies of Formation
Figure 5.25 Energy Consumption in the United States	5.8 Fuels and Foods

Animations:	**Section:**
Work of Gas Expansion	5.3 Enthalpy

Movies:	**Section:**
Thermite	5.2 The First Law of Thermodynamics
Formation of Water	5.4 Enthalpies of Reaction
Formation of Aluminum Bromide	5.7 Enthalpies of Formation
Nitrogen Triiodide	5.7 Enthalpies of Formation

Activities:	**Section:**
Sign Conventions for q and w	5.2 The First Law of Thermodynamics
Enthalpy of Solution	5.4 Enthalpies of Reaction
Calorimetry	5.5 Calorimetry

3-D Models:	**Section:**
Carbon Dioxide	5.8 Fuels and Foods
Oxygen	5.8 Fuels and Foods
Ethanol	5.8 Fuels and Foods
Sucrose	5.8 Fuels and Foods
Hydrogen	5.8 Fuels and Foods
Water	5.8 Fuels and Foods

Other Resources

Further Readings:	**Section:**
Weight-Loss Diets and the Law of Conservation of Energy	5.2 The First Law of Thermodynamics
Pictorial Analogies III: Heat Flow, Thermodynamics, and Entropy	5.3 Enthalpy
Analogical Demonstrations	5.3 Enthalpy
Heat Flow vs. Cash Flow: A Banking Analogy	5.3 Enthalpy
Three Forms of Energy	5.3 Enthalpy
A Specific Heat Analogy	5.5 Calorimetry
Heat Capacity, Body Temperature, and Hypothermia	5.6 Hess's Law
Calories–Who's Counting?	5.8 Foods and Fuels
The Conversion of Chemical Energy: Part 1. Technological Examples	5.8 Foods and Fuels
The Geochemistry of Coal. Part II: The Components of Coal	5.8 Foods and Fuels
Scientific American, **September 1990**	5.8 Foods and Fuels
Hydrogen: The Ultimate Fuel and Energy Carrier	5.8 Foods and Fuels
Chemical Fuels from the Sun	5.8 Foods and Fuels
"The Ice that Burns. Can Methane Hydrates Fuel the 21st Century?	5.8 Foods and Fuels

Live Demonstrations:	**Section:**
Evaporation as an Endothermic Process	5.2 The First Law of Thermodynamics
Flaming Cotton	5.4 Enthalpies of Reaction
Heat of Neutralization	5.4 Enthalpies of Reaction
Chemical Cold Pack	5.4 Enthalpies of Reaction
A Chemical Hand Warmer	5.4 Enthalpies of Reaction
Endothermic Reaction: Ammonium Nitrate	5.4 Enthalpies of Reaction
Boiling Water in a Paper Cup: Heat Capacity of Water	5.5 Calorimetry
Making Canned Heat	5.8 Foods and Fuels

Chapter 5. Thermochemistry

Common Student Misconceptions

- Students confuse power and energy.
- Students confuse heat with temperature.
- Students fail to note that the first law of thermodynamics *is* the law of conservation of energy.
- Students have difficulty in determining what constitutes the system and the surroundings.
- Sign conventions in thermodynamics are always problematic.
- Students do not realize that a chemical reaction carried out in an open container occurs at constant pressure.
- Since enthalpy is a state function, and $\Delta H = q_p$, students often think that *heat* is a state function.
- Students often cannot tell the difference between enthalpy of a reaction ΔH_{rxn} (in kJ) and molar enthalpy (per one mole of one of the reacting species, in kJ/mol).
- Students do not realize that Hess's law is a consequence of the fact that enthalpy is a state function.
- Students should be directed to Appendix C of the text for a list of standard enthalpy values. (They are unlikely to find this information on their own!)
- Students tend to have difficulties with calculating a value of ΔH°_f for a compound not listed in Appendix C from ΔH°_{rxn} and the available ΔH°_f values.
- Students tend to think that any reaction in which a given compound is formed, regardless of the type of reactants, should be called a *formation reaction*.
- Students often neglect to notice that a *formation reaction* leads to a formation of *1 mole* of a compound.

Teaching Tips

- Remind students that the values of ΔH°_f for the same compound but in a different phase are different; this is one of main causes of errors in calculations in section 5.7.
- Emphasize that molar heat capacity and specific heat capacity have different units; one is expressed on a per-mole basis while the other is expressed on a per-gram basis.

Lecture Outline

5.1 The Nature of Energy

- **Thermodynamics** is the study of energy and its transformations.
- **Thermochemistry** is the study of the relationships between chemical reactions and energy changes involving heat.
- Definitions:
  - **Energy** is the capacity to do work or to transfer heat.
  - **Work** is energy used to cause an object with mass to move.
$$w = F \times d$$
  - **Heat** is the energy used to cause the temperature of an object to increase.
  - A *force* is any kind of push or pull exerted on an object.
    - The most familiar force is the pull of gravity.

Kinetic Energy and Potential Energy

- **Kinetic energy** is the energy of motion:
$$E_k = \frac{1}{2}mv^2$$

- **Potential energy** is the energy an object possesses by virtue of its position or composition.
  - Electrostatic energy is an example.
    - It arises from interactions between charged particles.

$$E_{el} = \frac{\kappa Q_1 Q_2}{d}$$

  - Potential energy can be converted into kinetic energy.
    - An example is a ball of clay dropped off a building.

Units of Energy

- SI unit is the **joule** (J).
- From $E_k = \frac{1}{2}mv^2$, $1J = 1kg \times \frac{m^2}{s^2}$
- Traditionally, we use the **calorie** as a unit of energy.
  - 1 cal = 4.184 J (exactly)
- The nutritional Calorie, Cal = 1,000 cal = 1 kcal.

System and Surroundings

- A **system** is the part of the universe we are interested in studying.
- **Surroundings** are the rest of the universe (i.e., the surroundings are the portions of the universe that are not involved in the system).
- Example: If we are interested in the interaction between hydrogen and oxygen in a cylinder, then the H_2 and O_2 in the cylinder form a system.

Transferring Energy: Work and Heat

- From physics:
  - **Force** is a push or pull exerted on an object.
  - *Work* is the energy used to move an object against a force.
  $$w = F \times d$$
  - *Heat* is the energy transferred from a hotter object to a colder one.
  - *Energy* is the capacity to do work or to transfer heat.

FORWARD REFERENCES
  - The concepts of the system, surroundings, and universe will be used again in Chapter 19.
  - Energy in J will be used in Chapter 6 to express energy of a hydrogen atom and the energy of an emitted photon.
  - Energy in kJ/mol will be used in Chapter 7 for ionization energies and electron affinities.
  - Energy in kJ/mol will be used in Chapter 8 to measure lattice energy and average bond enthalpies and to calculate enthalpies of reactions.
  - Energy in J (and kJ) to energy of thermodynamic calculations throughout Chapters 19, 14 (Arrhenius equation in section 14.5), and Chapter 20 (Gibbs free energy vs. cell potential in section 20.5).

5.2 The First Law of Thermodynamics[1]

- **The first law of thermodynamics** states that energy cannot be created or destroyed.
- The first law of thermodynamics is the law of conservation of energy.
  - That is, the energy of system + surroundings is constant.
  - Thus, any energy transferred from a system must be transferred to the surroundings (and vice versa).

---

[1] "Weight-Loss Diets and the Law of Conservation of Energy" from Further Readings

Internal Energy[2]

- The total energy, E, of a system is called the **internal energy**.
  - It is the sum of all the kinetic and potential energies of all components of the system.
- Absolute internal energy cannot be measured, only changes in internal energy.
- Change in internal energy: $\Delta E = E_{final} - E_{initial}$.
- Thermodynamic quantities such as ΔE always have three parts:
  - a number,
  - a unit, and
  - a sign that gives direction.
- Example: A mixture of $H_2(g)$ and $O_2(g)$ has a higher internal energy than $H_2O(g)$.
- Going from $H_2(g)$ and $O_2(g)$ to $H_2O(g)$ results in a negative change in internal energy, indicating that the system has lost energy to the surroundings:
$$H_2(g) + O_2(g) \rightarrow 2H_2O(g) \qquad \Delta E < 0$$
- Going from $H_2O(g)$ to $H_2(g)$ and $O_2(g)$ results in a positive change in internal energy, indicating that the system has gained energy from the surroundings:
$$2H_2O \rightarrow H_2(g) + O_2(g) \qquad \Delta E > 0$$

Relating ΔE to Heat and Work[3]

- From the first law of thermodynamics:
  - When a system undergoes a physical or chemical change, the change in internal energy is given by the heat added to or liberated from the system plus the work done on or by the system:
$$\Delta E = q + w$$
- Heat flowing from the surroundings to the system is positive, $q > 0$.
- Work done by the surroundings on the system is positive, $w > 0$.

Endothermic and Exothermic Processes

- An **endothermic** process is one that *absorbs* heat from the surroundings.
  - An endothermic reaction feels cold.
- An **exothermic** process is one that *transfers* heat to the surroundings.
  - An exothermic reaction feels hot.

State Functions[4,5,6]

- A **state function** depends only on the initial and final states of a system.
  - Example: The altitude difference between Denver and Chicago does not depend on whether you fly or drive, only on the elevation of the two cities above sea level.
  - Similarly, the internal energy of 50 g of $H_2O(l)$ at 25 °C does not depend on whether we cool 50 g of $H_2O(l)$ from 100 °C to 25 °C or heat 50 g of $H_2O(l)$ at 0 °C to 25 °C.
- A state function does not depend on how the internal energy is used.
  - Example: A battery in a flashlight can be discharged by producing heat and light. The same battery in a toy car is used to produce heat and work. The change in internal energy of the battery is the same in both cases.

FORWARD REFERENCES

- Equilibria of endothermic vs. exothermic reactions will be differently affected by temperature changes in Chapter 15.
- Water autoionization is mentioned to be an endothermic process (Chapter 16, section 16.3).

---

[2] Figure 5.5 from Transparency Pack
[3] "Sign Conventions for q and w" Activity from Instructor's Resource CD/DVD
[4] "Thermite" Movie from Instructor's Resource CD/DVD
[5] "Evaporation as an Endothermic Process" from Live Demonstrations
[6] Figure 5.10 from Transparency Pack

- Solid→liquid→gas phase changes are endothermic, while gas→liquid→ solid phase changes are exothermic.
- Most spontaneous reactions (Chapter 19) are exothermic.
- State functions will be further discussed in Chapter 19 (entropy and Gibbs free energy).

5.3 Enthalpy[7,8,9,10,11]

- Chemical and physical changes that occur around us occur under essentially constant pressure of Earth's atmosphere.
  - Changes may be accompanied by work done by or on the system.
  - Changes may involve the release or absorption of heat.
    - We will focus much of our discussion on what we can learn from measurement of heat flow.
- **Enthalpy** (H) is defined as the internal energy (E) plus the product of the pressure and volume of the system.
$$H = E + PV$$
  - Enthalpy is useful for investigating heat flow in events that occur under constant pressure.
  - Again, we can only measure the change in enthalpy, ΔH.
- Mathematically,
$$\Delta H = H_{final} - H_{initial} = \Delta E + P\Delta V$$
$$w = -P\Delta V; \Delta E = q + w$$
$$\Delta H = \Delta E + P\Delta V = (q_p + w) - w = q_p$$
  - For most reactions $P\Delta V$ is small thus $\Delta H = \Delta E$
- Heat transferred from surroundings to the system has a positive enthalpy (i.e., $\Delta H > 0$ for an endothermic reaction).
- Heat transferred from the system to the surroundings has a negative enthalpy (i.e., $\Delta H < 0$ for an exothermic reaction).
- Enthalpy is a state function.

A Closer Look at Energy, Enthalpy, and P-V Work[12]

- Many chemical reactions involve work done on or by the system.
  - Work is often either electrical or mechanical work.
  - Mechanical work done by a system involving expanding gases is called **pressure-volume work** or *P-V* work.
- Consider:
  - A cylinder of cross-sectional area *A*,
  - A piston exerting a pressure, $P = F/A$, on a gas inside the cylinder,
  - The volume of gas expanding through ΔV while the piston moves a height $\Delta h = h_f - h_i$.
  - The magnitude of work done $= F \times \Delta h = P \times A \times \Delta h = P \times \Delta V$.
  - Since work is being done by the system on the surroundings,
    - $w = -P\Delta V$.
  - Using the first law of thermodynamics,
    - $\Delta E = q - P\Delta V$.
  - If the reaction is carried out under constant volume,
    - $\Delta V = 0$ and $\Delta E = q_v$.

---

[7] "Heat Flow vs. Cash Flow: A Banking Analogy" from Further Readings
[8] "Pictorial Analogies III: Heat Flow, Thermodynamics, and Entropy" from Further Readings
[9] "Analogical Demonstrations" from Further Readings
[10] "Work of Gas Expansion" Animation from Instructor's Resource CD/DVD
[11] "Three Forms of Energy" from Further Readings
[12] Figure 5.13 from Transparency Pack

- If the reaction is carried out under constant pressure,
  - $\Delta E = q_p - P\Delta V$, or
  - $q_p = \Delta H = \Delta E + P\Delta V$
  - and $\Delta E = \Delta H - P\Delta V$

5.4 Enthalpies of Reaction[13,14,15,16,17,18,19,20]

- For a reaction, $\Delta H_{rxn} = H_{products} - H_{reactants}$.
- The enthalpy change that accompanies a reaction is called the **enthalpy of reaction** or *heat of reaction* (ΔH_{rxn}).
- Consider the thermochemical equation for the production of water:

$$2H_2(g) + O_2(g) \rightarrow 2H_2O(g) \qquad \Delta H = -483.6 \text{ kJ}$$

  - The equation tells us that 483.6 kJ of energy are released to the surroundings when water is formed.
  - ΔH noted at the end of the balanced equation depends on the number of moles of reactants and products associated with the ΔH value.
  - These equations are called *thermochemical equations*.
- *Enthalpy diagrams* are used to represent enthalpy changes associated with a reaction.
- In the enthalpy diagram for the combustion of $H_2(g)$, the reactants, $2H_2(g) + O_2(g)$, have a higher enthalpy than the products $2H_2O(g)$; this reaction is exothermic.
- *Enthalpy is an extensive property.*
  - Therefore, the *magnitude* of enthalpy is directly proportional to the amount of reactant consumed.
  - Example: If one mol of CH_4 is burned in oxygen to produce CO_2 and water, 890 kJ of heat is released to the surroundings. If two mol of CH_4 is burned, then 1780 kJ of heat is released.
- The *sign* of ΔH depends on the direction of the reaction.
  - The enthalpy change for a reaction is equal in magnitude but opposite in sign to ΔH for the reverse reaction.
  - Example: $CH_4(g) + 2O_2(g) \rightarrow CO_2(g) + 2H_2O(l)$ $\Delta H = -890 \text{ kJ}$,
  - But $CO_2(g) + 2H_2O(l) \rightarrow CH_4(g) + 2O_2(g)$ $\Delta H = +890 \text{ kJ}$.
- Enthalpy change depends on *state of the products and reactants*.
  - $2H_2O(g) \rightarrow 2H_2O(l)$ $\Delta H = -88 \text{ kJ}$

FORWARD REFERENCES
  - Enthalpies of chemical reactions and physical processes will be used throughout the textbook.
  - Enthalpies of reactions will be calculated using average bond enthalpies in Chapter 8.
  - Enthalpy changes will be used in Chapter 19 to evaluate Gibbs free energy changes.

5.5 Calorimetry

- **Calorimetry** is a measurement of heat flow.
- A **calorimeter** is an apparatus that measures heat flow.

---

[13] "Enthalpy of Solution" Activity from Instructor's Resource CD/DVD
[14] "Formation of Water" Movie from Instructor's Resource CD/DVD
[15] "Flaming Cotton" from Live Demonstrations
[16] "Heat of Neutralization" from Live Demonstrations
[17] "Chemical Cold Pack" from Live Demonstrations
[18] "A Chemical Hand Warmer" from Live Demonstrations
[19] "Endothermic Reaction: Ammonium Nitrate" from Live Demonstrations
[20] "Beware-Fertilizer Can EXPLODE!" from Further Readings

Heat Capacity and Specific Heat[21]

- **Heat capacity** is the amount of energy required to raise the temperature of an object by 1 °C.
  - **Molar heat capacity** is the heat capacity of 1 mol of a substance.
  - **Specific heat**, or specific heat capacity, is the heat capacity of 1 g of a substance.
- Heat, q = (specific heat) × (grams of substance) × ΔT.
- Be careful with the sign of q.

Constant-Pressure Calorimetry[22,23]

- The most common technique is to use atmospheric pressure as the constant pressure.
- Recall $\Delta H = q_p$.
- The easiest method is to use a coffee cup calorimeter.

$$q_{soln} = \text{(specific heat of solution)} \times \text{(grams of solution)} \times \Delta T = -q_{rxn}$$

- For dilute aqueous solutions, the specific heat of the solution will be close to that of pure water.

Bomb Calorimetry (Constant-Volume Calorimetry)[24]

- Reactions can be carried out under conditions of constant volume instead of constant pressure.
- Constant volume calorimetry is carried out in a **bomb calorimeter**.
- The most common type of reaction studied under these conditions is combustion.
- If we know the heat capacity of the calorimeter, C_{cal}, then the heat of reaction,

$$q_{rxn} = -C_{cal} \times \Delta T.$$

- Since the reaction is carried out under constant volume, q relates to ΔE.

5.6 Hess's Law[25,26]

- **Hess's Law**: If a reaction is carried out in a series of steps, ΔH for the reaction is the sum of ΔH for each of the steps.
- The total change in enthalpy is independent of the number of steps.

$$
\begin{array}{ll}
CH_4(g) + 2O_2(g) \rightarrow CO_2(g) + 2H_2O(g) & \Delta H = -802 \text{ kJ} \\
2H_2O(g) \rightarrow 2H_2O(l) & \Delta H = -88 \text{ kJ} \\
\hline
CH_4(g) + 2O_2(g) \rightarrow CO_2(g) + 2H_2O(l) & \Delta H = -890 \text{ kJ}
\end{array}
$$

- Therefore, for the reaction $CH_4(g) + 2O_2(g) \rightarrow CO_2(g) + 2H_2O(l)$, $\Delta H = -890$ kJ.
- Note that ΔH is sensitive to the states of the reactants and products.
- Total ΔH is also independent of the nature of the path.
  - If we convert $CH_4(g) + 2O_2(g)$ to $CO_2(g) + 2H_2O(l)$ through a CO intermediate:

$$
\begin{array}{ll}
CH_4(g) + 2O_2(g) \rightarrow CO(g) + 2H_2O(l) + \tfrac{1}{2}O_2(g) & \Delta H_2 = -607 \text{ kJ} \\
CO(g) + 2H_2O(l) + \tfrac{1}{2}O_2(g) \rightarrow CO_2(g) + 2H_2O(l) & \Delta H_3 = -283 \text{ kJ},
\end{array}
$$

  Then ΔH for the overall reaction is the same:
$$\Delta H_2 + \Delta H_3 = -607 \text{ kJ} - 283 \text{ kJ} = -890 \text{ kJ} = \Delta H_1$$

FORWARD REFERENCES
- Similar rules will apply to ΔG and ΔS in Chapter 19.

---

[21] "Boiling Water in a Paper Cup: Heat Capacity of Water" from Live Demonstrations
[22] "A Specific Heat Analogy" from Further Readings
[23] "Calorimetry" Activity from Instructor's Resource CD/DVD
[24] Figure 5.19 from Transparency Pack
[25] "Heat Capacity, Body Temperature, and Hypothermia" from Further Readings
[26] Figure 5.22 from Transparency Pack

5.7 Enthalpies of Formation[27,28]

- If a compound is formed from its constituent elements, then the enthalpy change for the reaction is called the **enthalpy of formation**, ΔH_f.
- *Standard state* (standard conditions) refer to the substance at:
  - 1 atm and 25 °C (298 K).
- **Standard enthalpy**, $\Delta H°$, is the enthalpy measured when everything is in its standard state.
- **Standard enthalpy of formation** of a compound, $\Delta H°_f$, is the enthalpy change for *the formation of 1 mol of compound* with all substances in their *standard states*.
- $\Delta H°_f$ for selected substances are tabulated in Appendix C.
  - A large majority of $\Delta H°_f$ values tabulated in Appendix C are negative, meaning that most formation reactions are exothermic.
- If there is more than one state for a substance under standard conditions, the more stable one is used. Example: When dealing with carbon we use graphite because graphite is more stable than diamond or C_{60}.
- The standard enthalpy of formation of the most stable form of an element is zero.

Using Enthalpies of Formation to Calculate Enthalpies of Reaction[29,30]

- Use Hess's law!
- Example: Calculate ΔH for
$$C_3H_8(g) + 5O_2(g) \rightarrow 3CO_2(g) + 4H_2O(l)$$
- We start with the reactants, decompose them into elements, then rearrange the elements to form products. The overall enthalpy change is the sum of the enthalpy changes for each step.
  - Decomposing into elements (note O_2 is already elemental, so we concern ourselves with C_3H_8):
$$C_3H_8(g) \rightarrow 3C(s) + 4H_2(g) \qquad \Delta H_1 = -\Delta H°_f[C_3H_8(g)]$$
  - Next we form CO_2 and H_2O from their elements:
$$3C(s) + 3O_2(g) \rightarrow 3CO_2(g) \qquad \Delta H_2 = 3\,\Delta H°_f[CO_2(g)]$$
$$4H_2(g) + 2O_2(g) \rightarrow 4H_2O(l) \qquad \Delta H_3 = 4\,\Delta H°_f[H_2O(l)]$$
  - We look up the values and add:
$$\Delta H°_{rxn} = -1(-103.85\text{ kJ}) + 3(-393.5\text{ kJ}) + 4(-285.8\text{ kJ}) = -2220\text{ kJ}$$
- In general:
$$\Delta H°_{rxn} = \blacktriangleleft n\,\Delta H°_f(\text{products}) - \blacktriangleleft m\,\Delta H°_f(\text{reactants})$$
  - Where n and m are the stoichiometric coefficients.

FORWARD REFERENCES
- In Chapter 19 (section 19.5) Gibbs free energies of formation, $\Delta G°_f$, will used to find $\Delta G°_{rxn}$ in an analogical manner to how $\Delta H°_f$ values are used to find $\Delta H°_{rxn}$.

---

[27] "Formation of Aluminum Bromide" Movie from Instructor's Resource CD/DVD
[28] Table 5.3 from Transparency Pack
[29] "Nitrogen Triiodide" Movie from Instructor's Resource CD/DVD
[30] Figure 5.23 from Transparency Pack

5.8 Foods and Fuels

- **Fuel value** is the energy released when 1 g of substance is burned.
- The fuel value of any food or fuel is a positive value that must be measured by calorimetry.

Foods[31,32,33,34,35,36]

- Fuel value is usually measured in Calories (1 nutritional Calorie, 1 Cal = 1000 cal).
- Most energy in our bodies comes from the oxidation of carbohydrates and fats.
- In the intestines carbohydrates are converted into glucose, $C_6H_{12}O_6$, or blood sugar.
  - In the cells glucose reacts with O_2 in a series of steps, which produce CO_2, H_2O, and energy.
    $$C_6H_{12}O_6(s) + 6O_2(g) \rightarrow 6CO_2(g) + 6H_2O(l) \qquad \Delta H^\circ = -2803 \text{ kJ}$$
- Fats, for example tristearin, react with O_2 as follows:
  $$2C_{57}H_{110}O_6(s) + 163O_2(g) \rightarrow 114CO_2(g) + 110H_2O(l) \qquad \Delta H^\circ = -75,250 \text{ kJ}$$
- Fats contain more energy than carbohydrates. Fats are not water soluble. Therefore, fats are good for energy storage.

Fuels[37,38,39,40,41,42,43,44]

- In 2008 the United States consumed about 1.05×10^{17} kJ/year (9.4×10^5 kJ of fuel per person per day).
- Most of this energy comes from petroleum and natural gas.
- The remainder of the energy comes from coal, nuclear and hydroelectric sources.
- Coal, petroleum, and natural gas are **fossil fuels**. They are not renewable.
- **Natural gas** consists largely of carbon and hydrogen. Compounds such as CH_4, C_2H_6, C_3H_8 and C_4H_{10} are typical constituents.
- **Petroleum** is a liquid consisting of hundreds of compounds. Impurities include S, N, and O compounds.
- **Coal** contains high molecular weight compounds of C and H. In addition compounds containing S, O, and N are present as impurities that form air pollutants when burned in air.

Other Energy Sources[45]

- *Nuclear energy*: energy released in splitting or fusion of nuclei of atoms.
  - It is used to produce about 21% of the electric power in the US.
- Fossil fuels and nuclear energy are *nonrenewable* sources of energy.
- **Renewable energy** sources include:

---

[31] "Calories–Who's Counting?" from Further Readings
[32] "Sucrose" 3-D Model from Instructor's Resource CD/DVD
[33] "Carbon Dioxide" 3-D Model from Instructor's Resource CD/DVD
[34] "Oxygen" 3-D Model from Instructor's Resource CD/DVD
[35] "Water" 3-D Model from Instructor's Resource CD/DVD
[36] "Ethanol" 3-D Model from Instructor's Resource CD/DVD
[37] "Making Canned Heat" from Live Demonstrations
[38] Figure 5.25 from Transparency Pack
[39] "The Conversion of Chemical Energy. Part 1. Technological Examples" from Further Readings
[40] "The Geochemistry of Coal. Part II. The Components of Coal" from Further Readings
[41] *Scientific American*, **September, 1990** from Further Readings
[42] "Hydrogen: The Ultimate Fuel and Energy Carrier" from Further Readings
[43] "Chemical Fuels from the Sun" from Further Readings
[44] "The Ice that Burns. Can Methane Hydrates Fuel the 21st Century?" from Further Readings
[45] "Hydrogen" 3-D Model from Instructor's Resource CD/DVD

- Solar energy
- Wind energy
- Geothermal energy
- Hydroelectric energy
- Biomass energy
- These are virtually inexhaustible and will become increasingly important as fossil fuels are depleted.

FORWARD REFERENCES

- Pollution resulting from fossil-fuel combustion will be discussed in Chapter 18 (section 18.2).
- Pollution-free fuel cell-powered vehicles will be mentioned in Chapter 20 (section 20.7).

Further Readings:

1. John J. Fortman, "Pictorial Analogies III: Heat Flow, Thermodynamics, and Entropy," *J. Chem. Educ.*, Vol. 70, **1993**, 102–103.

2. John J. Fortman, "Analogical Demonstrations," *J. Chem. Educ.*, Vol. 69, **1992**, 323–324. This reference contains a quick analogical demonstration on heat transfer.

3. John W. Hill, "Weight-Loss Diets and the Law of Conservation of Energy," *J. Chem. Educ.*, Vol. 58, **1981**, 996.

4. Charles M. Wynn, Sr., "Heat Flow vs. Cash Flow: A Banking Analogy," *J. Chem. Educ.*, Vol. 74, **1997**, 3978.

5. Sigthor Petursson, "Three Forms of Energy," *J. Chem. Educ.,* Vol. 80, **2003**, 776–778.

6. Brother Thomas McCullogh CSC, "A Specific Heat Analogy," *J. Chem. Educ.*, Vol. 57, **1980**, 896.

7. Doris R. Kimbrough, "Heat Capacity, Body Temperature, and Hypothermia," *J. Chem. Educ.*, Vol. 75, **1998**, 48–49.

8.   JCE Editorial Staff, "JCE Classroom Activity #65: Calories–Who's Counting?," *J. Chem. Educ.*, Vol. 81, **2004**, 1440A.

9. Donald J. Wink, "The Conversion of Chemical Energy. Part 1. Technological Examples," *J. Chem. Educ.*, Vol. 69, **1992**, 108–111.

10. Harold H. Schobert, "The Geochemistry of Coal. Part II: The Components of Coal," *J. Chem. Educ.*, Vol. 66, **1989**, 290–293.

11. *Scientific American*, **September 1990**, Volume 263. This is a special issue devoted to uses of energy in our society.

12. Michael Laing, "Beware–Fertilizer Can EXPLODE!" *J. Chem. Educ.*, Vol. 70, **1993**, 392–394.

13. Gustav P. Dinga, "Hydrogen: The Ultimate Fuel and Energy Carrier," *J. Chem. Educ.*, Vol. 65, **1988**, 688–691.

14. Israel Dostrovsky, "Chemical Fuels from the Sun," *Scientific American*, Vol. 265, **1991**, 102–107.

15. Richard Monastersky, "The Ice that Burns. Can Methane Hydrates Fuel the 21st Century?" *Science News*, Vol. 154, **1998**, 312–313. This article explores a potential new source of natural gas.

Live Demonstrations:

1. Bassam A. Shakhashiri, "Evaporation as an Endothermic Process," *Chemical Demonstrations: A Handbook for Teachers of Chemistry, Volume 3* (Madison: The University of Wisconsin Press, **1989**). pp. 249–251.

2. Lee R. Summerlin, Christie L. Borgford, and Julie B Ealy, "Flaming Cotton," *Chemical Demonstrations, A Sourcebook for Teachers, Volume 2* (Washington: American Chemical Society, **1988**), p. 104. A cotton ball sprinkled with sodium peroxide bursts into flame upon addition of water.

3. Bassam Z. Shakhashiri, "Heat of Neutralization," *Chemical Demonstrations: A Handbook for Teachers of Chemistry, Volume 1* (Madison: The University of Wisconsin Press, **1983**), pp. 15–16.

4. Bassam Z. Shakhashiri, "Chemical Cold Pack," *Chemical Demonstrations: A Handbook for Teachers of Chemistry, Volume 1* (Madison: The University of Wisconsin Press, **1983**), pp. 8–9.

5. Lee. R. Summerlin,, Christie L. Borgford, and Julie B. Ealy, "A Chemical Hand Warmer," *Chemical Demonstrations, A Sourcebook for Teachers, Volume 2* (Washington: American Chemical Society, **1988**), pp.101–102. Oxidation of iron in a plastic baggie is used to prepare a hand-warmer.

6. Lee R. Summerlin and James L. Ealy, Jr. , "Endothermic Reaction: Ammonium Nitrate," *Chemical Demonstrations, A Sourcebook for Teachers,* (Washington: American Chemical Society, **1988**), p. 65. Temperature changes that accompany dissolution of ammonium nitrate in water are measured.

7. Bassam Z. Shakhashiri, "Boiling Water in a Paper Cup: Heat Capacity of Water," *Chemical Demonstrations: A Handbook for Teachers of Chemistry, Volume 3* (Madison: The University of Wisconsin Press, **1989**), pp. 239–241.

8. Lee. R. Summerlin,, Christie L. Borgford, and Julie B. Ealy, "Making Canned Heat," *Chemical Demonstrations, A Sourcebook for Teachers, Volume 2* (Washington: American Chemical Society, **1988**), pp. 111–112. Saponification of stearic acid by reaction with sodium hydroxide, in the presence of alcohol, is used to prepare a solid fuel--canned heat.

Chapter 6. Electronic Structure of Atoms

Media Resources

Figures and Tables in Transparency Pack:	Section:
Figure 6.3 Electromagnetic Waves	6.1 The Wave Nature of Light
Table 6.1 Common Wavelength Units for Electromagnetic Radiation	6.1 The Wave Nature of Light
Figure 6.4 The Electromagnetic Spectrum	6.1 The Wave Nature of Light
Figure 6.7 The Photoelectric Effect	6.2 Quantized Energy and Photons
Figure 6.9 Creating a Spectrum	6.3 Line Spectra and the Bohr Model
Figure 6.11 Line Spectra of Hydrogen and Neon	6.3 Line Spectra and the Bohr Model
Figure 6.12 Energy States in the Hydrogen Atom	6.3 Line Spectra and the Bohr Model
Figure 6.16 Electron-Density Distribution	6.5 Quantum Mechanics and Atomic Orbitals
Table 6.2 Relationship among Values of n, l, and m_l through $n = 4$	6.5 Quantum Mechanics and Atomic Orbitals
Figure 6.17 Energy Levels in the Hydrogen Atom	6.5 Quantum Mechanics and Atomic Orbitals
Figure 6.18 Radial Probability Distributions for the $1s$, $2s$, and $3s$ Orbitals of Hydrogen	6.6 Representations of Orbitals
Figure 6.21 Probability Density $[\psi(r)]^2$ in the $1s$, $2s$ and $3s$ Orbitals of Hydrogen	6.6 Representations of Orbitals
Figure 6.22 The p Orbitals	6.6 Representations of Orbitals
Figure 6.23 Contour Representations of the Five d Orbitals	6.6 Representations of Orbitals
Figure 6.24 General Energy Ordering of Orbitals for a Many-Electron Atom	6.7 Many-Electron Atoms
Table 6.3 Electron Configurations of Several Lighter Elements	6.8 Electron Configurations
Figure 6.30 Regions of the Periodic Table	6.9 Electron Configurations and the Periodic Table
Figure 6.31 Valence Electron Configurations of the Elements	6.9 Electron Configurations and the Periodic Table

Activities:	Section:
Electromagnetic Spectrum	6.1 The Wave Nature of Light
Bohr Model	6.3 Line Spectra and the Bohr Model
Quantum Numbers	6.5 Quantum Mechanics and Atomic Orbitals
Electron Configuration	6.8 Electron Configurations
Periodic Table	6.9 Electron Configurations and the Periodic Table

Animations:	Section:
Photoelectric Effect	6.2 Quantized Energy and Photons
Radial Electron Distribution	6.6 Representations of Orbitals
Electron Configuration	6.8 Electron Configurations

Movies:	Section:
Flame Tests for Metals	6.3 Line Spectra and the Bohr Model

Other Resources

Further Readings: **Section:**

Scientific American, **September 2004**   6.2 Quantized Energy and Photons
Put Body to Them!   6.2 Quantized Energy and Photons
Presenting the Bohr Atom   6.3 Line Spectra and the Bohr Model
Getting the Numbers Right–The Lonely Struggle   6.3 Line Spectra and the Bohr Model
    of Rydberg
Suitable Light Sources and Spectroscopes for   6.3 Line Spectra and the Bohr Model
    Student Observation of Emission Spectra in
    Lecture Halls
Niels Bohr   6.3 Line Spectra and the Bohr Model
100 Years of Quantum Mysteries   6.3 Line Spectra and the Bohr Model
On a Relation between the Heisenberg and   6.4 The Wave Behavior of Matter
    deBroglie Principles
Introducing the Uncertainty Principle Using   6.4 The Wave Behavior of Matter
    Diffraction of Light Waves
Perspectives on the Uncertainty Principle and   6.4 The Wave Behavior of Matter
    Quantum Reality
A Student's Travels, Close Dancing, Bathtubs,   6.5 Quantum Mechanics and Atomic Orbitals
    and the Shopping Mall: More Analogies in
    Teaching Introductory Chemistry
The Mole, the Periodic Table, and Quantum   6.5 Quantum Mechanics and Atomic Orbitals
    Numbers: An Introductory Trio
Electron Densities: Pictorial Analogies for   6.6 Representations of Orbitals
    Apparent Ambiguities in Probability
    Calculations
Mind over Matter   6.7 Many-Electron Atoms
Magnetic Whispers: Chemistry and Medicine   6.7 Many-Electron Atoms
    Finally Tune Into Controversial Molecular
    Chatter
Seeing Inside   6.8 Electron Configurations
The Nobel Prize in Medicine for Magnetic   6.8 Electron Configurations
    Resonance Imaging
Chemistry in Britain, **June 1996**   6.8 Electron Configurations
The Magnetic Eye   6.8 Electron Configurations
Demystifying Introductory Chemistry Part 1:   6.8 Electron Configurations
    Electron Configurations from Experiment
Quantum Analogies on Campus   6.8 Electron Configurations
The Origin of the s, p, d, f Orbital Labels   6.8 Electron Configurations
"New" Schemes for Applying the Aufbau Principle   6.8 Electron Configurations
A Low-Cost Classroom Demonstration of the   6.8 Electron Configurations
    Aufbau Principle
Housing Electrons: Relating Quantum Numbers,   6.8 Electron Configurations
    Energy Levels, and Electron Configurations
Pictorial Analogies VII: Quantum Numbers and   6.8 Electron Configurations
    Orbitals
The Quantum Shoe Store and Electron Structure   6.8 Electron Configurations
Some Analogies for Teaching Atomic Structure   6.8 Electron Configurations
    at the High School Level
Ionization Energies, Parallel Spins, and the Stability   6.8 Electron Configurations
    of Half-Filled Shells

The Noble Gas Configuration—Not the Driving
    Force but the Rule of the Game in Chemistry
The Periodic Table as a Mnemonic Device for
    Writing Electronic Configurations
The Periodic Table and Electron Configurations

6.8 Electron Configurations

6.9 Electron Configurations and the Periodic Table

6.9 Electron Configurations and the Periodic Table

Live Demonstrations:
Simple and Inexpensive Classroom Demonstration
    of Nuclear Magnetic Resonance and Magnetic
    Resonance Imaging

Section:
6.8 Electron Configurations

Chapter 6. Electronic Structure of Atoms

Common Student Misconceptions

- Some students have difficulty converting between angstroms, nanometers, etc. and meters.
- Students often have difficulty switching from the language of certainties to the language of probabilities.
- Students are often frightened or put off by the mathematics, vocabulary, foreign names, and an apparent intangibility of the information.
- Students are initially unaware that the quantum theory laid foundations for such areas as spectroscopy and nanotechnology, just to mention a few.
- Students confuse Bohr's *orbits* with *orbitals*; most spellcheckers do not recognize the word "orbital".
- Students mistakenly think that spectral lines represent energy levels; consequently…
- Students have difficulty associating a given line in an emission (or absorption) spectrum with a transition between *two* energy levels.
- When drawing the orbital diagrams, students often draw 2, 6, 10, and 14 "boxes" for *s, p, d,* and *f* orbitals, respectively.

Teaching Tips

- This is often students' first glimpse at the realm of quantum theory. They need to understand that the model has been built up to rationalize experimental data. They also need to know that elements of one theory are maintained in the subsequent theory.
- Students may not be familiar with the common symbol for wavelength (the lowercase lambda, λ) and the common symbol for frequency (the lowercase nu, ν).
- Using the unit s^{-1} for frequency makes the units cancel more easily.
- Many students will be familiar with the mnemonic for remembering the order of colors in the visible spectrum: ROY G BIV, which stands for red, orange, yellow, green, blue, indigo, and violet.
- A good analogy for the uncertainty principle: picture a busy intersection photographed at night. With a short exposure, you get a clear image of the position of every car, but you cannot tell how fast they are going or whether they are going forward or backward or about to swerve or turn. With a time-lapsed exposure, you can tell from the streaks of light the speed and direction of each car, but you cannot tell where each one currently is. You can know position or path, but not both.

Lecture Outline

6.1 The Wave Nature of Light[1,2,3,4]

- The **electronic structure** of an atom refers to the arrangement of electrons.
- Visible light is a form of **electromagnetic radiation** or *radiant energy*.
- Radiation carries energy through space.
- Electromagnetic radiation is characterized by its wave nature.
- All waves have a characteristic **wavelength**, λ (lambda), and amplitude, A.
- The **frequency**, ν (nu), of a wave is the number of cycles that pass a point in one second.
  - The units of ν are *hertz* (1 Hz = 1 s^{-1}).

---

[1] Figure 6.3 from Transparency Pack
[2] Figure 6.4 from Transparency Pack
[3] "Electromagnetic Spectrum" Activity from Instructor's Resource CD/DVD
[4] Table 6.1 from Transparency Pack

- The speed of a wave is given by its frequency multiplied by its wavelength.
  - For light, speed, $c = \lambda \nu$,
  - Electromagnetic radiation moves through a vacuum with a speed of 3.00×10^8 m/s.
- Electromagnetic waves have characteristic wavelengths and frequencies.
- The *electromagnetic spectrum* is a display of the various types of electromagnetic radiation arranged in order of increasing wavelength.
  - Example: visible radiation has wavelengths between 400 nm (violet) and 750 nm (red).

FORWARD REFERENCES
  - X-Ray diffraction will be discussed in Chapter 12.
  - Light emitting diodes will be described in Chapter 11 (section 11.7).
  - Different ranges of the electromagnetic spectrum will be mentioned in Chapters 18 and 23.
  - Gamma radiation will be further discussed in Chapter 21.

6.2 Quantized Energy and Photons
- Some phenomena can't be explained using a wave model of light:
  - *Blackbody radiation* is the emission of light from hot objects.
  - The *photoelectric effect* is the emission of electrons from metal surfaces on which light shines.
  - *Emission spectra* are the emissions of light from electronically excited gas atoms.

Hot Objects and the Quantization of Energy
- Heated solids emit radiation (black body radiation)
  - The wavelength distribution depends on the temperature (i.e., "red hot" objects are cooler than "white hot" objects).
- Planck investigated black body radiation.
  - He proposed that energy can only be absorbed or released from atoms in certain amounts.
  - These amounts are called quanta.
  - A **quantum** is the smallest amount of energy that can be emitted or absorbed as electromagnetic radiation.
  - The relationship between energy and frequency is:
$$E = h\nu$$
  - where h is **Planck's constant** (6.626×10^{-34} J-s).
- To understand quantization consider the notes produced by a violin (continuous) and a piano (quantized):
  - A violin can produce any note when the fingers are placed at an appropriate spot on the bridge.
  - A piano can only produce notes corresponding to the keys on the keyboard.

The Photoelectric Effect and Photons[5,6,7,8]
- The **photoelectric effect** provides evidence for the particle nature of light.
  - It also provides evidence for quantization.
- Einstein assumed that light traveled in energy packets called **photons**.
  - The energy of one photon is $E = h\nu$.
- Light shining on the surface of a metal can cause electrons to be ejected from the metal.
  - The electrons will only be ejected if the photons have sufficient energy (*work function*):
    - Below the threshold frequency no electrons are ejected.

---

[5] **September 2004** issue of *Scientific American* from Further Readings
[6] "Photoelectric Effect" Animation from Instructor's Resource CD/DVD
[7] Figure 6.7 from Transparency Pack
[8] "Put Body to Them!" from Further Readings

- Above the threshold frequency, the excess energy appears as the kinetic energy of the ejected electrons.
- Light has wave-like AND particle-like properties.

FORWARD REFERENCES
- *Photoconductivity* in solar energy conversions and emission of photons by semiconductor nanoparticles will be described in Chapter 12 (section 12.9).
- *Photodissociation*, i.e. bond breaking as a result of an absorption of a photon by a molecule, as well as *photodecomposition* will be discussed in Chapter 18 (section 18.2).
- The role of photons from sunlight in *photosynthesis* will be further discussed in Chapter 23 (section 23.3).

6.3 Line Spectra and the Bohr Model

Line Spectra[9,10,11]

- Radiation composed of only one wavelength is called *monochromatic*.
- Radiation that spans a whole array of different wavelengths is called *continuous*.
- When radiation from a light source, such as a lightbulb, is separated into its different wavelength components, a **spectrum** is produced.
  - White light can be separated into a **continuous spectrum** of colors.
    - A rainbow is a continuous spectrum of light produced by the dispersal of sunlight by raindrops or mist.
  - On the continuous spectrum there are no dark spots, which would correspond to different lines.
- Not all radiation is continuous.
  - A gas placed in a partially evacuated tube and subjected to a high voltage produces single colors of light.
  - The spectrum that we see contains radiation of only specific wavelengths; this is called a **line spectrum**.

Bohr's Model[12,13]

- Rutherford assumed that electrons orbited the nucleus analogous to planets orbiting the sun.
  - However, a charged particle moving in a circular path should lose energy.
  - This means that the atom should be unstable according to Rutherford's theory.
- Bohr noted the line spectra of certain elements and assumed that electrons were confined to specific energy states. These were called orbits.
- Bohr's model is based on three postulates:
  - Only orbits of specific radii, corresponding to certain definite energies, are permitted for electrons in an atom.
  - An electron in a permitted orbit has a specific energy and is an "allowed" energy state.
  - Energy is only emitted or absorbed by an electron as it moves from one allowed energy state to another.
    - The energy is gained or lost as a photon.

---

[9] Figure 6.9 from Transparency Pack
[10] "Flame Tests for Metals" Movie from Instructor's Resource CD/DVD
[11] Figure 6.11 from Transparency Pack
[12] "Presenting the Bohr Atom" from Further Readings
[13] "Bohr Model" Activity from Instructor's Resource CD/DVD

The Energy States of the Hydrogen Atom[14,15,16]

- Colors from excited gases arise because electrons move between energy states in the atom.
- Since the energy states are quantized, the light emitted from excited atoms must be quantized and appear as line spectra.
- Bohr showed mathematically that

$$E = -(hcR_H)\left(\frac{1}{n^2}\right) = (-2.18 \times 10^{-18}\,\text{J})\left(\frac{1}{n^2}\right)$$

  - where n is the *principal quantum number* (i.e., $n = 1, 2, 3, \ldots \infty$) and R_H is the Rydberg constant.
  - The product $hcR_H = 2.18 \times 10^{-18}$ J.
- The first orbit in the Bohr model has $n = 1$ and is closest to the nucleus.
- The furthest orbit in the Bohr model has $n = \infty$ and corresponds to $E = 0$.
- Electrons in the Bohr model can only move between orbits by absorbing and emitting energy in quanta ($E = h\nu$).
  - The **ground state** is the lowest energy state.
  - An electron in a higher energy state is said to be in an **excited state**.
- The amount of energy absorbed or emitted by moving between states is given by

$$|\Delta E| = |E_f - E_i| = h\nu = \left|\,-2.18 \times 10^{-18}\,\text{J}\left(\frac{1}{n_f^2} - \frac{1}{n_i^2}\right)\right|$$

Limitations of the Bohr Model[17,18]

- The Bohr Model has several limitations:
  - It cannot explain the spectra of atoms other than hydrogen.
  - Electrons do not move about the nucleus in circular orbits.
- However, the model introduces two important ideas:
  - The energy of an electron is quantized: electrons exist only in certain energy levels described by quantum numbers.
  - Energy gain or loss is involved in moving an electron from one energy level to another.

FORWARD REFERENCES

- Absorption of sufficient amount of energy to ionize an atom will be further discussed in Chapter 7 (section 7.4).
- Emission of light with characteristic colors (flame test) by excited atoms of Li, Na, and K is shown in Chapter 7 (section 7.7).
- Selective absorption of light by chemicals, e.g., organic dyes, will be described in Chapter 9.
- Absorption of wavelengths from the visible part of the electromagnetic spectrum by molecules of chlorophyll and other pigments will be discussed in Chapter 23 (section 23.3).
- Absorption in the visible range will be responsible for colors of many transition metal complexes (Chapter 23, section 23.5).

---

[14] "Getting the Numbers Right–The Lonely Struggle of Rydberg" from Further Readings
[15] Figure 6.12 from Transparency Pack
[16] "Suitable Light Sources and Spectroscopes for Student Observation of Emission Spectra in Lecture Halls" from Further Readings
[17] "Niels Bohr" from Further Readings
[18] "100 Years of Quantum Mysteries" from Further Readings

6.4 The Wave Behavior of Matter[19]

- Knowing that light has a particle nature, it seems reasonable to ask whether matter has a wave nature.
- This question was answered by Louis deBroglie.
- Using Einstein's and Planck's equations, deBroglie derived:

$$\lambda = h/mv$$

- The **momentum**, mv, is a particle property, whereas λ is a wave property.
    - **Matter waves** are the term used to describe wave characteristics of material particles.
    - Therefore, in one equation deBroglie summarized the concepts of waves and particles as they apply to low-mass, high-speed objects.
    - As a consequence of deBroglie's discovery, we now have techniques such as X-ray diffraction and electron microscopy to study small objects.

The Uncertainty Principle[20,21]

- **Heisenberg's uncertainty principle**: we cannot determine the *exact* position, direction of motion, and speed of subatomic particles simultaneously.
- For electrons: we cannot determine their momentum and position simultaneously.

FORWARD REFERENCES
- X-ray diffraction and X-ray crystallography will be further discussed in Chapter 12 (section 12.2).

6.5 Quantum Mechanics and Atomic Orbitals[22,23]

- Schrödinger proposed an equation containing both wave and particle terms.
- Solving the equation leads to **wave functions**, ψ.
- The wave function describes the electron's matter wave.
    - The square of the wave function, ψ^2, gives the probability of finding the electron.
    - That is, ψ^2 gives the electron density for the atom.
        - ψ^2 is called the **probability density**.
- **Electron density** is another way of expressing probability.
    - A region of high electron density is one where there is a high probability of finding an electron.

Orbitals and Quantum Numbers[24,25,26,27]

- If we solve the Schrödinger equation we get wave functions and energies for the wave functions.
- We call ψ **orbitals**.
- Schrödinger's equation requires three quantum numbers:
- *Principal quantum number, n*. This is the same as Bohr's n.
    - As n becomes larger, the atom becomes larger and the electron is further from the nucleus.
- *Angular momentum quantum number, l*. This quantum number depends on the value of n.

---

[19] "On a Relation between the Heisenberg and deBroglie Principles" from Further Readings
[20] "Introducing the Uncertainty Principle Using Diffraction of Light Waves" from Further Readings
[21] "Perspectives on the Uncertainty Principle and Quantum Reality" from Further Readings
[22] Figure 6.16 from Transparency Pack
[23] "A Student's Travels, Close Dancing, Bathtubs, and the Shopping Mall: More Analogies in Teaching Introductory Chemistry" from Further Readings
[24] "The Mole, the Periodic Table and Quantum Numbers: An Introductory Trio" from Further Readings
[25] "Quantum Numbers" Activity from Instructor's Resource CD/DVD
[26] Table 6.2 from Transparency Pack
[27] Figure 6.17 from Transparency Pack

- The values of l begin at 0 and increase to $n - 1$.
- We usually use letters for l (s, p, d and f for $l = 0, 1, 2,$ and 3). Usually we refer to the s, p, d and f orbitals.
- This quantum number defines the shape of the orbital.
- *Magnetic quantum number, m_l.*
  - This quantum number depends on l.
  - The magnetic quantum number has integer values between $-l$ and $+l$.
    - There are $(2l+1)$ possible values of m_l.
      - For example, for $l = \mathbf{1}$, there are $(2 \times \mathbf{1}+1) = 3$ values of m_l: 0, +1, and -1.
        - Consequently, for $l = 1$, there are 3 orbitals: p_x, p_y and p_z.
  - Magnetic quantum numbers give the three-dimensional orientation of each orbital.
- A collection of orbitals with the same value of n is called an **electron shell**.
  - There are n^2 orbitals in a shell described by a the n value.
    - For example, for $n = \mathbf{3}$, there are $\mathbf{3}^2 = 9$ orbitals.
  - A set of orbitals with the same n and l is called a **subshell**.
    - Each subshell is designated by a number and a letter.
      - For example, $3p$ orbitals have $n = 3$ and $l = 1$.
    - There are n types of subshells in a shell described by a the n value.
      - For example, for $n = \mathbf{3}$, there are $\mathbf{3}$ subshells: $3s$, $3p$ and $3d$.
- Orbitals can be ranked in terms of energy to yield an Aufbau diagram.
  - Note that this Aufbau diagram is for a single electron system.
- As n increases, note that the spacing between energy levels becomes smaller.

6.6 Representations of Orbitals[28,29]

The s Orbitals[30,31,32]

- All s orbitals are spherical.
- As n increases, the s orbitals get larger.
- As n increases, the number of **nodes** increases.
  - A node is a region in space where the probability of finding an electron is zero.
    - $\psi^2 = 0$ at a node.
  - For an s orbital the number of nodes is given by $n - 1$.
- We can plot a curve of *radial probability density* vs. distance (r) from the nucleus.
  - This curve is the **radial probability function** for the orbital.

The p Orbitals[33]

- There are three p orbitals: p_x, p_y and p_z.
  - The three p orbitals lie along the x-, y-, and z-axes of a Cartesian system.
  - The letters correspond to allowed values of m_l of -1, 0, and $+1$.
- The orbitals are dumbbell shaped; each has two *lobes*.
- As n increases, the p orbitals get larger.
- All p orbitals have a node at the nucleus.

---

[28] "The Origin of the s, p, d, f Orbital Labels" from Further Readings
[29] "Electron Densities: Pictorial Analogies for Apparent Ambiguities in Probability Calculations" from Further Readings
[30] "Radial Electron Distribution" Animation from Instructor's Resource CD/DVD
[31] Figure 6.18 from Transparency Pack
[32] Figure 6.21 from Transparency Pack
[33] Figure 6.22 from Transparency Pack

The *d* and *f* Orbitals[34]

- There are five *d* and seven f orbitals.
  - Three of the *d* orbitals lie in a plane bisecting the *x*-, *y*-, and *z*-axes.
  - Two of the *d* orbitals lie in a plane aligned along the *x*-, *y*-, and *z*-axes.
  - Four of the *d* orbitals have four lobes each.
  - One *d* orbital has two lobes and a collar.

FORWARD REFERENCES

- An overlap of atomic orbitals will be introduced in Chapter 9 (section 9.4).
- Hybridization of atomic orbitals will be discussed in Chapter 9 (section 9.5).
- Molecular orbitals will be introduced in Chapter 9 (section 9.7).
- Overlap of *p* orbitals on C atoms will be implicated in the formation of π bonds in organic chemistry, as mentioned in Chapters 9 and 22 (section 22.1; C vs. Si) and discussed in detail in Chapter 24.
- Energies of *d* orbitals in different crystal fields will be discussed in Chapter 23 (section 23.6).

6.7 Many-Electron Atoms

Orbitals and Their Energies[35,36,37]

- In a many-electron atom, for a given value of *n*,
  - The energy of an orbital increases with increasing value of *l*.
- Orbitals of the same energy are said to be **degenerate**.

Electron Spin and the Pauli Exclusion Principle[38]

- Line spectra of many electron atoms show each line as a closely spaced pair of lines.
- Stern and Gerlach designed an experiment to determine why.
  - A beam of atoms was passed through a slit and into a magnetic field and the atoms were then detected.
  - Two spots were found: one with the electrons spinning in one direction and one with the electrons spinning in the opposite direction.
- Since **electron spin** (electron as a tiny sphere spinning on its own axis) is quantized,
  - We define m_s = **spin magnetic quantum number** = $\pm$ 1/2.
- **Pauli's exclusion principle** states that no two electrons can have the same set of 4 quantum numbers.
  - Therefore, two electrons in the same orbital must have opposite spins.

FORWARD REFERENCES

- The roles of screening and penetration in determining the relative energies of subshells within a shell will be explained in Chapter 7.
- Pauli's exclusion principle will also apply to hybrid orbitals in Chapter 9 (sections 9.4-9.5) and molecular orbitals (sections 9.7-9.8).

---

[34] Figure 6.23 from Transparency Pack
[35] Figure 6.24 from Transparency Pack
[36] "'New' Schemes for Applying the Aufbau Principle" from Further Readings
[37] "A Low-Cost Classroom Demonstration of the Aufbau Principle" from Further Readings
[38] "Mind over Matter" from Further Readings

6.8 Electron Configurations[39,40,41,42,43]

- **Electron configurations** tell us how the electrons are distributed among the various orbitals of an atom.
- The most stable configuration, or ground state, is that in which the electrons are in the lowest possible energy state.
- When writing ground-state electronic configurations:
  - electrons fill orbitals in order of increasing energy with no more than two electrons per orbital.
  - no two electrons can fill one orbital with the same spin (Pauli).
  - for degenerate orbitals, electrons fill each orbital singly before any orbital gets a second electron.
  - How do we show spin?
    - An arrow pointing upwards has $m_s = + 1/2$ (spin up).
    - An arrow pointing downwards has $m_s = - 1/2$ (spin down).

Hund's Rule[44,45,46,47,48,49,50,51,52,53]

- **Hund's rule**: for degenerate orbitals, the lowest energy is attained when the number of electrons with the same spin is maximized.
  - Thus, electrons fill each orbital singly with their spins parallel before any orbital gets a second electron.
  - By placing electrons in different orbitals, electron-electron repulsions are minimized.

Condensed Electron Configurations[54]

- Electron configurations may be written using a shorthand notation (*condensed electron configuration*):
  - Write the **valence electrons** explicitly.
    - **Valence electrons** are electrons in the outer shell.
      - These electrons are gained and lost in reactions.
  - Write the **core electrons** corresponding to the filled noble gas in square brackets.
    - Core electrons are electrons in the inner shells.

---

[39] "Magnetic Whispers: Chemistry and Medicine Finally Tune Into Controversial Molecular Chatter" from Further Readings

[40] "Simple and Inexpensive Classroom Demonstration of Nuclear Magnetic Resonance and Magnetic Resonance Imaging" from Live Demonstrations

[41] "Seeing Inside" from Further Readings

[42] "The Nobel Prize in Medicine for Magnetic Resonance Imaging" from Further Readings

[43] **June 1996** issue of *Chemistry in Britain* from Further Readings

[44] "The Magnetic Eye" from Further Readings

[45] "Demystifying Introductory Chemistry; Part 1. Electron Configurations from Experiment" from Further Readings

[46] "Quantum Analogies on Campus" from Further Readings

[47] "Housing Electrons: Relating Quantum Numbers, Energy Levels, and Electron Configurations" from Further Readings

[48] "Pictorial Analogies VII: Quantum Numbers and Orbitals" from Further Readings

[49] "The Quantum Shoe Store and Electron Structure" from Further Readings

[50] Table 6.3 from Transparency Pack

[51] "Electron Configuration" Activity from Instructor's Resource CD/DVD

[52] "Some Analogies for Teaching Atomic Structure at the High School Level" from Further Readings

[53] " Ionization Energies, Parallel Spins, and the Stability of Half–Filled Shells" from Further Readings

[54] "The Noble Gas Configuration—Not the Driving Force but the Rule of the Game in Chemistry" from Further Readings

- • These are generally not involved in bonding.
- • Example:
  - • P is $1s^2 2s^2 2p^6 3s^2 3p^3$,
  - • but Ne is $1s^2 2s^2 2p^6$.
  - • Therefore, P is $[Ne]3s^2 3p^3$.

Transition Metals

- • After Ar the *d* orbitals begin to fill.
- • After the 3*d* orbitals are full the 4*p* orbitals begin to fill.
- • The ten elements between Ti and Zn are called the **transition metals** or **transition elements**.

The Lanthanides and Actinides

- • The 4*f* orbitals begin to fill with Ce.
  - • Note: The electron configuration of La is $[Xe]6s^2 5d^1$.
- • The 4*f* orbitals are filled for the elements Ce – Lu which are called **lanthanide elements** (or **rare earth elements**).
- • The 5*f* orbitals are filled for the elements Th – Lr which are called **actinide elements**.
  - • The actinide elements are radioactive and most are not found in nature.

FORWARD REFERENCES

- • Periodic properties associated with electron configurations, such as atomic radii, ionization energies and electron affinities, will be discussed throughout Chapter 7.
- • Valence electrons and the Octet Rule will be discussed in Chapter 8.
- • Valence electrons of atoms within molecules and ions will be added and distributed according to the VSEPR model in Chapter 9 to determine molecular shapes.
- • Electron configurations and the associated chemical properties of nonmetals in groups 4A-8A will be discussed in detail in Chapter 22.
- • Electron configurations and the associated properties of select transition metals will be discussed in Chapter 23.
- • High- and low-spin transition metal complexes will be discussed in Chapter 23 (section 23.6).
- • Electron configuration of the C atom will be highlighted in Chapter 24 on organic chemistry.

6.9 Electron Configurations and the Periodic Table[55,56,57,58,59]

- • The periodic table can be used as a guide for electron configurations.
- • The period number is the value of *n*.
- • Groups 1A and 2A have their *s* orbitals being filled.
- • Groups 3A–8A have their *p* orbitals being filled.
- • The *s*-block and *p*-block of the periodic table contain the representative, or main-group, elements.
- • Groups 3B–2B have their *d* orbitals being filled.
- • The lanthanides and actinides have their *f* orbitals being filled.
  - • The actinides and lanthanide elements are collectively referred to as the ***f*-block metals**.
- • Note that the 3*d* orbitals fill after the 4*s* orbital. Similarly, the 4*f* orbitals fill after the 5*d* orbitals.
- • In general, for representative elements we do not consider the electrons in completely filled d or f subshells to be valence electrons.

---

[55] Figure 6.30 from Transparency Pack
[56] "The Periodic Table as a Mnemonic Device for Writing Electronic Configurations" from Further Readings
[57] "The Periodic Table and Electron Configurations" from Further Readings
[58] Figure 6.31 from Transparency Pack
[59] "Periodic Table" Activity from Instructor's Resource CD/DVD

- In general, for transition elements we do not consider the electrons in a completely filled f subshell to be valence electrons.

Anomalous Electron Configurations

- There are many elements that appear to violate the electron configuration guidelines.
    - Examples:
        - Chromium is $[Ar]3d^54s^1$ instead of $[Ar]3d^44s^2$.
        - Copper is $[Ar]3d^{10}4s^1$ instead of $[Ar]3d^94s^2$.
    - Half-full (d^5) and full (d^{10}) d subshells are particularly stable.

FORWARD REFERENCES

- Electron configurations of ions of the main group elements will be covered in Chapter 8.
- Electron configurations of transition metal cations will be mentioned in Chapter 8 and further used in Chapter 23.

Further Readings:

1. Robert R. Perkins, "Put Body to Them!" *J. Chem. Educ.*, Vol. 72, **1995**, 151–152. This reference includes analogies for quantized states.

2. The **September 2004** issue of *Scientific American* is a special issue with numerous articles dealing with how Einstein's ideas reshaped the world.

3. Bianca L. Haendler, "Presenting the Bohr Atom," *J. Chem. Educ.*, Vol. 59, **1982**, 372–376. Presenting the role of the Bohr theory within the framework of the development of quantum mechanics.

4. Mike Sutton, "Getting the numbers Right–The Lonely Struggle of Rydberg," *Chemistry World*, **July 2004**, 38–41.

5. Elvin Hughes, Jr., and Arnold George, "Suitable Light Sources and Spectroscopes for Student Observation of Emission Spectra in Lecture Halls," *J. Chem. Educ.*, Vol. 61, **1984**, 908–909.

6. Max Tegmark and John Archibald Wheeler, "100 Years of Quantum Mysteries," *Scientific American*, **February 2001**, 68–75.

7. Dennis R. Sievers, "Niels Bohr," *J. Chem. Educ.*, Vol. 59, **1982**, 303–304. A short biography of Niels Bohr.

8. Pedro L. Muiño, "Introducing the Uncertainty Principle Using Diffraction of Light Waves," *J. Chem. Educ.*, Vol. 77, **2000**, 1025–1027.

9. Lawrence S. Bartell, "Perspectives on the Uncertainty Principle and Quantum Reality," *J. Chem. Educ.*, Vol. 62, **1985**, 192–196. This reading contains some practical applications of the uncertainty principle.

10. Oliver G. Ludwig, "On a Relation between the Heisenberg and deBroglie Principles," *J. Chem. Educ.*, Vol. 70, **1993**, 28.

11. Goeff Rayner-Canham, "A Student's Travels, Close Dancing, Bathtubs, and the Shopping Mall: More Analogies in Teaching Introductory Chemistry," *J. Chem. Educ.*, Vol. 71, **1994**, 943–944. This reference includes an analogy dealing with the probability model of the atom.

12. Mali Yin and Raymond S. Ochs, "The Mole, the Periodic Table, and Quantum Numbers: An Introductory Trio," *J. Chem. Educ.*, Vol. 78, **2001**, 1345–1347.

13. Ronald J. Gillespie, James N. Spencer and Richard S. Moog, "Demystifying Introductory Chemistry; Part 1. Electron Configurations from Experiment," *J. Chem. Educ.*, Vol. 73, **1996**, 617–622. The use of experimental data to investigate electron configurations is presented in this reference.

14. Ngai Ling Ma, "Quantum Analogies on Campus," *J. Chem. Educ.*, Vol. 73, **1996**, 1016–1017.

15. William B. Jensen, "The Origin of the s, p, d, f Orbital Labels," *J. Chem. Educ.*, Vol. 84, **2007**, 757–758.

16. Maria Gabriela Lagorio, "Electron Densities: Pictorial Analogies for Apparent Ambiguities in Probability Calculations," *J. Chem. Educ.*, Vol. 77, **2000**, 1444–1445.

17. Robin Hendry, "Mind over Water" *Chemistry in Britain*, **November 2000**, 35–37.

18. Peter Weiss, "Magnetic Whispers: Chemistry and Medicine Finally Tune Into Controversial Molecular Chatter," *Science News*, Vol. 159, **2001**, 42–44.

19. Anthony Garofalo, "Housing Electrons: Relating Quantum Numbers, Energy Levels, and Electron Configurations," *J. Chem. Educ.*, Vol. 74, **1997**, 709–719.

20. John J. Fortman, "Pictorial Analogies VII: Quantum Numbers and Orbitals," *J. Chem. Educ.*, Vol. 70, **1993**, 649–650.

21. M. Bonneau, "The Quantum Shoe Store and Electron Structure," *J. Chem. Educ.*, Vol. 68, **1991**, 837.

22. Robert D. Freeman, "'New' Schemes for Applying the Aufbau Principle," *J. Chem. Educ.*, Vol. 67, **1990**, 576.

23. James R. Hanley, III, and James R. Hanley, Jr., "A Low-Cost Classroom Demonstration of the Aufbau Principle," *J. Chem. Educ.*, Vol. 56, **1979**, 747.

24. Peter Cann, "Ionization Energies, Parallel Spins, and the Stability of Half-Filled Shells," *J. Chem. Educ.*, Vol. 77, **2000**, 1056–1061.

25. *Chemistry in Britain*, Vol. 32, **June, 1996**. This issue contains several articles on the uses of NMR–its developments and its uses in medicine.

26. Mark Fischetti, "Seeing Inside," *Scientific American*, **August 2004**, 92–93. A short article on medical imaging devices.

27. Lyn Gladden, "The Magnetic Eye," *Chemistry in Britain*, November **2000**, 35–37. A short article about the work of Wolfgang Pauli.

28. Roland Schmid, "The Noble Gas Configuration–Not the Driving Force but the Rule of the Game in Chemistry," *J. Chem. Educ.*, Vol. 80, **2003**, 931–937.

29. Charles G. Fry, "The Nobel Prize in Medicine for Magnetic Resonance Imaging," *J. Chem. Educ.*, Vol. 81, **2004**, 922–923.

30. Ngoh Khang Goh, Lian Sai Chia, and Daniel Tan, "Some Analogies for Teaching Atomic Structure at the High School Level," *J. Chem. Educ.*, Vol. 71, **1994**, 733–734. Analogies for orbitals, Hund's Rule, and the four quantum numbers are included in this reference.

31. Judith A. Strong, "The Periodic Table and Electron Configurations," *J. Chem. Educ.*, Vol. 63, **1986**, 834.

32. Suzanne T. Mabrouk, "The Periodic Table as a Mnemonic Device for Writing Electronic Configurations," *J. Chem. Educ.*, Vol. 80, **2003**, 894–898.

Live Demonstrations

1. Joel A. Olson, Karen J. Nordell, Marla A. Chesnik, Clark R. Landis, Arthur B. Ellis, M.S. Rzchowski, S. Michael Condren, George C. Lisensky, and James W. Long, "Simple and Inexpensive Classroom Demonstration of Nuclear Magnetic Resonance and Magnetic Resonance Imaging," *J. Chem. Educ.*, Vol. 77, **2000**, 882–889.

Chapter 7. Periodic Properties of the Elements

Media Resources

Figures and Tables in Transparency Pack:	**Section:**
Figure 7.2 Effective Nuclear Charge	7.2 Effective Nuclear Charge
Figure 7.3 2s and 2p Radial Probability Functions	7.2 Effective Nuclear Charge
Figure 7.4 Variations in Effective Nuclear Charge for Period 2 and Period 3 Elements	7.2 Effective Nuclear Charge
Figure 7.6 Trends in Bonding Atomic Radii for Periods 1 through 5	7.3 Sizes of Atoms and Ions
Figure 7.7 Cation and Anion Size	7.3 Sizes of Atoms and Ions
Table 7.2 Successive Values of Ionization Energies, I, for the Elements Sodium Through Argon (kJ/mol)	7.4 Ionization Energy
Figure 7.9 Trends in First Ionization Energies of the Elements	7.4 Ionization Energy
Figure 7.11 Electron Affinity in kJ/mol for Selected s- and p-Block Elements	7.5 Electron Affinities
Figure 7.12 Metals, Metalloids, and Nonmetals	7.6 Metals, Nonmetals, and Metalloids
Figure 7.14 Representative Oxidation States of the Elements	7.6 Metals, Nonmetals, and Metalloids
Table 7.4 Some Properties of the Alkali Metals	7.7 Trends for Group 1A and 2A Metals
Table 7.5 Some Properties of the Alkaline Earth Metals	7.7 Trends for Group 1A and 2A Metals
Table 7.6 Some Properties of the Group 6A Elements	7.8 Trends for Selected Nonmetals
Table 7.7 Some Properties of the Halogens	7.8 Trends for Selected Nonmetals
Table 7.8 Some Properties of the Noble Gases	7.8 Trends for Selected Nonmetals

Activities:	**Section:**
Periodic Table	7.1 Development of the Periodic Table
Ionization Energies	7.4 Ionization Energy

Animations:	**Section:**
Periodic Properties	7.1 Development of the Periodic Table
Effective Nuclear Charge	7.2 Effective Nuclear Charge
Periodic Trends: Atomic Radii	7.3 Sizes of Atoms and Ions
Gain and Loss of Electrons	7.3 Sizes of Atoms and Ions
Ionization Energy	7.4 Ionization Energy
Periodic Trends: Ionization Energies	7.4 Ionization Energy
Electron Affinity	7.5 Electron Affinities
Periodic Trends: Electron Affinity	7.5 Electron Affinities
Periodic Trends: Acid-Base Behavior of Oxides	7.6 Metals, Nonmetals, and Metalloids

Movies:	**Section:**
Sodium and Potassium in Water	7.7 Trends for Group 1A and 2A Metals
Flame Tests for Metals	7.7 Trends for Group 1A and 2A Metals
Physical Properties of the Halogens	7.8 Trends for Selected Nonmetals

Reactions with Oxygen

7.8 Trends for Selected Nonmetals

3-D Models:

Methanethiol (methyl mercaptan)
Water
Hydroxide Ion
Square Planar Structure
Oxygen
Sulfur
Chlorine
Bromine
Iodine

Section:
7.3 Sizes of Atoms and Ions
7.6 Metals, Nonmetals, and Metalloids
7.6 Metals, Nonmetals, and Metalloids
7.6 Metals, Nonmetals, and Metalloids
7.8 Trends for Selected Nonmetals
7.8 Trends for Selected Nonmetals
7.8 Trends for Selected Nonmetals
7.8 Trends for Selected Nonmetals
7.8 Trends for Selected Nonmetals

Other Resources

Further Readings:
Chemical and Engineering News, **September 8, 2003**

Using the Learning Cycle to Introduce Periodicity
The Nuts and Bolts of Chemistry
Mendeleev and Moseley: The Principal Discoverers of the Periodic Law
Mendeleev's Other Predictions
Atomic Numbers Before Moseley
D. I. Mendeleev and the English Chemists
The Evolution of the Periodic System
Periodic Table of Elemental Abundance
A Different Approach to a 3-D Periodic System Including Stable Isotopes
Screen Percentages Based on Slater Effective Nuclear Charge as a Versatile Tool for Teaching Periodic Trends
Pictorial Analogies VI: Radial and Angular Wave Function Plots
Using Balls from Different Sports to Model the Variation of Atomic Sizes
Periodic Contractions Among the Elements; Or, On Being the Right Size
Ionization Energies of Atoms and Atomic Ions
Trends in Ionization Energy of Transition-Metal Elements
Periodicity in the Acid-Base Behavior of Oxides and Hydroxides
Metalloids
A Variation on the Demonstration of the Properties of the Alkali Metals
A Little Lithium May be Just What the Doctor Ordered
The Legend of Dr. Pepper/Seven-Up
Update on Intake; Calcium Consumption Low

Section:
7.1 Development of the Periodic Table

7.1 Development of the Periodic Table
7.1 Development of the Periodic Table
7.1 Development of the Periodic Table

7.1 Development of the Periodic Table
7.1 Development of the Periodic Table
7.1 Development of the Periodic Table
7.1 Development of the Periodic Table
7.1 Development of the Periodic Table
7.1 Development of the Periodic Table

7.2 Effective Nuclear Charge

7.3 Sizes of Atoms and Ions

7.3. Sizes of Atoms and Ions

7.3 Sizes of Atoms and Ions

7.4 Ionization Energy
7.4 Ionization Energy

7.6 Metals, Nonmetals, and Metalloids

7.6 Metals, Nonmetals, and Metalloids
7.7 Trends for Group 1A and 2A Metals

7.7 Trends for Group 1A and 2A Metals

7.7 Trends for Group 1A and 2A Metals
7.7 Trends for Group 1A and 2A Metals

Life, Death, and Calcium	7.7 Trends for Group 1A and 2A Metals
A Second Note on the Term 'Chalcogen'	7.8 Trends for Selected Nonmetals
Allotropes and Polymorphs	7.8 Trends for Selected Nonmetals
The Origin of the Term Allotrope	7.8 Trends for Selected Nonmetals
Aqueous Hydrogen Peroxide: Its Household Uses and Concentration Units	7.8 Trends for Selected Nonmetals
The Chemistry of Swimming Pool Maintenance	7.8 Trends for Selected Nonmetals

Live Demonstrations: **Section:**

Halogens Compete for Electrons	7.5 Electron Affinities
Acidic and Basic Properties of Oxides	7.6 Metals, Nonmetals, and Metalloids
Disappearing Ink	7.6 Metals, Nonmetals, and Metalloids
A Dramatic Flame Test Demonstration	7.7 Trends for Group 1A and 2A Metals
Simple Flame Test Techniques Using Cotton Swabs	7.7 Trends for Group 1A and 2A Metals
Producing Hydrogen Gas from Calcium Metal	7.7 Trends for Group 1A and 2A Metals
Preparation and Properties of Oxygen	7.8 Trends for Selected Nonmetals
Plastic Sulfur	7.8 Trends for Selected Nonmetals

Chapter 7. Periodic Properties of the Elements

Common Student Misconceptions

- Students have difficulty with the concepts of shielding and effective nuclear charge. As you move to the right in a period, shielding does not increase appreciably but the nuclear charge does. Therefore, effective nuclear charge increases steadily as you move to the right along the period.
- Students are confused why, within a period, atomic radii decrease with increasing atomic number.
- Students often do not understand slight irregularities in periodic trends for elements in each row after each ns subshell becomes filled, and after np and $(n-1)d$ subshells become half-filled.
- Students often have problems with the signs of electron affinities; in particular, why group 1A metals have negative (exothermic) electronegativities.
- Students are often confused regarding the placement of hydrogen on the periodic table; despite its common placement in column 1A, hydrogen is a nonmetal.
- Students often confuse behavior of elements in *aqueous* phase with periodic properties determined in gas phase (*ionization energy, electron affinity*) or in solid phase (*ionic radius*).
- Students often confuse *isoelectronic* species with those with the same number of *valence electrons*.

Teaching Tips

- Students need to be shown how position on the periodic table and electron configurations can be used to highlight periodic properties.
- Emphasize the periodic table as an organizational tool; it will help students recall chemical facts.
- Students find the descriptive chemistry/group trends a bit overwhelming at first.
- Live demonstrations, CD videos, and web-based animations are very helpful in stimulating student interest in the group trends.

Lecture Outline

7.1 Development of the Periodic Table[1,2,3,4,5,6,7,8,9,10,11,12]

- The periodic table is the most significant tool that chemists use for organizing and recalling chemical facts.
- Elements in the same column contain the same number of outer-shell electrons or **valence electrons**.
- How do we organize the different elements in a meaningful way that will allow us to make predictions about undiscovered elements?

---

[1] "Periodic Properties" Animation from Instructor's Resource CD/DVD
[2] "Periodic Table" Activity from Instructor's Resource CD/DVD
[3] **September 8, 2003** issue of *Chemical and Engineering News* from Further Readings
[4] "Using the Learning Cycle to Introduce Periodicity" from Further Readings
[5] "The Nuts and Bolts of Chemistry" from Further Readings
[6] "Mendeleev and Moseley: The Principal Discoverers of the Periodic Law" from Further Readings
[7] "The Evolution of the Periodic System" from Further Readings
[8] "Mendeleev's Other Prediction" from Further Readings
[9] "Atomic Number Before Moseley" from Further Readings
[10] "D. I. Mendeleev and the English Chemists" from Further Readings
[11] "Periodic Tables of Elemental Abundance" from Further Readings
[12] "A Different Approach to a 3–D Periodic System Including Stable Isotopes" from Further Readings

- • Arrange elements to reflect the trends in chemical and physical properties.
- • The periodic table arises from the periodic patterns in the electronic configurations of the elements.
  - • Elements in the same column contain the same number of valence electrons.
  - • The trends within a row or column form patterns that help us make predictions about chemical properties and reactivity.
- • In the first attempt Mendeleev and Meyer arranged the elements in order of increasing atomic weight.
  - • Certain elements were missing from this scheme.
  - • For example, in 1871 Mendeleev noted that As properly belonged underneath P and not Si, which left a missing element underneath Si. He predicted a number of properties for this element.
    - • In 1886 Ge was discovered; the properties of Ge match Mendeleev's predictions well.
- • In the modern periodic table, elements are arranged in order of *increasing atomic number*.

FORWARD REFERENCES
- • Periodic trends and chemical properties of nonmetals will be further discussed in Chapter 22 (section 22.1).

7.2 Effective Nuclear Charge[13,14,15,16,17]

- • **Effective nuclear charge** (Z_{eff}) is the charge experienced by an electron on a many-electron atom.
- • The effective nuclear charge is not the same as the charge on the nucleus because of the effect of the inner electrons.
- • The electron is attracted to the nucleus, but repelled by electrons that *shield* or *screen* it from the full nuclear charge.
- • The nuclear charge experienced by an electron depends on its distance from the nucleus and the number of electrons in the spherical volume out to the electron in question.
- • As the average number of screening electrons (S) increases, the effective nuclear charge (Z_{eff}) decreases.

$$Z_{eff} = Z - S$$

- • As the distance from the nucleus increases, S increases and Z_{eff} decreases.
  - • S is called the *screening constant,* which represents the portion of the nuclear charge that is screened from the valence electron by other electrons in the atom.
  - • The value of S is usually close to the number of core electrons in an atom.

7.3 Sizes of Atoms and Ions[18,19,20]

- • Consider a collection of argon atoms in the gas phase.
  - • When they undergo collisions, they ricochet apart because electron clouds cannot penetrate each other to a significant extent.
  - • The *apparent* radius is determined by the closest distances separating the nuclei during such collisions.
  - • This radius is the *nonbonding radius*.
    - • Nonbonding atomic radii are also called *van der Waals radii*.
    - • These are used in space-filling models to represent the sizes of different elements.

---

[13] "Effective Nuclear Charge" Animation from Instructor's Resource CD/DVD
[14] Figure 7.2 from Transparency Pack
[15] Figure 7.3 from Transparency Pack
[16] "Screen Percentages Based on Slater Effective Nuclear Charge as a Versatile Tool for Teaching Periodic Trends" from Further Readings
[17] Figure 7.4 from Transparency Pack
[18] Figure 7.6 from Transparency Pack
[19] "Pictorial Analogies: VI: Radial and Angular Wave Function Plots" from Further Readings
[20] "Methanethiol (methyl mercaptan)" 3-D Model from Instructor's Resource CD/DVD

- Now consider a simple diatomic molecule.
  - The distance between the two nuclei is called the **bonding atomic radius**.
    - It is shorter than the nonbonding radius.
  - If the two atoms that make up the molecule are the same, then half the bond distance is called the covalent radius of the atom.

Periodic Trends in Atomic Radii[21,22]

- Atomic size varies consistently through the periodic table.
  - As we move down a group, the atoms become larger.
  - As we move across a period, atoms become smaller.
  - There are two factors at work:
    - the principal quantum number, n, and
    - the effective nuclear charge, Z_{eff}.
  - As the principal quantum number increases (i.e., we move down a group), the distance of the outermost electron from the nucleus becomes larger. Hence, the atomic radius increases.
  - As we move across the periodic table, the number of core electrons remains constant; however, the nuclear charge increases. Therefore, there is an increased attraction between the nucleus and the outermost electrons. This attraction causes the atomic radius to decrease.

Periodic Trends in Ionic Radii[23,24,25]

- Ionic size is important:
  - in predicting lattice energy and
  - in determining the way in which ions pack in a solid.
- Just as atomic size is periodic, ionic size is also periodic.
- In general:
  - Cations are smaller than their parent atoms.
    - Electrons have been removed from the most spatially extended orbital.
    - The effective nuclear charge has increased.
    - Therefore, the cation is smaller than the parent atom.
  - Anions are larger than their parent atoms.
    - Electrons have been added to the most spatially extended orbital.
    - This means total electron-electron repulsion has increased.
    - Therefore, anions are larger than their parent atoms.
- For ions with the same charge, ionic size increases down a group.
- All the members of an **isoelectronic series** have the same number of electrons.
  - As nuclear charge increases, in an isoelectronic series the ions become smaller:
$$O^{2-} > F^- > Na^+ > Mg^{2+} > Al^{3+}$$

FORWARD REFERENCES
- Sizes and charges of ions will be instrumental in determining lattice energies (Chapter 8).
- Structures of ionic solids in Chapter 12 (section 12.2).
- Atomic radii will affect relative strengths of binary acids of nonmetals from a given group, as discussed in Chapter 16 (section 16.10).
- Periodic properties of nonmetals in groups 4A-8A are tabulated throughout Chapter 22.
- Periodic properties for the first transition-series elements are shown in Chapter 23 (section 23.1).

---

[21] "Periodic Trends: Atomic Radii" Animation from Instructor's Resource CD/DVD
[22] "Using Balls from Different Sports to Model the Variation of Atomic Sizes" from Further Readings
[23] "Gain and Loss of Electrons" Animation from Instructor's Resource CD/DVD
[24] Figure 7.7 from Transparency Pack
[25] "Periodic Contractions Among the Elements; Or, On Being the Right Size" from Further Readings

7.4 Ionization Energy[26,27]

- The **ionization energy** of an atom or ion is the minimum energy required to remove an electron from the ground state of the isolated gaseous atom or ion.
- The *first ionization energy*, I_1, is the amount of energy required to remove an electron from a gaseous atom:

$$Na(g) \rightarrow Na^+(g) + e^-$$

- The *second ionization energy*, I_2, is the energy required to remove the second electron from a gaseous ion:

$$Na^+(g) \rightarrow Na^{2+}(g) + e^-$$

- The larger the ionization energy, the more difficult it is to remove the electron.
- There is a sharp increase in ionization energy when a core electron is removed.

Variations in Successive Ionization Energies[28,29]

- Ionization energies for an element increase in magnitude as successive electrons are removed.
    - As each successive electron is removed, more energy is required to pull an electron away from an increasingly more positive ion.
- A sharp increase in ionization energy occurs when an inner-shell electron is removed.

Periodic Trends in First Ionization Energies[30,31,32]

- Ionization energy generally increases across a period.
    - As we move across a period, Z_{eff} increases, making it more difficult to remove an electron.
    - Two exceptions are removing the first p electron and removing the fourth p electron.
        - The s electrons are more effective at shielding than p electrons. So, forming the s^2p^0 configuration is more favorable.
        - When a second electron is placed in a p orbital, the electron-electron repulsion increases. When this electron is removed, the resulting s^2p^3 configuration is more stable than the starting s^2p^4 configuration. Therefore, there is a decrease in ionization energy.
- Ionization energy decreases down a group.
    - This means that the outermost electron is more readily removed as we go down a group.
    - As the atom gets bigger, it becomes easier to remove an electron form the most spatially extended orbital.
        - Example: For the noble gases, the ionization energies follow the order:
          $$He > Ne > Ar > Kr > Xe$$
- The representative elements exhibit a larger range of values for I_1 than transition metals.

Electron Configurations of Ions

- These are derived from the electron configurations of elements with the required number of electrons added or removed from the most accessible orbital.
    - Li: [He]$2s^1$ becomes Li$^+$:   [He]
    - F: [He]$2s^2 2p^5$ becomes F$^-$:   [He]$2s^2 2p^6$ = [Ar]

---

[26] "Ionization Energy" Animation from Instructor's Resource CD/DVD
[27] "Ionization Energies of Atoms and Atomic Ions" from Further Readings
[28] "Ionization Energies" Activity from Instructor's Resource CD/DVD
[29] Table 7.2 from Transparency Pack
[30] Figure 7.9 from Transparency Pack
[31] "Periodic Trends: Ionization Energies" Animation from Instructor's Resource CD/DVD
[32] "Trends in Ionization Energy of Transition-Metal Elements" from Further Readings

- Transition metals tend to lose the valence shell electrons first and then as many d electrons as are required to reach the desired charge on the ion.
  - Thus electrons are removed from $4s$ _before_ the $3d$, etc.
  - In other words, when writing electron configurations of transition metal cations, the order of removal of electrons is **not** exactly opposite to the order in which subshells were occupied when an electron configuration of the parent atom was written.

FORWARD REFERENCES
  - Octet rule will be introduced in Chapter 8.
  - Discussion of electron configurations of the representative elements and transition metals will continue in Chapter 8.
  - Photoionization processes and ionization energies will be linked together in Chapter 18. (section 18.1).

7.5 Electron Affinities[33,34,35,36]

- **Electron affinity** is the energy change when a gaseous atom gains an electron to form a gaseous ion.
- Electron affinity and ionization energy measure the energy changes of opposite processes.
  - Electron affinity: $Cl(g) + e^- \rightarrow Cl^-(g)$ $\qquad \Delta E = -349$ kJ/mol
  - Ionization energy: $Cl(g) \rightarrow Cl^+(g) + e^-$ $\qquad \Delta E = 1251$ kJ/mol
- Electron affinity can either be exothermic (as the above example) or endothermic:

$$Ar(g) + e^- \rightarrow Ar^-(g) \qquad \Delta E > 0$$

- Look at electron configurations to determine whether electron affinity is positive or negative.
  - The extra electron in Ar needs to be placed in the $4s$ orbital, which is significantly higher in energy than the $3p$ orbital.
  - The added electron in Cl is placed in the $3p$ orbital to form the stable $3p^6$ electron configuration.
  - Electron affinities do not change greatly as we move down in a group.

7.6 Metals, Nonmetals, and Metalloids[37,38,39]

- **Metallic character** refers to the extent to which the element exhibits the physical and chemical properties of metals.
  - Metallic character increases down a group.
  - Metallic character decreases from left to right across a period.

Metals[40,41,42,43,44,45]

- Metals are shiny and lustrous, malleable and ductile.
- Metals are solids at room temperature (exception: mercury is liquid at room temperature; gallium and cesium melt just above room temperature) and have very high melting temperatures.

---

[33] "Electron Affinity" Animation from Instructor's Resource CD/DVD
[34] "Periodic Trends: Electron Affinity" Animation from Instructor's Resource CD/DVD
[35] Figure 7.11 from Transparency Pack
[36] "Halogens Compete for Electrons" from Live Demonstrations
[37] Figure 7.12 from Transparency Pack
[38] "Acidic and Basic Properties of Oxides" from Live Demonstrations
[39] "Water" 3-D Model from Instructor's Resource CD/DVD
[40] Figure 7.14 from Transparency Pack
[41] "Periodicity in the Acid-Base Behavior of Oxides and Hydroxides" from Further Readings
[42] "Periodic Trends: Acid-Base Behavior of Oxides" Animation from Instructor's Resource CD/DVD
[43] "Acidic and Basic Properties of Oxides" from Live Demonstrations
[44] "Disappearing Ink" from Live Demonstrations
[45] "Hydroxide Ion" 3-D Model from Instructor's Resource CD/DVD

- Metals tend to have low ionization energies and tend to form cations easily.
- Metals tend to be oxidized when they react.
- Compounds of metals with nonmetals tend to be ionic substances.
- Metal oxides form basic ionic solids.
  - Most metal oxides are basic:
    $$\text{Metal oxide + water} \rightarrow \text{metal hydroxide}$$
    $$Na_2O(s) + H_2O(l) \rightarrow 2NaOH(aq)$$
  - Metal oxides are able to react with acids to form salts and water:
    $$\text{Metal oxide + acid} \rightarrow \text{salt + water}$$
    $$NiO(s) + 2HNO_3(aq) \rightarrow Ni(NO_3)_2(aq) + H_2O(l)$$

Nonmetals[46]

- Nonmetals are more diverse in their behavior than metals.
- In general, nonmetals are nonlustrous, are poor conductors of heat and electricity, and exhibit lower melting points than metals.
- Seven nonmetallic elements exist as diatomic molecules under ordinary conditions:
  - $H_2(g)$, $N_2(g)$, $O_2(g)$, $F_2(g)$, $Cl_2(g)$, $Br_2(l)$, $I_2(s)$
- When nonmetals react with metals, nonmetals tend to gain electrons:
  $$\text{Metal + nonmetal} \rightarrow \text{salt}$$
  $$2Al(s) + 3Br_2(l) \rightarrow 2AlBr_3(s)$$
- Compounds composed entirely of nonmetals are molecular substances.
- Most nonmetal oxides are acidic:
  $$\text{Nonmetal oxide + water} \rightarrow \text{acid}$$
  $$CO_2(g) + H_2O(l) \rightarrow H_2CO_3(aq)$$
  $$P_4O_{10}(s) + 6H_2O(l) \rightarrow 4H_3PO_4(aq)$$
- Nonmetal oxides react with bases to form salts and water:
  $$\text{Nonmetal oxide + base} \rightarrow \text{salt + water}$$
  $$CO_2(g) + 2NaOH(aq) \rightarrow Na_2CO_3(aq) + H_2O(l)$$

Metalloids[47]

- Metalloids have properties that are intermediate between those of metals and nonmetals.
  - For example, Si has a metallic luster but it is brittle.
- Metalloids have found fame in the semiconductor industry.

FORWARD REFERENCES

- The role of metals and metalloids in semiconductors will be discussed in Chapter 12 (section 12.7).
- Arrhenius, Brønsted-Lowry, and Lewis acids and bases will be discussed in Chapter 16.
- Acids and bases as well as reactions between them will be discussed in Chapter 16.
- An in-depth discussion of nonmetals will be provided in Chapter 22.
- Physical properties for the first transition-series elements are tabulated in Chapter 23 (section 23.1)

7.7 Trends for Group 1A and Group 2A Metals

- The **alkali metals** (group 1A) and the **alkaline earth metals** (group 2A) are often called the active metals.

---

[46] "Square Planar Structure" 3-D Model from Instructor's Resource CD/DVD
[47] "Metalloids" from Further Readings

Group 1A: The Alkali Metals[48,49,50,51,52,53,54,55]

- The alkali metals are in Group 1A.
- Alkali metals are all soft.
- Their chemistry is dominated by the loss of their single s electron:

$$M \rightarrow M^+ + e^-$$

- Reactivity increases as we move down the group.
- Alkali metals react with hydrogen to form hydrides.
    - In hydrides, the hydrogen is present as H^-, called the **hydride ion**.

$$2M(s) + H_2(g) \rightarrow 2MH(s)$$

- Alkali metals react with water to form MOH and hydrogen gas:

$$2M(s) + 2H_2O(l) \rightarrow 2MOH(aq) + H_2(g)$$

- Alkali metals produce different oxides when reacting with O_2:
    - $4Li(s) + O_2(g) \rightarrow 2Li_2O(s)$ *(oxide)*
    - $2Na(s) + O_2(g) \rightarrow Na_2O_2(s)$ *(peroxide)*
    - $K(s) + O_2(g) \rightarrow KO_2(s)$ *(superoxide)*
- Alkali metals emit characteristic colors when placed in a high-temperature flame.
    - The s electron is excited by the flame and emits energy when it returns to the ground state.
    - The Na line occurs at 589 nm (yellow), characteristic of the $3p \rightarrow 3s$ transition.
    - The Li line is crimson red.
    - The K line is lilac.

Group 2A: The Alkaline Earth Metals[56,57,58,59]

- Alkaline earth metals are harder and more dense than the alkali metals.
- Their chemistry is dominated by the loss of two s electrons:

$$M \rightarrow M^{2+} + 2e^-$$
$$Mg(s) + Cl_2(g) \rightarrow MgCl_2(s)$$
$$2Mg(s) + O_2(g) \rightarrow 2MgO(s)$$

- Reactivity increases down the group.
    - Be does not react with water.
    - Mg will only react with steam.
    - Ca and the elements below it react with water at room temperature as follows:

$$Ca(s) + 2H_2O(l) \rightarrow Ca(OH)_2(aq) + H_2(g)$$

7.8 Trends for Selected Nonmetals

Hydrogen

- Hydrogen is a unique element.

---

[48] Table 7.4 from Transparency Pack
[49] "Sodium and Potassium in Water" Movie from Instructor's Resource CD/DVD
[50] "Flame Tests for Metals" Movie from Instructor's Resource CD/DVD
[51] "A Dramatic Flame Test Demonstration" from Live Demonstrations
[52] "Simple Flame Test Techniques Using Cotton Swabs" from Live Demonstrations
[53] "The Legend of Dr. Pepper/ Seven-Up" from Further Readings
[54] "A Little Lithium May Be Just What the Doctor Ordered" from Further Readings
[55] "A Variation on the Determination of the Properties of the Alkali Metals" from Further Readings
[56] Table 7.5 from Transparency Pack
[57] "Producing Hydrogen Gas from Calcium Metal" from Live Demonstrations
[58] "Life, Death, and Calcium" from Further Readings
[59] "Update on Intake: Calcium Consumption Low" from Further Readings

- It most often occurs as a colorless diatomic gas, H_2.
- Reactions between hydrogen and nonmetals can be very exothermic:
$$2H_2(g) + 2O_2(g) \rightarrow 2H_2O(l) \qquad \Delta H° = -571.7 \text{ kJ}$$
- It can either gain another electron to form the hydride ion, H^-, or lose its electron to become H^+:
$$2Na(s) + H_2(g) \rightarrow 2NaH(s)$$
$$2H_2(g) + O_2(g) \rightarrow 2H_2O(l)$$
- H^+ is a proton.
- The aqueous chemistry of hydrogen is dominated by $H^+(aq)$.

Group 6A: The Oxygen Group[60,61,62,63,64,65,66,67,68,69,70,71]

- As we move down the group, the metallic character increases.
  - O_2 is a gas, Te is a metalloid, Po is a metal.
- Two of the important forms of oxygen are O_2 and **ozone**, O_3.
  - O_2 and O_3 are allotropes.
    - Allotropes are different forms of the same element in the same state (in this case, gaseous).
    - Ozone can be prepared from oxygen:
$$3O_2(g) \rightarrow 2O_3(g) \qquad \Delta H° = +284.6 \text{ kJ}$$
  - Ozone is pungent and toxic.
  - Oxygen (or dioxygen, O_2) is a potent oxidizing agent since the O^{2-} ion has a noble gas configuration.
  - There are two oxidation states for oxygen: –2 (e.g., H_2O) and –1 (e.g., H_2O_2).
- Sulfur is another important member of this group.
  - The most common form of sulfur is yellow S_8.
  - Sulfur tends to form S^{2-} in compounds (sulfides).

Group 7A: The Halogens[72,73,74,75,76,77]

- Group 7A elements are known as the **halogens** ("salt formers").
- The chemistry of the halogens is dominated by gaining an electron to form an anion:
$$X_2 + 2e^- \rightarrow 2X^-$$
- Fluorine is one of the most reactive substances known:
$$2F_2(g) + 2H_2O(l) \rightarrow 4HF(aq) + O_2(g) \qquad \Delta H = -758.9 \text{ kJ}$$

---

[60] Table 7.6 from Transparency Pack
[61] "A Second Note on the Term Chalcogen" from Further Readings
[62] "Preparation and Properties of Oxygen" from Live Demonstrations
[63] "Plastic Sulfur" from Live Demonstrations
[64] "Allotropes and Polymorphs" from Further Readings
[65] "The Origin of the Term Allotrope" from Further Readings
[66] "Aqueous Hydrogen Peroxide: Its Household Uses and Concentration Units" from Further Readings
[67] "Preparation and Properties of Oxygen" from Live Demonstrations
[68] "Plastic Sulfur" from Live Demonstrations
[69] "Reactions with Oxygen" Movie from Instructor's Resource CD/DVD
[70] "Oxygen" 3-D Model from Instructor's Resource CD/DVD
[71] "Sulfur" 3-D Model from Instructor's Resource CD/DVD
[72] Table 7.7 from Transparency Pack
[73] "Physical Properties of the Halogens" Movie from Instructor's Resource CD/DVD
[74] "The Chemistry of Swimming Pool Maintenance" from Further Readings
[75] "Chlorine" 3-D Model from Instructor's Resource CD/DVD
[76] "Bromine" 3-D Model from Instructor's Resource CD/DVD
[77] "Iodine" 3-D Model from Instructor's Resource CD/DVD

- All halogens consist of diatomic molecules, X_2.
- Chlorine is the most industrially useful halogen.
  - In 2008 total production of chlorine was 21 billion pounds, making it one of the top ten most produced chemicals in the US.
  - The reaction between chorine and water produces hypochlorous acid (HOCl), which is used to disinfect swimming pool water:

$$Cl_2(g) + H_2O(l) \rightarrow HCl(aq) + HOCl(aq)$$

- Halogens react with hydrogen to form gaseous hydrogen halide compounds:

$$H_2(g) + X_2 \rightarrow 2HX(g)$$

- Hydrogen compounds of the halogens are all strong acids with the exception of HF.

Group 8A: The Noble Gases[78]

- The group 8A elements are known as the **noble gases**.
  - These are all nonmetals and monoatomic.
  - They are notoriously unreactive because they have completely filled s and p subshells.
- In 1962 the first compounds of the noble gases were prepared: XeF_2, XeF_4, and XeF_6.
- In 2000 Finnish scientists reported the first neutral molecule that contains argon: the HArF molecule, which is stable only at low temperatures.

FORWARD REFERENCES
  - Electron configurations of noble gases and the octet rule will be introduced in Chapter 8 (section 8.1).
  - The role of the expanded octet in the formation of compounds involving heavier noble gas atoms will be discussed in Chapter 8 (section 8.7).

---

[78] Table 7.8 from Transparency Pack

Further Readings:

1. The **September 8, 2003** issue of *Chemical and Engineering News* is a special issue celebrating the periodic table of the elements on C&EN's 80th anniversary. Approximately 90 short articles, each featuring a different element, are found in this issue.

2. N. K. Goh and L. S. Chia, "Using the Learning Cycle to Introduce Periodicity," *J. Chem. Educ.*, Vol. 66, **1989**, 747.

3. Mark J. Volkmann, "The Nuts and Bolts of Chemistry," *The Science Teacher*, Vol. 63, **1996**, 37–40. This activity introduces the periodic table.

4. George Gorin, "Mendeleev and Moseley: The Principal Discoverers of the Periodic Law," *J. Chem. Educ.*, Vol. 73, **1996**, 490–493. This article summarizes some contributions of Mendeleev and Moseley.

5. Eric R. Scerri, "The Evolution of the Periodic System," *Scientific American*, **September 1998,** 78–83.

6. Harold Goldwhite, "Mendeleev's Other Prediction," *J. Chem. Educ.*, Vol. 56, **1979**, 35–36.

7. Jan W. van Spronsen, "Atomic Number before Moseley," *J. Chem. Educ.*, Vol. 56, **1979**, 106.

8. Yu. I. Solov'ev, "D. I. Mendeleev and the English Chemists," *J. Chem. Educ.*, Vol. 61, **1984**, 1069–1071.

9. Steven I. Dutch, "Periodic Tables of Elemental Abundance," *J. Chem. Educ.*, Vol. 76, **1999**, 356–358.

10. Alexandru T. Balaban, "A Different Approach to a 3–D Periodic System Including Stable Isotopes," *J. Chem. Educ.*, Vol. 76, **1999**, 359.

11. Kimberley A. Waldron, Eric M. Fehringer, Amy E. Streeb, Jennifer E. Trosky, and Joshua J. Pearson, "Screen Percentages Based on Slater Effective Nuclear Charge as a Versatile Tool for Teaching Periodic Trends," *J. Chem. Educ.*, Vol. 78, **2001**, 635–639.

12. John J. Fortman, "Pictorial Analogies VI: Radial and Angular Wave Function Plots," *J. Chem. Educ.*, Vol. 70, **1993**, 549–550. Analogies for explaining probability distributions are presented.

13. Gabriel Pinto, "Using Balls from Different Sports to Model the Variation of Atomic Sizes," *J. Chem. Educ.*, Vol. 75, **1998**, 725–726. This reference involves analogies to investigate atomic and ionic radii.

14. Joan Mason, "Periodic Contractions Among the Elements; Or, On Being the Right Size," *J. Chem. Educ.*, Vol. 65, **1988**, 17–20. The importance of the size of atoms and ions is discussed.

15. Peter F. Lang and Barry C. Smith, "Ionization Energies of Atoms and Atomic Ions," *J. Chem. Educ.*, Vol. 80, **2003**, 938–946.

16. Paul S. Matsumoto, "Trends in Ionization Energy of Transition-Metal Elements," *J. Chem. Educ.*, Vol. 82, **2005**, 1660-1661.

17. Ronald L. Rich, "Periodicity in the Acid-Base Behavior of Oxides and Hydroxides," *J. Chem. Educ.*, Vol. 62, **1985**, 44. This article provides further information on the solubility of various oxides and hydroxides.

18. Robert H. Goldsmith, "Metalloids," *J. Chem. Educ.*, Vol. 59, **1982**, 526–527. This is a brief "thumbnail sketch" on metalloids.

19. Jeffrey L. Rodengen, "The Legend of Dr. Pepper/Seven-Up," (Write Stuff Syndicate: Ft. Lauderdale), **1995**.

20. Michael W. Miller, "A Little Lithium May Be Just What the Doctor Ordered," *Wall Street Journal*, **September 23, 1994**.

21. Joseph D. Ciparick and Richard F. Jones, "A Variation on the Demonstration of the Properties of the Alkali Metals," *J. Chem. Educ.*, Vol. 66, **1988**, 438.

22. G. Marino, "Update on Intake: Calcium Consumption Low," *Science News*, **June 18, 1994**, p. 390.

23. Malcolm East, "Life, Death and Calcium," *Chemistry in Britain*, **March 2002**, 42–44.

24. Werner Fischer, "A Second Note on the Term 'Chalcogen'," *J. Chem. Educ.*, Vol. 78, **2001**, 1333.

25. B. D. Sharma, "Allotropes and Polymorphs," *J. Chem. Educ.*, Vol. 64, **1987**, 404–407. Differences between polymorphs and allotropes are explored.

26. William B. Jensen, "The Origin of the Term Allotrope," *J. Chem. Educ.*, Vol. 83, **2006**, 838–839.

27. Carl Salter and David L. Langhus, "The Chemistry of Swimming Pool Maintenance," *J. Chem. Educ.*, Vol. 84, **2007**, 1124–1128.

28. Michael J. Webb, "Aqueous Hydrogen Peroxide: Its Household Uses and Concentration Units," *J. Chem. Educ.*, Vol. 62, **1985**, 152. This reference gives some examples of the uses of hydrogen peroxide.

Live Demonstrations:

1. Lee R. Summerlin, Christie L. Borgford, and Julie B. Ealy, "Halogens Compete for Electrons," *Chemical Demonstrations, A Sourcebook for Teachers, Volume 2* (Washington: American Chemical Society, **1988**), pp. 60–61. The relative tendency of halogens to gain (or lose) electrons is explored through the observation of color changes.

2. Bassam Z. Shakhashiri, "Preparation and Properties of Oxygen," *Chemical Demonstrations: A Handbook for Teachers of Chemistry, Volume 2* (Madison : The University of Wisconsin Press, **1985**), pp. 137–141. Oxygen gas, prepared from H_2O_2, is used to support combustion reactions.

3. Bassam Z. Shakhashiri, "Acidic and Basic Properties of Oxides," *Chemical Demonstrations: A Handbook for Teachers of Chemistry, Volume 3* (Madison: The University of Wisconsin Press, **1989**), pp. 109–113.

4. Lee. R. Summerlin, Christie L. Borgford, and Julie B. Ealy, "Disappearing Ink," *Chemical Demonstrations, A Sourcebook for Teachers, Volume 2* (Washington: American Chemical Society, **1988**), p. 176. "Disappearing ink" is made from thymolphthalein indicator and dilute sodium hydroxide.

5. Kristin A. Johnson, Rodney Schreiner, and Jon Loring, "A Dramatic Flame Test Demonstration," *J. Chem. Educ.*, Vol. 78, **2001**, 640–641.

6. Lee. R. Summerlin, Christie L. Borgford, and Julie B. Ealy, "Producing Hydrogen Gas from Calcium Metal," *Chemical Demonstrations, A Sourcebook for Teachers, Volume 2* (Washington: American Chemical Society, **1988**), pp. 51–52.

7. Lee. R. Summerlin, Christie L. Borgford, and Julie B. Ealy, "Plastic Sulfur," *Chemical Demonstrations, A Sourcebook for Teachers, Volume 2* (Washington: American Chemical Society, **1988**), p. 53. A flexible brown polymer is formed by pouring heated yellow sulfur into a beaker of water.

8. Michael J. Sanger and Amy J. Phelps, "Simple Flame Test Techniques Using Cotton Swabs," *J. Chem. Educ.*, Vol. 81, **2004**, 969–970.

Chapter 8. Basic Concepts of Chemical Bonding

Media Resources

Figures and Tables in Transparency Pack:	**Section:**
Figure 8.2 Reaction of Sodium Metal with Chlorine Gas to Form the Ionic Compound Sodium Chloride	8.2 Ionic Bonding
Table 8.2 Lattice Energies for Some Ionic Compounds	8.2 Ionic Bonding
Figure 8.5 Born-Haber Cycle for Formation of NaCl	8.2 Ionic Bonding
Figure 8.7 Electronegativity Values Based on Pauling's Thermochemical Data	8.4 Bond Polarity and Electronegativity
Figure 8.8 Electron Density Distribution	8.4 Bond Polarity and Electronegativity
Figure 8.11 Oxidation Number, Formal Charge, and Electron Density Distribution for the HCl Molecule	8.5 Drawing Lewis Structures
Table 8.4 Average Bond Enthalpies (kJ/mol)	8.8 Strengths of Covalent Bonds
Figure 8.15 Using Bond Enthalpies to Calculate ΔH_{rxn}	8.8 Strengths of Covalent Bonds
Table 8.5 Average Bond Lengths for Some Single, Double, and Triple Bonds	8.8 Strengths of Covalent Bonds

Activities:	**Section:**
Periodic Trends: Lewis Symbols	8.1 Lewis Symbols, and the Octet Rule
Octet Rule	8.1 Lewis Symbols, and the Octet Rule
Coulomb's Law	8.2 Ionic Bonding
Ion Electron Configurations	8.2 Ionic Bonding
Molecular Polarity	8.4 Bond Polarity and Electronegativity
Writing Lewis Structures I	8.5 Drawing Lewis Structures
Writing Lewis Structures II	8.5 Drawing Lewis Structures
Bond Enthalpy	8.8 Strengths of Covalent Bonds

Animations:	**Section:**
H_2 Bond Formation	8.3 Covalent Bonding
Periodic Trends: Electronegativity	8.4 Bond Polarity and Electronegativity
Formal Charges	8.5 Drawing Lewis Structures

Movies:	**Section:**
Formation of Sodium Chloride	8.2 Ionic Bonding

3-D Models:	**Section:**
Chlorine	8.1 Lewis Symbols, and the Octet Rule
Phosphorus	8.1 Lewis Symbols, and the Octet Rule
Sodium Chloride	8.2 Ionic Bonding

Methane	8.5 Drawing Lewis Structures
Carbon dioxide	8.5 Drawing Lewis Structures
Hydrogen Chloride	8.5 Drawing Lewis Structures
Ozone	8.6 Resonance Structures
Benzene	8.6 Resonance Structures
Phosphorus Pentachloride	8.7 Exceptions to the Octet Rule
Chloromethane	8.8 Strengths of Covalent Bonds

Other Resources

Further Readings:	Section:
The Chemical Bond as an Atomic Tug-of-War	8.1 Lewis Symbols, and the Octet Rule
Gilbert Newton Lewis and the Amazing Electron Dots	8.2 Ionic Bonding
The Chemical Bond	8.3 Covalent Bonding
Grade-12 Students' Misconceptions of Covalent Bonding and Structure	8.3 Covalent Bonding
The Role of Lewis Structures in Teaching Covalent Bonding	8.3 Covalent Bonding
Reflections on the Electron Theory of the Chemical Bond: 1900–1925	8.3 Covalent Bonding
Abegg, Lewis, Langmuir, and the Octet Rule	8.3 Covalent Bonding
G. N. Lewis and the Chemical Bond	8.3 Covalent Bonding
The Use of Dots in Chemical Formulas	8.3 Covalent Bonding
Electronegativity and Bond Type: Predicting Bond Type	8.4 Bond Polarity and Electronegativity
Electronegativity from Avogadro to Pauling Part I: Origins of the Electronegativity Concept	8.4 Bond Polarity and Electronegativity
Electronegativity from Avogadro to Pauling Part II: Late Nineteenth- and Early Twentieth-Century Developments	8.4 Bond Polarity and Electronegativity
Demystifying Introductory Chemistry Part 3: Ionization Energies, Electronegativity, Polar Bonds, and Partial Charges	8.4 Bond Polarity and Electronegativity
Electron Densities, Atomic Charges, and Ionic, Covalent, and Polar Bonds	8.4 Bond Polarity and Electronegativity
Drawing Lewis Structures from Lewis Symbols: A Direct Electron Pairing Approach	8.5 Drawing Lewis Structures
Lewis Structures Are Models for Predicting Molecular Structure, *Not* Electronic Structure	8.5 Drawing Lewis Structures
Teaching a Model for Writing Lewis Structures	8.5 Drawing Lewis Structures
Drawing Lewis Structures without Anticipating Octets	8.5 Drawing Lewis Structures
The '6N + 2 Rule' for Writing Lewis Octet Structures	8.5 Drawing Lewis Structures
Another Procedure for Writing Lewis Structures	8.5 Drawing Lewis Structures
Using Formal Charges in Teaching Descriptive Inorganic Chemistry	8.5 Drawing Lewis Structures

Lewis Structures, Formal Charge, and Oxidation Numbers: A More User-Friendly Approach	8.5 Drawing Lewis Structures
Valence, Oxidation Number, and Formal Charge: Three Related but Fundamentally Different Concepts	8.5 Drawing Lewis Structures
Lost in Lewis Structures: An Investigation of Student Difficulties in Developing Representational Competence	8.5 Drawing Lewis Structures
If It's Resonance, What Is Resonating?	8.6 Resonance Structures
Aromatic Bagels: An Edible Resonance Analogy	8.6 Resonance Structures
The Concept of Resonance	8.6 Resonance Structures
Explaining Resonance—A Colorful Approach	8.6 Resonance Structures
A Visual Aid for Teaching the Resonance Concept	8.6 Resonance Structures
The Origin of the Circle Symbol for Aromaticity	8.6 Resonance Structures
Nitric Oxide—Some Old and New Perspectives	8.7 Exceptions to the Octet Rule
Biological Roles of Nitric Oxide	8.7 Exceptions to the Octet Rule
The Relative Explosive Power of Some Explosives	8.8 Strengths of Covalent Bonds
Exothermic Bond Breaking: A Persistent Misconception	8.8 Strengths of Covalent Bonds

Chapter 8. Basic Concepts of Chemical Bonding

Common Student Misconceptions

- Students often think that a triple bond is three times as strong as a single bond. The fact that the *second* and *third* bonds (π bonds) are weaker than the first (σ bond) needs to be emphasized.
- Students confuse formal charges with real charges on atoms.
- The only place the $\leftrightarrow$ arrow is used is for resonance; students often want to use this to indicate equilibrium.
- Students do not appreciate that the exceptions to the octet rule are almost as common as the examples of substances that obey it.
- Students often confuse the octet rule with having *any* 8 valence electrons (e.g., $4s^2\,3d^6$ for iron).
- Students often think that all polar substances conduct electricity.

Teaching Tips

- Students need to be able to count the number of valence electrons in order to get the correct Lewis structure.
- Students need to be reminded that several *correct* Lewis structures can be often drawn for a molecule or an ion, but not all correct Lewis structures are equally good.

Lecture Outline

8.1 Lewis Symbols and the Octet Rule[1,2,3]

- The properties of many materials can be understood in terms of their microscopic properties.
- Microscopic properties of molecules include:
  - the connectivity between atoms and
  - the 3-D shape of the molecule.
- When atoms or ions are strongly attracted to one another, we say that there is a **chemical bond** between them.
  - In chemical bonds, electrons are shared or transferred between atoms.
- Types of chemical bonds include:
  - **ionic bonds** (electrostatic forces that hold ions together, e.g., NaCl);
  - **covalent bonds** (result from sharing electrons between atoms, e.g., Cl_2);
  - **metallic bonds** (refers to metal nuclei floating in a sea of electrons, e.g., Na).
- The electrons involved in bonding are called *valence electrons*.
  - Valence electrons are found in the incomplete, outermost shell of an atom.
- As a pictorial understanding of where the electrons are in an atom, we represent the electrons as dots around the symbol for the element.
  - The number of valence electrons available for bonding are indicated by unpaired dots.
  - These symbols are called **Lewis symbols** or Lewis electron-dot symbols.
  - We generally place the electrons on four sides of a square around the element's symbol.

---

[1] "The Chemical Bond as an Atomic Tug-of-War" from Further Readings
[2] "Chlorine" 3-D Model from Instructor's Resource CD/DVD
[3] "Phosphorus" 3-D Model from Instructor's Resource CD/DVD

The Octet Rule[4]
- Atoms tend to gain, lose, or share electrons until they are surrounded by eight valence electrons; this is known as the **octet rule**.
  - An octet consists of full s and p subshells.
  - We know that ns^2np^6 is a noble gas configuration.
  - We assume that an atom is stable when surrounded by eight electrons (four electron pairs).

FORWARD REFERENCES
- The octet rule will be brought up again in Chapters 22 and 23 for main group nonmetals and metals, respectively, and in Chapter 24 for carbon.

8.2 Ionic Bonding[5,6,7,8]
- Consider the reaction between sodium and chlorine:
$$Na(s) + \tfrac{1}{2} Cl_2(g) \rightarrow NaCl(s) \qquad \Delta H^{\circ}_f = -410.9 \text{ kJ/mol}$$
  - The reaction is violently exothermic.
  - We infer that the NaCl is more stable than its constituent elements.
    - Sodium has lost an electron to become Na^+ and chlorine has gained the electron to become Cl^-.
    - Note that Na^+ has an Ne electron configuration and Cl^- has an Ar configuration.
    - That is, both Na^+ and Cl^- have an octet of electrons.
- NaCl forms a very regular structure in which each Na^+ ion is surrounded by six Cl^- ions.
  - Similarly, each Cl^- ion is surrounded by six Na^+ ions.
  - There is a regular arrangement of Na^+ and Cl^-.
  - Note that the ions are packed as closely as possible.
- Ionic substances are often crystalline, brittle compounds with high melting points.

Energetics of Ionic Bond Formation[9,10,11]
- The heat of formation of NaCl(s) is exothermic:
$$Na(s) + \tfrac{1}{2} Cl_2(g) \rightarrow NaCl(s) \qquad \Delta H^{\circ}_f = -410.9 \text{ kJ/mol}$$
- Separation of the NaCl into sodium and chloride ions is endothermic:
$$NaCl(s) \rightarrow Na^+(g) + Cl^-(g) \qquad \Delta H^{\circ} = +788 \text{ kJ/mol}$$
  - The energy required to separate one mole of a solid ionic compound into gaseous ions is called the **lattice energy**, $\Delta H_{lattice}$.
  - Lattice energy depends on the charge on the ions and the size of the ions.
  - The stability of the ionic compound comes from the attraction between ions of unlike charge.
  - The specific relationship is given by Coulomb's equation:
$$E = k \frac{Q_1 Q_2}{d}$$
    - where E is the potential energy of the two interacting charged particles, Q_1 and Q_2 are the charges on the particles, d is the distance between their centers, and k is a constant:
$$k = 8.99 \times 10^9 \text{ J-m/C}^2.$$

---

[4] "Octet Rule" Activity from Instructor's Resource CD/DVD
[5] "Gilbert Newton Lewis and the Amazing Electron Dots" from Further Readings
[6] "Formation of Sodium Chloride" Movie from Instructor's Resource CD/DVD
[7] Figure 8.2 from Transparency Pack
[8] "Sodium Chloride" 3-D Model from Instructor's Resource CD/DVD
[9] "Coulomb's Law" Activity from Instructor's Resource CD/DVD
[10] Table 8.2 from Transparency Pack
[11] Figure 8.5 from Transparency Pack

- As Q_1 and Q_2 increase, E increases, and as d increases, E decreases.

Electron Configuration of Ions of the *s*- and *p*-Block Elements[12]

- These are derived from the electron configuration of elements with the required number of electrons added or removed from the most accessible orbital.
- Electron configuration of ions can predict stable ion formation:
  - Na: $[Ne]3s^1$
  - Na^+: $[Ne]$
  - Cl: $[Ne]3s^23p^5$
  - Cl^-: $[Ne]3s^23p^6 = [Ar]$

Transition-Metal Ions

- Lattice energies compensate for the loss of up to three electrons.
- We often encounter cations with charges of 1+, 2+, or 3+ in ionic compounds.
- However, transition metals can't attain a noble gas conformation (>3 electrons beyond a noble gas core).
  - Transition metals tend to lose the valence shell electrons first and then as many *d* electrons as are required to reach the desired charge on the ion.
  - Thus, electrons are removed from 4*s* *before* the 3*d*, etc.

FORWARD REFERENCES

- The link between lattice energy and solubility of ionic compounds will be made in Chapter 17 (section 17.4).
- The formation reaction of NaCl(s) from elements will be brought up in Chapter 19 (section 19.5) as an example of highly exothermic spontaneous processes with decreasing entropy of the system.
- Electron configurations of the first transition-series elements and chemistry of select main group and transition metals will be further discussed in Chapter 23 (sections 23.1).

8.3 Covalent Bonding[13,14,15]

- The majority of chemical substances do not have characteristics of ionic compounds.
- We need a different model for bonding between atoms.
- A chemical bond formed by sharing a pair of electrons is called a *covalent* bond.
- Both atoms acquire noble-gas electronic configurations.
- This is the "glue" to bind atoms together.

Lewis Structures[16,17,18,19,20]

- Formation of covalent bonds can be represented using Lewis symbols.
  - The structures are called **Lewis structures**.
  - We usually show each electron pair shared between atoms as a line and show unshared electron pairs as dots.
  - Each pair of shared electrons constitutes one chemical bond.

---

[12] "Ion Electron Configurations" Activity from Instructor's Resource CD/DVD
[13] "The Chemical Bond" from Further Readings
[14] "Grade-12 Students' Misconceptions of Covalent Bonding and Structure" from Further Readings
[15] "H₂ Bond Formation" Animation from Instructor's Resource CD/DVD
[16] "The Role of Lewis Structures in Teaching Covalent Bonding" from Further Readings
[17] "Reflections on the Electron Theory of the Chemical Bond: 1900–1925" from Further Readings
[18] "Abegg, Lewis, Langmuir, and the Octet Rule" from Further Readings
[19] "G.N. Lewis and the Chemical Bond" from Further Readings
[20] "The Use of Dots in Chemical Formulas" from Further Readings

- Example: •H + H• → H:H has electrons on a line connecting the two H nuclei (H–H).

Multiple Bonds

- It is possible for more than one pair of electrons to be shared between two atoms (e.g., **multiple bonding**):
- One shared pair of electrons is a **single bond** (e.g., H_2);
- Two shared pairs of electrons is a **double bond** (e.g., O_2);
- Three shared pairs of electrons is a **triple bond** (e.g., N_2).
- **Bond length** is the distance between the nuclei of the atoms in a bond.
- Generally, bond distances decrease as we move from single through double to triple bonds.

FORWARD REFERENCES
- Coordinate covalent bonds between Lewis acids and bases will be discussed in section 16.11.
- Covalent bonding between carbon atoms (and other nonmetals) will be highlighted throughout Chapter 24 on organic chemistry.

8.4 Bond Polarity and Electronegativity[21,22,23]

- The electron pairs shared between two different atoms are usually unequally shared.
- **Bond polarity** describes the sharing of the electrons in a covalent bond.
  - Two extremes:
    - In a **nonpolar covalent bond**, the electrons are shared equally.
      - An example is bonding between identical atoms (example: Cl_2).
    - In a **polar covalent bond**, one of the atoms exerts a greater attraction for bonding electrons than the other (example: HCl).
  - If the difference is large enough, an ionic bond forms (example: NaCl).

Electronegativity[24,25,26]

- The ability of an atom *in a molecule* to attract electrons to itself is its **electronegativity**.
- The electronegativity of an element is related to its ionization energy and electron affinity.
- Pauling electronegativity scale: from 0.7 (Cs) to 4.0 (F).
- Electronegativity increases across a period and decreases down a group.

Electronegativity and Bond Polarity[27,28,29]

- Electronegativity differences close to zero result in nonpolar covalent bonds.
  - The electrons are equally or almost equally shared.
- The greater the difference in electronegativity between two atoms, the more polar the bond (polar covalent bonds).
- There is no sharp distinction between bonding types.

---

[21] "Electronegativity and Bond Type: Predicting Bond Type" from Further Readings
[22] "Electronegativity from Avogadro to Pauling Part II: Late Nineteenth- and Early Twentieth-Century Developments" from Further Readings
[23] "Bending a Stream of Water" from Live Demonstrations
[24] "Periodic Trends: Electronegativity" Animation from Instructor's Resource CD/DVD
[25] Figure 8.7 from Transparency Pack
[26] "Electronegativity from Avogadro to Pauling Part I: Origins of the Electronegativity Concept" from Further Readings
[27] Figure 8.8 from Transparency Pack
[28] "Demystifying Introductory Chemistry: Part 3. Ionization Energies, Electronegativity, Polar Bonds, and Partial Charges" from Further Readings
[29] "Electron Densities, Atomic Charges, and Ionic, Covalent, and Polar Bonds" from Further Readings

Dipole Moments[30]

- Molecules like HF have centers of positive and negative charge that do not coincide.
- These are **polar molecules**.
- We indicate the polarity of molecules in two ways:
    - The positive end (or pole) in a polar bond may be represented with a "δ+" and the negative pole with a "δ−".
- We can also place an arrow over the line representing the bond.
    - The arrow points toward the more electronegative element and shows the shift in electron density toward that atom.
- We can quantify the polarity of the molecule.
    - When charges are separated by a distance, a **dipole** is produced.
    - The **dipole moment** is the quantitative measure of the magnitude of the dipole (μ)

$$\mu = Q\,r$$

    - The magnitude of the dipole moment is given in d*ebyes* (D).

Differentiating Ionic and Covalent Bonding

- Interactions of metals and nonmetals often yield ionic compounds.
    - When ionic bonding is dominant, we expect compounds to exhibit properties associated with ionic substances (high-melting solids, strong electrolyte behavior when dissolved in water, etc.).
- Interactions of nonmetals with other nonmetals often yield compounds that are covalent.
    - When covalent bonding is dominant, we expect compounds to exist as molecules and exhibit properties associated with molecular substances (low melting and boiling points, nonelectrolyte behavior when dissolved in water, etc.).
- Assigning the labels "ionic" and "covalent" to compounds is not necessarily straightforward.
    - There is a continuum between the extremes of ionic and covalent bonding.

FORWARD REFERENCES

- Bond polarities combined with molecular shapes (geometries) will be used to determine molecular polarity in Chapter 9 and physical properties of substances (Chapters 11, 13, 24).
- Polar covalent bonds between atoms of F, O, N, and H will be implicated in hydrogen bonding in Chapter 11 (section 11.2).
- The electronegativities of atoms in acids will be linked to acid strength in Chapter 16 (section 16.10).
- The electronegativities of nonmetals will be addressed again in sections 22.1 and 22.4.

8.5 Drawing Lewis Structures[31,32,33,34,35,36,37,38,39,40]

---

[30] "Molecular Polarity" Activity from Instructor's Resource CD/DVD

[31] "Drawing Lewis Structures from Lewis Symbols: A Direct Electron Pairing Approach" from Further Readings

[32] "Writing Lewis Structures I" Activity from Instructor's Resource CD/DVD

[33] "Writing Lewis Structures II" Activity from Instructor's Resource CD/DVD

[34] "Lewis Structures Are Models for Predicting Molecular Structure, *Not* Electronic Structure" from Further Readings

[35] "Teaching a Model for Writing Lewis Structures" from Further Readings

[36] "Drawing Lewis Structures without Anticipating Octets" from Further Readings

[37] "The '6N + 2 Rule' for Writing Lewis Octet Structures" from Further Readings

[38] "Another Procedure for Writing Lewis Structures" from Further Readings

[39] "Lost in Lewis Structures: An Investigation of Student Difficulties in Developing Representational Competence" from Further Readings

[40] "Methane" 3-D Model from Instructor's Resource CD/DVD

- Some simple guidelines for drawing Lewis structures:
  - **Sum the valence electrons from all atoms**.
    - For an anion, add electrons equal to the negative charge.
    - For a cation, subtract electrons equal to the positive charge.
  - **Write the symbols for the atoms, show which atoms are attached to which, and connect them with a single bond (a dash, representing two electrons).**
    - When a central atom has other atoms bound to it, the central atom is usually written first.
      - Example: In CO_3^{2-} the central atom is carbon.
    - Place the central atom in the center of the molecule and add all other atoms around it.
    - Place one bond (two electrons) between each pair of atoms.
  - **Complete the octets for all atoms connected to the central atom** (exception: hydrogen can only have two electrons).
  - **Place any leftover electrons on the central atom.**
  - **If there are not enough electrons to give the central atom an octet, try multiple bonds.**

Formal Charge and Alternative Lewis Structures[41,42,43,44,45,46,47]

- Sometimes it is possible to draw more than one Lewis structure with the octet rule obeyed for all the atoms.
- To determine which structure is most reasonable, we use formal charge.
- The **formal charge** of an atom is the charge that an atom (in a molecule) would have if all of the atoms had the same electronegativity.
- To calculate formal charge, electrons are assigned as follows:
  - All nonbonding (unshared) electrons are assigned to the atom on which they are found.
  - Half of the bonding electrons are assigned to each atom in a bond.
  - Formal charge is the number of valence electrons in the isolated atom, minus the number of electrons assigned to the atom in the Lewis structure.
- For example: consider CN^- (cyanide ion):
  - For carbon:
    - There are four valence electrons (from periodic table).
    - In the Lewis structure there are two nonbonding electrons and three electrons from the triple bond.
    - There are five electrons from the Lewis structure.
    - Formal charge: $4 - 5 = -1$.
  - For nitrogen:
    - There are five valence electrons.
    - In the Lewis structure there are two nonbonding electrons and three from the triple bond.
    - There are five electrons from the Lewis structure.
    - Formal charge $= 5 - 5 = 0$.
- Using formal charge calculations to distinguish between alternative Lewis structures:
  - the most stable structure has the smallest formal charge on each atom and

---

[41] "Using Formal Charges in Teaching Descriptive Inorganic Chemistry" from Further Readings

[42] "Formal Charges" Animation from Instructor's Resource CD/DVD

[43] "Lewis Structures, Formal Charge, and Oxidation Numbers: A More User-Friendly Approach" from Further Readings

[44] Figure 8.11 from Transparency Pack

[45] "Valence, Oxidation Number, and Formal Charge: Three Related but Fundamentally Different Concepts" from Further Readings

[46] "Hydrogen Chloride" 3-D Model from Instructor's Resource CD/DVD

[47] "Carbon Dioxide" 3-D Model from Instructor's Resource CD/DVD

- the most negative formal charge on the most electronegative atoms.
- It is important to keep in mind that formal charges do NOT represent REAL charges on atoms!

FORWARD REFERENCES
- Lewis structures of various species (neutral and charged) will appear throughout the textbook.
- Lewis structures can be considered starting points for the application of the VSEPR model or the Valence Bond theory in Chapter 9.

8.6 Resonance Structures[48,49,50,51]

- Some molecules are not adequately described by a single Lewis structure.
    - Typically, structures with multiple bonds can have similar structures with the multiple bonds between different pairs of atoms.
        - Example: Experimentally, ozone has two identical bonds, whereas the Lewis structure requires one single (longer) and one double bond (shorter).
- **Resonance structures** are attempts to represent a real structure that is a mix between several extreme possibilities.
    - Resonance structures are Lewis structures that differ only with respect to placement of the electrons.
    - The "true" arrangement is a blend or hybrid of the resonance structures.
    - Example: In ozone the extreme possibilities have one double and one single bond.
        - The resonance structure has two identical bonds of intermediate character.
    - We use a double-headed arrows (↔) to indicate resonance.
    - Common examples: O_3, NO_3^-, SO_3, NO_2, and benzene.

Resonance in Benzene[52,53,54,55]

- Benzene belongs to an important category of organic molecules called *aromatic* compounds.
- Benzene (C_6H_6) is a cyclic structure.
    - It consists of six carbon atoms in a hexagon.
    - Each carbon atom is attached to two other carbon atoms and one hydrogen atom.
    - There are alternating double and single bonds between the carbon atoms.
    - Experimentally, the C–C bonds in benzene are all the same length and benzene is planar.
- To emphasize the resonance between the two Lewis structures (hexagons with alternating single and double bonds), we often represent benzene as a hexagon with a circle in it.

FORWARD REFERENCES
- Ozone will be discussed in Chapter 18 (section 18.1).
- Benzene rings will be brought up in Chapter 11 (section 11.7) for liquid crystals and in Chapter 12 (section 12.8) for graphite and condensation polymers.
- Structure and reactivity of aromatic compounds will be further discussed in Chapter 24.

8.7 Exceptions to the Octet Rule

- There are three classes of exceptions to the octet rule:
    - molecules with an odd number of electrons,

---

[48] "If It's Resonance, What Is Resonating?" from Further Readings
[49] "Aromatic Bagels; An Edible Resonance Analogy" from Further Readings
[50] "The Concept of Resonance" from Further Readings
[51] "Ozone" 3-D Model from Instructor's Resource CD/DVD
[52] "The Origin of the Circle Symbol for Aromaticity" from Further Readings
[53] "Explaining Resonance—A Colorful Approach" from Further Readings
[54] "A Visual Aid for Teaching the Resonance Concept" from Further Readings
[55] "Benzene" 3-D Model from Instructor's Resource CD/DVD

- molecules in which one atom has less than an octet,
- molecules in which one atom has more than an octet.

Odd Number of Electrons[56,57]

- Most molecules have an even number of electrons and complete pairing of electrons occurs. although some molecules have an odd number of electrons.
- Examples: ClO_2, NO, and NO_2.

Less than an Octet of Valence Electrons

- Molecules with less than an octet are also relatively rare.
- Most often encountered in compounds of boron or beryllium.
  - A typical example is BF_3.

More than an Octet of Valence Electrons[58]

- This is the largest class of exceptions.
- Molecules and ions with more than an octet of electrons around the central atom are often called *hypervalent*.
- Atoms from the third period and beyond can accommodate more than an octet.
  - Examples: PCl_5, SF_4, AsF_6^-, and ICl_4^-.
- Elements from the third period and beyond have unfilled *d* orbitals that can be used to accommodate the additional electrons.
- Size also plays a role.
  - The larger the central atom, the larger the number of atoms that can surround it.
  - The size of the surrounding atoms is also important.
  - Expanded octets occur often when the atoms bound to the central atom are the smallest and most electronegative (e.g., F, Cl, O).

FORWARD REFERENCES
- Chemistry of species with an odd number of electrons (radicals) will be discussed in Chapter 18 (section 18.1).
- Electron deficiency of boron will be further discussed in section 22.11.
- Valence shell expansion will be used to explain the formation of noble-gas compounds in section 22.3.

8.8 Strengths of Covalent Bonds[59]

- The energy required to break a particular covalent bond in one mole of a gaseous substance is called the **bond enthalpy**, *D*.
  - That is, for the Cl_2 molecule, $D(Cl–Cl)$ is given by ΔH for the reaction:
$$Cl_2(g) \rightarrow 2Cl(g).$$
- When more than one bond is broken:
$$CH_4(g) \rightarrow C(g) + 4H(g) \qquad \Delta H = 1660 \text{ kJ}$$
  - The bond enthalpy is a fraction of ΔH for the atomization reaction:
$$D(C–H) = ¼ \ \Delta H = ¼ \ (1660 \text{ kJ}) = 415 \text{ kJ}.$$
- Bond enthalpy is always a positive quantity.

---

[56] "Nitric Oxide—Some Old and New Perspectives" from Further Readings
[57] "Biological Roles of Nitric Oxide" from Further Readings
[58] "Phosphorus Pentachloride" 3-D Model from Instructor's Resource CD/DVD
[59] Table 8.4 from Transparency Pack

Bond Enthalpies and the Enthalpies of Reactions[60,61,62,63,64]

- We can use bond enthalpies to calculate the enthalpy for a chemical reaction.
- We recognize that in any chemical reaction bonds need to be broken and then new bonds form.
- The enthalpy of the reaction, ΔH_{rxn}, is given by the sum of bond enthalpies for bonds broken (in reactants) less the sum of bond enthalpies for bonds formed (in products):

$$\Delta H_{rxn} = \sum D(\text{bonds broken}) - \sum D(\text{bonds formed})$$

- We illustrate the concept with the reaction between methane, CH_4, and chlorine:

$$CH_4(g) + Cl_2(g) \rightarrow CH_3Cl(g) + HCl(g)$$

  - In this reaction, one C–H bond and one Cl–Cl bond are broken, while one C–Cl bond and one H–Cl bond are formed.
  - So, $\Delta H_{rxn} = [D(\text{C–H}) + D(\text{Cl–Cl})] - [D(\text{C–Cl}) + D(\text{H–Cl})] = -104$ kJ.
  - The overall reaction is exothermic, which means that the bonds formed are stronger than the bonds broken.
  - The above result is consistent with Hess's law.

Bond Enthalpy and Bond Length[65]

- The distance between the nuclei of the atoms involved in a bond is called the **bond length**.
- Multiple bonds are shorter than single bonds.
  - We can show that multiple bonds are stronger than single bonds.
  - As the number of bonds between atoms increases, the atoms are held closer and more tightly together.

FORWARD REFERENCES

- Bond enthalpies and catalysis will be discussed in Chapter 14 (section 14.7).
- Relative length and strengths of X-H bonds (X = F, Cl, Br, I) will be important in determining strength of binary acids (e.g., HF vs. HCl) in Chapter 16 (section 16.10).
- Bond dissociation energies in N_2 vs. O_2 will be contrasted and linked to their reactivities in Chapter 18 (section 18.1).

---

[60] Figure 8.15 from Transparency Pack
[61] "Bond Enthalpy" Activity from Instructor's Resource CD/DVD
[62] "The Relative Explosive Power of Some Explosives" from Further Readings
[63] "Exothermic Bond Breaking: A Persistent Misconception" from Further Readings
[64] "Chloromethane" 3-D Model from Instructor's Resource CD/DVD
[65] Table 8.5 from Transparency Pack

Further Readings:

1. Georgios R. Tsaparlis, "The Chemical Bond as an Atomic Tug-of-War," *J. Chem. Educ.*, Vol. 61, **1984**, 677. An analogy between a covalent bond and a game of tug-and-war is suggested in this reference.

2. Natalie Foote Tiernan, "Gilbert Newton Lewis and the Amazing Electron Dots," *J. Chem. Educ.*, Vol. 62, **1985**, 569–570.

3. Roger L. DeKock, "The Chemical Bond," *J. Chem. Educ.*, Vol. 64, **1987**, 934–941. Chemical bonds and their properties are reviewed in this article.

4. Raymond F. Peterson and David F. Treagust, "Grade-12 Students' Misconceptions of Covalent Bonding and Structure," *J. Chem. Educ.*, Vol. 66, **1989**, 459–460. Common weaknesses in student comprehension of covalent bonding are explored in this article.

5. S. R. Logan, "The Role of Lewis Structures in Teaching Covalent Bonding," *J. Chem. Educ.*, Vol. 78, **2001**, 1457–1458.

6. Anthony N. Stranges, "Reflections on the Electron Theory of the Chemical Bond: 1900-1925," *J. Chem. Educ.*, Vol. 61, **1984**, 185–190.

7. William B. Jensen, "Abegg, Lewis, Langmuir, and the Octet Rule," *J. Chem. Educ.*, Vol. 61, **1984**, 191–200.

8. Linus Pauling, "G. N. Lewis and the Chemical Bond," *J. Chem. Educ.*, Vol. 61, **1984**, 201–203.

9. William B. Jensen, "The Use of Dots in Chemical Formulas," *J. Chem. Educ.*, Vol. 83, **2006**, 1590–1591.

10. Gordon Sproul, "Electronegativity and Bond Type: Predicting Bond Type," *J. Chem. Educ.*, Vol. 78, **2001**, 387–390.

11. William B. Jensen, "Electronegativity from Avogadro to Pauling, Part I: Origins of the Electronegativity Concept," *J. Chem. Educ.*, Vol. 73, **1996**, 11–20. The January 1996 edition of the *Journal of Chemical Education* is a special tribute to Linus Pauling and contains many interesting articles.

12. William B. Jensen, "Electronegativity from Avogrado to Pauling: II. Late Nineteenth- and Early Twentieth-Century Developments," *J. Chem. Educ.*, Vol. 80, **2003**, 279–287.

13. James N. Spencer, Richard S. Moog, and Ronald J. Gillespie, "Demystifying Introductory Chemistry: Part 3. Ionization Energies, Electronegativity, Polar Bonds, and Partial Charges," *J. Chem. Educ.*, Vol. 73, **1996**, 627–631.

14. Wan-Yaacob Ahmad and Mat B. Zakaria, "Drawing Lewis Structures from Lewis Symbols: A Direct Electron Pairing Approach," *J. Chem. Educ.*, Vol. 76, **1999**, 329–331.

15. Gordon H. Purser, "Lewis Structures Are Models for Predicting Molecular Structure, *Not* Electronic Structure," *J. Chem. Educ.*, Vol. 76, **1999**, 1013–1017.

16. Juan Quilez Pardo, "Teaching a Model for Writing Lewis Structures," *J. Chem. Educ.*, Vol. 66, **1989**, 456–458.

17. James Allen Carroll, "Drawing Lewis Structures without Anticipating Octets," *J. Chem. Educ.*, Vol. 63. **1986**, 28–31.

18. Melvin E. Zandler and Erach R. Talty, "The '6N + 2 Rule' for Writing Lewis Octet Structures," *J. Chem. Educ.*, Vol. 61, **1984**, 124–127.

19. Thomas J. Clark, "Another Procedure for Writing Lewis Structures," *J. Chem. Educ.*, Vol. 61, **1984**, 100.

20. Melanie M. Cooper, Nathaniel Gove, Sonia M. Underwood, and Michael W. Klymkowsky, "Lost in Lewis Structures: An Investigation of Student Difficulties in Developing Representational Competence," *J. Chem. Educ.*, Vol. 87, **2010**, 869–874.

21. David G. DeWit, "Using Formal Charges in Teaching Descriptive Inorganic Chemistry," *J. Chem. Educ.*, Vol. 71, **1994**, 750–755.

22. John E. Packer and Shiela D. Woodgate, "Lewis Structures, Formal Charge, and Oxidation Numbers: A More User-Friendly Approach," *J. Chem. Educ.*, Vol. 68, **1991**, 456–458. Simple rules for writing Lewis structures are discussed.

23. Gerard Parkin, "Valence, Oxidation Number, and Formal Charge: Three Related but Fundamentally Different Concepts," *J. Chem. Educ.*, Vol. 83, **2006**, 791–799.

24. Robert C. Kerber, "If it's Resonance, What is Resonating?" *J. Chem. Educ.*, Vol. 83, **2006**, 223–227.

25. Shirley Lin, "Aromatic Bagels: An Edible Resonance Analogy" *J. Chem. Educ.*, Vol. 84, **2007**, 779–780.

26. Donald G. Truhlar, "The Concept of Resonance" *J. Chem. Educ.*, Vol. 84, **2007**, 781–782.

27. William B. Jensen, "The Origin of the Circle Symbol for Aromaticity" *J. Chem. Educ.*, Vol. 86, **2009**, 423-424.

28. R. J. Gillespie, "Electron Densities, Atomic Charges, and Ionic, Covalent, and Polar Bonds," *J. Chem. Educ.*, Vol. 78, **2001**, 1688–1691.

29. Kenton B. Abel and William M Hemmerlin, "Explaining Resonance–A Colorful Approach," *J. Chem. Educ.*, Vol. 68, **1991**, 834.

30. Francis Delvigne, "A Visual Aid for Teaching the Resonance Concept," *J. Chem. Educ.*, Vol. 66, **1989**, 461–462.

31. Eric W. Ainscough and Andrew M. Brodie, "Nitric Oxide–Some Old and New Perspectives," *J. Chem. Educ.*, Vol. 72, **1995**, 686–692.

32. Solomon H. Snyder and David S. Bredt, "Biological Roles of Nitric Oxide," *Scientific American*, May **1992**, 68–77.

33. Marten J. Ten Hoor, "The Relative Explosive Power of Some Explosives," *J. Chem. Educ.*, Vol, 80, **2003**, 1397–1400.

34. William C. Galley, "Exothermic Bond Breaking: A Persistent Misconception," *J. Chem. Educ.*, Vol. 81, **2004**, 523–525.

35. A. A. Woolf, "Oxidation Numbers and Their Limitations," *J. Chem. Educ.*, Vol. 65, **1988**, 45–46.

36. Joel M. Kauffman, "Simple Method for Determination of Oxidation Numbers of Atoms in Compounds," *J. Chem. Educ.*, Vol. 63, **1986**, 474–475.

Live Demonstrations:

1. Lee. R. Summerlin,, Christie L. Borgford, and Julie B. Ealy, "Bending a Stream of Water," *Chemical Demonstrations, A Sourcebook for Teachers, Volume 2* (Washington: American Chemical Society, **1988**), p. 91. The polarity of water and cyclohexane are compared in this demonstration.

Chapter 9. Molecular Geometry and Bonding Theories

Media Resources

Figures and Tables in Transparency Pack:	**Section:**
Figure 9.2 Shapes of AB_2 and AB_3 Molecules	9.1 Molecular Shapes
Figure 9.3 Shapes Allowing Maximum Distances between Atoms in AB_n Molecules	9.1 Molecular Shapes
Table 9.1 Electron-Domain Geometries as a Function of Number of Electron Domains	9.2 VSEPR Model
Table 9.2 Electron-Domain and Molecular Geometries for Two, Three, and Four Electron Domains around a Central Atom	9.2 VSEPR Model
Table 9.3 Electron-Domain and Molecular Geometries for Five and Six Electron Domains around a Central Atom	9.2 VSEPR Model
Figure 9.12 Polar and Nonpolar Molecules Containing Polar Bonds	9.3 Molecular Shape and Molecular Polarity
Figure 9.14 Formation of the H_2 Molecule as Atomic Orbitals Overlap	9.4 Covalent Bonding and Orbital Overlap
Figure 9.15 Formation of sp Hybrid Orbitals	9.5 Hybrid Orbitals
Figure 9.17 Formation of sp^2 Hybrid Orbitals	9.5 Hybrid Orbitals
Figure 9.18 Formation of sp^3 Hybrid Orbitals	9.5 Hybrid Orbitals
Table 9.4 Geometric Arrangements Characteristic of Hybrid Orbital Sets	9.5 Hybrid Orbitals
Figure 9.23 The Orbital Structure of Ethylene	9.6 Multiple Bonds
Figure 9.24 Formation of Two π Bonds in Acetylene, C_2H_2	9.6 Multiple Bonds
Figure 9.26 σ and the π Bond Networks in Benzene, C_6H_6	9.6 Multiple Bonds
Figure 9.27 Delocalized π Bonds in Benzene	9.6 Multiple Bonds
Figure 9.32 The Two Molecular Orbitals of H_2, One a Bonding MO and One an Antibonding MO	9.7 Molecular Orbitals
Figure 9.35 Energy-level Diagram for the Li_2 Molecule	9.8 Period 2 Diatomic Molecules
Figure 9.36 Contour Representations of the Molecular Orbitals Formed by $2p$ Orbitals	9.8 Period 2 Diatomic Molecules
Figure 9.41 Energy-level Diagram for MOs of Period 2 Homonuclear Diatomic Molecules	9.8 Period 2 Diatomic Molecules
Figure 9.42 The Effect of Interactions between $2s$ and $2p$ Atomic Orbitals	9.8 Period 2 Diatomic Molecules

Activities:	**Section:**
Molecular Polarity	9.3 Molecular Shape and Molecular Polarity
s-p Hybridization	9.5 Hybrid Orbitals
Multiple Bonds	9.6 Multiple Bonds

Animations:	**Section:**
VSEPR	9.2 The VSEPR Model

Hybridization
Molecular Orbital Theory

9.5 Hybrid Orbitals
9.7 Molecular Orbitals

3-D Models:

Diazepam (valium)
Carbon Tetrachloride
Carbon Dioxide
Sulfur Dioxide
Sulfur Trioxide
Nitrogen Trifluoride
Chlorine Trifluoride
Ammonia
Ozone
Sulfur Tetrafluoride
Iodine Pentafluoride
Acetic Acid
Boron Trifluoride
Trichlorotin(II) Ion
VSEPR—Basic Molecular Configurations
Chloromethane
Hydrogen Chloride
Ethene (ethylene)
Ethyne (acetylene)
Benzene
Oxygen

Section:
Introduction
9.1 Molecular Shapes
9.1 Molecular Shapes
9.1 Molecular Shapes
9.1 Molecular Shapes
9.1 Molecular Shapes
9.1 Molecular Shapes
9.1 Molecular Shapes
9.2 VSEPR Model
9.2 VSEPR Model
9.2 VSEPR Model
9.2 VSEPR Model
9.2 VSEPR Model
9.2 VSEPR Model
9.2 VSEPR Model
9.3 Molecular Shape and Molecular Polarity
9.3 Molecular Shape and Molecular Polarity
9.6 Multiple Bonds
9.6 Multiple Bonds
9.6 Multiple Bonds
9.8 Period 2 Diatomic Molecules

Other Resources

Further Readings:
Molecular Geometry
Who Needs Lewis Structures to Get VSEPR
    Geometries?
Teaching Molecular Geometry with the VSEPR
    Model
Teaching VSEPR: The Plastic Egg Model
Multiple Bonds and the VSEPR Model
Lewis Structures Are Models for Predicting
    Molecular Structure, *Not* Electronic Structure
The Use of Molecular Modeling and VSEPR
    Theory in the Undergraduate Curriculum to
    Predict the Three-Dimensional Structure of
    Molecules
Tetrahedral Geometry and the Dipole Moment of
    Molecules
Difficulties with the Geometry and Polarity of
    Molecules: Beyond Misconceptions
The Ropes: A Molecular Polarity Activity
Identifying Polar and Nonpolar Molecules
The Significance of the Bond Angle in Sulfur
    Dioxide

Section:
9.1 Molecular Shapes
9.2 VSEPR Model

9.2 VSEPR Model

9.2 VSEPR Model
9.2 VSEPR Model
9.2 VSEPR Model

9.2 VSEPR Model

9.3 Molecular Shape and Molecular Polarity

9.3 Molecular Shape and Molecular Polarity

9.3 Molecular Shape and Molecular Polarity
9.3 Molecular Shape and Molecular Polarity
9.3 Molecular Shape and Molecular Polarity

Put the Body to Them!	9.3 Molecular Shape and Molecular Polarity
Demystifying Introductory Chemistry Part 2: Bonding and Molecular Geometry without Orbitals—The Electron-Domain Model	9.4 Covalent Bonding and Orbital Overlap
Grade-12 Students' Misconceptions of Covalent Bonding and Structure	9.4 Covalent Bonding and Orbital Overlap
A Colorful Demonstration to Simulate Orbital Hybridization	9.5 Hybrid Orbitals
The 'Big Dog–Puppy Dog' Analogy for Resonance	9.6 Multiple Bonds
Resonance Analogy Using Cartoon Characters	9.6 Multiple Bonds
Explaining Resonance—A Colorful Approach	9.6 Multiple Bonds
A Visual Aid for Teaching the Resonance Concept	9.6 Multiple Bonds
Delocalization—The Key Concept of Covalent Bonding	9.6 Multiple Bonds
Orbital Bartending	9.6 Multiple Bonds
Molecular Orbital Theory of Bond Order and Valency	9.7 Molecular Orbitals
The Eye's Photochemistry: A Quick Snap	9.7 Molecular Orbitals
The Molecules of Visual Excitation	9.7 Molecular Orbitals
The Relative Energies of Molecular Orbitals for Second-Row Homonuclear Diatomic Molecules: The Effect of s-p Mixing	9.8 Period 2 Diatomic Molecules

Live Demonstrations: **Section:**

Bending a Stream of Water	9.3 Molecular Shape and Molecular Polarity

Chapter 9. Molecular Geometry and Bonding Theories

Common Student Misconceptions

- Students find it difficult to think in three dimensions. Often, they believe that a square planar arrangement is the best arrangement for the least repulsion of four electron domains.
- Students often confuse the electron domain geometry and the molecular geometry (shape).
- Students need to realize that in order to determine whether a molecule is polar, they need to establish the correct molecular geometry.
- Students need to realize that large molecules with several central atoms do not have easily describable molecular shapes; geometry about each central atom has to be determined individually.
- Students often find it difficult to understand how a molecule with polar bonds can be nonpolar; a review of basic vector algebra to illustrate how the net dipole is derived may be needed.
- Students often attempt to determine polarity of ions.
- Students do not realize that hybridization is related to the electron-domain geometry, not the molecular geometry.
- Students need to realize that in wave mechanics bonding orbitals result from constructive interference and antibonding orbitals form destructive interference.

Teaching Tips

- Simple balloon models can be effectively used in classroom presentations of VSEPR.
- Referring to nonbonded electron pairs, single bonds, and multiple bonds as *regions of electron density* may help relieve any confusion that might arise from treating the various kinds of electron pairs differently.

Lecture Outline[1]

9.1 Molecular Shapes[2,3,4,5,6,7,8,9,10,11,12]

- Lewis structures give atomic connectivity: they tell us which atoms are physically connected to which atoms.
- The shape of a molecule is determined by its **bond angles**.
  - The angles made by the lines joining the nuclei of the atoms in a molecule are the bond angles.
- Consider CCl_4:
  - Experimentally we find all Cl–C–Cl bond angles are 109.5°.
  - Therefore, the molecule cannot be planar.

---

[1] "Diazepam (valium)" 3-D Model from Instructor's Resource CD/DVD
[2] "Carbon Tetrachloride" 3-D Model from Instructor's Resource CD/DVD
[3] Figure 9.2 from Transparency Pack
[4] Figure 9.3 from Transparency Pack
[5] "Carbon Dioxide" 3-D Model from Instructor's Resource CD/DVD
[6] "Sulfur Dioxide" 3-D Model from Instructor's Resource CD/DVD
[7] "Sulfur Trioxide" 3-D Model from Instructor's Resource CD/DVD
[8] "Nitrogen Trifluoride" 3-D Model from Instructor's Resource CD/DVD
[9] "Chlorine Trifluoride" 3-D Model from Instructor's Resource CD/DVD
[10] "Molecular Geometry" from Further Readings
[11] "Ammonia" 3-D Model from Instructor's Resource CD/DVD
[12] "Water" 3-D Model from Instructor's Resource CD/DVD

- All Cl atoms are located at the vertices of a tetrahedron with the C at its center.
- In order to predict molecular shape, we assume that the valence electrons repel each other.
  - Therefore, the molecule adopts the three-dimensional geometry that minimizes this repulsion.
  - We call this model the Valence-Shell Electron-Pair Repulsion (**VSEPR**) model.

FORWARD REFERENCES
  - Molecular shapes will affect such physical properties as viscosity (Chapter 11) and boiling points of structural isomers of organic compounds (Chapter 24).
  - Molecular shapes and structures of many compounds will be used throughout the textbook, but in particular in Chapters 22 and 24.

9.2 The VSEPR Model[13,14,15,16,17,18,19,20,21,22]

- A covalent bond forms between two atoms when a pair of electrons occupies the space between the atoms.
  - This is a **bonding pair** of electrons.
  - Such a region is an **electron domain**.
- A **nonbonding pair** or **lone pair** of electrons defines an electron domain located principally on one atom.
  - Example: NH_3 has three bonding pairs and one lone pair.
- VSEPR predicts that the best arrangement of electron domains is the one that minimizes the repulsions among them.
  - The arrangement of electron domains about the central atom of an AB_n molecule is its **electron-domain geometry**.
  - There are five different electron-domain geometries:
    - Linear (two electron domains), trigonal planar (three domains), tetrahedral (four domains), trigonal bipyramidal (five domains) and octahedral (six domains).
- The **molecular geometry** is the arrangement of the atoms in space.
  - To determine the shape of a molecule we distinguish between lone pairs and bonding pairs.
  - We use the electron domain geometry to help us predict the molecular geometry.
    - Draw the Lewis structure.
    - Count the total number of electron domains around the central atom.
    - Arrange the electron domains in one of the above geometries to minimize electron-electron repulsion.
  - Next, determine the three-dimensional structure of the molecule.
    - We ignore lone pairs in the molecular geometry.
    - Describe the molecular geometry in terms of the angular arrangement of the bonded atoms.
    - Multiple bonds are counted as one electron domain.

---

[13] "Who Needs Lewis Structures To Get VSEPR Geometries?" from Further Readings

[14] "VSEPR" Animation from Instructor's Resource CD/DVD

[15] Table 9.1 from Transparency Pack

[16] "Teaching Molecular Geometry with the VSEPR Model" from Further Readings

[17] "Teaching VSEPR: The Plastic Egg Model" from Further Readings

[18] "VSEPR—Basic Molecular Configurations" 3-D Model from Instructor's Resource CD/DVD

[19] Table 9.2 from Transparency Pack

[20] "Ozone" 3-D Model from Instructor's Resource CD/DVD

[21] "Boron Trifluoride" 3-D Model from Instructor's Resource CD/DVD

[22] "Trichlorotin(II) Ion" 3-D Model from Instructor's Resource CD/DVD

Effect of Nonbonding Electrons and Multiple Bonds on Bond Angles[23,24]

- We refine VSEPR to predict and explain slight distortions from "ideal" geometries.
- Consider three molecules with tetrahedral electron domain geometries:
  - CH_4, NH_3, and H_2O.
  - By experiment, the H–X–H bond angle decreases from C (109.5° in CH_4) to N (107° in NH_3) to O (104.5° in H_2O).
  - A bonding pair of electrons is attracted by two nuclei. They do not repel as much as lone pairs which are primarily attracted by only one nucleus.
  - Electron domains for nonbonding electron pairs thus exert greater repulsive forces on adjacent electron domains.
    - They tend to compress the bond angles.
    - The bond angle decreases as the number of nonbonding pairs increases.
  - Similarly, electrons in multiple bonds repel more than electrons in single bonds. (e.g. in Cl_2CO the O–C–Cl angle is 124.3°, and the Cl–C–Cl bond angle is 111.4°).
- We will encounter 11 basic molecular shapes:
  - Three atoms (AB_2)
    - Linear
    - Bent
  - Four atoms (AB_3)
    - Trigonal planar
    - Trigonal pyramidal
    - T-shaped
  - Five atoms (AB_4)
    - Tetrahedral
    - Square planar
    - Seesaw
  - Six atoms (AB_5)
    - Trigonal bipyramidal
    - Square pyramidal
  - Seven atoms (AB_6)
    - Octahedral

Molecules with Expanded Valence Shells[25,26,27]

- Atoms that have expanded octets have five electron domains (trigonal bipyramidal) or six electron domains (octahedral) electron-domain geometries.
  - Trigonal bipyramidal structures have a plane containing three electron pairs.
    - The fourth and fifth electron pairs are located above and below this plane.
    - In this structure two trigonal pyramids share a base.
  - For octahedral structures, there is a plane containing four electron pairs.
    - Similarly, the fifth and sixth electron pairs are located above and below this plane.
    - Two square pyramids share a base.
- Consider a trigonal bipyramid.
  - The three electron pairs in the plane are called *equatorial*.

---

[23] "Multiple Bonds and the VSEPR Model" from Further Readings
[24] "Lewis Structures are Models for Predicting Molecular Structure, *Not* Electronic Structure" from Further Readings
[25] Table 9.3 from Transparency Pack
[26] "Sulfur Tetrafluoride" 3-D Model from Instructor's Resource CD/DVD
[27] "Iodine Pentafluoride" 3-D Model from Instructor's Resource CD/DVD

- The two electron pairs above and below this plane are called *axial*.
- The axial electron pairs are 180° apart and 90° to the equatorial electrons.
- The equatorial electron pairs are 120° apart.
- To minimize electron–electron repulsion, nonbonding pairs are always placed in equatorial positions and bonding pairs in either axial or equatorial positions.
- Consider an octahedron.
  - The four electron pairs in the plane are at 90° to each other.
  - The two axial electron pairs are 180° apart and at 90° to the electrons in the plane.
  - Because of the symmetry of the system, each position is equivalent.
  - If we have five bonding pairs and one lone pair, it doesn't matter where the lone pair is placed.
    - The molecular geometry is square pyramidal.
  - If two nonbonding pairs are present, the repulsions are minimized by pointing them toward opposite sides of the octahedron.
    - The molecular geometry is square planar.

Shapes of Larger Molecules[28,29]

- In acetic acid, CH_3COOH, there are three interior atoms: two C and one O.
- We assign the molecular (and electron-domain) geometry about each interior (central) atom separately.
  - The geometry around the first C is tetrahedral.
  - The geometry around the second C is trigonal planar.
  - The geometry around the O is bent (tetrahedral).

FORWARD REFERENCES
- The consequence of water having an sp^3 hybridized oxygen atom and bent molecular shape will be linked to its the ability to form 4 hydrogen bonds in the structure of ice in Chapter 11 (section 11.2).
- Octahedral vs. tetrahedral metal complexes will be discussed in Chapter 23 (section 23.6).

9.3 Molecular Shape and Molecular Polarity[30,31,32,33,34,35,36,37,38,39,40]

- Polar molecules interact with electric fields.
- We previously saw that binary compounds are polar if their centers of negative and positive charge do not coincide.

---

[28] "The Use of Molecular Modeling and VSEPR Theory in the Undergraduate Curriculum to Predict the Three-Dimensional Structure of Molecules" from Further Readings
[29] "Acetic Acid" 3-D Model from Instructor's Resource CD/DVD
[30] Figure 9.12 from Transparency Pack
[31] "Molecular Polarity" Activity from Instructor's Resource CD/DVD
[32] "Tetrahedral Geometry and the Dipole Moment of Molecules" from Further Readings
[33] "Bending a Stream of Water" from Live Demonstrations
[34] "Difficulties with the Geometry and Polarity of Molecules: Beyond Misconceptions" from Further Readings
[35] "The Ropes: A Molecular Polarity Activity" from Further Readings
[36] "Identifying Polar and Nonpolar Molecules" from Further Readings
[37] "The Significance of the Bond Angle in Sulfur Dioxide" from Further Readings
[38] "Put the Body to Them!" from Further Readings
[39] "Chloromethane" 3-D Model from Instructor's Resource CD/DVD
[40] "Hydrogen Chloride" 3-D Model from Instructor's Resource CD/DVD

- • If two charges, equal in magnitude and opposite in sign, are separated by a distance d, then a *dipole* is established.
  - • The dipole moment, μ, is given by:

$$\mu = Qr$$

  - • where Q is the magnitude of the charge.
- • We can extend this to polyatomic molecules.
  - • For each bond in a polyatomic molecule, we can consider the **bond dipole**.
    - • The dipole moment due only to the two atoms in the bond is the bond dipole.
  - • Because bond dipoles and dipole moments are *vector quantities*, the orientation of these individual dipole moments determines whether the molecule has an overall dipole moment.
  - • Examples:
    - • In CO_2 each $^{\delta+}C-O^{\delta-}$ dipole is canceled because the molecule is linear.
    - • In H_2O, the $^{\delta+}H-O^{\delta-}$ dipoles do not cancel because the molecule is bent.
- • It is possible for a molecule with polar bonds to be either polar or nonpolar.
  - • Example:
    - • For diatomic molecules:
      - • polar bonds always result in an overall dipole moment.
    - • For triatomic molecules:
      - • if the molecular geometry is bent, there is an overall dipole moment.
      - • if the molecular geometry is linear, and the B atoms are the same, there is no overall dipole moment.
      - • if the molecular geometry is linear and the B atoms are different, there is an overall dipole moment.
    - • For molecules with four atoms:
      - • if the molecular geometry is trigonal pyramidal, there is an overall dipole moment;
      - • if the molecular geometry is trigonal planar, and the B atoms are identical, there is no overall dipole moment;
      - • if the molecular geometry is trigonal planar and the B atoms are different, there is an overall dipole moment.

FORWARD REFERENCES
- • Molecular polarity will affect such physical properties as viscosity, vapor pressure and energy changes associated with phase changes of compounds (Chapter 11).
- • Molecular polarity vs. miscibility will be discussed in Chapter 13 (section 13.3).
- • Polar functional groups in otherwise nonpolar organic compounds will be further discussed in Chapter 24 (section 24.4).

9.4 Covalent Bonding and Orbital Overlap[41,42,43]

- • Lewis structures and VSEPR theory give us the shape and location of electrons in a molecule.
  - • They do not explain why a chemical bond forms.
- • How can quantum mechanics be used to account for molecular shape? What are the orbitals that are involved in bonding?
- • We use **valence-bond theory**:
  - • A covalent bond forms when the orbitals on two atoms *overlap*.
    - • The shared region of space between the orbitals is called the *orbital overlap*.
    - • There are two electrons (usually one from each atom) of opposite spin in the orbital overlap.

---

[41] "Demystifying Introductory Chemistry Part 2: Bonding and Molecular Geometry without Orbitals—The Electron-Domain Model" from Further Readings
[42] "Grade-12 Students' Misconceptions of Covalent Bonding and Structure" from Further Readings
[43] Figure 9.14 from Transparency Pack

- As two nuclei approach each other, their atomic orbitals overlap.
- As the amount of overlap increases, the energy of the interaction decreases.
- At some distance the minimum energy is reached.
  - The minimum energy corresponds to the bonding distance (or bond length).
- As the two atoms get closer, their nuclei begin to repel and the energy increases.
- At the bonding distance, the attractive forces between nuclei and electrons just balance the repulsive forces (nucleus-nucleus, electron-electron).

9.5 Hybrid Orbitals[44,45]

- We can apply the idea of orbital overlap and valence-bond theory to polyatomic molecules.

sp Hybrid Orbitals[46]

- Consider the BeF_2 molecule.
  - Be has a $1s^2 2s^2$ electron configuration.
  - There is no unpaired electron available for bonding.
  - We conclude that the atomic orbitals are not adequate to describe orbitals in molecules.
- We know that the F–Be–F bond angle is 180° (VSEPR theory).
- We also know that one electron from Be is shared with each one of the unpaired electrons from F.
- We assume that the Be orbitals in the Be–F bond are 180° apart.
- We could promote an electron from the 2s orbital on Be to the 2p orbital to get two unpaired electrons for bonding.
  - BUT the geometry is still not explained.
- We can solve the problem by allowing the 2s and one 2p orbital on Be to mix or form two new **hybrid orbitals** (a process called **hybridization**).
  - The two equivalent hybrid orbitals that result from mixing an *s* and a *p* orbital and are called *sp* hybrid orbitals.
  - The two lobes of an *sp* hybrid orbital are 180° apart.
  - According to the valence-bond model, a linear arrangement of electron domains implies *sp* hybridization.
  - Since only one of 2p orbitals of Be has been used in hybridization, there are two unhybridized *p* orbitals remaining on Be.
  - The electrons in the *sp* hybrid orbitals form shared electron bonds with the two fluorine atoms.

*sp*² and *sp*³ Hybrid Orbitals[47,48,49]

- Important: when we mix *n* atomic orbitals, we must get *n* hybrid orbitals.
- Three *sp*² hybrid orbitals are formed from hybridization of one *s* and two *p* orbitals.
  - Thus, there is one unhybridized *p* orbital remaining.
  - The large lobes of the *sp*² hybrids lie in a trigonal plane.
  - Molecules with trigonal planar electron-pair geometries have *sp*² orbitals on the central atom.
- Four *sp*³ hybrid orbitals are formed from hybridization of one *s* and three *p* orbitals.
  - Therefore, there are four large lobes.
  - Each lobe points towards the vertex of a tetrahedron.
  - The angle between the large lobes is 109.5°.
  - Molecules with tetrahedral electron pair geometries are *sp*³ hybridized.

---

[44] "A Colorful Demonstration to Simulate Orbital Hybridization" from Further Readings
[45] "Hybridization" Animation from Instructor's Resource CD/DVD
[46] Figure 9.15 from Transparency Pack
[47] Figure 9.17 from Transparency Pack
[48] Figure 9.18 from Transparency Pack
[49] "s-p Hybridization" Activity from Instructor's Resource CD/DVD

- Since there are only three *p* orbitals, trigonal bipyramidal and octahedral electron-pair geometries must involve *d* orbitals.
- Trigonal bipyramidal electron pair geometries require sp^3d hybridization.
- Octahedral electron pair geometries require sp^3d^2 hybridization.
- Note that the electron pair VSEPR geometry corresponds well with the hybridization.
  - Use of *d* orbitals in making hybrid orbitals corresponds well with the idea of an expanded octet.

Hybrid Orbital Summary[50]

- We need to know the electron-domain geometry before we can assign hybridization.
- To assign hybridization:
  - Draw a Lewis structure.
  - Assign the electron-domain geometry using VSEPR theory.
  - Specify the hybridization required to accommodate the electron pairs based on their geometric arrangement.
  - Name the geometry by the positions of the atoms.

FORWARD REFERENCES

  - Hybridization of C atoms in carbon nanotubes and polymers will be mentioned in Chapter 12 (section 12.9).
  - *sp*, sp^2 and sp^3 hybridizations will be utilized throughout Chapter 24.
  - Hybrid orbitals will be utilized in the metal-ligand bond formation in Chapter 23 (section 23.6).

9.6 Multiple Bonds[51,52,53,54,55]

- In the covalent bonds we have seen so far the electron density has been concentrated symmetrically about the *internuclear axis*.
- **Sigma (σ) bonds**: electron density lies on the axis between the nuclei.
  - All single bonds are σ bonds.
- What about overlap in multiple bonds?
  - **Pi (π) bonds**: electron density lies above and below the plane of the nuclei.
    - A double bond consists of one σ bond and one π bond.
    - A triple bond has one σ bond and two π bonds.
- Often, the *p* orbitals involved in π bonding come from unhybridized orbitals.
- For example: ethylene, C_2H_4, has a C=C double bond:
  - One σ and one π bond.
  - Both C atoms sp^2 hybridized.
  - Both C atoms with trigonal planar electron-pair and molecular geometries.
- For example: acetylene, C_2H_2, has a C≡C triple bond
  - The electron-domain geometry of each C is linear.
  - Therefore, the C atoms are *sp* hybridized.
  - The *sp* hybrid orbitals form the C–C and C–H σ bonds.
  - There are *two* unhybridized *p* orbitals on each C atom.
  - *Both* unhybridized *p* orbitals form the *two* π bonds;
    - One π bond is above and below the plane of the nuclei;

---

[50] Table 9.4 from Transparency Pack
[51] Figure 9.23 from Transparency Pack
[52] "Multiple Bonds" Activity from Instructor's Resource CD/DVD
[53] Figure 9.24 from Transparency Pack
[54] "Ethene (ethylene)" 3-D Model from Instructor's Resource CD/DVD
[55] "Ethyne (acetylene)" 3-D Model from Instructor's Resource CD/DVD

- One π bond is in front and behind the plane of the nuclei.
- When triple bonds form (e.g., N_2), one π bond is always above and below and the other is in front and behind the plane of the nuclei.

Resonance Structures, Delocalization, and π Bonding[56,57,58,59,60,61,62,63]

- So far all the bonds we have encountered are localized between two nuclei.
- In the case of benzene:
  - There are six localized C–C σ bonds and six localized C–H σ bonds
    - Each C atom is sp^2 hybridized.
  - There is one unhybridized p orbital on each carbon atom, resulting in six unhybridized carbon p orbitals in a ring.
- In benzene the three π bonds are **delocalized** over the entire ring (i.e., the π electrons are shared by all six carbon atoms).
- Experimentally, all C–C bonds are the same length in benzene.
  - Therefore, all C–C bonds are of the same type (recall single bonds are longer than double bonds).

General Conclusions[64]

- Every pair of bonded atoms shares one or more pairs of electrons.
- Two electrons shared between atoms on the same axis as the nuclei are σ bonds.
- σ Bonds are always localized in the region between two bonded atoms.
- If two atoms share more than one pair of electrons, the additional pairs form π bonds.
- When resonance structures are possible, delocalization is also possible.

FORWARD REFERENCES

- Delocalized electrons in metallic solids will be mentioned in Chapter 12 (section 12.3).
- Delocalized π bonds in graphite will be further discussed in Chapter 12 (section 12.7).
- Multiple bonds in polymerization, rubber, and biopolymers will be discussed in Chapter 12 (section 12.8).
- Effectiveness of orbital overlap in the formation of π bonds in 2nd vs. 3rd row elements will be compared in Chapter 22 (section 22.1).
- The role of π bonds in O_2 and other oxygen containing compounds, as well as a delocalized π bond in ozone will be discussed in Chapter 22 (section 22.5).
- Alternating double bonds in chlorophyll will be discussed in Chapter 23 (section 23.3).
- π bonds in alkenes and alkynes will be discussed in Chapter 24 (section 24.3).
- Delocalized π bonds in aromatic compounds will be mentioned in Chapter 24 (section 24.3).

9.7 Molecular Orbitals[65,66,67,68]

- Some aspects of bonding are not explained by Lewis structures, VSEPR theory and hybridization.

[56] "The 'Big Dog-Puppy Dog' Analogy for Resonance" from Further Readings
[57] Figure 9.26 from Transparency Pack
[58] Figure 9.27 from Transparency Pack
[59] "Resonance Analogy Using Cartoon Characters" from Further Readings
[60] "Explaining Resonance—A Colorful Approach" from Further Readings
[61] "A Visual Aid for Teaching the Resonance Concept" from Further Readings
[62] "Delocalization—The Key Concept of Covalent Bonding" from Further Readings
[63] "Benzene" 3-D Model from Instructor's Resource CD/DVD
[64] "Orbital Bartending" from Further Readings
[65] "Molecular Orbital Theory" Animation from Instructor's Resource CD/DVD
[66] "Molecular Orbital Theory of Bond Order and Valency" from Further Readings
[67] "The Eye's Photochemistry: A Quick Snap" from Further Readings
[68] "The Molecules of Visual Excitation" from Further Readings

- For example:
  - Why does O_2 interact with a magnetic field?
  - Why are some molecules colored?
- For these molecules, we use **molecular orbital theory**.
- Just as electrons in atoms are found in atomic orbitals, electrons in molecules are found in **molecular orbitals (MO)**.
- Molecular orbitals:
  - Some characteristics are similar to those of atomic orbitals.
    - Each contains a maximum of two electrons with opposite spins.
    - Each has a definite energy.
    - Electron density distribution can be visualized with contour diagrams.
  - However, unlike atomic orbitals, molecular orbitals are associated with an *entire molecule*.

The Hydrogen Molecule[69]

- When two AOs overlap, two MOs form.
- Therefore, $1s$ (H) + $1s$ (H) must result in two MOs for H_2:
  - One has electron density between the nuclei (**bonding MO**);
  - One has little electron density between the nuclei (**antibonding MO**).
- **Sigma (σ) MOs** have electron density in both molecular orbitals centered about the internuclear axis.
- The σ bonding MO is lower in energy than the σ^* (antibonding) MO.
- **The energy-level diagram** or **MO diagram** shows the energies of the orbitals in a molecule.
  - The total number of electrons in all atoms are placed in the MOs starting from lowest energy (σ_{1s}) and ending when all electrons have been accommodated.
  - Note that electrons in MOs have opposite spins.

Bond Order

- Define **bond order** = ½ (bonding electrons – antibonding electrons).
  - Bond order = 1 for single bond.
  - Bond order = 2 for double bond.
  - Bond order = 3 for triple bond.
    - Fractional bond orders are possible.
- For example, consider the molecule H_2.
  - H_2 has two bonding electrons.
  - Bond order for H_2 is:
    ½ (bonding electrons - antibonding electrons) = ½ (2 − 0) = 1.
  - Therefore, H_2 has a single bond.
- For example, consider the species He_2.
  - He_2 has two bonding electrons and two antibonding electrons.
  - Bond order for He_2 is:
    ½ (bonding electrons - antibonding electrons) = ½ (2 − 2) = 0.
  - Therefore He_2 is *not* a stable molecule.
- MO theory correctly predicts that hydrogen forms a diatomic molecule but that helium does not!

FORWARD REFERENCES
  - Molecular orbitals in silicon-containing materials will be mentioned in Chapter 12 (section 12.7).

----

[69] Figure 9.32 from Transparency Pack

9.8 Period 2 Diatomic Molecules

- We look at homonuclear diatomic molecules (e.g., Li_2, Be_2, B_2 etc.).
- AOs combine according to the following rules:
  - The number of MOs = number of AOs.
  - AOs of similar energy combine (e.g., $1s + 1s$ rather than $1s + 2s$).
  - As overlap increases, the energy of the bonding MO decreases and the energy of the antibonding MO increases.
  - Pauli: each MO has at most two electrons, with spins paired.
  - Hund: for degenerate orbitals, each MO is first occupied singly before spin pairing occurs.

Molecular Orbitals for Li_2 and Be_2[70]

- Each $1s$ orbital combines with another $1s$ orbital to give one σ_{1s} and one σ^*_{1s} orbital, both of which are occupied (since Li and Be have $1s^2$ electron configurations).
- Each $2s$ orbital combines with another $2s$ orbital to give one σ_{2s} and one σ^*_{2s} orbital.
- The energies of the $1s$ and $2s$ orbitals are sufficiently different so that there is no cross mixing of orbitals (i.e., we do not get $1s + 2s$).
- Consider the bonding in Li_2.
  - There are a total of six electrons in Li_2.
    - 2 electrons in σ_{1s}.
    - 2 electrons in σ^*_{1s}.
    - 2 electrons in σ_{2s}.
    - 0 electrons in σ^*_{2s}.
    - Therefore the bond order is ½ $(4 - 2) = 1$.
- Since the $1s$ AOs are completely filled, the σ_{1s} *and* σ^*_{1s} are filled.
  - We generally ignore core electrons in MO diagrams.
  - Core electrons usually don't contribute significantly to bonding in molecule formation.
- Consider bonding in Be_2.
  - There are a total of eight electrons in Be_2.
    - 2 electrons in σ_{1s}.
    - 2 electrons in σ^*_{1s}.
    - 2 electrons in σ_{2s}.
    - 2 electrons in σ^*_{2s}.
    - Therefore the bond order is ½ $(4 - 4) = 0$.
  - Be_2 does not exist.

Molecular Orbitals from $2p$ Atomic Orbitals[71]

- There are two ways in which two p orbitals can overlap:
  - End on so that the resulting MO has electron density on the axis between nuclei (i.e., σ type orbital).
  - Sideways, so that the resulting MO has electron density above and below the axis between nuclei.
    - These are called **pi (π) molecular orbitals**.
- The six p-orbitals (two sets of three) must give rise to six MOs:
  - σ_{2p}, σ_{2p}^*, π_{2p}, π_{2p}^*, π_{2p} and π_{2p}^*.
  - Therefore, there are a maximum of two π bonds which can come from p orbitals.
  - The relative energies of these six orbitals can change.

---

[70] Figure 9.35 from Transparency Pack
[71] Figure 9.36 from Transparency Pack

Electron Configurations for B₂ through Ne₂[72,73,74]

- Features of the energy-level diagrams for these elements:
  - $2s$ orbitals are lower in energy than $2p$ orbitals so both σ_{2s} orbitals (σ_{2s} and σ^*_{2s}) are lower in energy than the lowest energy MO derived from the $2p$ AOs.
  - There is greater overlap between $2p_z$ orbitals.
    - They point directly towards one another, so the σ_{2p} MO is lower in energy than the π_{2p} orbitals.
    - The σ^*_{2p} MO is higher in energy than the π^*_{2p} orbitals.
  - The π_{2p} and π^*_{2p} orbitals are doubly degenerate.
  - As the atomic number decreases, it becomes more likely that a $2s$ orbital on one atom can interact with the $2p$ orbital on the other.
  - As the $2s$–$2p$ interaction increases, the σ_{2s} MO lowers and the σ_{2p} MO increases in energy.
    - For B₂, C₂ and N₂ the σ_{2p} orbital is higher in energy than the π_{2p}.
    - For O₂, F₂ and Ne₂ the σ_{2p} orbital is lower in energy than the π_{2p}.
  - Once we know the relative orbital energies, we add the required number of electrons to the MOs, taking into account Pauli's exclusion principle and Hund's rule.
- As bond order increases,
  - bond length decreases.
  - bond energy increases.

Electron Configurations and Molecular Properties[75]

- Two types of magnetic behavior:
  - **paramagnetism** (unpaired electrons in molecule)
    - strong attraction between magnetic field and molecule
  - **diamagnetism** (no unpaired electrons in molecule)
    - weak repulsion between magnetic field and molecule
- Magnetic behavior is detected by determining the mass of a sample in the presence and absence of a magnetic field:
  - A large increase in mass indicates paramagnetism.
  - A small decrease in mass indicates diamagnetism.
- Experimentally, O₂ is paramagnetic, has a short bond length (1.21 Å) and high bond dissociation energy (495 kJ/mol).
  - The Lewis structure for O₂ shows no unpaired electrons.
  - The MO diagram for O₂ shows 2 unpaired electrons in the π^*_{2p} orbital.
    - This suggests a double bond.
    - The MO diagram for O₂ predicts both paramagnetism and the double bond (bond order = 2).

Heteronuclear Diatomic Molecules

- Heteronuclear diatomic molecules contain 2 different elements.
- If both atoms do not differ greatly in electronegativity, the description of their MOs will be similar to those for homonuclear diatomic molecules.

FORWARD REFERENCES
- The HOMO and LUMO gap will be mentioned in Chapter 12 (section 12.7).
- Magnetism in coordination chemistry will be discussed in Chapter 23 (section 23.5).

---

[72] Figure 9.41 from Transparency Pack
[73] Figure 9.42 from Transparency Pack
[74] "The Relative Energies of Molecular Orbitals for Second-Row Homonuclear Diatomic Molecules: The Effect of *s-p* Mixing" from Further Readings
[75] "Oxygen" 3-D Model from Instructor's Resource CD/DVD

Further Readings:

1. H. O. Desseyn, M. A. Herman, and J. Mullens, "Molecular Geometry," *J. Chem. Educ.*, Vol. 62, **1985**, 220–222.

2. Alan F. Lindmark, "Who Needs Lewis Structures To Get VSEPR Geometries?" *J. Chem. Educ.*, Vol. 87, **2010**, 487–491.

3. James P. Birk and Soraya Abbassian, "Teaching VSEPR: The Plastic Egg Model," *J. Chem. Educ.*, Vol. 73, **1996**, 636–637. The use of inexpensive models for teaching VSEPR is covered in this short article.

4. Ronald J. Gillespie, "Teaching Molecular Geometry with the VSEPR Model," *J. Chem. Educ.*, Vol. 81, **2004**, 298–304.

5. Ronald J. Gillespie, "Multiple Bonds and the VSEPR Model," *J. Chem. Educ.*, Vol. 69, **1992**, 116–121.

6. Brian W. Pfennig and Richard L. Frock, "The Use of Molecular Modeling and VSEPR Theory in the Undergraduate Curriculum to Predict the Three-Dimensional Structure of Molecules," *J. Chem. Educ.*, Vol. 76, **1999**, 1018–1022.

7. Gordon H. Purser, "Lewis Structures Are Models for Predicting Molecular Structure, *Not* Electronic Structure," *J. Chem. Educ.*, Vol. 76, **1999**, 1013–1017.

8. Carlos Furio and Ma. Luisa Calatayud, "Difficulties with the Geometry and Polarity of Molecules: Beyond Misconceptions," *J. Chem. Educ.*, Vol. 73, **1996**, 36–41.

9. Thomas H. Bindel and Timothy C. Smiley, "The Ropes: A Molecular Polarity Activity," *J. Chem. Educ.*, Vol. 71, **1994**, 945.

10. R. J. Tykodi, "Identifying Polar and Nonpolar Molecules," *J. Chem. Educ.*, Vol. 66, **1989**, 1007–1011.

11. Gordon H. Purser, "The Significance of the Bond Angle in Sulfur Dioxide," *J. Chem. Educ.*, Vol. 66, **1989**, 710–713.

12. Robert R. Perkins, "Put the Body to Them!" *J. Chem. Educ.*, Vol. 72, **1995**, 151–152. This reference includes an analogical demonstration of the concept of molecular polarity.

13. Ronald J. Gillespie, James N. Spencer and Richard S. Moog, "Demystifying Introductory Chemistry Part 2: Bonding and Molecular Geometry without Orbitals—The Electron-Domain Model," *J. Chem. Educ.*, Vol. 73, **1996**, 622–627.

14. Raymond F. Peterson and David F. Treagust, "Grade-12 Students' Misconceptions of Covalent Bonding and Structure," *J. Chem. Educ.*, Vol. 66, **1989**, 459–460.

15. D. W. Emerson, "A Colorful Demonstration to Simulate Orbital Hybridization," *J. Chem. Educ.*, Vol. 65, **1988**, 454.

16. Ronald Starkey, "Resonance Analogy Using Cartoon Characters," *J. Chem. Educ.*, Vol. 72, **1995**, 542.

17. Kenton B. Abel and William M. Hemmerlin, "Explaining Resonance—A Colorful Approach," *J. Chem. Educ.*, Vol. 8, **1991**, 834.

18. Francis Delvigne, "A Visual Aid for Teaching the Resonance Concept," *J. Chem. Educ.*, Vol. 66, **1989**, 461–462.

19. A. B. Sannigrahi and Tapas Kar, "Molecular Orbital Theory of Bond Order and Valency," *J. Chem. Educ.*, Vol. 65, **1988**, 674–676.

20. John Barbaro, "Orbital Bartending," *J. Chem. Educ.*, Vol. 71, **1994**, 1012. An analogy for orbital hybridization is suggested in this short article.

21. Albert Haim, "The Relative Energies of Molecular Orbitals for Second-Row Homonuclear Diatomic Molecules: The Effect of *s-p* Mixing," *J. Chem. Educ.*, Vol. 68, **1991**, 737–738.

22. Lubert Stryer, "The Molecules of Visual Excitation," *Scientific American*, Vol. 255 (7), **1987**, 42–50.

23. Sture Nordholm, "Delocalization---The Key Concept of Covalent Bonding," *J. Chem. Educ.*, Vol. 65, **1988**, 581–584.

24. Todd P. Silverstein, "The 'Big Dog-Puppy Dog' Analogy for Resonance," *J. Chem. Educ.*, Vol. 76, **1999**, 206–208.

25. Sara N. Mendiara and Luis J. Perissionotti, "Tetrahedral Geometry and the Dipole Moment of Molecules," *J. Chem. Educ.*, Vol. 79, **2002**, 64–66.

Live Demonstrations:

1. Lee. R. Summerlin, Christie L. Borgford, and Julie B. Ealy, "Bending a Stream of Water," *Chemical Demonstrations, A Sourcebook for Teachers, Volume 2* (Washington: American Chemical Society, **1988**), p. 91. The polarity of water and cyclohexane are compared in this demonstration.

Chapter 10. Gases

Media Resources

Figures and Tables in Transparency Pack: **Section:**
Figure 10.1 Calculating Atmospheric Pressure   10.2 Pressure
Figure 10.2 A Mercury Barometer   10.2 Pressure
Figure 10.3 A Mercury Manometer   10.2 Pressure
Figure 10.7 Boyle's Law   10.3 The Gas Laws
Figure 10.11 Comparison of Molar Volumes at STP   10.4 The Ideal-Gas Equation
Figure 10.17 Distribution of Molecular Speeds for   10.7 Kinetic-Molecular Theory of Gases
    Nitrogen Gas
Figure 10.18 The Effect of Molecular Mass on   10.8 Molecular Effusion and Diffusion
    Molecular Speed at 25 °C.
Figure 10.22 The Effect of Pressure on the Behavior 10.9 Real Gases: Deviations from Ideal Behavior
    of Several Real Gases
Figure 10.23 The Effect of Temperature and Pressure 10.9 Real Gases: Deviations from Ideal Behavior
    on the Behavior of Nitrogen Gas

Activities: **Section:**
Manometer   10.2 Pressure
Gas Laws   10.3 Gas Laws
Density of Gases   10.5 Further Applications of the Ideal-Gas
                                                        Equation
Partial Pressures   10.6 Gas Mixtures and Partial Pressures
Motions of a Gas   10.7 Kinetic-Molecular Theory of Gases
Gas Phase: Boltzmann Distribution   10.7 Kinetic-Molecular Theory of Gases
Gas Diffusion and Effusion   10.8 Molecular Effusion and Diffusion
Nonideal Gas Behavior   10.9 Real Gases: Deviations from Ideal Behavior

Animations: **Section:**
P-V Relationships   10.3 The Gas Laws
Airbags   10.5 Further Applications of the Ideal-Gas
                                                        Equation
Kinetic Energy of a Gas   10.7 Kinetic-Molecular Theory of Gases

Movies: **Section:**
Diffusion of Bromine Vapor   10.8 Molecular Effusion and Diffusion

3-D Molecules: **Section:**
Nitrogen   10.7 Kinetic-Molecular Theory of Gases

Other Resources

Further Readings:
Gases and Their Behavior
Carbon Dioxide Flooding: A Classroom Case Study
    Derived from Surgical Practice
Gay-Lussac: Chemist Extraordinary
Gay-Lussac after 200 Years
The Chemistry behind the Air Bag

Chemistry of Air Bags

Cinema, Flirts, Snakes, and Gases
Toy Flying Saucers and Molecular Speeds

Section:
10.1 Characteristics of Gases
10.1 Characteristics of Gases

10.4 The Ideal-Gas Equation
10.4 The Ideal-Gas Equation
10.5 Further Applications of the Ideal-Gas
    Equation
10.5 Further Applications of the Ideal-Gas
    Equation
10.7 Kinetic-Molecular Theory of Gases
10.7 Kinetic-Molecular Theory of Gases

Live Demonstrations:
Boiling at Reduced Pressure
Boyle's Law
Boyle's Law and the Monster Marshmallow
Robert Boyle: The Founder of Modern Chemistry
Boyle's Law and the Mass of a Textbook
Effect of Pressure on the Size of a Balloon
Thermal Expansion of Gases
Charles' Law of Gases: A Simple Experimental
    Demonstration
Charles' Law: The Relationship between Volume
    and Temperature of a Gas
Collapsing Can
Determining the Molecular Weight of a Gas
Diffusion of Gases
Overhead Projection of Graham's Law of Gaseous
    Diffusion
Relative Velocity of Sound Propagation: Musical
    Molecular Weights

Section:
10.2 Pressure
10.3 The Gas Laws
10.3 The Gas Laws
10.3 The Gas Laws
10.3 The Gas Laws
10.3 The Gas Laws
10.3 The Gas Laws
10.3 The Gas Laws

10.3 The Gas Laws

10.4 The Ideal-Gas Equation
10.6 Gas Mixtures and Partial Pressures
10.8 Molecular Effusion and Diffusion
10.8 Molecular Effusion and Diffusion

10.8 Molecular Effusion and Diffusion

Chapter 10. Gases

Common Student Misconceptions

- Students need to be told to *always* use temperature in Kelvin in gas problems.
- Due to several systems of units, students often use ideal gas constants with units inconsistent with values.
- Students often confuse the standard conditions for gas behavior (STP) with the standard conditions in thermodynamics.
- Ideal gas behavior should discussed as just that, *ideal*; students should be reminded that real gases do not behave ideally, especially at high pressures and/or low temperatures.
- Students expect a change in the gas particle distribution upon temperature changes at constant *V*.
- Students commonly confuse effusion and diffusion.

Teaching Tips

- Students should always use units in gas-law problems to keep track of required conversions. Encourage them to use dimensional analysis to detect conversion errors.
- Students may be used to seeing densities given in units of g/mL; this is the case for liquids and solids. The densities of gases are usually expressed in g/L.
- It is helpful to remind students that the sum of the mole fractions of a mixture must equal 1, i.e., $\Sigma X_i = 1$.

Lecture Outline

10.1 Characteristics of Gases[1,2]

- All substances have three phases: solid, liquid and gas.
- Substances that are liquids or solids under ordinary conditions may also exist as gases.
  - These are often referred to as **vapors**.
- Many of the properties of gases differ from those of solids and liquids:
  - Gases are highly compressible and occupy the full volume of their containers.
  - When a gas is subjected to pressure, its volume decreases.
  - Gases always form homogeneous mixtures with other gases.
- Gases only occupy a small fraction of the volume of their containers.
  - As a result, each molecule of gas behaves largely as though other molecules were absent.

FORWARD REFERENCES
  - Thermodynamics of phase changes will be discussed in Chapter 19.
  - Such important gaseous reactions as the Haber process or equilibria involving nitrogen oxides will be covered in Chapter 15.

10.2 Pressure

- **Pressure** is the force acting on an object per unit area:

$$P = \frac{F}{A}$$

---

[1] "Gases and Their Behavior" from Further Readings

Atmospheric Pressure and the Barometer[3,4,5,6,7]

- The SI unit of force is the *newton* (N).
  - $1 \text{ N} = 1 \text{ kg-m/s}^2$
- The SI unit of pressure is the **pascal** (Pa).
  - $1 \text{ Pa} = 1 \text{ N/m}^2$
  - A related unit is the **bar,** which is equal to 10^5 Pa.
  - Another pressure unit is pounds per square inch (psi, lbs/in^2).
- Gravity exerts a force on the Earth's atmosphere.
  - A column of air 1 m^2 in cross section extending to the upper atmosphere exerts a force of 10^5 N.
  - Thus, the pressure of a 1 m^2 column of air extending to the upper atmosphere is 100 kPa.
    - Atmospheric pressure at sea level is about 100 kPa or 1 bar or 14.7 psi.
    - The actual atmospheric pressure at a specific location depends on the altitude and weather conditions.
- Atmospheric pressure is measured with a *barometer*.
  - If a tube is completely filled with mercury and then inverted into a container of mercury open to the atmosphere, the mercury will rise 760 mm up the tube.
  - **Standard atmospheric pressure** is the pressure required to support 760 mm of Hg in a column.
  - Important non-SI units used to express gas pressure include:
    - **atmospheres** (atm)
    - *millimeter of mercury* (mm Hg) or **torr**
    - $1 \text{ atm} = 760 \text{ mm Hg} = 760 \text{ torr} = 1.01325 \times 10^5 \text{ Pa} = 101.325 \text{ kPa} = 1.01325 \text{ bar}$.
- The pressure of enclosed gases is measured with a *manometer*.

FORWARD REFERENCES

- Osmotic pressure (in atm) will be calculated in Chapter 13 (section 13.5).
- K_p's and thermodynamic equilibrium constants in Chapter 15 will use pressure (in atm).
- Pressure and Le Châtelier's principle will be discussed in Chapter 15 (section 15.7).

10.3 The Gas Laws

- The equations that express the relationships among T (temperature), P (pressure), V (volume), and n (number of moles of gas) are known as *gas laws*.

The Pressure-Volume Relationship: Boyle's Law[8,9,10,11,12,13]

- Weather balloons are used as a practical application of the relationship between pressure and volume of a gas.
  - As the weather balloon ascends, the volume increases.
  - As the weather balloon gets further from Earth's surface, the atmospheric pressure decreases.

---

[2] "Carbon Dioxide Flooding: A Classroom Case Study Derived from Surgical Practice" from Further Readings
[3] Figure 10.1 from Transparency Pack
[4] Figure 10.2 from Transparency Pack
[5] "Boiling at Reduced Pressure" from Live Demonstrations
[6] "Manometer" Activity from Instructor's Resource CD/DVD
[7] Figure 10.3 from Transparency Pack
[8] "Boyle's Law" from Live Demonstrations
[9] "Boyle's Law and the Monster Marshmallow" from Live Demonstrations
[10] "Robert Boyle: The Founder of Modern Chemistry" from Live Demonstrations
[11] Figure 10.7 from Transparency Pack
[12] "Boyle's Law and the Mass of a Textbook" from Live Demonstrations
[13] "P-V Relationships" Animation from Instructor's Resource CD/DVD

- **Boyle's law**: The volume of a fixed quantity of gas, at constant temperature, is inversely proportional to its pressure.
- Mathematically:

$$V = \text{constant} \times \frac{1}{P} \text{ or } PV = \text{constant}$$

- A plot of V versus P is a hyperbola.
- A plot of V versus $1/P$ must be a straight line passing through the origin.
- The working of the lungs illustrates Boyle's law.
  - As we breathe in, the diaphragm moves down, and the ribs expand; therefore, the volume of the lungs increases.
  - According to Boyle's law, when the volume of the lungs increases, the pressure decreases; therefore, the pressure inside the lungs is less than atmospheric pressure.
  - Atmospheric pressure then forces air into the lungs until the pressure once again equals atmospheric pressure.
  - As we breathe out, the diaphragm moves up and the ribs contract. Therefore, the volume of the lungs decreases.
  - By Boyle's law, the pressure increases and air is forced out.

The Temperature-Volume Relationship: Charles's Law[14,15,16]

- We know that hot-air balloons expand when they are heated.
- **Charles's law**: The volume of a fixed quantity of gas at constant pressure is directly proportional to its absolute temperature.
- Mathematically:

$$V = \text{constant} \times T \text{ or } \frac{V}{T} = \text{constant}$$

- Note that the value of the constant depends on the pressure and number of moles of gas.
- A plot of V versus T is a straight line.
- When T is measured in °C, the intercept on the temperature axis is –273.15 °C.
- We define *absolute zero*, 0 K = –273.15 °C.

The Quantity-Volume Relationship: Avogadro's Law[17,18]

- Gay-Lussac's *law of combining volumes*: At a given temperature and pressure the volumes of gases that react with one another are ratios of small whole numbers.
- **Avogadro's hypothesis**: Equal volumes of gases at the same temperature and pressure contain the same number of molecules.
- **Avogadro's law**: The volume of gas at a given temperature and pressure is directly proportional to the number of moles of gas.
  - Mathematically:
$$V = \text{constant} \times n$$
  - We can show that 22.4 L of any gas at 0 °C and 1 atmosphere contains 6.02×10^{23} gas molecules.

FORWARD REFERENCES
- Vapor pressure vs. temperature will be discussed in Chapter 13 (section 13.5).

---

[14] "Effect of Pressure on the Size of a Balloon" from Live Demonstrations
[15] "Charles' Law of Gases" from Live Demonstrations
[16] "Charles' Law: The Relationship Between Volume and Temperature of a Gas" from Live Demonstrations
[17] "Thermal Expansion of Gases" from Live Demonstrations
[18] "Gas Laws" Activity from Instructor's Resource CD/DVD

- Increasing entropy of gases with temperature as well as entropy of gases vs. other states of matter will be discussed in Chapter 19 (section 19.3).

10.4 The Ideal-Gas Equation[19,20,21,22]

- Summarizing the gas laws:
  - Boyle: $V \propto 1/P$ (constant n, T)
  - Charles: $V \propto T$ (constant n, P)
  - Avogadro: $V \propto n$ (constant P, T)
  - Combined: $V \propto nT/P$
- **Ideal-gas equation** or **ideal-gas law**: $PV = nRT$
  - An **ideal gas** is a hypothetical gas whose P, V, and T behavior is completely described by the ideal-gas equation.
  - R = **gas constant** = 0.08206 L-atm/mol-K
    - Other numerical values of R in various units are given in Table 10.2.
- Define **STP (standard temperature and pressure)** = 0 °C, 273.15 K, 1 atm.
  - The molar volume of 1 mol of an ideal gas at STP is 22.41 L.

Relating the Ideal-Gas Equation and the Gas Laws

- If $PV = nRT$ and n and T are constant, then PV is constant and we have Boyle's law.
  - Other laws can be generated similarly.
- In general, if we have a gas under two sets of conditions, then

$$\frac{P_1 V_1}{n_1 T_1} = \frac{P_2 V_2}{n_2 T_2}$$

- We often have a situation in which P, V, and T all change for a fixed number of moles of gas.
  - For this set of circumstances,

$$\frac{PV}{T} = nR = \text{constant}$$

  - Which gives the *combined gas law*.

$$\frac{P_1 V_1}{T_1} = \frac{P_2 V_2}{T_2}$$

FORWARD REFERENCES
- The ideal gas constant will be used in Chapter 14 in the Arrhenius equation (section 14.5).
- The ideal gas constant will be used in Chapter 15 in conversions between K_c and K_p (section 15.2) and to relate Gibbs free energy with the equilibrium constant in Chapter 19 (section 19.7) as well as with the cell potentials in Chapter 20 (sections 20.5 and 20.6).

10.5 Further Applications of the Ideal-Gas Equation

Gas Densities and Molar Mass[23]

- Density has units of mass over volume.

---

[19] "Gay-Lussac: Chemist Extraordinary" from Further Readings
[20] "Gay-Lussac after 200 Years" from Further Readings
[21] "Collapsing Can" from Live Demonstrations
[22] Figure 10.11 from Transparency Pack
[23] "Density of Gases" Activity from Instructor's Resource CD/DVD

- Rearranging the ideal-gas equation with M as molar mass we get

$$\frac{n}{V} = \frac{P}{RT}$$

$$\frac{nM}{V} = \frac{PM}{RT}$$

$$\therefore d = \frac{nM}{V} = \frac{PM}{RT}$$

- The molar mass of a gas can be determined as follows:

$$M = \frac{dRT}{P}$$

Volumes of Gases in Chemical Reactions[24,25,26]
- The ideal-gas equation relates P, V, and T to number of moles of gas.
- The n can then be used in stoichiometric calculations.

FORWARD REFERENCES
- Solubility of gases vs. temperature (Henry's law) will be covered in Chapter 13 (section 13.3).

10.6 Gas Mixtures and Partial Pressures[27]
- Since gas molecules are so far apart, we can assume they behave independently.
- Dalton observed:
  - The total pressure of a mixture of gases equals the sum of the pressures that each would exert if present alone.
  - **Partial pressure** is the pressure exerted by a particular component of a gas mixture.
- **Dalton's law of partial pressures**: In a gas mixture the total pressure is given by the sum of partial pressures of each component:

$$P_t = P_1 + P_2 + P_3 + \ldots$$

- Each gas obeys the ideal gas equation.
  - Thus,

$$P_t = (n_1 + n_2 + n_3 + \cdots)\frac{RT}{V} = n_t \frac{RT}{V}$$

Partial Pressures and Mole Fractions
- Let n_1 be the number of moles of gas 1 exerting a partial pressure P_1, then

$$P_1 = X_1 P_t$$

  - Where X_1 is the **mole fraction** (n_1/n_t).
  - Note that a mole fraction is a dimensionless number.

Collecting Gases over Water[28]
- It is common to synthesize gases and collect them by displacing a volume of water.

---

[24] "The Chemistry Behind the Air Bag" from Further Readings
[25] "The Chemistry of Air Bags" from Further Readings
[26] "Air Bags" Animation from Instructor's Resource CD/DVD
[27] "Partial Pressures" Activity from Instructor's Resource CD/DVD
[28] "Determining the Molecular Weight of a Gas" from Live Demonstrations

- To calculate the amount of gas produced, we need to correct for the partial pressure of the water:

$$P_{\text{total}} = P_{\text{gas}} + P_{\text{water}}$$

- The vapor pressure of water varies with temperature.
  - Values can be found in Appendix B.

FORWARD REFERENCES
- Vapor pressure, volatility, and temperature relationships will be introduced in Chapter 11 (section 11.5) and further applied to Raoult's Law in Chapter 13 (section 13.5).
- Air – a mixture of gases – will be discussed in Chapter 18 (section 18.1) and 22 (section 22.7).

10.7 Kinetic-Molecular Theory of Gases[29,30,31,32,33,34]

- The **kinetic molecular theory of gases** was developed to *explain* gas behavior.
  - It is a theory of moving molecules.
- Summary:
  - 1. Gases consist of a large number of molecules in constant random motion.
  - 2. The combined volume of all the molecules is negligible compared with the volume of the container.
  - 3. Intermolecular forces (forces between gas molecules) are negligible.
    - Energy can be transferred between molecules during collisions, but the average kinetic energy is constant at constant temperature.
  - 4. Energy can be transferred between molecules during collisions but, as long as the temperature remains constant, the *average* kinetic energy of the molecules does not change with time (the collisions are perfectly elastic.
  - 5. The average kinetic energy of the gas molecules is proportional to the absolute temperature.
- Kinetic molecular theory gives us an *understanding* of pressure and temperature on the molecular level.
  - The pressure of a gas results from the collisions with the walls of the container.
  - The magnitude of the pressure is determined by how often and how hard the molecules strike.
- The absolute temperature of a gas is a measure of the average kinetic energy.
  - Some molecules will have less kinetic energy or more kinetic energy than the average (distribution).
    - There is a spread of individual energies of gas molecules in any sample of gas.
    - As the temperature increases, the average kinetic energy of the gas molecules increases.

Distributions of Molecular Speed[35]
- As kinetic energy increases, the velocity of the gas molecules increases.
  - **Root-mean-square (rms) speed**, u_{rms}, is the speed of a gas molecule having average kinetic energy.
- Average kinetic energy, ε, is related to rms speed:

$$\varepsilon = \tfrac{1}{2}\,mu^2$$

  - where m = mass of the molecule.

---

[29] "Cinema, Flirts, Snakes, and Gases" from Further Readings
[30] "Kinetic Energy of a Gas" Animation from Instructor's Resource CD/DVD
[31] "Motions of a Gas" Activity from Instructor's Resource CD/DVD
[32] Figure 10.17 from Transparency Pack
[33] "Gas Phase: Boltzmann Distribution" Activity from Instructor's Resource CD/DVD
[34] "Toy Flying Saucers and Molecular Speeds" from Further Readings
[35] "Nitrogen" 3-D Model from Instructor's Resource CD/DVD

Application of Kinetic-Molecular Theory to the Gas-Laws

- We can understand empirical observations of gas properties within the framework of the kinetic-molecular theory.
- *Effect of an increase in volume (at constant temperature):*
  - As volume increases at constant temperature, the average kinetic of the gas remains constant.
  - Therefore, u is constant.
  - However, volume increases, so the gas molecules have to travel further to hit the walls of the container.
  - Therefore, pressure decreases.
- *Effect of an increase in temperature (at constant volume):*
  - If temperature increases at constant volume, the average kinetic energy of the gas molecules increases.
  - There are more collisions with the container walls.
  - Therefore, u increases.
  - The change in momentum in each collision increases (molecules strike harder).
  - Therefore, pressure increases.

FORWARD REFERENCES
- The collision model in Chapter 14 (section 14.5) will be based on the kinetic-molecular theory.

10.8 Molecular Effusion and Diffusion[36,37]

- The average kinetic energy of a gas is related to its mass:

$$\varepsilon = \tfrac{1}{2}\, mu^2$$

- Consider two gases at the same temperature: the lighter gas has a higher rms speed than the heavier gas.
  - Mathematically:

$$u_{rms} = \sqrt{\frac{3RT}{M}}$$

  - The lower the molar mass, M, the higher the rms speed for that gas at a constant temperature.
- Two consequences of the dependence of molecular speeds on mass are:
  - **Effusion** is the escape of gas molecules through a tiny hole into an evacuated space.
  - **Diffusion** is the spread of one substance throughout a space or throughout a second substance.

Graham's Law of Effusion[38,39]

- The rate of effusion can be quantified.
- Consider two gases with molar masses M_1 and M_2, with effusion rates, r_1 and r_2, respectively:
  - The relative rate of effusion is given by **Graham's law**:

$$\frac{r_1}{r_2} = \sqrt{\frac{M_2}{M_1}}$$

  - Only those molecules that hit the small hole will escape through it.
  - Therefore, the higher the rms speed, the more likely that a gas molecule will hit the hole.

---

[36] Figure 10.18 from Transparency Pack
[37] "Diffusion of Gases" from Live Demonstrations
[38] "Gas Diffusion and Effusion" Activity from Instructor's Resource CD/DVD
[39] "Overhead Projection of Graham's Law of Gaseous Diffusion" from Live Demonstrations

- We can show that:

$$\frac{r_1}{r_2} = \frac{u_1}{u_2} = \sqrt{\frac{3RT/M_1}{3RT/M_2}} = \sqrt{\frac{M_2}{M_1}}$$

Diffusion and Mean Free Path[40,41]

- Diffusion is faster for light gas molecules.
- Diffusion is significantly slower than the rms speed.
  - Diffusion is slowed by collisions of gas molecules with one another.
  - Consider someone opening a perfume bottle: It takes awhile to detect the odor, but the average speed of the molecules at 25 °C is about 515 m/s (1150 mi/hr).
- The average distance traveled by a gas molecule between collisions is called the **mean free path**.
- At sea level, the mean free path for air molecules is about 6×10^{-6} cm.

FORWARD REFERENCES
  - Similar molar mass related issues (e.g., passing of particles of solute through semipermeable membranes) for solutions will be discussed in Chapter 13 (section 13.5).

10.9 Real Gases: Deviations from Ideal Behavior[42,43]

- From the ideal gas equation:

$$\frac{PV}{RT} = n$$

- For 1 mol of an ideal gas, $PV/RT = 1$ for all pressures.
  - In a real gas, PV/RT varies from 1 significantly.
  - The higher the pressure, the more the deviation from ideal behavior.
- For 1 mol of an ideal gas, $PV/RT = 1$ for all temperatures.
  - As temperature increases, the gases behave more ideally.
- The assumptions in the kinetic-molecular theory show where ideal gas behavior breaks down:
  - The molecules of a gas *have* finite volume.
  - Molecules of a gas *do* attract each other.
- As the pressure on a gas increases, the molecules are forced closer together.
  - As the molecules get closer together, the free space in which the molecules can move gets smaller.
  - The smaller the container, the more of the total space the gas molecules occupy.
  - Therefore, the higher the pressure, the less the gas resembles an ideal gas.
  - As the gas molecules get closer together, the intermolecular distances decrease.
  - The smaller the distance between gas molecules, the more likely that attractive forces will develop between the molecules.
  - Therefore, the less the gas resembles an ideal gas.
- As temperature increases, the gas molecules move faster and further apart.
  - Also, higher temperatures mean more energy available to break intermolecular forces.
  - As temperature increases, the negative departure from ideal-gas behavior disappears.

---

[40] "Diffusion of Bromine Vapor" Movie from Instructor's Resource CD/DVD
[41] "Relative Velocity of Sound Propagation: Musical Molecular Weights" from Live Demonstrations
[42] Figure 10.22 from Transparency Pack
[43] Figure 10.23 from Transparency Pack

The van der Waals Equation[44]

- We add two terms to the ideal gas equation to correct for
  - The volume of molecules: $(V - nb)$

  - For molecular attractions:

  $$\left(\frac{n^2 a}{V^2}\right)$$

    - The correction terms generate the **van der Waals equation**:

    $$\left(P + \frac{n^2 a}{V^2}\right)(V - nb) = nRT$$

      - where a and b are empirical constants (van der Waals constants) that differ for each gas.
      - van der Waals constants for some common gases can be found in Table 10.3.
- To understand the effect of intermolecular forces on pressure, consider a molecule that is about to strike the wall of the container.
  - The striking molecule is attracted by neighboring molecules.
  - Therefore, the impact on the wall is lessened.

FORWARD REFERENCES
  - The name of van der Waals will come up again in Chapter 11 for van der Waals forces.

---

[44] "Nonideal Gas Behavior" Activity from Instructor's Resource CD/DVD

Further Readings:

1. Joseph S. Schmuckler, "Gases and Their Behavior," *J. Chem. Educ.*, Vol. 57, **1980**, 885. A collection of gas law references from past editions of the *Journal of Chemical Education*

2. Robert C. Kerber, "Carbon Dioxide Flooding: A Classroom Case Study Derived from Surgical Practice," *J. Chem. Educ.*, Vol. 80, **2003**, 1437–1438.

3. R. P. Graham, "Gay-Lussac: Chemist Extraordinary," *J. Chem. Educ.*, Vol. 58, **1981**, 789.

4. Harold Goldwhite, "Gay-Lussac after 200 Years," *J. Chem. Educ.*, Vol. 55, **1978**, 366–368.

5. Andreas Madlung, "The Chemistry Behind the Air Bag," *J. Chem. Educ.*, Vol. 73, **1996**, 347–348.

6. William L. Bell, "Chemistry of Air Bags," *J. Chem. Educ.*, Vol. 67, **1990**, 61.

7. Dacio R. Hartwig and Romeu C. Rocha Filho, "Cinema, Flirts, Snakes, and Gases," *J. Chem. Educ.*, Vol. 59, **1982**, 295. The kinetic theory of gases is explored with an analogy in this short reference.

8. Reggie L. Hudson, "Toy Flying Saucers and Molecular Speeds," *J. Chem. Educ.*, Vol. 59, **1982**, 1025–1026. An analogy for molecular speed distributions features a common toy: the Frisbee®.

Live Demonstrations:

1. Lee R. Summerlin, Christie L. Borgford and Julie B. Ealy, "Boiling at Reduced Pressure," *Chemical Demonstrations, A Sourcebook for Teachers, Volume 2* (Washington: American Chemical Society, **1988**), pp 24-25. The volume of a gas-filled balloon is changed by immersion in an ice bath or a warm water bath in this demonstration of Charles's Law.

2. Rick Broniec, "Boyle's Law and the Monster Marshmallow," *J. Chem. Educ.*, Vol. 59, **1982**, 974. A quick demonstration of Boyle's law.

3. Kathryn R. Williams, "Robert Boyle: The Founder of Modern Chemistry," *J. Chem. Educ.*, Vol. 86, **2010**, 148-149.

4. Bassam Z. Shakhashiri, "Effect of Pressure on the Size of a Balloon", *Chemical Demonstrations: A Handbook for Teachers of Chemistry, Volume 2* (Madison: The University of Wisconsin Press, **1985**), pp. 12–13.

5. Bassam Z. Shakhashiri, "Boyle's Law and the Mass of a Textbook," *Chemical Demonstrations: A Handbook for Teachers of Chemistry, Volume 2* (Madison: The University of Wisconsin Press, **1985**), pp. 20–23.

6. Bassam Z. Shakhashiri, "Boyle's Law," *Chemical Demonstrations: A Handbook for Teachers of Chemistry, Volume 2* (Madison: The University of Wisconsin Press, **1985**), pp. 14–19. The relationship between gas pressure and volume at constant temperature is explored.

7. Bassam Z. Shakhashiri, "Thermal Expansion of Gases," *Chemical Demonstrations: A Handbook for Teachers of Chemistry, Volume 2* (Madison: The University of Wisconsin Press, **1985**), pp. 24–27.

8. John T. Petty, "Charles' Law of Gases: A Simple Experimental Demonstration," *J. Chem. Educ*, Vol. 72, **1995**, 257. A short demonstration of Charles's Law.

9. Lee R. Summerlin, Christie L. Borgford, and Julie B. Ealy, "Charles' Law: The Relationship Between Volume and Temperature of a Gas," *Chemical Demonstrations, A Sourcebook for Teachers, Volume 2* (Washington: American Chemical Society, **1988**), p. 23. The volume of a gas-filled balloon is changed by immersion in an ice bath or a warm water bath in this demonstration of Charles's Law.

10. Bassam Z. Shakhashiri, "Collapsing Can", *Chemical Demonstrations: A Handbook for Teachers of Chemistry, Volume 2* (Madison: The University of Wisconsin Press, **1985**), pp. 6–8.

11. Lee R. Summerlin and James L. Ealy, Jr., "Determining the Molecular Weight of a Gas," *Chemical Demonstrations, A Sourcebook for Teachers, Volume 1, 2nd edition* (Washington: American Chemical Society, **1988**), pp. 19–20. The molar mass of butane is determined from its mass and the volume of water it displaces.

12. Lee R. Summerlin and James L. Ealy, Jr., "Diffusion of Gases," *Chemical Demonstrations, A Sourcebook for Teachers, Volume 1, 2nd edition* (Washington: American Chemical Society, **1988**), pp. 14–15. Graham's Law is checked by timing color changes in pH paper caused by $HCl(g)$ or $NH_3(g)$.

13. Dianne N. Epp. "Overhead Projection of Graham's Law of Gaseous Diffusion," *J. Chem. Educ.*, Vol. 67, **1990**, 1061. $HCl(g)$ or $NH_3(g)$ are used in this demonstration of Graham's Law.

14. Bassam Z. Shakhashiri, "Relative Velocity of Sound Propagation: Musical Molecular Weights," *Chemical Demonstrations: A Handbook for Teachers of Chemistry, Volume 2* (Madison: The University of Wisconsin Press, **1985**), pp. 88–89. The relationship between the pitch of a pipe organ and the molar mass of gas passed through it is explored.

Chapter 11. Liquids and Intermolecular Forces

Media Resources

Figures and Tables in Transparency Pack:	Section:
Figure 11.2 Gases, Liquids, and Solids	11.1 A Molecular Comparison of Gases, Liquids, and Solids
Figure 11.4 Dispersion Forces	11.2 Intermolecular Forces
Figure 11.6 Molecular Shape Affects Intermolecular Attraction	11.2 Intermolecular Forces
Figure 11.9 Boiling Points of the Covalent Hydrides of the Elements in Groups 4A-7A as a Function of Molecular Weight	11.2 Intermolecular Forces
Figure 11.10 Hydrogen Bonding	11.2 Intermolecular Forces
Figure 11.14 Flowchart for Determining Intermolecular Forces	11.2 Intermolecular Forces
Figure 11.20 Phase Changes and the Names Associated with Them	11.4 Phase Changes
Figure 11.22 Heating Curve for Water	11.4 Phase Changes
Figure 11.25 Vapor Pressure for Four Liquids as a Function of Temperature	11.5 Vapor Pressure
Figure 11.27 Generic Phase Diagram for a Pure Substance	11.6 Phase Diagrams
Figure 11.28 Phase Diagram of H_2O	11.6 Phase Diagrams
Figure 11.32 Molecular Order in Nematic and Smectic Liquid Crystals	11.7 Liquid Crystals
Figure 11.33 Molecular Structure and Liquid Crystal Temperature Range for Two Typical Liquid Crystalline Materials	11.7 Liquid Crystals
Figure 11.36 Schematic Illustration of the Operation of a Twisted Nematic Liquid Crystal Display (LCD)	11.7 Liquid Crystals

Activities:	Section:
Phases of Matter	11.1 A Molecular Comparison of Gases, Liquids, and Solids
Hydrogen Bonding in Water	11.2 Intermolecular Forces
Intermolecular Forces	11.2 Intermolecular Forces
Heating Curves	11.4 Phase Changes
Equilibrium Vapor Pressure	11.5 Vapor Pressure
Boltzmann Distribution	11.5 Vapor Pressure
Phase Diagram	11.6 Phase Diagrams

Animations:	Section:
Hydrogen Bonding	11.2 Intermolecular Forces
Changes of State	11.4 Phase Changes
Vapor Pressure versus Temperature	11.5 Vapor Pressure
Phase Diagram of Water	11.6 Phase Diagrams

Movies:	Section:
Physical Properties of the Halogens	11.1 A Molecular Comparison of Gases, Liquids,

3-D Models:

and Solids

Section:

Chlorine	11.1 A Molecular Comparison of Gases, Liquids, and Solids
Bromine	11.1 A Molecular Comparison of Gases, Liquids, and Solids
Iodine	11.1 A Molecular Comparison of Gases, Liquids, and Solids
Fluorine	11.1 A Molecular Comparison of Gases, Liquids, and Solids
Hydrogen Chloride	11.2 Intermolecular Forces
Hydrogen Fluoride	11.2 Intermolecular Forces
Pentane	11.2 Intermolecular Forces
Neopentane (dimethylpropane)	11.2 Intermolecular Forces
Acetonitrile	11.2 Intermolecular Forces
Propane	11.2 Intermolecular Forces
Dimethyl Ether	11.2 Intermolecular Forces
Acetaldehyde	11.2 Intermolecular Forces
Ice	11.2 Intermolecular Forces
Water	11.2 Intermolecular Forces
Ammonia	11.2 Intermolecular Forces
Methane	11.2 Intermolecular Forces
Acetic Acid	11.2 Intermolecular Forces
1-Propanol	11.2 Intermolecular Forces
2-Propanol	11.2 Intermolecular Forces
Ethyl Methyl Ether	11.2 Intermolecular Forces
Sulfur Dioxide	11.2 Intermolecular Forces
Methylpropane (isobutane)	11.2 Intermolecular Forces
1,2,3-Ethanetriol (glycerol)	11.3 Intermolecular Forces
Butane	11.4 Phase Changes

Other Resources

Further Readings:

Section:

Pictorial Analogies I: States of Matter	11.1 A Molecular Comparison of Gases, Liquids, and Solids
Molecular Handshake: Recognition through Weak Noncovalent Interactions	11.2 Intermolecular Forces
Put the Body to Them!	11.2 Intermolecular Forces
Students as Solids, Liquids, and Gases	11.2 Intermolecular Forces
Solving the Mystery of Fading Fingerprints with London-Dispersion Forces	
London-Dispersion Forces and 'The Wave'	11.2 Intermolecular Forces
A People-and-Velcro Model for Hydrogen Bonding	11.2 Intermolecular Forces
Tears of Wine	11.3 Select Properties of Liquids
Why do Alcoholic Beverages Have 'Legs'?	11.3 Select Properties of Liquids
Past, Present, and Possible Future Applications of Supercritical Fluid Extraction Technology	11.4 Phase Changes
Supercritical Chemistry: Synthesis with a Spanner	11.6 Phase Diagrams
Journey Around a Phase Diagram	11.6 Phase Diagrams
There is No Perceptible Inflection at the Triple Point	11.6 Phase Diagrams

Liquid Crystal Inquiries: Add a New Phase to Your Curriculum	11.7 Liquid Crystals
Liquid Crystals Display New Potential	11.7 Liquid Crystals
Preparation and Properties of Cholesteric Liquid Crystals	11.7 Liquid Crystals
OLEDs Set to Glow	11.7 Liquid Crystals
Shining Examples	11.7 Liquid Crystals

Live Demonstrations: **Section:**

Dancing Crystals: A Dramatic Illustration of Intermolecular Forces	11.2 Intermolecular Forces
Viscosity Races	11.3 Select Properties of Liquids
Surface Tension of Water: The Magic Touch	11.3 Select Properties of Liquids
At the Water's Edge: Surface Spreading and Surface Tension	11.3 Select Properties of Liquids
Demonstration of Surface Tension	11.3 Select Properties of Liquids
Polarity, Miscibility, and Surface Tension of Liquids	11.3 Select Properties of Liquids
Lowering the Surface Tension of Water: An Illustration of the Scientific Method	11.3 Select Properties of Liquids
Evaporation as an Endothermic Process	11.4 Phase Changes
The Effect of Pressure on Boiling Point	11.5 Vapor Pressure
A Simple Experiment for Demonstration of Phase Diagram of Carbon Dioxide	11.6 Phase Diagrams
Colors in Liquid Crystals	11.7 Liquid Crystals

Chapter 11. Liquids and Intermolecular Forces

Common Student Misconceptions

- Students confuse *inter*molecular and *intra*molecular forces.
- Students often do not appreciate how important information from earlier chapters is for the understanding of concepts in this chapter.
- Students have difficulty predicting the relative strength of intermolecular forces involved in different materials.
- Students are unaware that there can be *intra*molecular hydrogen bonding.
- Students confuse cohesion and adhesion.
- Students do not realize that, under the right set of conditions, water also sublimes.
- Students often think that more viscous necessarily means more dense.
- Student often think that the "*liquid*" in liquid crystals refers to these materials being pliable rather than actually being liquid.
- Students often confuse LCD and plasma TV technologies.

Teaching Tips

- Ion-dipole interactions are technically inter*particular* forces.
- The term volatile is often used incorrectly, especially in the media.
- Emphasize that *dynamic equilibrium* is one of the most important concepts used in the latter half of the course.
- The term *boiling point* is often used to refer to the *normal boiling point*, that is, the boiling point at 1.0 atm external pressure. If the external pressure is varied, the boiling point will also vary.
- The term *melting point* is often used when referring to the *normal melting point*, that is, the melting point at 1.0 atm external pressure. Like the boiling point, the melting point also varies with external pressure. The melting point is less sensitive to external pressure than is the boiling point.

11.1 A Molecular Comparison of Gases, Liquids, and Solids[1,2,3,4,5,6,7,8]

- Physical properties of substances are understood in terms of kinetic-molecular theory:
  - Gases are highly compressible and assume the shape and volume of their container.
    - Gas molecules are far apart and do not interact much with one another.
  - Liquids are almost incompressible and assume the shape but not the volume of the container.
    - Liquids molecules are held together more closely than gas molecules but not so rigidly that the molecules cannot slide past each other.
  - Solids are incompressible and have a definite shape and volume.
    - Solid molecules are packed closely together.
    - The molecules are so rigidly packed that they cannot easily slide past each other.
- Solids and liquids are *condensed phases*.
  - Solids with highly ordered structures are said to be *crystalline*.
- Converting a gas into a liquid or solid requires the molecules to get closer to each other.

---

[1] "Physical Properties of the Halogens" Movie from Instructor's Resource CD/DVD
[2] "Pictorial Analogies I: States of Matter" from Further Readings
[3] Figure 11.2 from Transparency Pack
[4] "Phases of Matter" Activity from Instructor's Resource CD/DVD
[5] "Chlorine" 3-D Model from Instructor's Resource CD/DVD
[6] "Bromine" 3-D Model from Instructor's Resource CD/DVD
[7] "Iodine" 3-D Model from Instructor's Resource CD/DVD
[8] "Fluorine" 3-D Model from Instructor's Resource CD/DVD

- • We can accomplish this by cooling or compressing the gas.
- Converting a solid into a liquid or gas requires the molecules to move further apart.
  - • We can accomplish this by heating or reducing the pressure on the gas.
- The forces holding solids and liquids together are called intermolecular forces.
- Physical properties of liquids and solids are due to **intermolecular forces**.
  - These are forces *between* molecules.

FORWARDS REFERENCES
- • A comparison of phases in terms of entropy will be performed in Chapter 19 (section 19.3).

11.2 Intermolecular Forces[9,10,11,12]

- The attraction between molecules is an *inter*molecular force.
  - Intermolecular forces are much weaker than ionic or covalent bonds.
- When a substance melts or boils, intermolecular forces are broken.
- When a substances condenses, intermolecular forces are formed.
  - Boiling points reflect intermolecular force strength.
    - A high boiling point indicates strong attractive forces.
- Melting points also reflect the strength of attractive forces.
  - A high melting point indicates strong attractive forces.
- *van der Waals* forces are the intermolecular forces that exist between neutral molecules.
  - These include Dispersion forces, dipole-dipole forces, and hydrogen-bonding forces.
  - Ion-dipole interactions are important in solutions.
    - These are all weak (<15% as strong as a covalent or ionic bond) electrostatic interactions.

Dispersion Forces[13,14,15,16,17,18,19]

- These are the weakest of all intermolecular forces.
- It is possible for two adjacent neutral molecules to affect each other.
  - The nucleus of one molecule (or atom) attracts the electrons of the adjacent molecule (or atom).
  - For an instant, the electron clouds become distorted.
  - In that instant a dipole is formed (called an *instantaneous* or momentary dipole).
  - One instantaneous dipole can induce another instantaneous dipole in an adjacent molecule (or atom).
  - These two temporary dipoles attract each other.
  - The attraction is called the **dispersion force**, or London dispersion force.
    - Dispersion forces exist between all molecules.
- What affects the strength of a dispersion force?
  - Molecules must be very close together for these attractive forces to occur.
  - **Polarizability** is the ease with which an electron distribution can be deformed.
    - The larger the molecule (the greater the number of electrons) the more polarizable it is.

---

[9] "Molecular Handshake; Recognition through Weak Noncovalent Interactions" from Further Readings
[10] "Dancing Crystals: A Dramatic Illustration of Intermolecular Forces" from Live Demonstrations
[11] "Hydrogen Chloride" 3-D Model from Instructor's Resource CD/DVD
[12] "Hydrogen Fluoride" 3-D Model from Instructor's Resource CD/DVD
[13] Figure 11.4 from Transparency Pack
[14] Figure 11.6 from Transparency Pack
[15] "Solving the Mystery of Fading Fingerprints with London-Dispersion Forces" from Further Readings
[16] "London-Dispersion Forces and 'The Wave'" from Further Readings
[17] Figure 11.9 from Transparency Pack
[18] "Pentane" 3-D Model from Instructor's Resource CD/DVD
[19] "Neopentane (dimethylpropane)" 3-D Model from Instructor's Resource CD/DVD

- Dispersion forces increase as molecular weight increases.
- Dispersion forces depend on the shape of the molecule.
  - The greater the surface area available for contact, the greater the dispersion forces.
  - Dispersion forces between spherical molecules are smaller than those between more cylindrically shaped molecules.
    - Example: *n*-pentane vs. neopentane.

Dipole-Dipole Forces[20,21,22,23,24]

- **Dipole-dipole forces** exist between neutral polar molecules.
  - Compare two molecules with similar molecular weight: acetonitrile and propane.
  - With similar molecular weights, we expect similar magnitudes for the dispersion forces.
  - Acetonitrile, (polar) however, has a much higher boiling point than propane (nonpolar)
    - The higher boiling point reflects the dipole-dipole forces present.
- Polar molecules attract each other.
  - The partially positive end of one molecule attracts the partially negative end of another.
- Polar molecules need to be close together to form strong dipole-dipole interactions.
- If two molecules have about the same mass and size, then dipole-dipole forces increase with increasing polarity.

Hydrogen Bonding[25,26,27,28,29,30,31]

- Experiments show that the boiling points of compounds with H–F, H–O, and H–N bonds are abnormally high.
  - Their intermolecular forces are abnormally strong.
- **Hydrogen bonding** is a special type of intermolecular attraction.
  - This is a special case of dipole-dipole interactions.
  - H-bonding requires:
    - H bonded to a small electronegative element (most important for compounds of F, O, and N).
    - an unshared electron pair on a nearby small electronegative ion or atom (usually F, O, or N on another molecule).
  - Electrons in the H–X bond (X is the more electronegative element) lie much closer to X than H.
  - H has only one electron, so in the H–X bond, the H^+ presents an almost bare proton to the X^-.
    - Bond energies of hydrogen bonds vary from about 4 kJ/mol to 25 kJ/mol.
    - They are much weaker than ordinary chemical bonds.
- Intermolecular and intramolecular hydrogen bonds have exceedingly important biological significance.
  - They are important in stabilizing protein structure, in DNA structure and function, etc.
- An interesting consequence of H-bonding is that ice floats.

---

[20] "Students as Solids, Liquids, and Gases" from Further Readings
[21] "Acetonitrile" 3-D Model from Instructor's Resource CD/DVD
[22] "Propane" 3-D Model from Instructor's Resource CD/DVD
[23] "Dimethyl Ether" 3-D Model from Instructor's Resource CD/DVD
[24] "Acetaldehyde" 3-D Model from Instructor's Resource CD/DVD
[25] Hydrogen Bonding" Animation from Instructor's Resource CD/DVD
[26] "Hydrogen Bonding in Water" Activity from Instructor's Resource CD/DVD
[27] "A People-and-Velcro Model for Hydrogen Bonding" from Further Readings
[28] Figure 11.10 from Transparency Pack
[29] "Water" 3-D Model from Instructor's Resource CD/DVD
[30] "Ice" 3-D Model from Instructor's Resource CD/DVD
[31] "Ammonia" 3-D Model from Instructor's Resource CD/DVD

- The molecules in solids are usually more closely packed than those in liquids.
  - Therefore, solids are usually more dense than liquids.
- Ice is ordered with an open structure to optimize H-bonding.
  - Water molecules in ice are arranged in an open, regular hexagon.
    - Each δ^+ H points towards a lone pair on O.
  - Therefore, ice is less dense than water.
- Ice floats, so it forms an insulating layer on top of lakes, rivers, etc. Therefore, aquatic life can survive in winter.
- Water expands when it freezes.
  - Frozen water in pipes may cause them to break in cold weather.

Ion-Dipole Forces[32]

- An **ion-dipole** force is an interaction between an ion (e.g., Na^+) and the partial charge on the end of a polar molecule/dipole (e.g., water).
- It is especially important for solutions of ionic substances in polar liquids.
  - Example: NaCl(*aq*)

Comparing Intermolecular Forces[33,34,35,36,37,38,39,40]

- Dispersion forces are found in all substances.
  - Their strength depends on molecular shapes and molecular weights.
- Dipole-dipole forces add to the effect of dispersion forces.
  - They are found only in polar molecules.
- H-bonding is a special case of dipole-dipole interactions.
  - It is the strongest of the intermolecular forces involving neutral species.
  - H-bonding is most important for H compounds of N, O, and F.
- If ions are involved, ion-dipole (if a dipole is present) and ionic bonding are possible.
  - Ion-dipole interactions are stronger than H-bonds.
- When comparing the relative strengths of intermolecular attractions:
  - If the molecules of the two substances have similar molecular weights and shapes, dispersion forces will be similar in magnitude.
    - Differences in the magnitudes of the intermolecular forces are due to dipole-dipole attractions
    - The greater the molecular polarity, the stronger the intermolecular forces.
  - If the molecules of the two substances have very different molecular weights, dispersion forces will have a significant impact on the intermolecular attractions.
    - Intermolecular attractive forces will generally be greater in the substance with the higher molecular weight.
- Keep in mind that ordinary ionic or covalent bonds are much stronger than these interactions!

FORWARDS REFERENCES

  - Soft molecular materials held together by intermolecular forces will be in Chapter 12 (section 12.6).

---

[32] "Put the Body to Them!" from Further Readings
[33] "Intermolecular Forces" Activity from Instructor's Resource CD/DVD
[34] Figure 11.14 from Transparency Pack
[35] "Acetic Acid" 3-D Model from Instructor's Resource CD/DVD
[36] "1-Propanol" 3-D Model from Instructor's Resource CD/DVD
[37] "2-Propanol" 3-D Model from Instructor's Resource CD/DVD
[38] "Methylpropane" 3-D Model from Instructor's Resource CD/DVD
[39] "Ethyl Methyl Ether" 3-D Model from Instructor's Resource CD/DVD
[40] "Sulfur Dioxide" 3-D Model from Instructor's Resource CD/DVD

- Breaking of solute-solute and solvent-solvent intermolecular forces and replacing them with solute-solvent interactions will take place in the solution process (Ch. 13).
- The binding between the substrate and the active site in the enzyme action thanks to the intermolecular forces will be discussed in Chapter 14 (section 14.7).
- Hydrogen bonding and the formation of hydrated hydronium ions will be discussed in Chapter 16 (section 16.2).
- Hydrogen bonding will be partially responsible for the relative weakness of HF compared to the strength of other binary acids involving halides (section 16.10).
- Hydrogen bonding and high heat capacity, high melting and boiling points of water will be mentioned again in Chapter 18 (sections 18.2 and 18.3).
- Intermolecular attractions in ice will be discussed in Chapter 19 (section 19.3).
- Hydrogen bonding in alcohols will be discussed in Chapter 24 (section 24.4).
- Hydrogen bonding in the α helix of a protein will be discussed in Chapter 24 (section 24.10).

11.3 Select Properties of Liquids

Viscosity[41,42]

- **Viscosity** is the resistance of a liquid to flow.
- A liquid flows by sliding molecules over one another.
- Viscosity depends on:
  - the attractive forces between molecules.
    - The stronger the intermolecular forces, the higher the viscosity.
  - the tendency of molecules to become entangled.
    - Viscosity increases as molecules become entangled with one another.
  - the temperature.
    - Viscosity usually decreases with an increase in temperature.

Surface Tension[43,44,45,46,47,48,49]

- Bulk molecules (those in the liquid) are equally attracted to their neighbors.
- Surface molecules are only attracted inward towards the bulk molecules.
  - Therefore, surface molecules are packed more closely than bulk molecules.
  - This causes the liquid to behave as if it had a "skin".
- **Surface tension** is the amount of energy required to increase the surface area of a liquid by a unit amount.
- Stronger intermolecular forces cause higher surface tension.
  - Water has a high surface tension (H-bonding)
  - Hg(l) has an even higher surface tension (there are very strong metallic bonds between Hg atoms).
- Cohesive and adhesive forces are at play.
  - *Cohesive forces* are intermolecular forces that bind molecules to one another.

---

[41] "Viscosity Races" from Live Demonstrations
[42] "1,2,3-Ethanetriol (glycerol)" 3-D Model from Instructor's Resource CD/DVD
[43] "Demonstration of Surface Tension" from Live Demonstrations
[44] "Polarity, Miscibility, and Surface Tension of Liquids" from Live Demonstrations
[45] "Lowering the Surface Tension of Water: An Illustration of the Scientific Method" from Live Demonstrations
[46] "Tears of Wine" from Further Readings
[47] "Why Do Alcoholic Beverages Have 'Legs'?" from Further Readings
[48] "Surface Tension of Water: The Magic Touch" from Live Demonstrations
[49] "At the Water's Edge: Surface Spreading and Surface Tension" from Live Demonstrations

- *Adhesive forces* are intermolecular forces that bind molecules to a surface.
- Illustrate this by looking at the meniscus in a tube filled with liquid.
  - The *meniscus* is the shape of the liquid surface.
  - If adhesive forces are greater than cohesive forces, the liquid surface is attracted to its container more than the bulk molecules. Therefore, the meniscus is U-shaped (e.g., water in glass).
  - If cohesive forces are greater than adhesive forces, the meniscus is curved downwards (e.g., $Hg(l)$ in glass)
- **Capillary action** is the rise of liquids up very narrow tubes.
  - The liquid climbs until adhesive and cohesive forces are balanced by gravity.

FORWARDS REFERENCES
- Viscosity of organic compounds, such as polyhydroxyl alcohols, will be mentioned in Chapter 24 (section 24.4).

11.4 Phase Changes[50]

- **Phase changes** are changes of state.
  - Matter in one state is converted into another state.
    - *Sublimation*: solid → gas.
    - *Melting* or *fusion*: solid → liquid.
    - *Vaporization*: liquid → gas.
    - *Deposition*: gas → solid.
    - *Condensation*: gas → liquid.
    - *Freezing*: liquid → solid.

Energy Changes Accompanying Phase Changes[51,52,53]
- Energy changes of the system for the above processes are:
  melting or *fusion*: $\Delta H_{fus} > 0$ (endothermic).
    - The enthalpy of fusion is known as the **heat of fusion**.
  - *vaporization*: $\Delta H_{vap} > 0$ (endothermic).
    - The enthalpy of vaporization is known as the **heat of vaporization**.
  - *sublimation*: $\Delta H_{sub} > 0$ (endothermic).
    - The enthalpy of sublimation is called the **heat of sublimation.**
  - *deposition*: $\Delta H_{dep} < 0$ (exothermic).
  - *condensation*: $\Delta H_{con} < 0$ (exothermic).
  - *freezing*: $\Delta H_{fre} < 0$ (exothermic).
- Generally the heat of fusion (enthalpy of fusion) is less than heat of vaporization.
  - It takes more energy to completely separate molecules, than to partially separate them.
- All phase changes are possible under the right conditions (e.g., water sublimes when snow disappears without forming puddles).
  - The following sequence is endothermic:
    heat solid → melt → heat liquid → boil → heat gas
  - The following sequence is exothermic:
    cool gas → condense → cool liquid → freeze → cool solid

[50] Figure 11.20 from Transparency Pack
[51] "Evaporation As an Endothermic Process" from Live Demonstrations
[52] "Changes of State" Animation from Instructor's Resource CD/DVD
[53] "Butane" 3-D Model from Instructor's Resource CD/DVD

Heating Curves[54,55]

- Plot of temperature change versus heat added is a *heating curve*.
- During a phase change, adding heat causes no temperature change.
  - The added energy is used to break intermolecular bonds rather than cause a temperature change.
  - These points are used to calculate ΔH_{fus} and ΔH_{vap}.
- *Supercooling*: When a liquid is cooled below its freezing point and it still remains a liquid.

Critical Temperature and Pressure[56]

- Gases may be liquefied by increasing the pressure at a suitable temperature.
- **Critical temperature** is the highest temperature at which a substance can exist as a liquid.
- **Critical pressure** is the pressure required for liquefaction at this critical temperature.
  - The greater the intermolecular forces, the easier it is to liquefy a substance.
    - Thus, the higher the critical temperature.
- A substance at temperatures and pressures higher than its critical temperature and pressure is in a state called a **supercritical fluid**.
  - *Supercritical fluid extraction* is a used to separate complex mixtures.
    - Supercritical carbon dioxide is widely used for these applications.

FORWARDS REFERENCES
- Supercritical fluids in green chemistry will be discussed in Chapter 18 (section 18.5).
- Thermodynamics of phase changes will be further discussed throughout Chapter 19.

11.5 Vapor Pressure

- Some of the molecules on the surface of a liquid have enough energy to escape the attraction of the bulk liquid.
  - These molecules move into the gas phase.
- As the number of molecules in the gas phase increases, some of the gas phase molecules strike the surface and return to the liquid.
- After some time, the pressure of the gas will be constant.
  - A **dynamic equilibrium** has been established.
    - Dynamic equilibrium is a condition in which two opposing processes occur simultaneously at equal rates.
    - In this case, it is the point when as many molecules escape the surface as strike the surface.
  - **Vapor pressure** of a liquid is the pressure exerted by its vapor when the liquid and vapor are in dynamic equilibrium.
    - The pressure of the vapor at this point is called the equilibrium vapor pressure.

Volatility, Vapor Pressure, and Temperature[57,58,59]

- If equilibrium is never established, the vapor continues to form.
  - Eventually, the liquid evaporates to dryness.
- Liquids that evaporate easily are said to be **volatile**.
  - The higher the temperature, the higher the average kinetic energy, the faster the liquid evaporates.

---

[54] "Heating Curves" Activity from Instructor's Resource CD/DVD
[55] Figure 11.22 from Transparency Pack
[56] "Past, Present, and Possible Future Applications of Supercritical Fluid Extraction Technology" from Further Readings
[57] "Vapor Pressure vs. Temperature" Animation from Instructor's Resource CD/DVD
[58] Figure 11.25 from Transparency Pack
[59] "Boltzmann Distribution" Activity from Instructor's Resource CD/DVD

Vapor Pressure and Boiling Point[60,61]

- Liquids boil when the external pressure at the liquid surface equals the vapor pressure.
  - The **normal boiling point** is the boiling point at 760 mm Hg (1 atm).
- The temperature of the boiling point increases as the external pressure increases.
- Two ways to get a liquid to boil: increase temperature or decrease pressure.
  - Pressure cookers operate at high pressure.
  - At high pressure, the boiling point of water is higher than at 1 atm.
  - Therefore, food is cooked at a higher temperature.

FORWARDS REFERENCES
- Vapor pressure reduction of the solvent in a solution – a colligative property – will be discussed in Chapter 13 (section 13.5).

11.6 Phase Diagrams[62,63,64,65,66]

- **A phase diagram** is a plot of pressure vs. temperature summarizing all equilibria between phases.
- Phase diagrams tell us which phase will exist at a given temperature and pressure.
- Features of a phase diagram include:
  - *vapor-pressure curve*: generally as temperature increases, vapor pressure increases.
  - *critical point*: critical temperature and pressure for the gas.
  - *supercritical fluid:* state of matter beyond the critical point.
  - *sublimation curve*: separates the solid and gas phases.
  - *melting curve*: separates the solid phase and liquid phases.
  - **normal melting point**: melting point at 1 atm.
  - **triple point**: temperature and pressure at which all three phases are in equilibrium.
  - Any temperature and pressure combination not on a curve represents a single phase.

Phase Diagrams of H_2O and CO_2[67,68,69,70]

- *Water*:
  - In general, an increase in pressure favors the more compact phase of the material.
    - This is usually the solid.
  - Water is one of the few substances whose solid form is less dense than the liquid form.
    - The melting point curve for water slopes to the left.
  - The triple point occurs at 0.0098 °C and 4.58 mm Hg.
  - The normal melting (freezing) point is 0 °C.
  - The normal boiling point is 100 °C.
  - The critical point is 374 °C and 218 atm.
- *Carbon Dioxide*:
  - The triple point occurs at –56.4 °C and 5.11 atm.

---

[60] "Equilibrium Vapor Pressure" Activity from Instructor's Resource CD/DVD
[61] "The Effect of Pressure on Boiling Point" from Live Demonstrations
[62] "Journey Around a Phase Diagram" from Further Readings
[63] Figure 11.27 from Transparency Pack
[64] "Phase Diagram" Activity from Instructor's Resource CD/DVD
[65] "There is No Perceptible Inflection at the Triple Point" from Further Readings
[66] "Supercritical Chemistry: Synthesis with a Spanner" from Further Readings
[67] "A Simple Experiment for Demonstration of the Phase Diagram of Carbon Dioxide" from Live Demonstrations
[68] Figure 11.28 from Transparency Pack
[69] "Phase Diagram of Water" Animation from Instructor's Resource CD/DVD
[70] "Methane" 3-D Model from Instructor's Resource CD/DVD

- The normal sublimation point is −78.5 °C. (At 1 atm CO_2 sublimes, it does not melt.)
- The critical point occurs at 31.1 °C and 73 atm.
- Freeze drying: Frozen food is placed in a low pressure (< 4.58 torr) chamber.
  - The ice sublimes.

FORWARDS REFERENCES
- Phase diagrams for a pure solvent and for a solution of a nonvolatile solute will be discussed in Chapter 13 (section 13.5).
- Phase equilibria at melting and boiling points will be further analyzed in Chapter 19.

11.7 Liquid Crystals[71,72]

- Solids are characterized by their order.
- Liquids are characterized by almost random ordering of molecules.
- There is an intermediate phase where liquids show a limited amount of ordering.
  - **Liquid crystals** are substances that exhibit one or more ordered phases at a temperature above the melting point.
  - Example: The first systematic report of a liquid crystal was cholesteryl benzoate.
    - It melts at 145 °C.
    - Between 145 °C and 179 °C cholesteryl benzoate is milky and liquid crystalline.
    - At 179 °C the milky liquid suddenly clears.
    - Cholesteryl benzoate passes through an intermediate liquid crystalline phase.
      - It has some properties of liquids and some of solids.
    - The liquid flows (liquid properties) but has some order (crystal properties).

Types of Liquid-Crystalline Phases[73,74,75,76,77,78,79]

- Liquid crystal molecules are usually long and rodlike.
  - In normal liquid phases they are randomly oriented.
  - In liquid crystals, the molecules are arranged in specific patterns.
- Classification of liquid crystals depend on the ordering of the molecules.
  - **Nematic liquid crystals** (least ordered).
    - Ordered along the long axis of the molecule only.
  - **Smectic A and smectic C liquid crystals**.
    - Ordered along the long axis of the molecule *and* packed into layers.
    - Intermolecular forces limit the ability of the molecules to slide past one another.
  - **Cholesteric liquid crystals**.
    - Molecules are aligned along their long axis.
    - In addition, the molecules are arranged in layers.
    - Molecules in each plane are twisted slightly relative to molecules in neighboring layers.
    - Many of the molecules are derivatives of cholesterol.
      - An example is cholesteryl octanoate.
      - The molecules are long, flat, and rod-like with a flexible tail.

---

[71] "Liquid Crystal Inquiries: Add a New Phase to Your Curriculum" from Further Readings
[72] "Colors in Liquid Crystals" from Live Demonstrations
[73] Figure 11.32 from Transparency Pack
[74] Figure 11.33 from Transparency Pack
[75] "Liquid Crystals Display New Potential" from Further Readings
[76] "Preparation and Properties of Cholesteric Liquid Crystals" from Further Readings
[77] Figure 11.36 from Transparency Pack
[78] "OLEDs Set to Glow" from Further Readings
[79] "Shining Examples" from Further Readings

- - The flexible tail causes the twist between the layers.
  - The flexible tail usually contains many C–C bonds (e.g., the hydrocarbon tail in cholesteryl octanoate).
  - The rings in the cholesterol portion are not planar, but give the molecule a flat, sausage-like shape.
- Changes in temperature and pressure cause ordering between layers to change.
- This results in color changes.

Further Readings:

1. John J. Fortman, "Pictorial Analogies I: States of Matter," *J. Chem. Educ.*, Vol. 70, **1993**, 56–57.

2. Parvathi S. Murthy, "Molecular Handshake: Recognition through Weak Noncovalent Interactions," *J. Chem. Educ.*, Vol. 83, **2006**, 1010–1013.

3. Robert R. Perkins, "Put the Body to Them!" *J. Chem. Educ.*, Vol. 72, **1995**, 151–152. The difference between an intermolecular change and an intramolecular change is explored by analogy in this short reference.

4. Ponnadurai Ramasami, "Students as Solids, Liquids, and Gases," *J. Chem. Educ.*, Vol. 76, **1999**, 485.

5. Doris R. Kimbrough and Ronald DeLorenzo, "Solving the Mystery of Fading Fingerprints with London-Dispersion Forces," *J. Chem. Educ.*, Vol. 75, **1998**, 1300–1301. This is a forensic chemistry application of London dispersion forces.

6. C. Jayne Wilcox, "London-Dispersion Forces and 'The Wave'", *J. Chem. Educ.*, Vol. 75, **1998**, 1301. This is a sports analogy to introduce London-dispersion forces.

7. John W. Hill, "A People-and-Velcro Model for Hydrogen Bonding," *J. Chem. Educ.*, Vol. 67, **1990**, 223. An analogy for hydrogen bonding is presented in this very short reading.

8. Todd P. Silverstein, "Why Do Alcoholic Beverages Have 'Legs'?" *J. Chem. Educ.*, Vol. 75, **1998**, 723–724. Adhesive and cohesive forces are explored in this analogy involving the behavior of liquid in an alcoholic beverage.

9. Marcos Gugliotti, "Tears of Wine," *J. Chem. Educ.*, Vol. 81, **2004**, 67–68. This is a new look at the "legs" of alcoholic beverages, tested by Todd Silverstein.

10. Cindy L. Phelps, Neil G. Smart, and C. M. Wai. "Past, Present, and Possible Future Applications of Supercritical Fluid Extraction Technology," *J. Chem. Educ.*, Vol. 73, **1996**, 1163–1168. This provides an in-depth look at supercritical fluid extraction.

11. Martyn Poliakoff and Steve Howdle, "Supercritical Chemistry: Synthesis with a Spanner," *Chemistry in Britain*, **February 1995**, 118–121.

12. Nicholas K Kildahl, "Journey Around a Phase Diagram," *J. Chem. Educ.*, Vol. 71, **1994**, 1052–1054.

13. Stephen J. Hawkes, "There is No Perceptible Inflection at the Triple Point," *J. Chem. Educ.*, Vol. 76, **1999**, 226.

14. Renata-Maria Marroum, "Liquid Crystal Inquiries: Add a New Phase to Your Curriculum," *The Science Teacher*, Vol. 65, **1996**, 32–35. Liquid crystals are used as tools to demonstrate phase transitions.

15. Richard Bissell and Neville Boden, "Liquid Crystals Display New Potential," *Chemistry in Britain*, Vol. 31(1), **January 1995**, 38–41.

16. Graeme Patch and Gregory A. Hope, "Preparation and Properties of Cholesteric Liquid Crystals," *J. Chem. Educ.*, Vol. 62, **1985**, 454–455. The liquid crystal properties of cholesterol compounds are studied

as a function of temperature and composition. This reference includes instructions for the preparation of a number of such compounds.

17. Richard Stevenson, "OLEDs Set to Glow," *Chemistry in Britain*, **January 2003**, 33.

18. Stephen Kelly, "Shining Examples," *Chemistry in Britain*, **January 2003**, 34–37. A short article on organic light emitting molecules.

Live Demonstrations:

1. Donald W. Mundell and James H. Maynard, "Dancing Crystals: A Dramatic Illustration of Intermolecular Forces," *J. Chem. Educ.*, Vol. 84, **2007**, 1773-1775.

2. William M. Hemmerlin and Kenton Abel, "Viscosity Races," *J. Chem. Educ.*, Vol. 68, **1991**, 417. This is a simple demonstration to illustrate the relationship between molecular size and viscosity.

3. Lee. R. Summerlin, and James. L. Ealy, Jr., "Surface Tension of Water: The Magic Touch," *Chemical Demonstrations, A Sourcebook for Teachers, Volume 1* (Washington: American Chemical Society, **1988**), p. 45. The effect of a wetting agent on surface tension is demonstrated.

4. Bassam Z. Shakhashiri, "At the Water's Edge: Surface Spreading and Surface Tension," *Chemical Demonstrations: A Handbook for Teachers of Chemistry, Volume 3* (Madison: The University of Wisconsin Press, **1989**), pp. 301–304.

5. Andrew J. Rosenthal, "Demonstration of Surface Tension," *J. Chem. Educ.*, Vol. 78, **2001**, 332–333.

6. Todd P. Silverstein, "Polarity, Miscibility, and Surface Tension of Liquids," *J. Chem. Educ.*, Vol. 70, **1993**, 253.

7. Paul G. Jasien, Glenn Barnett, and David Speckhard, "Lowering the Surface Tension of Water: An Illustration of the Scientific Method," *J. Chem. Educ.*, Vol. 70, **1993**, 67–68.

8. Bassam Z. Shakhashiri, "Evaporation As an Endothermic Process," *Chemical Demonstrations: A Handbook for Teachers of Chemistry, Volume 3* (Madison: The University of Wisconsin Press, **1989**), pp. 249–251. A "drinking duck" toy and a beaker of water are used to demonstrate the endothermic nature of evaporation.

9. Lee. R. Summerlin, and James. L. Ealy, Jr., "The Effect of Pressure on Boiling Point," *Chemical Demonstrations, A Sourcebook for Teachers, Volume 1* (Washington: American Chemical Society, **1988**), p. 21.

10. Van T. Lieu, "A Simple Experiment for Demonstration of Phase Diagram of Carbon Dioxide," *J. Chem. Educ.*, Vol. 73, **1996**, 837–838. A syringe filled with dry ice is used in this simple and quick demonstration.

11. George Lisensky and Elizabeth Boatman, "Colors in Liquid Crystals," *J. Chem. Educ.*, Vol. 82, **2005**, 1360A.

Chapter 12. Solids and Modern Materials

Media Resources

Figures and Tables in Transparency Pack:	Section:
Figure 12.11 The Structures of (a) Primitive Cubic, (b) Body-centered Cubic, and (c) Face-centered Cubic Metals	12.3 Metallic Solids
Figure 12.12 A Space-filling View of Unit Cells for Metals with a Cubic Structure	12.3 Metallic Solids
Figure 12.13 Close Packing of Equal-sized Spheres	12.3 Metallic Solids
Figure 12.22 The Melting Points of Metals from Periods 4, 5, and 6	12.4 Metallic Bonding
Figure 12.24 The Electronic Band Structure of Nickel	12.4 Metallic Bonding
Figure 12.27 Coordination Environments in CsCl, NaCl, and ZnS	12.5 Ionic Solids
Figure 12.30 The Structures of (a) Diamond and (b) Graphite	12.7 Covalent-Network Solids
Figure 12.31 The Electronic Band Structure of Semiconductors that have the Diamond Crystal Structure	12.7 Covalent-Network Solids
Table 12.5 Polymers of Commercial Importance	12.8 Polymeric Solids
Figure 12.48 Atomic Models of Carbon Nanotubes	12.9 Nanomaterials

Activities:	Section:
Close Packing	12.3 Metallic Solids
Metallic Bonding	12.4 Metallic Bonding
Band Structure	12.7 Covalent-Network Solids

Movies:	Section:
Close Packing	12.3 Metallic Solids
Synthesis of Nylon 6,10	12.8 Polymeric Solids

3-D Models:	Section:
Water	12.1 Classifications of Solids
Silicon Carbide	12.1 Classifications of Solids
Primitive Cubic	12.2 Structures of Solids
Simple Cubic	12.2 Structures of Solids
Body-Centered Cubic	12.2 Structures of Solids
Face-Centered Cubic	12.2 Structures of Solids
Orthorhombic Sulfur	12.2 Structures of Solids
Sulfur	12.4 Metallic Bonding
Chlorine	12.4 Metallic Bonding
Cesium Chloride (unit cell)	12.5 Ionic Solids
Sodium Chloride	12.5 Ionic Solids
Rutile	12.5 Ionic Solids
Fluorite	12.5 Ionic Solids
Diamond	12.7 Covalent-Network Solids
Graphite	12.7 Covalent-Network Solids
Zinc Sulfide (crystal structure)	12.7 Covalent-Network Solids

162 Chapter 12

Phosphorus
Polyethylene
Buckminsterfullerene

12.7 Covalent-Network Solids
12.8 Polymeric Solids
12.9 Nanomaterials

Other Resources

	Section:
Pictorial Analogies II: Types of Solids	12.1 Classifications of Solids
The Importance of Understanding Structure	12.2 Structures of Solids
The Fifth Bragg Lecture; W. L. Bragg-Scientific Revolutionary	12.2 Structures of Solids
Revealing the Backbone Structure of B-DNA from Laser Optical Simulations of its X-Ray Diffraction Diagram	12.2 Structures of Solids
A-DNA and B-DNA: Comparing their Historical X-ray Fiber Diffraction Images	12.2 Structures of Solids
The Discovery of X-ray Diffraction by Crystals	12.2 Structures of Solids
On the Occurrence of Metallic Character in the Periodic Table of the Elements	12.3 Metallic Solids
Intelligent Materials	12.3 Metallic Solids
Nickel-Titanium Memory Metal: A "Smart" Material Exhibiting a Solid-State Phase Change and Superelasticity	12.3 Metallic Solids
Conducting Midshipmen–A Classroom Activity Modeling Extended Bonding in Solids	12.4 Metallic Bonding
An Ionic Model for Metallic Bonding	12.4 Metallic Bonding
A Model to Illustrate the Brittleness of Ionic and Metallic Crystals	12.5 Ionic Solids
The Future's Bright, The Future's Blue	12.7 Covalent-Network Solids
Pictorial Analogies V: Polymers	12.8 Polymeric Solids
Polymer Literature and Samples for Classroom Use	12.8 Polymeric Solids
Alkanes: Abundant, Pervasive, Important, and Essential	12.8 Polymeric Solids
Polymer Structure–Organic Aspects (Definitions)	12.8 Polymeric Solids
Polymers Are Everywhere	12.8 Polymeric Solids
JCE Resources for Chemistry and Recycling	12.8 Polymeric Solids
How to Learn and Have Fun with Poly(Vinyl Alcohol) and White Glue	12.8 Polymeric Solids
Polymers and Processes	12.8 Polymeric Solids
Wallace Hume Carothers and Nylon, the First Completely Synthetic Fiber	12.8 Polymeric Solids
Neoprene and Nylon Stockings; The Legacy of Wallace Hume Carothers	12.8 Polymeric Solids
The Origin of the Name 'Nylon'	12.8 Polymeric Solids
Dr. Baekeland's Bakelite	12.8 Polymeric Solids
Thermosetting Resins	12.8 Polymeric Solids
Performance Polymers	12.8 Polymeric Solids
Elastomers I: Natural Rubber	12.8 Polymeric Solids
Rubber Reclamation	12.8 Polymeric Solids
Plastic Fantastic	12.8 Polymeric Solids
It's a Small World	12.9 Nanomaterials

Copyright © 2012 Pearson Education, Inc.

Fishing for New Materials	12.9 Nanomaterials
Big Bucks from Small Science	12.9 Nanomaterials
The Smallest Revolution	12.9 Nanomaterials
A Tube of Tubes	12.9 Nanomaterials
Water-Filled Polymer Tubes	12.9 Nanomaterials
A Quantum Paintbox	12.9 Nanomaterials
Fullerenes	12.9 Nanomaterials
Buckytubes	12.9 Nanomaterials

Live Demonstrations: **Section:**

Kixium Monolayers: A Simple Alternative to the Bubble Raft Model for Close-Packed Spheres	12.2 Structures of Solids
Paper-and-Glue Unit Cell Models	12.2 Structures of Solids
Close Packing of Identical Spheres	12.3 Metallic Solids
Memory Metal	12.3 Metallic Solids
Slime: Gelation of Poly(vinyl alcohol) with Borax	12.8 Polymeric Solids
The Gelation of Polyvinyl Alcohol with Borax. A Novel Class Participation Experiment Involving the Preparation and Properties of a 'Slime'	12.8 Polymeric Solids
Synthesis of Nylon	12.8 Polymeric Solids
The Disappearing Coffee Cup	12.8 Polymeric Solids
Solid Foams	12.8 Polymeric Solids
Polyurethane Foams	12.8 Polymeric Solids

Chapter 12. Solids and Modern Materials

Common Student Misconceptions

- Students tend to have difficulty in "seeing" unit cells and crystal lattices; the use of models is often helpful.
- Students often equate the word "solution" with something liquid; they do not realize that, mixtures of such solids as metals are also solutions (alloys); similarly, liquids or solids dissolved in gases are also solutions, which we call foams.
- Students often do not realize that, in ionic solids, it is not just the strength of the electrostatic interactions but the *multitude* of such interactions that affects such properties as solubility, hardness and melting point.
- Students are not always aware that many *nano*materials naturally occur in the environment and living organisms and have existed prior to nanotechnology becoming a popular new field of research.

Teaching Tips

- It should be stressed that nanoscience is an interdisciplinary science and background knowledge in physics, chemistry and biology is needed in order to understand how nanomaterials are designed, made and applied.
- It should be pointed out to students that, due to the fact that most of the manmade nanomaterials are quite new and nature has not yet evolved to handle (dispose of) these materials, the impact of nanomaterials on human health and the environment has not been properly studied yet, and hence, it is not fully understood.
- Students should be made familiar with recycling symbols and importance of recycling. When teaching about polymers, plastics in particular, both positive and negative aspects should be mentioned.

Lecture Outline

12.1 Classifications of Solids[1,2,3]

- Solids are classified by the types of bonds that hold the atoms in place.
  - **Metallic solids**: held together by a delocalized "sea" of shared valence electrons.
  - **Ionic solids**: held together by mutual attraction between cations and anions.
  - **Covalent-network solids**: held together by an extended network of covalent bonds.
  - **Molecular solids**: held together by relatively weak intermolecular forces.
- Some solids to are harder to categorize:
  - **Polymers**: long chains of atoms held together by covalent bonds.
    - The chains are often held to one another by weaker intermolecular forces.
  - **Nanomaterials**: solids whose crystals have dimensions on the order of 1-100nm.

12.2 Structures of Solids

- Solids may be classified according to their level of order.
  - **Crystalline solids** have atoms and ions arranged in an orderly repeating pattern.
    - Examples: NaCl, quartz, diamond
  - **Amorphous solids** lack the order of crystalline solids.
    - Examples: rubber and glass

---

[1] "Pictorial Analogies II: Types of Solids" from Further Readings
[2] "Silicon Carbide" 3-D Model from Instructor's Resource CD/DVD
[3] "Water" 3-D Model from Instructor's Resource CD/DVD

Unit Cells and Crystal Lattices[4,5,6,7,8,9,10,11,12,13,14,15]

- Crystalline solids have an ordered, repeating structure.
- The smallest repeating unit in a crystal is a **unit cell**.
  - The unit cell is the smallest unit with all the symmetry of the entire crystal.
  - The three-dimensional stacking of unit cells is the **crystal lattice**.
    - Each point in the lattice is a **lattice point** that represents an identical environment within the solid.
    - The position of lattice points are defined by the **lattice vectors**.
      - A parallelogram formed by the lattice vectors defines the unit cells.
      - In two dimensions, the unit cells must *tile* or fit together in space so that they completely cover the area of the lattice with no gaps.
      - In three dimensions, the unit cells must stack together to fill all space.
- In a two-dimensional lattice, the unit cells can take on only one of four shapes:
  - An *oblique lattice*: lattice vectors have different lengths.
    - The angle between the lattice vectors is of arbitrary size.
    - The unit cells is an arbitrarily shaped parallelogram.
  - A *square lattice*: lattice vectors are equal in length and perpendicular to each other.
  - A *rectangular lattice*: the lattice vectors are perpendicular but of different lengths.
  - A *hexagonal lattice*: the lattice vectors are of the same length and the angle between them is 120°.
- In three dimensions a lattice is defined by three lattice vectors: a, b, c.
  - These define a parallelepiped: a 6-sided figure whose faces are all parallelograms.
  - This figure is described by the length of the cell edges (a, b, c) and the angles between the edges (α, β, γ).
  - There are seven possible shapes for a three-dimensional unit cell:
    - cubic
    - tetragonal
    - orthorhombic
    - rhombohedral
    - hexagonal
    - monoclinic
    - triclinic
  - A **primitive lattice** has a lattice point at each corner of the unit cell.
  - *Centered lattices*: lattices with additional lattice points in specific locations in the unit cells.

---

[4] "Primitive Cubic" 3-D Model from Instructor's Resource CD/DVD

[5] "Simple Cubic" 3-D Model from Instructor's Resource CD/DVD

[6] "Body-Centered Cubic" 3-D Model from Instructor's Resource CD/DVD

[7] "Face-Centered Cubic" 3-D Model from Instructor's Resource CD/DVD

[8] "The Importance of Understanding Structure" from Further Readings

[9] "The Fifth Bragg Lecture; W. L. Bragg-Scientific Revolutionary" from Further Readings

[10] "Revealing the Backbone Structure of B-DNA from Laser Optical Simulations of its X-Ray Diffraction Diagram" from Further Readings

[11] "A-DNA and B-DNA: Comparing their Historical X-ray Fiber Diffraction Images" from Further Readings

[12] "The Discovery of X-ray Diffraction by Crystals" from Further Readings

[13] "Paper-and-Glue Unit Cell Models" from Live Demonstrations

[14] "Kixium Monolayers: A Simple Alternative to the Raft Model for Close-Packed Spheres" from Live Demonstrations

[15] "Orthorhombic Sulfur" 3-D Model from Instructor's Resource CD/DVD

- Example: A **body-centered cubic lattice** has one lattice point at each of the 8 corners plus one at the center of the unit cell.
- Example: A **face-centered cubic lattice** has one lattice point at each of the 8 corners plus one at the center of each of the 6 faces of the unit cell.

Filling the Unit Cell

- A crystal structure is defined by the lattice as well as the location of the atoms relative to the lattice points.
  - Simplest case: a crystal structure made of identical atoms with each atom exactly coincident with a lattice point.
    - Here the crystal structure and the lattice points have the same pattern.
    - Many metallic elements have this structure.
    - Only elements can form this structure.
  - Most crystals have groups of atoms called a **motif** associated with each lattice point.
  - The crystal structure is built up by repeating the unit cell over and over again.
    - Bonds may form between atoms in neighboring unit cells.
    - This happens in many metallic, ionic, and network-covalent solids.

FORWARD REFERENCES

- Quartz – a crystalline solid, and glass – an amorphous solid, will be discussed in Chapter 22 (section 22.10).

12.3 Metallic Solids[16]

- **Metallic solids** or *metals* consist solely of metal atoms.
- *Metallic bonding* results from *delocalization* of valence electrons throughout the solid.
  - The metal nuclei are seen to exist in a "sea" of delocalized valence electrons.
- Important physical properties of pure metals:
  - *malleable*: can be hammered into thin sheets
  - *ductile*: can be pulled into wires
  - good electrical and thermal conductivity

The Structures of Metallic Solids[17,18]

- The crystal structures of many metals correspond to one of three cubic lattices:
  - Primitive cubic (examples: polonium); 1 atom per unit cell.
  - Body-centered cubic (examples: sodium and chromium); 2 atoms per unit cell.
  - Face-centered cubic (examples: silver, gold, copper, aluminum, lead); 4 atoms per unit cell.

Close Packing[19,20,21,22]

- The sharing of valence electrons makes it favorable for the atoms in a metal to pack closely together.
  - Layers of atoms are efficiently packed by surrounding each atom by six neighbors.
  - A three dimensional structure is formed by stacking additional layers on top of the base layer.
    - The second layer packs most efficiently if the atoms sit in the depressions formed by the atoms in the first layer.

---

[16] "On the Occurrence of Metallic Character in the Periodic Table of the Elements" from Further Readings
[17] Figure 12.11 from Transparency Pack
[18] Figure 12.12 from Transparency Pack
[19] "Close Packing of Identical Spheres" from Live Demonstrations
[20] Figure 12.13 from Transparency Pack
[21] "Close Packing" Activity from Instructor's Resource CD/DVD
[22] "Close Packing" Movie from Instructor's Resource CD/DVD

- There are two choices for the arrangement of the atoms in the third layer.
  - **Hexagonal close packing** (hcp): The third layer atoms are in the depressions that lie directly over the first layer.
  - **Cubic close packing** (ccp): The third layer atoms do not sit directly above the spheres in either of the first two layers.
  - In both hcp and ccp each sphere has 12 equidistant nearest neighbors:
    - Six neighbors in the same layer,
    - three from the layer above, and
    - three from the layer below.
    - Each sphere has a **coordination number** of 12.
      - The coordination number is the number of atoms immediately surrounding a given atom in the crystal structure.

Alloys[23,24,25]

- **Alloys** contain more than one element and have the characteristic properties of metals.
  - Pure metals and alloys have different physical properties.
  - An alloy of gold and copper is used in jewelry (the alloy is harder than the relatively soft pure 24 karat gold).
    - 14 karat gold is an alloy containing 58% gold.
- Alloys can be divided into 4 categories:
  - **Substitutional alloys** (the solute atoms take the positions normally occupied by a solvent atom)
    - The atoms must have similar atomic radii.
    - The elements must have similar bonding characteristics.
  - **Interstitial alloys** (the solute occupies interstitial sites in the metallic lattice)
    - One element (usually a nonmetal) must have a significantly smaller radius than the other (in order to fit into the interstitial site).
    - The alloy is much harder, stronger and less ductile than the pure metal (increased bonding between nonmetal and metal).
      - An example is steel (contains up to 3% carbon).
        - *mild steels* (<0.2% carbon; useful for chains, nails, etc)
        - *medium steels* (0.2–0.6% carbon; useful for girders, rails, etc.)
        - *high-carbon steels* (0.6–1.5% carbon; used in cutlery, tools, springs)
      - Other elements may also be added to make *alloy steels*.
        - Addition of V and Cr increases the strength of the steel and improves its resistance to stress and corrosion.
      - The most important iron alloy is stainless steel. It contains C, Cr (from *ferrochrome*, $FeCr_2$), and Ni.
  - **Heterogeneous alloys**: The components are not dispersed uniformly (e.g., pearlite steel has two phases: almost pure Fe and cementite, Fe_3C).
  - **Intermetallic compounds**: homogeneous alloys with definite properties and compositions.
    - Examples include:
    - Ni_3Al (a major component of jet aircraft engines).
    - Cr_3Pt (used to coat razor blades (to increase hardness and ability to maintain a sharp edge),
    - Co_5Sm (used in permanent magnets in lightweight headsets).
    - LaN_5 (used as the anode in nickel-metal hydride batteries).

---

[23] "Intelligent Materials" from Further Readings
[24] "Nickel-Titanium Memory Metal: A "Smart" Material Exhibiting a Solid-State Phase Change and Superelasticity" from Further Readings
[25] "Memory Metal" from Live Demonstrations

FORWARD REFERENCES
- Coordination numbers in the context of coordination transition metal compounds will be discussed in detail throughout Chapter 23.

12.4 Metallic Bonding[26,27,28,29,30]

Electron-Sea Model

- A simple model that accounts for many properties of metals is the **electron-sea model**.
  - An array of metal cations exist in a "sea" of valence electrons.
  - No electrons are localized between any two metal atoms.
  - Therefore, the electrons can flow freely through the metal.
  - Without any definite bonds, the metals are easy to deform (and are malleable and ductile) and exhibit high thermal and electrical conductivity.

Molecular-Orbital Model[31,32]

- Problems with the electron-sea model:
  - As the number of electrons increases, the strength of bonding should increase, and the melting point should increase.
  - *However*, group 6B metals (at the center of the transition metals) have the highest melting points in their respective periods.
  - We turn to molecular-orbital theory for a more general model.
- Review of molecular-orbital theory:
  - Atomic orbitals combine to make molecular orbitals that can extend over the entire molecule.
  - A molecular orbital can contain zero, one, or two electrons.
  - The number of molecular orbitals in a molecule equals the number of atomic orbitals that combine to form molecular orbitals.
- Consider how the molecular-orbital diagram for a chain of lithium atoms changes as we increase the length of the chain.
  - As the chain length increases, the number of molecular orbitals increases.
  - If the chain becomes very long, there are so many molecular orbitals that the energy separation between orbitals becomes vanishingly small.
    - As the number of orbitals increases, their energy spacing decreases.
      - As the chain length goes to infinity the allowed energy states become a continuous **band**.
      - The complex electronic structure of a bulk solid is call a **band structure**.
  - Many of the properties of metals can be understood in terms of its band structure.
  - The available electrons do not completely fill the band of orbitals.
    - Therefore, electrons can be promoted to unoccupied energy *bands*.
    - Because the energy differences between orbitals are small the promotion of electrons requires little energy.

FORWARD REFERENCES
- Molecular orbitals will be discussed in the context of the crystal field theory in Chapter 23 (Section 23.6).

---

[26] "Metallic Bonding" Activity from Instructor's Resource CD/DVD
[27] "Conducting Midshipmen – A Classroom Activity Modeling Extended Bonding in Solids" from Further Readings
[28] "An Ionic Model for Metallic Bonding" from Further Readings
[29] "Sulfur" 3-D Model from Instructor's Resource CD/DVD
[30] "Chlorine" 3-D Model from Instructor's Resource CD/DVD
[31] Figure 12.22 from Transparency Pack
[32] Figure 12.24 from Transparency Pack

12.5 Ionic Solids[33]

- Ionic solids are held together by ionic bonds: electrostatic attraction between cations and anions.
  - The high melting and boiling points reflect the strength of ionic bonds.
  - The strength depends on the charges and sizes of the ions.
    - Attractions increase in strength as the charges of the ions go up.
    - Attractions also increase as the ions get smaller.
- Valence electrons in ionic compounds are confined to the anions rather than being delocalized.
  - Thus, ionic solids tend to be electrical insulators.
- Ionic solids tend to be brittle.
  - Stress applied to an ionic solid may shift the alignment of ions and create repulsive interactions between ions of like charge.

Structures of Ionic Solids[34,35,36,37,38]

- Ionic solids tend to have close-packed arrangements of ions.
  - The arrangement is different from that of metallic solids due to the different radii and different charges of the cations and anions.
- Three common ionic structure types are commonly found for ionic solids:
  - Structure based on a primitive cubic lattice: anions sit on the lattice points at the corners of the unit cell and one cation sits inside each cell.
    - Example: CsCl
  - Structure based on a face-centered cubic lattice: anions sit on the lattice points that lie on the corners and faces of the unit cell.
    - Differences in the two-atom motif for different ionic solids yields different coordination numbers.
      - Example: NaCl: face-centered cubic lattice with sodium ions displaced from the chloride ions along the edge of the unit cell.
      - Coordination number: 6
      - Octahedral coordination environment.
      Example: ZnS: face-centered cubic lattice with zinc ions displaced from sulfide ions along the body diagonal of the unit cell.
      - Coordination number: 4
      - Tetrahedral coordination environment.
- The relative number of cations and anions determines the most stable structure type.

FORWARD REFERENCES
  - Chemistry of nonmetals forming anions in ionic solids will be discussed in Chapter 22.
  - Electrical conductivity of solutions of soluble ionic compounds will be exploited in electrochemical cells in Chapter 20 (Sections 20.3 and 20.9).
  - Many ionic solids, such as transition metal coordination compounds, will be discussed throughout Chapter 23.

12.6 Molecular Solids

- **Molecular solids** consist of atoms or molecules held together by intermolecular forces.
- Weak intermolecular forces give rise to low melting points.

---

[33] "A Model to Illustrate Brittleness of Ionic and Metallic Crystals" from Further Readings
[34] Figure 12.27 from Transparency Pack
[35] "Sodium Chloride" 3-D Model from Instructor's Resource CD/DVD
[36] "Cesium Chloride (unit cell)" 3-D Model from Instructor's Resource CD/DVD
[37] "Rutile" 3-D Model from Instructor's Resource CD/DVD
[38] "Fluorite" 3-D Model from Instructor's Resource CD/DVD

- • Intermolecular forces include dipole-dipole, dispersion forces and H-bonds.
  - • Molecular solids are usually soft.
  - • They are often gases or liquids are room temperature.
- • Efficient packing of molecules is important (because they are not regular spheres).
- • Molecular solids show poor thermal and electrical conductivity.
- • Examples: Ar(s), $CH_4(s)$, $CO_2(s)$, sucrose.

FORWARD REFERENCES
  - • Chapter 24 on organic chemistry will discuss formation and properties of many molecular substances that are solids at room temperature.

12.7 Covalent-Network Solids[39,40,41]

- • **Covalent-network solids** consist of atoms held together, in large networks or chains, with covalent bonds.
- • They have much higher melting points and are much harder than molecular solids.
  - • This is a consequence of the strong covalent bonds that connect the atoms.
- • Examples are diamond, graphite, quartz (SiO_2), and silicon carbide (SiC).
- • In diamond:
  - • each C atom has a coordination number of 4.
  - • each C atom is tetrahedral.
  - • there is a three-dimensional array of atoms.
  - • Diamond is hard, and has a high melting point (3550 °C).
- • In graphite:
  - • each C atom is arranged in a planar hexagonal ring.
  - • layers of interconnected rings are placed on top of each other.
  - • the distance between adjacent C atoms in the same layer is close to that seen in benzene (1.42 Å vs. 1.395 Å in benzene).
  - • electrons move in delocalized orbitals (good conductor).
  - • the distance between layers is large (3.41 Å).
  - • the layers are held together by weak dispersion forces.
    - • They slide easily past each other.
    - • Graphite is a good lubricant.

Semiconductors[42,43,44,45,46]

- • Semiconductors can be divided into two classes.
  - • **Elemental semiconductors** (made of only one type of atom)
    - • Elemental semiconductors include silicon, germanium, and gray tin.
    - • These elements adopt the crystal structure of diamond.
    - • In this structure, four atoms in a tetrahedral coordination geometry surround each atom.
    - • There are 4 valence electrons per atom thus, each hybrid orbital contains a single electron.
    - • This yields a structure that has an energy gap that separates totally filled and empty bands.

---

[39] Figure 12.30 from Transparency Pack
[40] "Diamond" 3-D Model from Instructor's Resource CD/DVD
[41] "Graphite" 3-D Model from Instructor's Resource CD/DVD
[42] "Band Structure" Activity from Instructor's Resource CD/DVD
[43] "The Future's Bright, the Future's Blue" from Further Readings
[44] Figure 12.31 from Transparency Pack
[45] "Zinc Sulfide (crystal structure)" 3-D Model from Instructor's Resource CD/DVD
[46] "Phosphorus" 3-D Model from Instructor's Resource CD/DVD

- The **band gap** is the energy gap between a filled **valence band** and an empty **conduction band**.
- Valence band: forms from bonding molecular orbitals.
- Conduction band: forms from antibonding molecular orbitals.
- The two bands are separated by the band gap, E_g.
  - The result is that semiconductors are conductive but less so than metals due to the presence of the band gap.
- **Compound semiconductors** (made up of two or more elements)
  - Compound semiconductors include GaAs, InP, and CdTe.
  - These also maintain the average valence electron count as elemental semiconductors (4 per atom)
- The band gaps of semiconductors range from a few tenths of an electron volt to about 3 eV.
- Periodic trends are seen.
  - Moving down a group, the band gap decreases.
    - C → Si → Ge → Sn
  - The band gap increases as the difference in group numbers of elements increases.

Semiconductor Doping

- Electrical conductivity may be influenced by **doping**.
  - Doping is the addition of small amounts of impurity atoms to the semiconductors.
  - Doping yields different kinds of semiconductors.
    - *n-type:* The dopant atom has more valence electrons than the host atom.
      - This adds electrons to the conduction band.
      - An example is phosphorous doped into silicon.
    - *p-type:* The dopant atom has fewer valence electrons than the host atom.
      - This leads to more electron vacancies or **holes** in the valence band.
    - An example is boron doped into silicon.

FORWARD REFERENCES

- Network-covalent solids will be discussed further in Chapter 22.
- The chemistry of Si and Ge will be discussed in Chapter 22 (section 22.10).

12.8 Polymeric Solids[47,48,49,50]

- **Polymers** are molecules of high molecular weight that are made by *polymerization* (joining together) of smaller molecules of low molecular mass.
- The building block small molecules for polymers are called **monomers**.
  - Examples of polymers include plastics, DNA, proteins, and rubber.
- **Plastics** are materials that can be formed into various shapes, usually with heat and pressure.
  - **Thermoplastic** materials can be reshaped.
    - Recycling of *polypropylene* takes advantage of this property!
  - **Thermosetting plastic** materials are shaped by an irreversible process.
    - They are not readily reshaped.
  - **Elastomers** are materials that exhibit elastic or rubbery behavior.
    - If a moderate amount of a deforming force is added, the elastomer will return to its original shape.

---

[47] "Pictorial Analogies V: Polymers" from Further Readings
[48] "Polymer Literature and Samples for Classroom Use" from Further Readings
[49]"Thermosetting Resins" from Further Readings
[50] "Polymers Are Everywhere" from Further Readings

Making Polymers[51,52,53,54,55,56,57,58,59,60,61,62,63,64]

- Many synthetic polymers have a backbone of C–C bonds.
- Carbon atoms have the ability to form unusually strong stable bonds with each other.
  - Example: Ethylene $H_2C=CH_2$.
    - Ethylene can polymerize by opening the C–C π bond to form C–C σ bonds with adjacent ethylene molecules.
      - The result is polyethylene.
  - This is an example of **addition polymerization**.
    - Ethylene molecules are added to each other.
- In **condensation polymerization** two molecules are joined to form a larger molecule by the elimination of a small molecule (like water).
  - An example of such a **condensation reaction**:
    - An amine ($R–NH_2$) condenses with a carboxylic acid ($R–COOH$) to form water and an amide.
    - A biological example of this reaction is the linking of amino acids to form polymer chains–proteins!
      - A protein is an example of a **copolymer**–a polymer formed from different monomers.
  - Another example of condensation polymerization is the formation of nylon 6,6.
    - Diamine and adipic acid are joined to form nylon 6,6.

Structure and Physical Properties of Polymers[65,66,67,68,69,70,71,72,73]

- Synthetic and natural polymers commonly consist of a collection of *macromolecules* of different molecular weights.
- Polymers are fairly amorphous (noncrystalline).
  - Polymer chains tend to be flexible and easily entangled or folded.

---

[51] "Alkanes: Abundant, Pervasive, Important, and Essential" from Further Readings
[52] "Polyethylene" 3-D Model from Instructor's Resource CD/DVD
[53] "Slime: Gelation of Poly(vinyl alcohol) with Borax" From Live Demonstrations
[54] "The Gelation of Polyvinyl Alcohol with Borax. A Novel Class Participation Experiment Involving the Preparation and Properties of a 'Slime'" from Live Demonstrations
[55] "How to Learn and Have Fun with Poly(Vinyl Alcohol) and White Glue" from Further Readings
[56] "Polymers and Processes" from Further Readings
[57] "JCE Resources for Chemistry and Recycling" from Further Readings
[58] "Wallace Hume Carothers and Nylon, the First Completely Synthetic Fiber" from Further Readings
[59] "Neoprene and Nylon Stockings: The Legacy of Wallace Hume Carothers" from Further Readings
[60] Table 12.5 from Transparency Pack
[61] "Dr. Baekeland's Bakelite" from Further Readings
[62] "Synthesis of Nylon 6,10" Movie from Instructor's Resource CD/DVD
[63] "Synthesis of Nylon" from Live Demonstrations
[64] "The Origin of the Name 'Nylon'" from Further Readings
[65] "Polymer Structure–Organic Aspects (Definitions)" from Further Readings
[66] "Performance Polymers" from Further Readings
[67] "The Disappearing Coffee Cup" from Live Demonstrations
[68] "Solid Foams" from Live Demonstrations
[69] "Polyurethane Foams" from Live Demonstrations
[70] "Thermosetting Resins" from Further Readings
[71] "Elastomers I: Natural Rubber" from Further Readings
[72] "Plastic Fantastic" from Further Readings
[73] "Rubber Reclamation" from Further Readings

- They soften over a wide range of temperatures.
- They may show some ordering.
  - The degree of *crystallinity* reflects the extent of the order.
- Stretching or extruding a polymer can increase crystallinity.
- The degree of crystallinity is also strongly influenced by average molecular mass:
  - Low-density polyethylene (LDPE), which is used in plastic wrap, has an average molecular mass of 10^4 amu.
  - High-density polyethylene (HDPE), which is used in milk cartons, has an average molecular mass of 10^6 amu.
- We can modify the polymeric properties by the addition of substances with lower molecular mass.
  - **Plasticizers** are molecules that interfere with interactions between polymer chains.
    - These make polymers more pliable.
- Bonds formed between polymer chains make the polymer stiffer.
  - Forming such bonds is referred to as **cross-linking**.
    - The greater the number of cross-links, the more rigid the polymer becomes.
- Example: Natural rubber is too soft and too chemically reactive to be useful.
  - **Vulcanization** of rubber involves the formation of cross-links in the polymer chain.
  - Rubber is cross-linked in a process employing short chains of sulfur atoms.
  - Vulcanized rubber has more useful properties.
    - It is more elastic and less susceptible to chemical reaction than natural rubber.

FORWARD REFERENCES
- Further mention of sulfur chemistry, including vulcanization of rubber, will be made in Chapter 22 (section 22.6).
- The use of halogens in lubricants and plastics (Teflon) will be described in Chapter 22 (section 22.4).
- Condensation reaction in polymerization of phosphates will be described in Chapter 22 (section 22.8).

12.9 Nanomaterials

- **Nanomaterials** have dimensions on the 1 – 100 nm scale.

Semiconductors on the Nanoscale[74,75,76,77,78,79,80]

- Semiconductor particles with diameters in the 1 to 10 nm range are called *quantum dots*.
- Semiconductor band gaps change substantially with size in the 1-10 nm range.
  - The smaller the particle, the larger the band gap. Consider cadmium phosphide.
    - On a macrolevel it looks black. The band gap is small and it absorbs most of the visible light.
    - When the particle is made smaller, the color changes until it looks white.
      - No visible light is absorbed.
      - The band gap is so large that only UV light can excite electrons to the conduction band.
  - By appropriately tuning the band gap of the quantum dots, all colors of the rainbow can be obtained from one material.

---

[74] "It's a Small World" from Further Readings
[75] "Fishing for New Materials" from Further Readings
[76] "Big Bucks from Small Science" from Further Readings
[77] "The Smallest Revolution" from Further Readings
[78] "A Tube of Tubes" from Further Readings
[79] "Water-Filled Polymer Tubes" from Further Readings
[80] "A Quantum Paintbox" from Further Readings

- *Quantum wires* have also been produced. A quantum wire is a semiconductor wire that may have a very long length but a diameter that is only a few nanometers.

Metals on the Nanoscale

- The *mean free path* of an electron is the average distance it moves before bumping into something and being scattered.
- The mean free path of an electron in a metal at room temperature is on the 1-100 nm scale.
  - Metals with particle sizes of 1-100 nm have unusual properties.
  - Unusual properties of metal nanoproperties that are being explored include applications in biomedical imaging and chemical detection.

Fullerenes, Carbon Nanotubes, and Graphene[81,82,83,84]

- In 1985 molecules composed of 60 carbon atoms, C_{60} molecules, were first described.
  - C_{60} molecules are among a class of molecules of carbon atoms known as fullerenes.
  - Buckyball or buckminsterfullerene may be prepared by electrically evaporating graphite in a helium atmosphere.
- Because fullerenes are composed of individual molecules, they dissolve in various organic solvents while diamond and graphite do not.
- Carbon nanotubes are sheets of graphite rolled up and capped at one or both ends by half of a C_{60} molecule.
  - May be either *multiwall* or *single-walled*.
    - Multiwall tubes consist of tubes within tubes.
    - Single-walled tubes may be 1000 nm or longer but only 1 nm in diameter.
- Carbon nanotubes may be made either semiconducting or metallic without the need for doping.
- Carbon nanotubes are also being explored for their mechanical properties.
- The two-dimensional form of carbon, graphene, is the most recent low-dimensional form of carbon to be isolated and studied.
  - In 2004 sheets of carbon atoms with a honeycomb structure were isolated and identified.
  - Graphene has interesting properties:
    - It is very strong and has a high thermal conductivity.
    - Its electronic structure is like that of a semiconductor with an energy gap of zero.
    - It can sustain very high electrical current densities.

FORWARD REFERENCES

- The work of Michael Faraday will be discussed in Chapter 20 (section 20.5).
- Fullerenes will be further discussed in Chapter 22 (section 22.9).

---

[81] Figure 12.48 from Transparency Pack
[82] "Fullerenes" from Further Readings
[83] "Buckytubes" from Further Readings
[84] "Buckminsterfullerene" 3-D Model from Instructor's Resource CD/DVD

Further Readings:

1. John J. Fortman, "Pictorial Analogies II: Types of Solids," *J. Chem. Educ.,* Vol. 70, **1993**, 57–58.

2. Frank Galasso, "The Importance of Understanding Structure," *J. Chem. Educ.*, Vol. 70, **1993**, 287–290. The relationship between unit cells and the structure of solids is covered in this article.

3. Henry S. Lipson, "The Fifth Bragg Lecture; W. L. Bragg-Scientific Revolutionary," *J. Chem. Educ.*, Vol. 60, **1983**, 405–407.

4. Amand A. Lucas, P. Lambin, R. Mairesse and M. Mathot, "Revealing the Backbone Structure of B-DNA from Laser Optical Simulations of its X-ray Diffraction Diagram," *J. Chem. Educ.*, Vol. 76, **1999**, 378–383.

5. Amand L. Lucas, "A-DNA and B-DNA: Comparing their Historical X-ray Fiber Diffraction Images," *J. Chem. Educ.*, Vol. 85, **2008**, 737–743.

6. J. C. Speckman, "The Discovery of X-ray Diffraction by Crystals," *J. Chem. Educ.*, Vol. 57, **1980**, 489–490.

7. Peter P. Edwards and M. J. Sienko, "On the Occurrence of Metallic Character in the Periodic Table of the Elements," *J. Chem. Educ.*, Vol. 60, **1983**, 691–696.

8. Craig A. Rogers, "Intelligent Materials," *Scientific American,* **September 1995**, 154–157.

9. Kathleen R. C. Gissser, Margaret J. Geselbracht, Ann Cappellari, Lynn Hunsberger, Arthur B. Ellis, John Perepezko, and George Lisensky, "Nickel-Titanium Memory Metal: A "Smart" Material Exhibiting a Solid-State Phase Change and Superelasticity," *J. Chem. Educ.*, Vol. 71, **1994**, 334–340.

10. Joseph F. Lomax, "Conducting Midshipmen-A Classroom Activity Modeling Extended Bonding in Solids," *J. Chem. Educ.*, Vol. 69, **1992**, 794–795.

11. Frank Rioux, "An Ionic Model for Metallic Bonding" ," *J. Chem. Educ.*, Vol. 62, **1985**, 383–384.

12. James P. Birk, "A Model to Illustrate the Brittleness of Ionic and Metallic Crystals," *J. Chem. Educ.*, Vol. 62, **1985**, 667. Models made from magnets and plexiglass are used to illustrate some properties of crystals.

13. John Emsley, "The Future's Bright, the Future's Blue," *Chemistry World,* **March 2004**, 30–33. A short article on promising semiconductors.

14. John H. Fortman, "Pictorial Analogies V: Polymers," *J. Chem. Educ.*, Vol. 70, **1993**, 403–404. Several analogies for polymer formation are featured in this reference.

15. John J. Meister, "Polymer Literature and Samples for Classroom Use," *J. Chem. Educ.*, Vol. 72, **1995**, 593–595. This reference provides a list of sources for suppliers of polymer samples as well as polymer literature references.

16. Raymond B. Seymour, "Polymers Are Everywhere," *J. Chem. Educ.*, Vol. 65, **1988**, 327–334. Uses of polymers throughout history are outlined in this reference.

17. William B. Jensen, "The Origin of the Name "Nylon," *J. Chem. Educ.*, Vol. 82, **2005**, 676.

18. Charles E. Carraher, Jr. and Raymond B. Seymour, "Polymer Structure–Organic Aspects (Definitions)," *J. Chem. Educ.*, Vol. 65, **1988**, 314–319.

19. Raymond B. Seymour, "Alkanes: Abundant, Pervasive, Important, and Essential," *J. Chem. Educ.*, Vol. 66, **1989**, 59–63.

20. Erica K. Jacobsen, "JCE Resources for Chemistry and Recycling," *J. Chem. Educ.*, Vol. 84, **2007**, 212–213. An annotated bibliography of past *Journal of Chemical Education* articles dealing with recycling.

21. V. de Zea Bermudez, P. Passos de Almeida, and J. Feria Seita, "How to Learn and Have Fun with Poly(Vinyl Alcohol) and White Glue," *J. Chem. Educ.*, Vol. 75, **1998**, 1410–1418.

22. Melissa Lee, "Polymers and Processes," *Chemistry in Britain*, Vol. 31(9), **September 1998**.

23. George B. Kauffman, "Wallace Hume Carothers and Nylon, the First Completely Synthetic Fiber," *J. Chem. Educ.*, Vol. 65, **1988**, 803–808.

24. Carol Cummings, "Neoprene and Nylon Stockings: The Legacy of Wallace Hume Carothers," *J. Chem. Educ.*, Vol. 61, **1984**, 241–242.

25. Alan Gray, "Performance Polymers," *Chemistry in Britain*, Vol. 34(3), **March 1998**, 44–45. A short article on innovations in engineering thermoplastics.

26. Miriam C. Nagel, "Dr. Baekeland's Bakelite," *J. Chem. Educ.*, Vol. 57, **1980**, 811–812. A short historical article about the scientist who prepared the first commercially successful plastic.

27. W. Peng and B. Riedl, "Thermosetting Resins," *J. Chem. Educ.*, Vol. 72, **1995**, 587–592. A general description of resins or thermosets, their applications and manner of curing is featured in this reference.

28. Kathryn R. Williams, "Rubber Reclamation," *J. Chem. Educ.*, Vol. 84, **2007**, 217-218.

29. George B. Kauffman and Raymond B. Seymour, "Elastomers I: Natural Rubber," *J. Chem. Educ.*, Vol. 67, **1990**, 422–425.

30. Michael Chisholm, "Plastic Fantastic," *Chemistry in Britain*, Vol. 34(4), **April 1998**, 33–36. An article looking at the uses of polymethyl methacrylate.

31. Mary E. Harris, "Polymers in the Field and Track," *J. Chem. Educ.*, Vol. 85, **2008**, 1323-1325.

32. Sandy Van Natta and John P. Williams, "Impact of Polymers in Impact Sports," *J. Chem. Educ.*, Vol. 85, **2008**, 1326-1329.

33. William B. Jensen, "The Origin of the Polymer Concept," *J. Chem. Educ.*, Vol. 85, **2008**, 624-625.

34. Philip Ball, "It's a Small World," *Chemistry World*, **February 2004**, 30–36.

35. Michael Gross, "Fishing for New Materials," *Chemistry World,* **July 2003**, 33–35.

36. Michael Kenward, "Big Bucks from Small Science," *Chemistry in Britain*, **April 2003**, 24–26.

37. Michael Gross, "The Smallest Revolution," *Chemistry in Britain*, **May 2002**, 36–39.

38. Bethany Halford, "A Tube of Tubes," *Chem. Eng. News*, **August 1, 2004**, 23.

39. Michael Freemantle, "Water-Filled Polymer Tubes," *Chem. Eng. News*, **July 12, 2004**, 7.

40. Jonathan Cox, "A Quantum Paintbox," *Chemistry in Britain*, **September 2003**, 21–25. A short article on quantum dots.

41. Robert F. Curl and Richard E. Smalley, "Fullerenes," *Scientific American*, **October 1991**, 54–63. This is an early review on fullerenes.

42. Philip E. Ross, "Buckytubes," *Scientific American*, **December 1991**, 24.

Live Demonstrations:

1. Keenan E. Dungey, George Lisensky, and S. Michael Condren, "Kixium Monolayers: A Simple Alternative to the Bubble Raft Model for Close-Packed Spheres," *J. Chem. Educ.*, Vol. 76, **1999**, 618–619.

2. Daryl L. Ostercamp, "Close Packing of Identical Spheres," *J. Chem. Educ.*, Vol. 69, **1992**, 162. An overhead projector demonstration of close packing.

3. James Birk, and Ellen Yezierski, "Paper-and-Glue Unit Cell Models," *J. Chem. Educ.*, Vol. 80, **2003**, 157–159. This is an origami-inspired demonstration, tested by Michael Laing.

4. Anthony T. Jacob, Charles I. Pechmann, and Arthur B. Ellis, "A Double-Decker Levitation Experiment Using a Sandwich of Superconductors," *J. Chem. Educ.*, Vol. 65, **1988**, 1094–1095.

5. Ethel Z. Casassa, Arlyne M. Sarquis, and C. H. Van Dyke, "The Gelation of Polyvinyl Alcohol with Borax. A Novel Class Participation Experiment Involving the Preparation and Properties of a 'Slime'," *J. Chem. Educ.*, Vol. 63, **1986**, 57–60. A classic demonstration of polymer formation! Making SLIME!!

6. Bassam Z. Shakhashiri, "'Slime': Gelation of Poly(vinyl alcohol) with Borax," *Chemical Demonstrations: A Handbook for Teachers of Chemistry, Volume 3* (Madison: The University of Wisconsin Press, **1989**), pp. 362–363.

7. Bassam Z. Shakhashiri, "Solid Foams," *Chemical Demonstrations: A Handbook for Teachers of Chemistry, Volume 3* (Madison: The University of Wisconsin Press, **1989**), pp. 348–350. A demonstration of the formation and destruction of solid foams.

8. Bassam Z. Shakhashiri, "Polyurethane Foam," *Chemical Demonstrations: A Handbook for Teachers of Chemistry, Volume 1* (Madison: The University of Wisconsin Press, **1983**), pp. 216–218. Polyurethane foam is prepared in this demonstration of polymer formation.

9. Lee. R. Summerlin, Christie L. Borgford, and Julie B. Ealy, "The Disappearing Coffee Cup," *Chemical Demonstrations, A Sourcebook for Teachers*, Volume 2 (Washington: American Chemical Society, **1988**), pp. 96. A polystyrene coffee cup is "melted" in a pool of acetone.

10. Lee. R. Summerlin, and James. L. Ealy, Jr., "Synthesis of Nylon," *Chemical Demonstrations, A Sourcebook for Teachers*, Volume 1 (Washington: American Chemical Society, **1988**), pp.172–173.

Chapter 13. Properties of Solutions

Media Resources

Figures and Tables in Transparency Pack:	**Section:**
Figure 13.3 Dissolution of an Ionic Solid in Water	13.1 The Solution Process
Figure 13.4 Enthalpy Changes Accompanying the Solution Process	13.1 The Solution Process
Figure 13.11 Hydrogen Bonding Involving OH Groups	13.3 Factors Affecting Solubility
Figure 13.18 Solubilities of Some Ionic Compounds in Water as a Function of Temperature	13.3 Factors Affecting Solubility
Figure 13.19 Solubilities of Four Gases in Water as a Function of Temperature	13.3 Factors Affecting Solubility
Figure 13.20 Calculating Molality and Molarity from Solute Mass, Solvent Mass, and Solution Density	13.4 Expressing Solution Concentration
Figure 13.23 Phase Diagram Illustrating Boiling-Point Elevation	13.5 Colligative Properties
Figure 13.24 Phase Diagram Illustrating Freezing-Point Depression	13.5 Colligative Properties
Figure 13.25 Osmosis	13.5 Colligative Properties
Figure 13.27 Ion Pairing and Colligative Properties	13.5 Colligative Properties

Activities:	**Section:**
Boiling-Point Elevation and Freezing-Point Depression	13.5 Colligative Properties
Determination of Molar Mass	13.5 Colligative Properties

Animations:	**Section:**
Dissolution of NaCl in Water	13.1 The Solution Process
Henry's Law	13.3 Factors Affecting Solubility
Raoult's Law	13.5 Colligative Properties
Osmosis and Osmotic Pressure	13.5 Colligative Properties

Movies:	**Section:**
Dissolution of $KMnO_4$ in Water	13.1 The Solution Process

3-D Models:	**Section:**
Water	13.1 The Solution Process
Sodium Chloride (1 × 1 Unit Cell)	13.1 The Solution Process
Hydrated Magnesium Cation	13.1 The Solution Process
Deprotonated Hydrated Aluminum Cation	13.1 The Solution Process
Hydrated Aluminum Cation	13.1 The Solution Process
Pentane	13.1 The Solution Process
Acetone	13.1 The Solution Process
Chloroform	13.1 The Solution Process
Ethanol	13.1 The Solution Process
Vitamin C (ascorbic acid)	13.3 Factors Affecting Solubility
Vitamin A	13.3 Factors Affecting Solubility

Cyclohexane	13.3 Factors Affecting Solubility
Glucose	13.3 Factors Affecting Solubility
Ibuprofen	13.3 Factors Affecting Solubility
Alanine	13.3 Factors Affecting Solubility
Caffeine	13.4 Expressing Solution Concentration
Adrenaline	13.5 Colligative Properties

Other Resources

Further Readings:	**Section:**
The Use of Dots in Chemical Formulas	13.1 The Solution Process
Crystallization from a Supersaturated Solution of Sodium Acetate	13.2 Saturated Solutions and Solubility
Polarity, Miscibility, and Surface Tension	13.3 Factors Affecting Solubility
An Analogy to Illustrate Miscibility of Liquids	13.3 Factors Affecting Solubility
Using Computer-Based Visualization Strategies to Improve Students' Understanding of Molecular Polarity and Miscibility	13.3 Factors Affecting Solubility
Applications of Solubility Data	13.3 Factors Affecting Solubility
Henry's Law and Noisy Knuckles	13.3 Factors Affecting Solubility
Henry's Law: A Retrospective	13.3 Factors Affecting Solubility
Soft Drink Bubbles	13.3 Factors Affecting Solubility
Candy Sprinkles to Illustrate One Part Per Million	13.4 Expressing Solution Concentration
An Alternative Introduction to the Mole Fraction	13.4 Expressing Solution Concentration
Mole Fraction Analogies	13.4 Expressing Solution Concentration
One Cool Chemist	13.5 Colligative Properties
Antifreeze Solutions: The Colligative Properties of Antifreeze	13.5 Colligative Properties
Freeze-Proof Bugs	13.5 Colligative Properties
Seawater Gets Fresh	13.5 Colligative Properties
Salts Are Mostly NOT Ionized	13.5 Colligative Properties
J. H. van't Hoff	13.5 Colligative Properties
The Impact of Colloid Science	13.6 Colloids
Colloidal Systems	13.6 Colloids
Put the Brakes on Wastewater Emulsions	13.6 Colloids
Surfactants: The Ubiquitous Amphiphiles	13.6 Colloids
Clearly Cleaner	13.6 Colloids
Blood-Chemistry Tutorials: Teaching Biological Applications of General Chemistry Material	13.6 Colloids
Chemistry and Physics in the Kitchen	13.6 Colloids

Live Demonstrations:	**Section:**
Copper Sulfate: Blue to White	13.1 The Solution Process
Supersaturation	13.2 Saturated Solutions and Solubility
Crystallization from Supersaturated Solutions of Sodium Acetate	13.3 Factors Affecting Solubility
Nonadditivity of Volumes	13.3 Factors Affecting Solubility
Solubility of Alcohols	13.3 Factors Affecting Solubility
Why Don't Water and Oil Mix?	13.3 Factors Affecting Solubility
Effect of Temperature and Pressure on the Solubility of Gases in Liquids	13.3 Factors Affecting Solubility

A Simple Demonstration Model of Osmosis   13.5 Colligative Properties

Osmotic Pressure of a Sugar Solution   13.5 Colligative Properties

Osmosis through the Membrane of an Egg   13.5 Colligative Properties

Osmosis and the Egg Membrane   13.5 Colligative Properties

Color of the Sunset: The Tyndall Effect   13.6 Colloids

Illustrating the Properties of Magic Sand   13.6 Colloids

Chapter 13. Properties of Solutions

Common Student Misconceptions

- Students often confuse dilute and concentrated; weak and strong are often confused.
- Students often do not appreciate the *driving forces* behind the formation of a solution.
- Students often confuse dissolution with melting.
- Students do not realize that crystallization is the reverse of dissolution.
- Many student think that solutions can only be made either by mixing two liquids or dissolving a solid in a liquid.
- Students often confuse solution with solvation.
- Students often think that every mixture is a solution.
- Students often do not appreciate how *unusual* water is.
- Students often forget that calculations of molality require the mass of *solvent*, not *solution*.
- Students often do not realize that colloids, like solutions, can occur in all three states of matter.

Teaching Tips

- Remind students that even the so-called *insoluble* compounds dissolve to *some* extent in water.
- The differences between the definitions of molarity (*M*) and molality (*m*) and between their respective notations and pronunciations must be emphasized to avoid confusion.
- Remind students that, for more concentrated solutions, the density of the solution is needed to relate molarity and molality.
- The assumption that the density of a dilute aqueous solution is identical to that of pure water (1 g/mL) is a valid at normal temperatures (to two significant figures).
- It may be helpful to note the similarity between Raoult's law ($P_A = X_A P°_A$) and the expression for partial pressures in a mixture of gases derived from Dalton's law ($P_A = X_A P_{tot}$).

Lecture Outline

13.1 The Solution Process[1,2,3,4]

- A *solution* is a homogeneous mixture of solute and solvent.
- Solutions may be gases, liquids, or solids,
- Each substance present is a *component* of the solution.
    - The *solvent* is the component present in the largest amount.
    - The other components are the *solutes*.
    - We will be particularly interested in *aqueous solutions* which contain water as the solvent.

The Natural Tendency Toward Mixing

- Consider the formation of a gaseous solution of $O_2(g)$ and $Ar(g)$.
    - Initially they are separated by a barrier.
    - When the barrier is removed, the gases mix to form a homogeneous mixture, or solution.
    - The mixing of gases is a *spontaneous* process.
        - It occurs without input of energy from the surroundings.

---

[1] "Dissolution of NaCl in Water" Animation from Instructor's Resource CD/DVD
[2] Figure 13.3 from Transparency Pack
[3] "Sodium Chloride (1 × 1 Unit Cell)" 3-D Model from Instructor's Resource CD/DVD
[4] "Dissolution of $KMnO_4$ in Water" Movie from Instructor's Resource CD/DVD

- *Entropy* is the thermodynamic quantity that measures the extent of the spreading of the molecules and their associated kinetic energies.
  - The mixing that occurs as the solution is formed represents an increase in entropy.
  - Formation of a solution is favored by the increase in entropy that accompanies mixing.

The Effect of Intermolecular Forces on Solution Formation[5,6,7,8,9]

- Intermolecular forces become rearranged in the process of making solutions with condensed phases.
- Intermolecular forces operate between solute and solvent particles in a solution.
  - Three kinds of intermolecular interactions are involved in solution formation:
    - *Solute-solute* interactions between solute particles.
      - These must be overcome in order to disperse the particles through the solvent.
    - *Solvent-solvent* interactions between solvent particles.
      - These must be overcome to make room for the solute particles in the solvent.
    - *Solvent-solute* interactions between solvent and solute particles.
      - These occur as the particles mix.
  - Consider NaCl (solute) dissolving in water (solvent):
    - Water molecules orient themselves on the NaCl crystals.
    - H-bonds between the water molecules have to be broken.
    - NaCl dissociates into Na^+ and Cl^-.
    - Ion-dipole forces form between the Na^+ and the negative end of the water dipole.
      - Similar ion-dipole interactions form between the Cl^- and the positive end of the water dipole.
    - Such an interaction between solvent and solute is called **solvation**.
      - If water is the solvent, the interaction is called **hydration**.

Energetics of Solution Formation[10]

- There are three steps involving energy in the formation of a solution:
  - Separation of solute molecules (ΔH_{solute}),
  - Separation of solvent molecules ($\Delta H_{solvent}$), and
  - Formation of solute-solvent interactions (ΔH_{mix}).
- We define the enthalpy change in the solution process as:

$$\Delta H_{soln} = \Delta H_{solute} + \Delta H_{solvent} + \Delta H_{mix}$$

- ΔH_{soln} can either be positive or negative, depending on the intermolecular forces.
  - To determine whether ΔH_{soln} is positive or negative, we consider the strengths of all solute-solute, solvent-solvent, and solute-solvent interactions:
  - Breaking attractive intermolecular forces is always endothermic.
    - ΔH_{solute} and $\Delta H_{solvent}$ are both positive.
  - Forming attractive intermolecular forces is always exothermic.
    - ΔH_{mix} is always negative.
- It is possible to have either $\Delta H_{mix} > (\Delta H_{solute} + \Delta H_{solvent})$ or $\Delta H_{mix} < (\Delta H_{solute} + \Delta H_{solvent})$.
  - Examples:
    - $MgSO_4$ added to water has $\Delta H_{soln} = -91.2$ kJ/mol.
    - NH_4NO_3 added to water has $\Delta H_{soln} = + 26.4$ kJ/mol.

---

[5] "Water" 3-D Model from Instructor's Resource CD/DVD
[6] "Pentane" 3-D Model from Instructor's Resource CD/DVD
[7] "Acetone" 3-D Model from Instructor's Resource CD/DVD
[8] "Chloroform" 3-D Model from Instructor's Resource CD/DVD
[9] "Ethanol" 3-D Model from Instructor's Resource CD/DVD
[10] Figure 13.4 from Transparency Pack

- MgSO$_4$ is often used in instant heat packs and NH$_4$NO$_3$ is often used in instant cold packs.
- How can we predict if a solution will form?
  - In general, solutions form if the ΔH_{soln} is negative.
  - If ΔH_{soln} is too endothermic, a solution will not form.
  - "Rule of thumb": polar solvents dissolve polar solutes.
    - Nonpolar solvents dissolve nonpolar solutes.
  - Consider the process of mixing NaCl in gasoline.
    - Only weak interactions are possible because gasoline is nonpolar.
    - These interactions do not compensate for the separation of ions from one another.
      - Result: NaCl doesn't dissolve to any great extent in gasoline.
  - Consider the process of mixing a polar liquid solute (water) with a nonpolar liquid solvent (octane (C$_8$H$_{18}$)).
    - Water has strong H-bonds.
    - The energy required to break these H-bonds is not compensated for by interactions between water and octane.
      - Result: water and octane do not mix.

Solution Formation and Chemical Reactions[11,12,13,14]

- Some solutions form by physical processes and some by chemical processes.
  - Consider:
$$Ni(s) + 2HCl(aq) \rightarrow NiCl_2(aq) + H_2(g)$$
  - Note that the chemical form of the substance being dissolved has changed during this process (Ni $\rightarrow$ NiCl$_2$)
  - When all the water is removed from the solution, no Ni is found, only NiCl$_2$·6H$_2$O remains.
  - Therefore, the dissolution of Ni in HCl is a chemical process.
  - By contrast:
$$NaCl(s) + H_2O\ (l) \rightarrow Na^+(aq) + Cl^-(aq).$$
  - When the water is removed from the solution, NaCl is found.
  - Therefore, NaCl dissolution is a physical process.

FORWARDS REFERENCES
- Hydrolysis of metal ions will be brought up again in Chapter 16 (section 16.11).
- Thermodynamics of processes will be further discussed throughout Chapter 19.
- Rust is a hydrate (Chapter 20, section 20.8).

13.2 Saturated Solutions and Solubility[15,16,17]
- As a solid dissolves, a solution forms:
  - Solute + solvent $\rightarrow$ solution
- The opposite process is **crystallization**.
  - Solution $\rightarrow$ solute + solvent
- If crystallization and dissolution are in equilibrium with undissolved solute, the solution is **saturated**.
  - There will be no further increase in the amount of dissolved solute.

---

[11] "The Use of Dots in Chemical Formulas" from Further Readings
[12] "Hydrated Magnesium Cation" 3-D Model from Instructor's Resource CD/DVD
[13] "Deprotonated Hydrated Aluminum Cation" 3-D Model from Instructor's Resource CD/DVD
[14] "Hydrated Aluminum Cation" 3-D Model from Instructor's Resource CD/DVD
[15] "Crystallization from a Supersaturated Solution of Sodium Acetate" from Further Readings
[16] "Supersaturation" from Live Demonstrations
[17] "Crystallization from Supersaturated Solutions of Sodium Acetate" from Live Demonstrations

- **Solubility** is the amount of solute required to form a saturated solution.
    - A solution with a concentration of dissolved solute that is less than the solubility is said to be **unsaturated**.
    - A solution is said to be **supersaturated** if more solute is dissolved than in a saturated solution.

FORWARDS REFERENCES
- Solubility equilibria will be further discussed in Chapter 17 (section 17.4).
- Various crystalline substances (anhydrous and hydrated) for transition metal compounds will be described throughout Chapter 23.

13.3 Factors Affecting Solubility[18,19,20,21]

- The tendency of a substance to dissolve in another depends on:
    - the nature of the solute.
    - the nature of the solvent.
    - the temperature.
    - the pressure (for gases).

Solute-Solvent Interactions[22,23,24,25,26,27,28,29,30,31]

- Intermolecular forces are an important factor in determining solubility of a solute in a solvent.
    - The stronger the attraction between solute and solvent molecules, the greater the solubility.
        - For example, polar liquids tend to dissolve in polar solvents.
        - Favorable dipole-dipole interactions exist (solute-solute, solvent-solvent, and solute-solvent).
- Pairs of liquids that mix in any proportions are said to be **miscible**.
    - Example: Ethanol and water are miscible liquids.
- In contrast, **immiscible** liquids do not mix significantly.
    - Example: Gasoline and water are immiscible.
- Consider the solubility of alcohols in water.
    - Water and ethanol are miscible because the broken hydrogen bonds in both pure liquids are re-established in the mixture.
- However, not all alcohols are miscible with water.
    - Why?
    - The number of carbon atoms in a chain affects solubility.
        - The greater the number of carbons in the chain, the more the molecule behaves like a hydrocarbon.
        - Thus, the more C atoms in the alcohol, the lower its solubility in water.

---

[18] "Vitamin C (ascorbic acid)" 3-D Model from Instructor's Resource CD/DVD
[19] "Vitamin A" 3-D Model from Instructor's Resource CD/DVD
[20] "Alanine" 3-D Model from Instructor's Resource CD/DVD
[21] "Ibuprofen" 3-D Model from Instructor's Resource CD/DVD
[22] "Nonadditivity of Volumes" from Live Demonstrations
[23] Figure 13.11 from Transparency Pack
[24] "Polarity, Miscibility, and Surface Tension" from Further Readings
[25] "An Analogy to Illustrate Miscibility of Liquids" from Further Readings
[26] "Solubility of Alcohols" from Live Demonstrations
[27] "Using Computer-Based Visualization Strategies to Improve Students' Understanding of Molecular Polarity and Miscibility" from Further Readings
[28] "Applications of Solubility Data" from Further Readings
[29] "Why Don't Water and Oil Mix?" from Live Demonstrations
[30] "Cyclohexane" 3-D Model from Instructor's Resource CD/DVD
[31] "Glucose" 3-D Model from Instructor's Resource CD/DVD

- Increasing the number of –OH groups within a molecule increases its solubility in water.
  - The greater the number of –OH groups along the chain, the more solute-water H-bonding is possible.
- Generalization: "like dissolves like".
  - Substances with similar intermolecular attractive forces tend to be soluble in one another.
    - The more polar bonds in the molecule, the better it dissolves in a polar solvent.
    - The less polar the molecule the less likely it is to dissolve in a polar solvent and the more likely it is to dissolve in a nonpolar solvent.
- Network solids do not dissolve because the strong intermolecular forces in the solid are not reestablished in any solution.

Pressure Effects[32,33,34,35]

- The solubility of a gas in a liquid is a function of the partial pressure of the gas over the solution.
  - Solubilities of solids and liquids are not greatly affected by pressure.
- With higher gas pressure, more molecules of gas are close to the surface of the solution and the probability of a gas molecule striking the surface and entering the solution is increased.
  - Therefore, the higher the pressure, the greater the solubility.
- The lower the pressure, the smaller the number of molecules of gas close to the surface of the solution resulting in a lower solubility.
  - The solubility of a gas in a liquid solvent is directly proportional to the partial pressure of the gas above the solution.
  - This statement is called **Henry's law**.
  - Henry's law may be expressed mathematically as:
  $$S_g = kP_g$$
    - Where S_g is the solubility of gas, P_g the partial pressure, k = Henry's law constant.
    - Note that the Henry's law constant differs for each solute-solvent pair and differs with temperature.
- An application of Henry's law is the preparation of carbonated soda.
  - Carbonated beverages are bottled under $P_{CO_2} > 1$ atm.
  - As the bottle is opened, P_{CO_2} *decreases* and the solubility of CO_2 decreases.
  - Therefore, bubbles of CO_2 escape from solution.

Temperature Effects[36,37,38]

- Experience tells us that sugar dissolves better in warm water than in cold water.
  - The solubility of most solid solutes in water increases as the solution temperature increases.
  - Sometimes solubility decreases as temperature increases (e.g., $Ce_2(SO_4)_3$).
- Experience tells us that carbonated beverages go flat as they get warm.
  - The solubility of gas in water decreases with increasing temperature.
- An environmental application of this is thermal pollution.
  - *Thermal pollution*: if lakes get too warm, CO_2 and O_2 become less soluble and are not available for plants or animals.
    - Fish suffocate.

---

[32] "Effect of Temperature and Pressure on the Solubility of Gases in Liquids" from Live Demonstrations
[33] "Henry's Law and Noisy Knuckles" from Further Readings
[34] "Henry's Law: A Retrospective" from Further Readings
[35] "Henry's Law" Animation from Instructor's Resource CD/DVD
[36] Figure 13.18 from Transparency Pack
[37] Figure 13.19 from Transparency Pack
[38] "Soft Drink Bubbles" from Further Readings

FORWARDS REFERENCES
- The dynamic equilibrium between a solid solute and its solution will be mentioned in Chapter 14 (section 14.7).
- Factors affecting solubility will be discussed in detail in Chapter 17 (section 17.5).
- Temperature effects on solubility of NaCl will be mentioned in Chapter 19 (section 19.7).
- Reactions involving CO_2, HCO_3^- and H_2CO_3 will be discussed in Chapter 22 (section 22.9).
- Solubility of organic substances in polar solvents will be mentioned in Chapter 24 (section 24.1).

13.4 Expressing Solution Concentration[39]
- All methods involve quantifying the amount of solute per amount of solvent (or solution).
- Concentration may be expressed qualitatively or quantitatively.
  - The terms *dilute* and *concentrated* are qualitative ways to describe concentration.
    - A dilute solution has a relatively small concentration of solute.
    - A concentrated solution has a relatively high concentration of solute.
- Quantitative expressions of concentration require specific information regarding such quantities as masses, moles, or liters of the solute, solvent, or solution.
  - The most commonly used expressions for concentration are:
    - mass percentage.
    - mole fraction.
    - molarity.
    - molality.

Mass Percentage, ppm, and ppb[40]
- **Mass percentage** is one of the simplest ways to express concentration.
  - By definition:

$$\text{Mass \% of component} = \frac{\text{mass of component in soln}}{\text{total mass of solution}} \times 100$$

- Similarly, **parts per million (ppm)** can be expressed as the number of mg of solute per kilogram of solution.
  - By definition:

$$\text{Parts per million (ppm) of component} = \frac{\text{mass of component in soln}}{\text{total mass of solution}} \times 10^6$$

  - The density of a very dilute aqueous solution is similar to that of pure water (1g/mL)
    - If the density of the solution is 1g/mL, then 1 ppm = 1 mg solute per liter of solution.
- We can extend this again!
  - Parts per billion (ppb) can be expressed as the number of μg of solute per kilogram of solution.
  - By definition:

$$\text{Parts per billion (ppb) of component} = \frac{\text{mass of component in soln}}{\text{total mass of solution}} \times 10^9$$

  - If the density of the solution is 1g/mL, then 1 ppb = 1 μg solute per liter of solution.

---

[39] "Caffeine" 3-D Model from Instructor's Resource CD/DVD
[40] "Candy Sprinkles to Illustrate One Part Per Million" from Further Readings

Mole Fraction, Molarity, and Molality[41,42,43]

- Common expressions of concentration are based on the number of moles of one or more components.
- Recall that mass can be converted to moles using the molar mass.
- Recall:

$$\text{Mole fraction of component, } X = \frac{\text{moles of component}}{\text{total moles of all components}}$$

- Note that mole fraction has no units.
- Note that mole fractions range from 0 to 1.
- Recall:

$$\text{Molarity, } M = \frac{\text{moles of solute}}{\text{liters of solution}}$$

- Note that molarity will change with a change in temperature (as the solution volume increases or decreases).
- We can define **molality** (*m*), yet another concentration unit:

$$\text{Molality, } m = \frac{\text{moles of solute}}{\text{kilograms of solvent}}$$

- Molality does not vary with temperature.
- Note that converting between molarity (*M*) and molality (*m*) requires density.
- The molarity and molality of dilute solutions are often very similar.

FORWARD REFERENCES
- Molar concentrations will be used in rate law expressions in Chapter 14.
- Molar concentrations will be used in equilibrium constant and reaction quotient expressions in Chapters 15, 16, 17, 19, and 20.
- Concentrations (ppm) of trace constituents in mixtures will be re-introduced in Chapter 18 (section 18.1) and used throughout Chapter 18.

13.5 Colligative Properties

- Colligative properties depend on number of solute particles.
- There are four colligative properties to consider:
  - vapor pressure lowering (Raoult's law).
  - boiling point elevation.
  - freezing point depression.
  - osmotic pressure.

Vapor-Pressure Lowering[44,45]

- Consider a *volatile* liquid in a closed container.
  - After a period of time, an equilibrium will be established between the liquid and its vapor.
  - The partial pressure exerted by the vapor is the *vapor pressure*.
- *Nonvolatile* solutes (with no measurable vapor pressure) reduce the ability of the surface solvent molecules to escape the liquid.
  - Therefore, vapor pressure is lowered.

---

[41] "An Alternative Introduction to the Mole Fraction" from Further Readings
[42] "Mole Fraction Analogies" from Further Readings
[43] Figure 13.20 from Transparency Pack
[44] "Raoult's Law" Animation from Instructor's Resource CD/DVD
[45] "One Cool Chemist" from Further Readings

- • The amount of vapor pressure lowering depends on the amount of solute.
- **Raoult's law** quantifies the extent to which a nonvolatile solute lowers the vapor pressure of the solvent.
  - • If $P_{solution}$ is the vapor pressure of the solution, $P°_{solvent}$ is the vapor pressure of the pure solvent, and X_{solute} is the mole fraction of solute, then
$$P_{solution} = X_{solvent}P°_{solvent}$$
  - • The vapor-pressure lowering, ΔP, is directly proportional to the mole fraction of the solute, X_{solute}.
$$\Delta P = X_{solute}P°_{solvent}$$
- An **ideal solution** is one that obeys Raoult's law.
  - • Real solutions show approximately ideal behavior when:
    - • the solute concentration is low.
    - • the solute and solvent have similarly sized molecules.
    - • the solute and solvent have similar types of intermolecular attractions.
  - • Raoult's law breaks down when the solvent-solvent and solute-solute intermolecular forces are much greater or weaker than solute-solvent intermolecular forces.

Boiling-Point Elevation[46,47,48]

- • A nonvolatile solute lowers the vapor pressure of a solution.
- • At the normal boiling point of the pure liquid, the solution has a has a vapor pressure less than 1 atm.
  - • Therefore, a higher temperature is required to reach a vapor pressure of 1 atm for the solution (ΔT_b).
- • The **molal boiling-point-elevation constant**, K_b, expresses how much ΔT_b changes with molality, m:
$$\Delta T_b = K_b m$$
- • The nature of the solute (electrolyte vs. nonelectrolyte) will impact the colligative molality of the solute.

Freezing-Point Depression[49,50,51]

- • When a solution freezes, crystals of almost pure solvent are formed first.
  - • Solute molecules are usually not soluble in the solid phase of the solvent.
  - • Therefore, the triple point occurs at a lower temperature because of the lower vapor pressure for the solution.
- • The melting-point (freezing-point) curve is a vertical line from the triple point.
  - • Therefore, the solution freezes at a lower temperature (ΔT_f) than the pure solvent.
  - • The decrease in freezing point (ΔT_f) is directly proportional to molality.
- • K_f is the **molal freezing-point-depression constant**.
$$\Delta T_f = K_f m$$
  - • Values of K_f and K_b for most common solvents can be found in Table 13.4.

---

[46] Figure 13.23 from Transparency Pack
[47] "Boiling-Point Elevation and Freezing-Point Depression" Activity from Instructor's Resource CD/DVD
[48] "Adrenaline" 3-D Model from Instructor's Resource CD/DVD
[49] "Antifreeze Solutions: The Colligative Properties of Antifreeze" from Further Readings
[50] "Freeze-Proof Bugs" from Further Readings
[51] Figure 13.24 from Transparency Pack

Osmosis[52,53,54,55,56,57,58]

- *Semipermeable* membranes permit passage of some components of a solution.
  - Often they permit passage of water but not larger molecules or ions.
  - Examples of semipermeable membranes are cell membranes and cellophane.
- **Osmosis** is the net movement of a solvent from an area of low solute concentration to an area of high solute concentration.
- Consider a U-shaped tube with a two liquids separated by a semipermeable membrane.
  - One arm of the tube contains pure solvent.
  - The other arm contains a solution.
  - There is movement of solvent in both directions across a semipermeable membrane.
    - As solvent moves across the membrane, the fluid levels in the arms become uneven.
      - The vapor pressure of solvent is higher in the arm with pure solvent.
  - Eventually the pressure difference due to the difference in height of liquid in the arms stops osmosis.
- **Osmotic pressure**, π, is the pressure required to prevent osmosis.
  - Osmotic pressure obeys a law similar in form to the ideal-gas law.
    - For n moles, V= volume, M= molarity, R= the ideal gas constant, and an absolute temperature, T, the osmotic pressure is:

$$\pi = \left(\frac{n}{V}\right)RT = MRT$$

  - Two solutions are said to be *isotonic* if they have the same osmotic pressure.
    - *Hypotonic* solutions have a lower π, relative to a more concentrated solution.
    - *Hypertonic* solutions have a higher π, relative to a more dilute solution.
- We can illustrate this with a biological system: red blood cells.
  - Red blood cells are surrounded by semipermeable membranes.
    - If red blood cells are placed in a hypertonic solution (relative to intracellular solution), there is a lower solute concentration in the cell than the surrounding tissue.
      - Osmosis occurs and water passes through the membrane out of the cell.
      - The cell shrivels up.
      - This process is called *crenation*.
    - If red blood cells are placed in a hypotonic solution, there is a higher solute concentration in the cell than outside the cell.
      - Osmosis occurs and water moves into the cell.
      - The cell bursts (*hemolysis*).
  - To prevent crenation or hemolysis, IV (intravenous) solutions must be isotonic relative to the intracellular fluids of cells.
- Everyday examples of osmosis include:
  - If a cucumber is placed in NaCl solution, it will lose water to shrivel up and become a pickle.
  - A limp carrot placed in water becomes firm because water enters via osmosis.
  - Eating large quantities of salty food causes retention of water and swelling of tissues (*edema*).
  - Water moves into plants, to a great extent, through osmosis.

---

[52] "A Simple Demonstration Model of Osmosis" from Live Demonstrations
[53] "Osmotic Pressure of a Sugar Solution" from Live Demonstrations
[54] "Osmosis Through the Membrane of an Egg" from Live Demonstrations
[55] "Osmosis and Osmotic Pressure" Animation from Instructor's Resource CD/DVD
[56] "Osmosis and the Egg Membrane" from Live Demonstrations
[57] "Seawater Gets Fresh" from Further Readings
[58] Figure 13.25 from Transparency Pack

- Salt may be added to meat (or sugar added to fruit) as a preservative.
  - Salt prevents bacterial infection: A bacterium placed on the salt will lose water through osmosis and die.
- *Active transport* is the movement of nutrients and waste material through a biological membrane against a concentration gradient.
  - Movement is from an area of low concentration to an area of high concentration.
  - Active transport is not spontaneous.
    - Energy must be expended by the cell to accomplish this.

Determination of Molar Mass[59,60,61,62]

- Any of the four colligative properties may be used to determine molar mass.

FORWARDS REFERENCES
  - Desalination via reverse osmosis will be described in Chapter 18 (section 18.4).

13.6 Colloids[63,64,65]

- **Colloids** or **colloidal dispersions** are suspensions in which the suspended particles are larger than molecules but too small to separate out of the suspension due to gravity.
  - Particle size: 5 to 1000 nm.
  - A colloid particle may consist of a single giant molecule.
    - Example: hemoglobin has molecular dimensions of $6.5 \times 5.5 \times 5.0$ nm and a molar mass of 64,500 g/mol.
- There are several types of colloids:
  - aerosol: gas + liquid or solid (e.g., fog and smoke),
  - foam: liquid + gas (e.g., whipped cream),
  - emulsion: liquid + liquid (e.g., milk),
  - sol: liquid + solid (e.g., paint),
  - solid foam: solid + gas (e.g., marshmallow),
  - solid emulsion: solid + liquid (e.g., butter),
  - solid sol: solid + solid (e.g., ruby glass).
- The **Tyndall effect** is the ability of colloidal particles to scatter light.
  - The path of a beam of light projected through a colloidal suspension can be seen through the suspension.

Hydrophilic and Hydrophobic Colloids[66,67]

- Focus on colloids in water.
  - Water-loving colloids are **hydrophilic**.
  - Water-hating colloids are **hydrophobic**.
- In the human body, large biological molecules such as proteins are kept in suspension by association with surrounding water molecules.

---

[59] "Determination of Molar Mass" Activity from Instructor's Resource CD/DVD

[60] Figure 13.27 from Transparency Pack

[61] "Salts Are Mostly NOT Ionized" from Further Readings

[62] "J.H. van't Hoff" from Further Readings

[63] "The Impact of Colloid Science" from Further Readings

[64] "Colloidal Systems" from Further Readings

[65] "Color of the Sunset: The Tyndall Effect" from Live Demonstrations

[66] "Illustrating the Properties of Magnetic Sand" from Live Demonstrations

[67] "Put the Brakes on Wastewater Emulsions" from Further Readings

- These macromolecules fold up so that hydrophobic groups are away from the water (inside the folded molecule).
- Hydrophilic groups are on the surface of these molecules and interact with solvent (water) molecules.
  - Typical hydrophilic groups are polar (containing C–O, O–H, N–H bonds) or charged.
- Hydrophobic colloids need to be stabilized in water.
  - One way to stabilize hydrophobic colloids is to adsorb ions on their surface.
    - *Adsorption*: when something sticks to a surface, we say that it is adsorbed.
  - If ions are adsorbed onto the surface of a colloid, the colloid appears hydrophilic and is stabilized in water.
  - Consider a small drop of oil in water.
    - Add a small amount of sodium stearate.
    - Sodium stearate has a long hydrophobic hydrocarbon tail and a small hydrophilic head.
    - The hydrophobic tail can be absorbed into the oil drop, leaving the hydrophilic head on the surface.
    - The hydrophilic heads then interact with the water and the oil drop is stabilized in water.
  - A soap acts in a similar fashion.
    - Soaps are molecules with long hydrophobic tails and hydrophilic heads that remove dirt by stabilizing the colloid in water.
    - Most dirt stains on people and clothing are oil-based.
- Biological application of this principle:
  - The gallbladder excretes a fluid called bile.
  - Bile contains substances (bile salts) that form an emulsion with fats in our small intestine.
  - Emulsifying agents help form an emulsion.
    - Emulsification of dietary fats and fat-soluble vitamins is important in their absorption and digestion by the body.

Removal of Colloid Particles[68,69,70,71]

- We often need to separate colloidal particles from the dispersing medium.
- This may be problematic.
  - Colloid particles are too small to be separated by physical means (e.g., filtration).
  - However, colloid particles often may be *coagulated* (enlarged) until they can be removed by filtration.
- There are various methods of coagulation.
  - Colloid particles move more rapidly when the colloidal dispersion is heated, increasing the number of collisions. The particles stick to each other when they collide.
  - Adding an electrolyte neutralizes the surface charges on the colloid particles.
- A biological application of another approach to separating colloidal particles from the suspending medium is dialysis.
  - In *dialysis*, a semipermeable membrane is used to separate ions from colloidal particles.
  - In kidney dialysis, the blood is allowed to pass through a semipermeable membrane immersed in a washing solution.
  - The washing solution is isotonic in ions that must be retained.
  - The washing solution does not have the waste products that are found in the blood.

---

[68] "Surfactants: The Ubiquitous Amphiphiles" from Further Readings
[69] "Clearly Cleaner" from Further Readings
[70] "Blood-Chemistry Tutorials: Teaching Biological Applications of General Chemistry Material" from Further Readings
[71] "Chemistry and Physics in the Kitchen" from Further Readings

- Wastes therefore dialyze out of the blood (move from the blood into the washing solution).
- The "good" ions remain in the blood.

FORWARDS REFERENCES
- Adsorption and absorption in heterogeneous catalysis will be mentioned in Chapter 14 (section 14.7).
- A model of hemoglobin in blood will be provided in Chapter 23 and (sections 23.3 and 23.6) and Chapter 24 (section 24.9).
- Surfactant organic molecules will be mentioned again in Chapter 24 (section 24.1).

Further Readings:

1. William B. Jensen, "The Use of Dots in Chemical Formulas," *J. Chem. Educ.*, Vol. 83, **2006**, 1590-1591.

2. Jamil Ahmad, "Crystallization from a Supersaturated Solution of Sodium Acetate," *J. Chem. Educ.*, Vol. 77, **2000**, 1446.

3. Todd P. Silverstein, "Polarity, Miscibility, and Surface Tension," *J. Chem. Educ.*, Vol. 70., **1993**, 253.

4. Barry K. Thornton, "An Analogy to Illustrate Miscibility of Liquids," *J. Chem. Educ.*, Vol. 71, **1994**, 156.

5. Michael J. Sanger and Steven M. Badger III, "Using Computer-Based Visualization Strategies to Improve Students' Understanding of Molecular Polarity and Miscibility," *J. Chem. Educ.*, Vol. 78, **2001**, 1412–1416.

6. Reginald P. T. Tomkins, "Applications of Solubility Data," *J. Chem. Educ.*, Vol. 85, **2008**, 310–316.

7. Doris R. Kimbrough, "Henry's Law and Noisy Knuckles," *J. Chem. Educ.*, Vol. 76, **1999**, 1509–1510.

8. Robert M. Rosenberg and Warner L. Peticolas, "Henry's Law: A Retrospective," *J. Chem. Educ.*, Vol. 81, **2004**, 1647–1652.

9. James H. Cragin, "Soft Drink Bubbles," *J. Chem. Educ.*, Vol. 60, **1983**, 71. A short Henry's Law reference.

10. Clifton E Meloan, Mindy L. Meloan, and John M. Meloan, "Candy Sprinkles to Illustrate One Part Per Million," *J. Chem. Educ.*, Vol. 71, **1994**, 658.

11. Alvin D. White, "An Alternative Introduction to the Mole Fraction," *J. Chem. Educ.*, Vol. 59, **1982**, 153.

12. Ronald DeLorenzo, "Mole Fraction Analogies," *J. Chem. Educ.*, Vol. 57, **1980**, 733.

13. Michael Sutton, "One Cool Chemist," *Chemistry in Britain*, **July 2001**, 66–68. An article on Raoult's Law and the preparation of ice cream.

14. Sarah F. McDuffie and Catherine E. Matthews, "Antifreeze Solutions: The Colligative Properties of Antifreeze," *The Science Teacher*, Vol. 63, **1996**, 41–43.

15. Ronald DeLorenzo, "Freeze-Proof Bugs," *J. Chem. Educ.*, Vol. 58, **1981**, 788.

16. Gerald Parkinson, Charlene Crabb, and Takeshi Kamiya, "Seawater Gets Fresh," *Chemical Engineering*, Vol. 106(3), **March, 1999**, 32–35. An article that looks at the role of desalination and reverse osmosis in providing drinking water.

17. Stephen J. Hawkes, "Salts Are Mostly NOT Ionized," *J. Chem. Educ.*, Vol. 73, **1996**, 421–423.

18. W. A. E. McBryde, "J. H. van't Hoff," *J. Chem. Educ.*, Vol. 64, **1987**, 573–575.

19. Mike Garvey, "The Impact of Colloid Science," *Chemistry in Britain,* **February 2003,** 28–32.

20. Jerry Sarquis, "Colloidal Systems," *J. Chem. Educ.,* Vol. 57, **1980,** 602–605.

21. George Alther, "Put the Brakes on Wastewater Emulsions," *Chemical Engineering,* Vol. 105(3), **1998,** 82–88.

22. Tony Hargreaves, "Surfactants: The Ubiquitous Amphiphiles," *Chemistry in Britain,* **July 2003,** 38–41.

23. Jia-Qian Jiang and Nigel Graham, "Clearly Cleaner," *Chemistry in Britain,* Vol. 34(3), **March 1998,** 38–41. An article that explores the use of coagulants to help treat water.

24. Rachel E. Casiday, Dewey Holten, Richard Krathen, and Regina F. Frey, "Blood–Chemistry Tutorials: Teaching Biological Applications of General Chemistry Material," *J. Chem. Educ.,* Vol. 78, **2001,** 1210–1214. The relationship between oxygen transport, iron transport, blood buffering, kidney dialysis and general chemistry topics is discussed.

25. Nicholas Kurti and Hervé This-Benckhard, "Chemistry and Physics in the Kitchen," *Scientific American,* **April 1994,** 66–71.

Live Demonstrations:

1. Lee. R. Summerlin, Christie L. Borgford, and Julie B. Ealy, "Copper Sulfate: Blue to White," *Chemical Demonstrations, A Sourcebook for Teachers, Volume 2* (Washington: American Chemical Society, **1988**), pp. 69–70. An exploration of color change associated with the dehydration of copper sulfate.

2. Lee R. Summerlin, Christie L. Borgford, and Julie B. Ealy, "Supersaturation," *Chemical Demonstrations, A Sourcebook for Teachers, Volume 2* (Washington: American Chemical Society, **1988**), pp. 121–122. Disruption of a supersaturated solution of sodium acetate results in a sudden formation of solid in this demonstration.

3. Bassam Z. Shakhashiri, "Crystallization from Supersaturated Solutions of Sodium Acetate," *Chemical Demonstrations: A Handbook for Teachers of Chemistry, Volume 1* (Madison: The University of Wisconsin Press, **1983**), pp. 27–30.

4. Lee. R. Summerlin, Christie L. Borgford, and Julie B. Ealy, "Nonadditivity of Volumes," *Chemical Demonstrations, A Sourcebook for Teachers, Volume 2* (Washington: American Chemical Society, **1988**), p.14. Two miscible liquids are mixed and the final volume measured in this short demonstration.

5. Walter H. Corkern and Linda L Munchausen, "Solubility of Alcohols," *J. Chem. Educ.,* Vol. 69, **1992,** 928. An overhead projector demonstration of solubility.

6. Katia Pravia and David F. Maynard, "Why Don't Water and Oil Mix?" *J. Chem. Educ.,* Vol. 73, **1996,** 497. A simple overhead projector demonstration.

7. Bassam Z. Shakhashiri, "Effect of Temperature and Pressure on the Solubility of Gases in Liquids," *Chemical Demonstrations: A Handbook for Teachers of Chemistry, Volume 3* (Madison: The University of Wisconsin Press, **1989**), pp. 280–282.

8. Joseph G. Morse, "A Simple Demonstration Model of Osmosis," *J. Chem. Educ.*, Vol. 76, **1999**, 64–65.

9. Bassam Z. Shakhashiri, "Osmotic Pressure of a Sugar Solution," *Chemical Demonstrations: A Handbook for Teachers of Chemistry, Volume 3* (Madison: The University of Wisconsin Press, **1989**), pp. 286–289. A sugar solution placed in dialysis tubing is used to demonstrate osmotic pressure.

10. Bassam Z. Shakhashiri, "Osmosis Through the Membrane of an Egg," *Chemical Demonstrations: A Handbook for Teachers of Chemistry, Volume 3* (Madison: The University of Wisconsin Press, **1989**), pp. 283–285.

11. Lee. R. Summerlin, Christie L. Borgford, and Julie B. Ealy, "Osmosis and the Egg Membrane," *Chemical Demonstrations, A Sourcebook for Teachers, Volume 2* (Washington: American Chemical Society, **1988**), pp. 136–137. Movement of water through the membrane of an egg is explored in this demonstration of osmosis.

12. Bassam Z. Shakhashiri, "Color of the Sunset: The Tyndall Effect," *Chemical Demonstrations: A Handbook for Teachers of Chemistry, Volume 3* (Madison: The University of Wisconsin Press, **1989**), pp. 353–357. Several procedures for demonstrating the Tyndall Effect are presented in this demonstration.

13. Robert H. Goldsmith, "Illustrating the Properties of Magic Sand," *J. Chem. Educ.*, Vol. 76, **1999**, 41. An overhead projector demonstration illustrating the differences between hydrophobic and hydrophilic materials.

Chapter 14. Chemical Kinetics

Media Resources

Figures and Tables in Transparency Pack:	Section:
Figure 14.4 Concentration of Butyl Chloride (C_4H_9Cl) as a Function of Time	14.2 Reaction Rates
Figure 14.6 Components of a Spectrometer	14.2 Reaction Rates
Figure 14.8 Kinetic Data for Conversion of Methyl Isonitrile into Acetonitrile	14.4 The Change of Concentration with Time
Figure 14.9 Kinetic Data for Decomposition of NO_2	14.4 The Change of Concentration with Time
Figure 14.14 Temperature Dependence of the Rate Constant for Methyl Isonitrile Conversion to Acetonitrile	14.5 Temperature and Rate
Figure 14.15 Molecular Collisions May or May Not Lead to a Chemical Reaction Between Cl and NOCl	14.5 Temperature and Rate
Figure 14.17 Energy Profile for Conversion of Methyl Isonitrile (H_3CNC) to Its Isomer Acetonitrile (H_3CCN)	14.5 Temperature and Rate
Figure 14.18 The Effect of Temperature on the Distribution of Kinetic Energies of Molecules in a Sample	14.5 Temperature and Rate
Figure 14.22 Homogeneous Catalysis	14.7 Catalysis
Figure 14.27 Lock-and-Key Model for Enzyme Action	14.7 Catalysis

Activities:	Section:
Progress of Reaction	14.2 Reaction Rates
Decomposition of N_2O_5	14.3 Concentration and Rate Laws
Rates of Reaction	14.3 Concentration and Rate Laws
Arrhenius Model	14.5 Temperature and Rate

Animations:	Section:
First-Order Process	14.4 The Change of Concentration with Time
Bimolecular Reaction	14.6 Reaction Mechanisms
Surface Reaction-Hydrogenation	14.7 Catalysis

Movies:	Section:
CFCs and Stratospheric Ozone	14.4 The Change of Concentration with Time
Catalysis	14.7 Catalysis

3-D Models:	Section:
Chlorine	14.3 Concentration and Rate Laws
Acetonitrile	14.4 The Change of Concentration with Time
Methyl Isonitrile	14.4 The Change of Concentration with Time
Fluorine	14.6 Reaction Mechanisms
Oxygen	14.7 Catalysis
Bromine	14.7 Catalysis

Hydrogen Peroxide   14.7 Catalysis
Ethylene   14.7 Catalysis
Ethane   14.7 Catalysis
FeMo-cofactor of Nitrogenase   14.7 Catalysis
Nitrogen Dioxide   14.7 Catalysis

Other Resources

Further Readings: **Section:**
The Fizz Keeper, a Case Study in Chemical Education, Equilibrium, and Kinetics   14.1 Factors that Affect Reaction Rates
Inflation Rates, Car Devaluation, and Chemical Kinetics   14.3 Concentration and Rate Laws
An Analogy to Help Students Understand Reaction Orders   14.3 Concentration and Rate Laws
Don't Be Tricked by Your Integrated Rate Plot!   14.4 The Change of Concentration with Time
Mice in the Box for Zero-Order Kinetics   14.4 The Change of Concentration with Time
Light Sticks   14.5 Temperature and Rate
Audience-Appropriate Analogies: Collision Theory   14.5 Temperature and Rate
The Collision Theory and an American Tradition   14.5 Temperature and Rate
Just What Is a Transition State?   14.5 Temperature and Rate
The Arrhenius Law and Storage of Food   14.5 Temperature and Rate
Visualizing the Transition State: A Hands-On Approach to the Arrhenius Equation   14.5 Temperature and Rate
Pictorial Analogies XIII: Kinetics and Mechanisms   14.6 Reaction Mechanisms
Doing the Dishes: An Analogy for Use in Teaching Reaction Kinetics   14.6 Reaction Mechanisms
Auto Analogies   14.6 Reaction Mechanisms
Another Auto Analogy: Rate-Determining Steps   14.6 Reaction Mechanisms
Catalysis   14.7 Catalysis
Catalysis: New Reaction Pathways, Not Just a Lowering of the Activation Energy   14.7 Catalysis
Catalysis on Surfaces   14.7 Catalysis
Solid Acid Catalysts   14.7 Catalysis
Getting Auto Exhausts to Pristine   14.7 Catalysis
Driving Down Emissions   14.7 Catalysis
Enzyme Catalysis: Cleaner, Safer, Energy Efficient   14.7 Catalysis
Environmental Catalysts   14.7 Catalysis
Practical Enzyme Kinetics   14.7 Catalysis
Breaking Bonds versus Chopping Heads: The Enzyme as Butcher   14.7 Catalysis
Biocatalysis Makes Headway in Chemicals   14.7 Catalysis
The Catalytic Function of Enzymes   14.7 Catalysis
Frank Westheimer's Early Demonstration of Enzymatic Specificity   14.7 Catalysis
Enzyme Activity: A Simple Analogy   14.7 Catalysis

Live Demonstrations: **Section:**
Appearing Red   14.1 Factors that Affect Reaction Rates
A New Twist on the Iodine Clock Reaction: 14.1 Factors that Affect Reaction Rates

Determining the Order of a Reaction

Hydrogen Peroxide Iodine Clock: Oxidation of
  Potassium Iodide by Hydrogen Peroxide   14.1 Factors that Affect Reaction Rates

The Starch-Iodine Clock Reaction   14.1 Factors that Affect Reaction Rates

Lightsticks   14.5 Temperature and Rate

Cool-Light Chemiluminescence   14.5 Temperature and Rate

Catalytic Decomposition of Hydrogen Peroxide: 14.7 Catalysis
  Foam Production

Enzyme Kinetics: Effects of Temperature and an 14.7 Catalysis
  Inhibitor on Catalase Extracted from Potato

Chapter 14. Chemical Kinetics

Common Student Misconceptions

- Students often assume that reaction orders may be determined from stoichiometric coefficients *regardless* of the reaction mechanism.
- Students have difficulty comprehending zero-order processes.
- Students have difficulty understanding the relationship between various experimental results and the rate of reaction.
- Students often confuse fast reactions with those with large reaction yields.
- Students have difficulty distinguishing between kinetic and thermodynamic control of reactions.
- Students often confuse intermediates and transition states.
- Students often confuse *ad*sorption and *ab*sorption.

Teaching Tips

- It is possible for mathematics to get in the way of some students' understanding of the chemistry of this chapter.
- Remind students that the term *change in* a quantity always refers to the *final* minus the *initial* value.
- Remind students to use the absolute temperature (in Kelvin) when manipulating the Arrhenius equation.
- Emphasize to students that the coefficients of the balanced chemical equation do not necessarily correspond to the reaction orders in the rate law. However, the rate law of an elementary step *does* follow from the coefficients of the balanced equation of the step.

Lecture Outline

14.1 Factors that Affect Reaction Rates[1,2,3,4]

- The speed at which a chemical reaction occurs is the **reaction rate**.
- **Chemical kinetics** is the study of how fast chemical reactions occur.
- There are several important factors that affect rates of reactions:
    - physical state of the reactants.
    - concentration of the reactants.
    - temperature of the reaction.
    - presence or absence of a catalyst.
- The goal is to understand chemical reactions at the molecular level.

14.2 Reaction Rates[5,6]

- The speed of a reaction is defined as the change that occurs per unit time.

---

[1] "Appearing Red" from Live Demonstrations
[2] "A New Twist on the Iodine Clock Reaction: Determining the Order of a Reaction" from Live Demonstrations
[3] "Hydrogen Peroxide Iodine Clock: Oxidation of Potassium Iodide by Hydrogen Peroxide" from Live Demonstrations
[4] "The Starch-Iodine Clock Reaction" from Live Demonstrations
[5] "Progress of Reaction" Activity from Instructor's Resource CD/DVD
[6] "The Fizz Keeper, A Case Study in Chemical Education, Equilibrium, and Kinetics" from Further Readings

- It is often determined by measuring the change in concentration of a reactant or product with time.
- For a reaction A → B

$$\text{Average rate with respect to B} = \frac{\text{change in the concentration of B}}{\text{change in time}}$$

  - Here the change in the concentration of B is defined as:

  Δ (concentration of B) = (concentration of B at final time) – (concentration of B at initial time)
- Illustrate this with an example:
  - Suppose A reacts to form B. Let us begin with 1.00 M A.
  - At $t = 0$ (time zero) there is 1.00 M A and no B present.
  - At $t = 20$ s, there is 0.54 M A and 0.46 M B.
  - At $t = 40$ s, there is 0.30 M A and 0.70 M B.
  - We can uses this information to find the average rate with respect to B:

$$\text{Avg Rate} = \frac{\Delta (\text{Conc B})}{\Delta t} = \frac{(\text{Conc of B at } t = 20s) - (\text{Conc of B at } t = 0 \, s)}{20s - 0 \, \text{min}}$$

$$\text{Avg Rate} = \frac{0.46M - 0.00\,M}{20\,s - 0\,s} = 0.023\frac{M}{s}$$

- For the reaction A → B there are two ways of measuring rate:
  - the rate of appearance of product B (i.e., change in moles of B per unit time) as in the preceding example, and
  - the rate of disappearance of reactant A (i.e., the change in moles of A per unit time).

$$\text{Average Rate} = \frac{-\Delta[A]}{\Delta t}$$

  - Note the negative sign! This reminds us that rate is being expressed in terms of the *disappearance* of a reactant.
  - A plot of number of moles versus time shows that as the reactants (A) disappear, the products (B) appear.

Change of Rate with Time[7]

- In most chemical reactions we will determine the reaction rate by monitoring a change in concentration (of a reactant or product).
  - The most useful unit to use for rate is molarity.
    - Since volume is constant, molarity and moles are directly proportional.
  - Consider the following reaction:

$$C_4H_9Cl(aq) + H_2O(l) \rightarrow C_4H_9OH(aq) + HCl(aq)$$

- We can calculate the average rate in terms of the disappearance of C_4H_9Cl.
- The units for average rate are *mol/Ls* or *M/s*.
- The average rate decreases with time.

Instantaneous Rate

- We can plot [C_4H_9Cl] versus time.
  - The rate at any instant in time is called the **instantaneous rate.**
  - It is the slope of the straight line tangent to the curve at that instant.
  - Instantaneous rate is different from average rate.

---

[7] Figure 14.4 from Transparency Pack

- It is the rate at that particular instant in time.
- For our discussion we will call the "instantaneous rate" the rate, unless otherwise indicated.

Reaction Rates and Stoichiometry[8]

- For the reaction:

$$C_4H_9Cl(aq) + H_2O(l) \rightarrow C_4H_9OH(aq) + HCl(aq)$$

   - The rate of appearance of C_4H_9OH must equal the rate of disappearance of C_4H_9Cl.

$$Rate = -\frac{\Delta[C_4H_9Cl]}{\Delta t} = \frac{\Delta[C_4H_9OH]}{\Delta t}$$

- What if the stoichiometric relationships are not one-to-one?
   - For the reaction:

$$2HI(g) \rightarrow H_2(g) + I_2(g)$$

   - The rate may be expressed as:

$$Rate = -\frac{1}{2}\frac{\Delta[HI]}{\Delta t} = \frac{\Delta[H_2]}{\Delta t} = \frac{\Delta[I_2]}{\Delta t}$$

- We can generalize this equation a bit.
   - For the reaction:

$$aA + bB \rightarrow cC + dD$$

   - The rate may be expressed as:

$$Rate = -\frac{1}{a}\frac{\Delta[A]}{\Delta t} = -\frac{1}{b}\frac{\Delta[B]}{\Delta t} = \frac{1}{c}\frac{\Delta[C]}{\Delta t} = \frac{1}{d}\frac{\Delta[D]}{\Delta t}$$

14.3 Concentration and Rate Laws[9,10,11]

- In general, rates:
   - increase when reactant concentration is increased.
   - decrease as the concentration of reactants is reduced.
- We often examine the effect of concentration on reaction rate by measuring the way in which reaction rate at the beginning of a reaction depends on starting conditions.
- Consider the reaction:

$$NH_4^+(aq) + NO_2^-(aq) \rightarrow N_2(g) + 2H_2O(l)$$

   - We measure initial reaction rates.
      - The initial rate is the instantaneous rate at time $t = 0$.
   - We find this at various initial concentrations of each reactant.
   - As $[NH_4^+]$ doubles with $[NO_2^-]$ constant the rate doubles.
      - We conclude the rate is proportional to $[NH_4^+]$.
   - As $[NO_2^-]$ doubles with $[NH_4^+]$ constant the rate doubles.
      - We conclude that the rate is proportional to $[NO_2^-]$.
- The overall concentration dependence of reaction rate is given in a **rate law,** or rate expression.
   - For our example, the rate law is:

$$Rate = k[NH_4^+][NO_2^-]$$

   - The proportionality constant k is called the **rate constant**.

---

[8] Figure 14.6 from Transparency Pack
[9] "Decomposition of N_2O_5" Activity from Instructor's Resource CD/DVD
[10] "Inflation Rates, Car Devaluation, and Chemical Kinetics" from Further Readings
[11] "Rates of Reaction" Activity from Instructor's Resource CD/DVD

- Once we have determined the rate law and the rate constant, we can use them to calculate initial reaction rates under any set of initial concentrations.

Reaction Orders: The Exponents in the Rate Law[12]

- For a general reaction with rate law:
$$\text{Rate} = k[\text{reactant 1}]^m[\text{reactant 2}]^n$$
- The exponents m and n are called **reaction orders**.
  - The **overall reaction order** is the sum of the reaction orders.
    - The overall order of reaction is $m + n + \dots$.
- Note that reaction orders must be determined experimentally.
  - They do not necessarily correspond to the stoichiometric coefficients in the balanced chemical equation!
  - We commonly encounter reaction orders of 0, 1, or 2.
  - Even fractional or negative values are possible.

Magnitudes and Units of Rate Constants

- In comparing reactions to evaluate which ones are relatively fast and which are relative slow, the rate constants are compared:
  - A large value of k (10^9 or greater): the reaction is fast.
  - A small value of k (10 or lower): the reaction is slow.
- Units of the rate constant depend on the overall reaction order.

Using Initial Rates to Determine Rate Laws[13]

- To determine the rate law, we observe the effect of changing initial concentrations.
  - If a reaction is zero order in a reactant, changing the initial concentration of that reactant will have no effect on rate (as long as *some* reactant is present).
  - If a reaction is first order, doubling the concentration will cause the rate to double.
  - If a reaction is second order, doubling the concentration will result in a 2^2 increase in rate.
    - Similarly, tripling the concentration results in a 3^2 increase in rate.
  - A reaction is n^{th} order if doubling the concentration causes a 2^n increase in rate.
- Note that the rate, not the rate constant, depends on concentration.
- The rate constant IS affected by temperature and by the presence of a catalyst.

FORWARD REFERENCES
  - The importance of pH in determining the rates of proton transfer reactions in biological systems will be mentioned in Chapter 16 (section 16.4).

14.4 The Change of Concentration with Time[14]

- Goal: Convert the rate law into a convenient equation that gives concentration as a function of time.

First-Order Reactions[15,16,17,18]

- For a **first-order reaction**, the rate doubles as the concentration of a reactant doubles.
  - Therefore, we can write the *differential rate law*:

---

[12] "An Analogy to Help Students Understand Reaction Orders" from Further Readings
[13] "Chlorine" 3-D Model from Instructor's Resource CD/DVD
[14] "CFCs and Stratospheric Ozone" Movie from Instructor's Resource CD/DVD
[15] "First-Order Process" Animation from Instructor's Resource CD/DVD
[16] "Don't Be Tricked by Your Integrated Rate Plot!" from Further Readings
[17] "Acetonitrile" 3-D Model from Instructor's Resource CD/DVD
[18] "Methyl Isonitrile" 3-D Model from Instructor's Resource CD/DVD

$$\text{Rate} = -\frac{\Delta[A]}{\Delta t} = k[A]$$

- Integrating, we get the *integrated rate law*:

$$\ln[A]_t - \ln[A]_0 = -kt$$

- Rearranging:

$$\ln[A]_t = -kt + \ln[A]_0$$

- An alternate form:

$$\ln\frac{[A]_t}{[A]_0} = -kt$$

- A plot of $\ln[A]_t$ versus t is a straight line with slope $-k$ and intercept $\ln[A]_0$.
- Note that in this equation we use the natural logarithm, ln (log to the base e).

Second-Order Reactions[19,20]

- A **second-order reaction** is one whose rate depends on the reactant concentration to the second power or on the concentration of two reactants, each raised to the first power.
- For a second-order reaction with just one reactant, we write the differential rate law:

$$\text{Rate} = -\frac{\Delta[A]}{\Delta t} = k[A]^2$$

- Integrating, we get the integrated form of the rate law:

- A plot of $1/[A]_t$ versus t is a straight line with slope k and intercept $1/[A]_0$.

$$\frac{1}{[A]_t} = kt + \frac{1}{[A]_0}$$

- For a second-order reaction, a plot of $\ln[A]_t$ vs. t is not linear.
- Note that a second-order process can have a rate constant expression of the form:
$$\text{Rate} = k[A][B]$$
- That is, the reaction is second order overall, but has first-order dependence on A and B.

Zero-Order Reactions[21]

- A **zero-order reaction** is one whose rate is independent of the reactant concentration.

$$\text{Rate} = -\frac{\Delta[A]}{\Delta t} = k$$

- The integrated rate law for a zero-order reaction is:

$$[A]_t = -kt + [A]_0$$

---

[19] Figure 14.8 from Transparency Pack
[20] Figure 14.9 from Transparency Pack
[21] "Mice in the Box for Zero-Order Kinetics" from Further Readings

Half-life

- **Half-life**, $t_{1/2}$, is the time required for the concentration of a reactant to decrease to half its original value.
  - That is, half life, $t_{1/2}$, is the time taken for $[A]_0$ to reach $\frac{1}{2} [A]_0$.
  - Mathematically, the half life of a first-order reaction is:

$$\ln \frac{[A]_t}{[A]_0} = -kt$$

- So, for $t = t_{1/2}$ and $[A]_t = \frac{1}{2} [A]_0$

$$\ln \frac{\frac{1}{2}[A]_0}{[A]_0} = -kt_{1/2}$$

$$\ln \frac{1}{2} = -kt_{1/2}$$

$$\therefore t_{1/2} = -\frac{\ln 1/2}{k} = \frac{0.693}{k}$$

- Note that the half-life of a first-order reaction is independent of the initial concentration of the reactant.
- We can show that the half-life of a second order reaction is:

$$t_{1/2} = \frac{1}{k[A]_0}$$

- Note that, unlike for the first-order reaction, the half-life of a second-order reaction is dependent on the initial concentration of the reactant.

FORWARD REFERENCES
- Rates of radioactive decay processes, half-lives of radioactive isotopes, and radiocarbon dating will be further discussed in Chapter 21 (section 21.4).

14.5 Temperature and Rate[22,23,24,25]

- Most reactions speed up as temperature increases.
- We can illustrate this with chemiluminescent Cyalume® light sticks.
  - A chemiluminescent reaction produces light.
  - Two light sticks are placed in water, one at room temperature and one in ice.
    - The one at room temperature is brighter than the one in ice.
    - Its luminescence also fades more quickly.
  - The chemical reaction responsible for chemiluminescence is dependent on temperature, the higher the temperature, the faster the reaction and the brighter the light.
- As temperature increases, the rate increases.
- How is the relationship between temperature and rate reflected in the rate expression?

---

[22] "Lightsticks" from Live Demonstrations
[23] "Cool-Light Chemiluminescence" from Live Demonstrations
[24] "Light Sticks" from Further Readings
[25] Figure 14.14 from Transparency Pack

- The rate law has no temperature term in it, so the rate constant must depend on temperature.
- Consider the first-order reaction $CH_3NC \rightarrow CH_3CN$.
  - As temperature increases from 190 °C to 250 °C, the rate constant increases.
    - The temperature effect is quite dramatic.
- We see an approximate doubling of the rate of the reaction with each 10 °C increase in temperature.

The Collision Model[26,27,28]

- Rates of reactions are affected by concentration and temperature.
- We need to develop a model that explains this observation.
- An explanation is provided by the **collision model**, based on kinetic-molecular theory.
  - In order for molecules to react, they must collide.
  - The greater the number of collisions, the faster the rate.
  - The more molecules present, the greater the probability of collision and the faster the rate.
    - Thus, reaction rate should increase with an increase in the concentration of reactant molecules.
  - The higher the temperature, the more energy available to the molecules and the more frequently the molecules collide.
    - Thus, reaction rate should increase with an increase in temperature.
  - However, not all collisions lead to products.
    - In fact, only a small fraction of collisions lead to products.
    - In order for a reaction to occur, the reactant molecules must collide in the correct orientation and with enough energy to form products.

The Orientation Factor[29]

- The orientation of a molecule during collision can have a profound effect on whether or not a reaction occurs.
- Consider the reaction between Cl and NOCl:

$$Cl + NOCl \rightarrow NO + Cl_2$$

  - If the Cl collides with the Cl of NOCl, the products are Cl_2 and NO.
  - If the Cl collides with the O of NOCl, no products are formed.

Activation Energy[30,31,32]

- Arrhenius: Molecules must posses a minimum amount of energy to react. Why?
  - In order to form products, bonds must be broken in the reactants.
  - Bond breakage requires energy.
  - Molecules moving too slowly, with too little kinetic energy, don't react when they collide.
- **Activation energy**, E_a, is the minimum energy required to initiate a chemical reaction.
  - E_a will vary with the reaction.
- Consider the rearrangement of methyl isonitrile to form acetonitrile:
  - Energy is required to stretch the bond between the CH_3 group and the $N\equiv C$ group to allow the $N\equiv C$ to rotate.
  - The C–C bond begins to form.

---

[26] "Audience-Appropriate Analogies: Collision Theory" from Further Readings
[27] "Arrhenius Model" Activity from Instructor's Resource CD/DVD
[28] "The Collision Theory and an American Tradition" from Further Readings
[29] Figure 14.15 from Transparency Pack
[30] Figure 14.17 from Transparency Pack
[31] Figure 14.18 from Transparency Pack
[32] "Just What Is a Transition State?" from Further Readings

- The energy associated with the molecule drops.
- The energy barrier between the starting molecule and the highest energy state found along the reaction pathway is the activation energy.
  - The species at the top of the barrier is called the **activated complex** or **transition state**.
- The change in energy for the reaction is the difference in energy between CH_3NC and CH_3CN.
  - ΔE_{rxn} has no effect on reaction rate.
- The activation energy is the difference in energy between reactants, (CH_3NC) and the transition state.
  - The rate depends on the magnitude of the E_a.
    - In general, the lower the E_a, the faster the rate.
- Notice that if a forward reaction is exothermic ($CH_3NC \rightarrow CH_3CN$), then the reverse reaction is endothermic ($CH_3CN \rightarrow CH_3NC$).
- How does this relate to temperature?
  - At any particular temperature, the molecules present have an average kinetic energy associated with the population.
  - In the same distribution, some molecules have less energy than the average while others have more than the average value.
    - The fraction of molecules with an energy equal to or greater than E_a is given by:

$$f = e^{\frac{-E_a}{RT}}$$

  - R is the gas constant (8.314 J/mol·K) and T is the absolute temperature.
  - Molecules that have an energy equal to or greater than E_a have sufficient energy to react.
  - As we increase the temperature, the fraction of the population that has an energy equal to or greater than E_a increases.
    - Thus, more molecules can react.

The Arrhenius Equation[33,34]

- Arrhenius discovered that most reaction-rate data obeyed an equation based on three factors:
  - The number of collisions per unit time.
  - The fraction of collisions that occur with the correct orientation.
  - The fraction of the colliding molecules that have an energy equal to or greater than E_a.
- From these observations Arrhenius developed the **Arrhenius equation**.

$$k = Ae^{\frac{-E_a}{RT}}$$

  - Where k is the rate constant, E_a is the activation energy, R is the gas constant (8.314 J/K·mol), and T is the temperature in K.
  - A is called the **frequency factor**.
    - It is related to the frequency of collisions and the probability that a collision will have a favorable orientation.
  - Both A and E_a are *specific to a given reaction*.

Determining the Activation Energy

- E_a may be determined experimentally.
  - We need to take the natural log of both sides of the Arrhenius equation:

$$\ln k = -\frac{E_a}{RT} + \ln A$$

---

[33] "The Arrhenius Law and Storage of Food" from Further Readings
[34] "Visualizing the Transition State: A Hands-On Approach to Arrhenius Equation" from Further Readings

- A graph of ln k vs $1/T$ will have a slope of $-E_a/R$ and a y-intercept of ln A.
- Alternatively we can use:

$$\ln\frac{k_1}{k_2} = \frac{E_a}{R}\left(\frac{1}{T_2} - \frac{1}{T_1}\right)$$

FORWARD REFERENCES
- The role of temperature in affecting the position of equilibrium will be discussed in Chapter 15 (section 15.7).

14.6 Reaction Mechanisms[35,36]

- The balanced chemical equation provides information about substances present at the beginning and end of the reaction.
- The **reaction mechanism** is the process by which the reaction occurs.
- Mechanisms provide a picture of which bonds are broken and formed during the course of a reaction.

Elementary Reactions[37]

- **Elementary reactions** or elementary processes are any processes that occur in a single step.
- The number of molecules present in an elementary step is the **molecularity** of that elementary step.
  - **Unimolecular** reactions involve one molecule.
  - **Bimolecular** elementary reactions involve the collision of two molecules.
  - **Termolecular** elementary reactions involve the simultaneous collision of three molecules.
    - It is not common to see termolecular processes (statistically improbable).

Multistep Mechanisms[38]

- A multistep mechanism consists of a sequence of elementary steps.
  - The elementary steps must add to give the balanced chemical equation.
  - Some multistep mechanisms will include **intermediates**.
    - These are species that appear in an elementary step but are neither a reactant nor product.
    - Intermediates are formed in one elementary step and consumed in another.
    - They are not found in the balanced equation for the overall reaction.
    - Intermediates are NOT the same as transition states.

Rate Laws of Elementary Reactions

- The rate laws of the elementary steps determine the overall rate law of the reaction.
- The rate law of an elementary step is determined by its molecularly.
  - Unimolecular processes are first order.
  - Bimolecular processes are second order.
  - Termolecular processes are third order.

The Rate-Determining Step for a Multistep Mechanism[39,40]

- Most reactions occur by mechanisms with more than one elementary step.
  - Often one step is much slower than the others.
  - The slow step limits the overall reaction rate.
    - This is called the **rate-determining step** (*rate-limiting step*) of the reaction.

---

[35] "Pictorial Analogies XIII: Kinetics and Mechanisms" from Further Readings
[36] "Doing the Dishes: An Analogy for Use in Teaching Reaction Kinetics" from Further Readings
[37] "Bimolecular Reaction" Animation from Instructor's Resource CD/DVD
[38] "Fluorine" 3-D Model from Instructor's Resource CD/DVD
[39] "Auto Analogies" from Further Readings
[40] "Another Auto Analogy: Rate Determining Steps" from Further Readings

- This step governs the overall rate law for the overall reaction.

Mechanisms with a Slow Initial Step

- Consider the reaction:
$$NO_2(g) + CO(g) \rightarrow NO(g) + CO_2(g)$$
- The experimentally derived rate law is: Rate $= k[NO_2]^2$
- We propose a mechanism for the reaction:

  - Step 1: $NO_2(g) + NO_2(g) \xrightarrow{k_1} NO_3(g) + NO(g)$ slow step

  - Step 2: $NO_3(g) + CO(g) \xrightarrow{k_2} NO_2(g) + CO_2(g)$ fast step

    - Note that NO_3 is an intermediate.
- If $k_2 \gg k_1$, then the overall reaction rate will depend on the first step (the rate-determining step).
  - Rate $= k_1[NO_2]^2$
  - This theoretical rate law is in agreement with the experimental rate law.
  - This supports (but does not prove) our mechanism.

Mechanisms with a Fast Initial Step

- Consider the reaction:
$$2NO(g) + Br_2(g) \rightarrow 2NOBr(g)$$
- The experimentally determined rate law is:
$$Rate = k[NO]^2[Br_2]$$
- Consider the following proposed mechanism:

  - Step 1: $NO(g) + Br_2(g) \underset{k_{-1}}{\overset{k_1}{\rightleftharpoons}} NOBr_2(g)$ fast step

  - Step 2: $NOBr_2(g) + NO(g) \xrightarrow{k_2} 2NOBr(g)$ slow step

  - The theoretical rate law for this mechanism is based on the rate-determining step, step 2:
$$Rate = k_2[NOBr_2][NO]$$
- Problem: This rate law depends on the concentration of an intermediate species.
  - Intermediates are usually unstable and have low/unknown concentrations.
  - We need to find a way to remove this term from our rate law.
  - We can express the concentration of $[NOBr_2]$ in terms of NOBr and Br_2 by assuming that there is an equilibrium in step 1.
- In a dynamic equilibrium, the forward rate equals the reverse rate.
  - Therefore, by definition of equilibrium we get:
$$k_1[NO][Br_2] = k_{-1}[NOBr_2]$$
  - Solving for $NOBr_2$ we get:

$$[NOBr_2] = \frac{k_1}{k_{-1}}[NO][Br_2]$$

  - Therefore, the overall rate law becomes:

$$Rate = k_2 \frac{k_1}{k_{-1}}[NO][Br_2][NO] = k[NO]^2[Br_2]$$

- Note that the final rate law is consistent with the experimentally observed rate law.

FORWARD REFERENCES

- The relationship between k_1 and k_{-1} will be exploited in Chapter 15 (section 15.1).
- Mechanism of organic addition reactions will be discussed in Chapter 24 (section 24.4).

14.7 Catalysis[41,42]

- A **catalyst** is a substance that changes the rate of a chemical reaction without itself undergoing a permanent chemical change in the process.
- There are two types of catalysts:
  - homogeneous and
  - heterogeneous.
- Catalysts are common in the body, in the environment, and in the chemistry lab!

Homogeneous Catalysis[43,44,45,46,47,48]

- A **homogeneous catalyst** is one that is present in the same phase as the reacting molecules.
- For example, hydrogen peroxide decomposes very slowly in the absence of a catalyst:

$$2H_2O_2(aq) \rightarrow 2H_2O(l) + O_2(g)$$

- In the presence of bromide ion, the decomposition occurs rapidly in acidic solution:

$$2Br^-(aq) + H_2O_2(aq) + 2H^+(aq) \rightarrow Br_2(aq) + 2H_2O(l)$$

$$Br_2(aq) + H_2O_2(aq) \rightarrow 2Br^-(aq) + 2H^+(aq) + O_2(g)$$

  - Br^- is a catalyst because it is regenerated at the end of the reaction.
  - The net reaction is still:

$$2H_2O_2(aq) \rightarrow 2H_2O(l) + O_2(g)$$

- How do catalysts increase reaction rates?
  - In general, catalysts operate by *lowering the overall activation energy for a chemical reaction.*
  - However, catalysts can operate by increasing the number of effective collisions.
    - That is, from the Arrhenius equation catalysts increase k by increasing A or decreasing E_a.
  - A catalyst usually provides a completely different mechanism for the reaction.
    - In the preceding peroxide decomposition example, in the absence of a catalyst, H_2O_2 decomposes directly to water and oxygen.
    - In the presence of Br^-, $Br_2(aq)$ is generated as an intermediate.
  - When a catalyst adds an intermediate, the activation energies for *both* steps must be lower than the activation energy for the uncatalyzed reaction.

---

[41] "Catalysis" from Further Readings
[42] "Catalysis" Movie from Instructor's Resource CD/DVD
[43] "Catalytic Decomposition of Hydrogen Peroxide: Foam Production" from Live Demonstrations
[44] Figure 14.22 from Transparency Pack
[45] "Catalysis: New Reaction Pathways, Not Just a Lowering of the Activation Energy" from Further Readings
[46] "Hydrogen Peroxide" 3-D Model from Instructor's Resource CD/DVD
[47] "Oxygen" 3-D Model from Instructor's Resource CD/DVD
[48] "Bromine" 3-D Model from Instructor's Resource CD/DVD

Heterogeneous Catalysis[49,50,51,52,53,54,55]

- A **heterogeneous catalyst** exists in a different phase than the reactants.
- Often we encounter a situation involving a solid catalyst in contact with gaseous reactants and gaseous products (example: catalytic converters in cars) or with reactants in a liquid.
    - Many industrial catalysts are heterogeneous.
- How do they do their job?
    - The first step is **adsorption** (the binding of reactant molecules to the catalyst surface).
    - Adsorption occurs due to the high reactivity of atoms or ions on the surface of the solid.
        - *Absorption* refers to the uptake of molecules into the interior of another substance.
    - Molecules are adsorbed onto the catalyst surface.
        - The number of active sites on a given amount of catalyst depends on several factors such as:
            - the nature of the catalyst.
            - how the catalyst was prepared.
            - how the catalyst was treated prior to use.
    - For example, consider the hydrogenation of ethylene to form ethane:

$$C_2H_4(g) + H_2(g) \rightarrow C_2H_6(g) \qquad \Delta H° = -137 \text{ kJ/mol}$$

    - The reaction is slow in the absence of a catalyst.
    - In the presence of a finely divided metal catalyst (Ni, Pt, or Pd) the reaction occurs quickly at room temperature.
    - First, the ethylene and hydrogen molecules are adsorbed onto active sites on the metal surface.
    - The H–H bond breaks and the H atoms migrate about the metal surface.
    - When an H atom collides with an ethylene molecule on the surface, the C–C π bond breaks and a C–H σ bond forms.
    - An *ethyl group*, C_2H_5, is weakly bonded to the metal surface with a metal-carbon σ bond.
    - When C_2H_6 forms, it desorbs from the surface.
    - When ethylene and hydrogen are adsorbed onto a surface, less energy is required to break the bonds.
    - The activation energy for the reaction is lowered.
        - Thus, the reaction rate is increased.

---

[49] "Catalysis on Surfaces" from Further Readings
[50] "Surface Reaction-Hydrogenation" Animation from Instructor's Resource CD/DVD
[51] "Solid Acid Catalysts" from Further Readings
[52] "Getting Auto Exhausts to Pristine" from Further Readings
[53] "Driving Down Emissions" from Further Readings
[54] "Ethylene" 3-D Model from Instructor's Resource CD/DVD
[55] "Ethane" 3-D Model from Instructor's Resource CD/DVD

Enzymes[56,57,58,59,60,61,62,63,64,65]

- **Enzymes** are biological catalysts.
- Most enzymes are large protein molecules.
  - Molar masses are in the range of 10^4 to 10^6 amu.
- Enzymes are capable of catalyzing very specific reactions.
- For example, *catalase* is an enzyme found in blood and liver cells.
  - It catalyzes the decomposition of hydrogen peroxide:
  $$2H_2O_2(aq) \rightarrow 2H_2O(l) + O_2(g)$$
  - This reaction is important in removing peroxide, a potentially harmful oxidizing agent.
- The enzyme catalyzes the reaction at its **active site**.
- The substances that undergo reaction at the active site on enzymes are called **substrates**.
- A simple view of enzyme specificity is the **lock-and-key model**.
  - Here, a substrate is pictured as fitting into the active site of an enzyme in a manner similar to a specific key fitting into a lock. This forms an *enzyme-substrate (ES) complex*.
  - Only substrates that fit into the enzyme lock can be involved in the reaction.
  - The enzyme's active site and the substrate thus have complementary shapes.
  - However, there may be a significant amount of flexibility at the active site.
    - It may change shape as it binds substrate.
  - A reaction occurs very quickly once substrate is bound.
  - Products depart the active site at the end of the reaction.
  - This allows new substrate molecules to bind to the enzyme.
- If a molecule binds so tightly to an enzyme that substrate molecules cannot displace it, then the active site is blocked and the catalyst is inhibited.
  - Such molecules are called *enzyme inhibitors*.
  - Many poisons act by binding to the active site, blocking the binding of substrates.
  - Some poisons bind to *other* locations on the enzyme.
    - Binding ultimately causes a change in the enzyme that interferes with enzyme activity.
- Enzymes are extremely efficient catalysts.
  - The number of individual catalytic events occurring at an active site per unit time is called the *turnover number*.
  - Large turnover numbers correspond to very low E_a values.
  - For enzymes, turnover numbers are very large (typically $10^3 - 10^7$ per second).

Nitrogen Fixation and Nitrogenase[66,67]

- Nitrogen gas cannot be used in the soil for plants or animals.
- Nitrogen compounds, NH_3, NO_2^-, and NO_3^- are used in the soil.

---

[56] "Enzyme Catalysis: Cleaner, Safer, Energy Efficient" from Further Readings
[57] "Environmental Catalysts" from Further Readings
[58] "Practical Enzyme Kinetics" from Further Readings
[59] Figure 14.27 from Transparency Pack
[60] "Breaking Bonds versus Chopping Heads: The Enzyme as Butcher" from Further Readings
[61] "Biocatalysis Makes Headway in Chemicals" From Further Readings
[62] "The Catalytic Function of Enzymes" from Further Readings
[63] "Frank Westheimer's Early Demonstration of Enzymatic Specificity" from Further Readings
[64] "Enzyme Activity: A Simple Analogy" from Further Readings
[65] "Enzyme Kinetics: Effects of Temperature and an Inhibitor on Catalase Extracted from Potato" from Live Demonstrations
[66] "FeMo-cofactor of Nitrogenase" 3-D Model from Instructor's Resource CD/DVD
[67] "Nitrogen Dioxide" 3-D Model from Instructor's Resource CD/DVD

- The conversion between N_2 and NH_3 is a process with a high activation energy (the N_2 triple bond needs to be broken).
- Nitrogenase, an enzyme in bacteria that lives in root nodules of legumes such as clover and alfalfa, catalyses the reduction of nitrogen to ammonia.
- The fixed nitrogen (NH_3, NO_2^-, and NO_3^-) is consumed by plants and then eaten by animals.
- Animal waste and dead plants are attacked by bacteria that break down the fixed nitrogen and produce N_2 gas for the atmosphere.

FORWARD REFERENCES
- The effect of catalysts on equilibrium and catalytic converters will be discussed in Chapter 15 (section 15.7).
- Metal ions will be mentioned as integral parts of many enzymes in Chapter 23 (section 23.4).
- Chiral enzymes will be mentioned in Chapter 23 (section. 23.4).
- The degree of subdivision of a catalyst will be mentioned in Chapter 24 (section 24.4).
- The role of proteins as enzymes will be discussed in Chapter 24 (section 24.10).

Further Readings:

1. Reed A. Howald, "The Fizz Keeper, a Case Study in Chemical Education, Equilibrium, and Kinetics," *J. Chem. Educ.*, Vol. 76, **1999**, 208–209.

2. Lionello Pobliani and Mario N. Berberan-Santos, "Inflation Rates, Car Devaluation, and Chemical Kinetics," *J. Chem. Educ.*, Vol. 73, **1996**, 950–952.

3. Charles J. Marzzacco, "An Analogy to Help Students Understand Reaction Orders," *J. Chem. Educ.*, Vol. 75, **1998**, 482.

4. Edward Todd Urbansky, "Don't Be Tricked by Your Integrated Rate Plot!," *J. Chem. Educ.*, Vol. 78, **2001**, 921–923.

5. Francisco J. Arnaiz, "Mice in the Box for Zero-Order Kinetics," *J. Chem. Educ.*, Vol. 76, **1999**, 1458.

6. Elizabeth Wilson, "Light Sticks," *Chemical and Engineering News*, **January 18, 1999**, 65. A brief article on chemiluminescent light sticks.

7. Kent W. Piepgrass, "Audience-Appropriate Analogies: Collision Theory," *J. Chem. Educ.*, Vol. 75, **1998**, 72.

8. Lee A. Krug, "The Collision Theory and an American Tradition," *J. Chem. Educ.*, Vol. 64, **1987**, 1000.

9. Keith J. Laidler, "Just What Is a Transition State?," *J. Chem. Educ.*, Vol. 64, **1988**, 540–542.

10. Ilya A. Leenson, "The Arrhenius Law and Storage of Food," *J. Chem. Educ.*, Vol. 76, **1999**, 504–505.

11. Thomas S. Kuntzleman, Matthew S. Swanson, and Deborah K. Sayers, "Visualizing the Transition State: A Hands-On Approach to the Arrhenius Equation," *J. Chem. Educ.*, Vol. 84, **2007**, 1776–1778.

12. John J. Fortman, "Pictorial Analogies XIII: Kinetics and Mechanisms," *J. Chem. Educ.*, Vol. 71, **1994**, 848–849.

13. Arthur M. Last, "Doing the Dishes: An Analogy for Use in Teaching Reaction Kinetics," *J. Chem. Educ.*, Vol. 62, **1985**, 1015–1016.

14. Richard A. Potts, "Auto Analogies," *J. Chem. Educ.*, Vol. 62, **1985**, 579. This brief article includes analogies for reaction mechanisms and rate-determining steps of a reaction.

15. David W. Ball, "Another Auto Analogy: Rate Determining Steps," *J. Chem. Educ.*, Vol. 64, **1987**, 486–487.

16. Doris Kolb, "Catalysis," *J. Chem. Educ.*, Vol. 56, **1979**, 743–747.

17. Albert Haim, "Catalysis: New Reaction Pathways, Not Just a Lowering of the Activation Energy," *J. Chem. Educ.*, Vol. 66, **1989**, 935–937.

18. Cynthia M. Friend, "Catalysis on Surfaces," *Scientific American*, **April 1993**, 74–79.

19. Sir John Meurig Thomas, "Solid Acid Catalysts," *Scientific American*, **April 1992**, 112–118.

20. Mitch Jacoby, "Getting Auto Exhausts to Pristine," *Chemical and Engineering News*, **January 25, 1999**, 36–44.

21. Rosslyn Nicholson, "Driving Down Emissions," *Chemistry World*, **March 2004**, 50–53.

22. Jim Lalonde, "Enzyme Catalysis: Cleaner, Safer, Energy Efficient," *Chemical Engineering*, Vol. 104(9), **1997**, 108–112.

23. Robert J. Farrauto, Ronald M. Heck, and Barry K. Speronello, "Environmental Catalysts," *Chemical and Engineering News*, **September 7, 1992**, 34–44.

24. H. Alan Rowe and Morris Brown, "Practical Enzyme Kinetics," *J. Chem. Educ.*, Vol. 65, **1988**, 548–549.

25. Todd P. Silverstein, "Breaking Bonds versus Chopping Heads: The Enzyme as Butcher," *J. Chem. Educ.*, Vol. 72, **1995**, 645–646.

26. Rita L. D'Aquino, "Biocatalysis Makes Headway in Chemicals," *Chemical Engineering*, Vol. 106(3), **1999**, 37–43.

27. Allan G. Splittgerber, "The Catalytic Function of Enzymes," *J. Chem. Educ.*, Vol. 62, **1985**, 1008–1010.

28. Addison Ault, "Frank Westheimer's Early Demonstration of Enzymatic Specificity," *J. Chem. Educ.*, Vol. 85, **2008**, 1246-1249.

29. Kenton B. Abel and Donald R. Halenz, "Enzyme Activity: A Simple Analogy," *J. Chem. Educ.*, Vol. 69, **1992**, 9.

Live Demonstrations:

1. Lee. R. Summerlin, Christie L. Borgford, and Julie B. Ealy, "Appearing Red," *Chemical Demonstrations, A Sourcebook for Teachers, Volume 2* (Washington: American Chemical Society, **1988**), pp. 145–146. An introductory kinetics experiment.

2. Xavier Creary and Karen M. Morris, "A New Twist on the Iodine Clock Reaction: Determining the Order of a Reaction," *J. Chem. Educ.*, Vol. 76, **1999**, 530–531.

3. Bassam Z. Shakhashiri, "Hydrogen Peroxide Iodine Clock: Oxidation of Potassium Iodide by Hydrogen Peroxide", *Chemical Demonstrations: A Handbook for Teachers of Chemistry, Volume 4* (Madison: The University of Wisconsin Press, **1992**), pp. 37–43.

4. Lee. R. Summerlin, and James. L. Ealy, Jr., "The Starch-Iodine Clock Reaction," *Chemical Demonstrations, A Sourcebook for Teachers, Volume 1* (Washington: American Chemical Society, **1988**), pp.107–108. The classic iodine clock experiment.

5. Bassam Z. Shakhashiri, "Lightsticks," *Chemical Demonstrations: A Handbook for Teachers of Chemistry, Volume 1* (Madison: The University of Wisconsin Press, **1983**), pp. 146–152.

6. Bassam Z Shakhashiri, Lloyd G. Williams, Glen E. Dirreen, and Ann Francis, "Cool-Light Chemiluminescence," *J. Chem. Educ.*, Vol. 58, **1981**, 70–72. The dependence of reaction rates on temperature is demonstrated with chemiluminescent light sticks.

7. Lee. R. Summerlin, Christie L. Borgford, and Julie B. Ealy, "Enzyme Kinetics: Effects of Temperature and an Inhibitor on Catalase Extracted from Potato," *Chemical Demonstrations, A Sourcebook for Teachers, Volume 2* (Washington: American Chemical Society, **1988**), pp. 152–153. An exploration of enzyme-catalyzed decomposition of hydrogen peroxide.

8. Lee R. Summerlin and James L. Ealy, Jr., "Catalytic Decomposition of Hydrogen Peroxide: Foam Production," *Chemical Demonstrations, A Sourcebook for Teachers* (Washington: American Chemical Society, **1988**), pp. 101–102. Potassium iodide (or manganese dioxide) is the catalyst in this demonstration; oxygen gas produced in the presence of detergent gives rise to a large quantity of foam.

Chapter 15. Chemical Equilibrium

Media Resources

Figures and Tables in Transparency Pack:

	Section:
Figure 15.2 Achieving Chemical Equilibrium in the $N_2O_4(g) \rightleftharpoons 2\,NO_2(g)$ Reaction	15.1 The Concept of Equilibrium
Figure 15.9 Effect of Temperature and Pressure on NH_3 Yield in the Haber Process	15.7 Le Châtelier's Principle
Figure 15.10 Effect of Adding H_2 to an Equilibrium Mixture of N_2, H_2, and NH_3	15.7 Le Châtelier's Principle

Activities:

	Section:
Chemical Equilibrium	15.1 The Concept of Equilibrium
NO_2-N_2O_4 Equilibrium	15.1 The Concept of Equilibrium
Equilibrium Constant	15.2 The Equilibrium Constant
Using an Equilibrium Table	15.5 Calculating Equilibrium Constants
Le Châtelier's Principle	15.7 Le Châtelier's Principle

Animations:

	Section:
NO_2-N_2O_4 Equilibrium	15.1 The Concept of Equilibrium
Temperature Dependence of Equilibrium	15.7 Le Châtelier's Principle

Movies:

	Section:
Nitrogen Dioxide and Dinitrogen Tetroxide	15.1 The Concept of Equilibrium
Formation of Water	15.7 Le Châtelier's Principle

3-D Models:

	Section:
Dinitrogen Tetroxide	15.1 The Concept of Equilibrium
Nitrogen Dioxide	15.1 The Concept of Equilibrium
Oxygen	15.1 The Concept of Equilibrium
Carbon Dioxide	15.4 Heterogeneous Equilibria
Nitrogen	15.7 Le Châtelier's Principle
Hydrogen	15.7 Le Châtelier's Principle
Ammonia	15.7 Le Châtelier's Principle
Tetrachlorocobaltate(III)	15.7 Le Châtelier's Principle

Other Resources

Further Readings:

	Section:
Fritz Haber	15.2 The Equilibrium Constant
An Elementary Discussion of Chemical Equilibrium	15.2 The Equilibrium Constant
Chemical Equilibrium in the General Chemistry Course	15.2 The Equilibrium Constant
The Complexity of Teaching and Learning Chemical Equilibrium	15.2 The Equilibrium Constant
Equilibrium: A Teaching/Learning Activity	15.2 The Equilibrium Constant

Introducing Dynamic Equilibrium as an Explanatory Model — 15.2 The Equilibrium Constant

Simulations for Teaching Chemical Equilibrium — 15.2 The Equilibrium Constant

Applying the Reaction Table Method for Chemical Reaction Problems (Stoichiometry and Equilibrium) — 15.5 Calculating Equilibrium Constants

Amounts Tables as a Diagnostic Tool for Flawed Stoichiometric Reasoning — 15.7 Le Châtelier's Principle

Calculating Equilibrium Concentrations by Iteration: Recycle Your Approximations — 15.7 Le Châtelier's Principle

Man of Principle — 15.7 Le Châtelier's Principle

Chemical Equilibrium and Polynomial Equations: Beware of Roots — 15.7 Le Châtelier's Principle

Le Châtelier's Principle — 15.7 Le Châtelier's Principle

The Fizz Keeper, a Case Study in Chemical Education, Equilibrium, and Kinetics — 15.7 Le Châtelier's Principle

Live Demonstrations:

Section:

Equilibrium and Le Châtelier's Principle — 15.2 The Equilibrium Constant

Effect of Concentration on Equilibrium: Cobalt Complex — 15.7 Le Châtelier's Principle

Effect of Temperature Change on Equilibrium: Cobalt Complex — 15.7 Le Châtelier's Principle

Equilibrium in the Gas Phase — 15.7 Le Châtelier's Principle

From Chicken Breath to the Killer Lakes of Cameroon: Uniting Seven Interesting Phenomena with a Single Chemical Underpinning — 15.7 Le Châtelier's Principle

Chapter 15. Chemical Equilibrium

Common Student Misconceptions

- Students confuse the arrows used for resonance and equilibrium.
- Students often incorrectly include concentrations of pure liquids and solids in equilibrium constant expressions.
- Students often have problems distinguishing between K and Q.
- Students struggle with the idea that K and Q have no units.
- Students often do not know (or check) whether an approximate equilibrium calculation is valid.

Teaching Tips

- Many students need to see how the numerical problems in this chapter are solved.
- Students who have difficulty with some of the mathematical manipulations in this chapter should be directed to Appendix A of the text.
- It is useful to stress that concentrations in equilibrium constant expressions are merely approximations of activities. Since activities of pure substances are 1, they do not appear in equilibrium constant expressions, and neither should their approximations, i.e. concentrations.
- Students might find it helpful to consider changing the concentration or pressure of a substance in a reaction at equilibrium as creating stress. The removal of something creates a "deficit stress," and adding something creates an "excess stress." Reactions will always respond to stress by reducing the deficit (making more of what was removed) or by reducing the excess (consuming some of what was added). This description works regardless of which side of the reaction is changed.
- Students should be reminded that principles of general equilibria taught in this chapter are very universal and need to be mastered in order to understand concepts in future chapters.

Lecture Outline

15.1 The Concept of Equilibrium[1,2,3,4,5,6,7,8]

- Consider colorless frozen N_2O_4.
  - At room temperature, it decomposes to brown NO_2.
    $$N_2O_4(g) \leftrightarrows 2NO_2(g)$$
  - At some time, the color stops changing and we have a mixture of N_2O_4 and NO_2.
  - **Chemical equilibrium** is the point at which the concentrations of all species are constant.
    - Opposing reactions proceed at equal rates.
  - Assume that both the forward and reverse reactions are elementary processes.
  - We can write rate expressions for each reaction.
    - Forward reaction: $N_2O_4(g) \rightarrow 2NO_2(g)$
      - $Rate_f = k_f[N_2O_4]$ $\quad k_f$ = rate constant (forward reaction)

---

[1] "Chemical Equilibrium" Activity from Instructor's Resource CD/DVD
[2] Figure 15.2 from Transparency Pack
[3] "NO₂-N₂O₄ Equilibrium" Activity from Instructor's Resource CD/DVD
[4] "NO₂-N₂O₄ Equilibrium" Animation from Instructor's Resource CD/DVD
[5] "Nitrogen Dioxide and Dinitrogen Tetroxide" Movie from Instructor's Resource CD/DVD
[6] "Dinitrogen Tetroxide" 3-D Model from Instructor's Resource CD/DVD
[7] "Nitrogen Dioxide" 3-D Model from Instructor's Resource CD/DVD
[8] "Oxygen" 3-D Model from Instructor's Resource CD/DVD

- Reverse reaction: $2NO_2(g) \rightarrow N_2O_4(g)$
  - $Rate_r = k_r[NO_2]^2$ k_r = rate constant (reverse reaction)
- Place some pure N_2O_4 into a closed container.
  - As N_2O_4 reacts to form NO_2, the concentration of N_2O_4 will decrease and the concentration of NO_2 will increase.
  - Thus, we expect the forward reaction rate to slow and the reverse reaction rate to increase.
  - Eventually we get to equilibrium where the forward and reverse rates are equal.
  - At equilibrium:
$$k_f[N_2O_4] = k_r[NO_2]^2$$
  - Rearranging, we get:
$$k_f/k_r = \text{a constant}$$
- At equilibrium the concentrations of N_2O_4 and NO_2 do not change.
  - This mixture is called an *equilibrium mixture*.
    - The equilibrium mixture results because the reaction is *reversible*.
  - This is an example of a dynamic equilibrium.
    - A dynamic equilibrium exists when the rates of the forward and reverse reactions are equal.
    - No further net change in reactant or product concentration occurs.
    - The double arrow $\rightleftharpoons$ implies that the process is dynamic.

FORWARD REFERENCES
- Equilibria involving acids and bases will be the subject of Chapters 16 and 17.
- Solubility equilibria will be discussed in Chapter 17 (section 17.4).
- The concept of equilibrium will be important throughout Chapter 19.

15.2 The Equilibrium Constant[9,10,11,12,13,14,15,16,17]

- Consider the **Haber process**:
$$N_2(g) + 3H_2(g) \rightleftharpoons 2NH_3(g)$$
- It is used for the preparation of ammonia from nitrogen and hydrogen.
- The process is carried out at high temperature and pressure.
  - Ammonia is a good source of fixed nitrogen for plants.
    - Much of the NH_3 produced industrially is used as a fertilizer.
- If we start with a mixture of nitrogen and hydrogen (in any proportions), the reaction will reach equilibrium with constant concentrations of nitrogen, hydrogen, and ammonia.
- However, if we start with just ammonia and no nitrogen or hydrogen, the reaction will proceed and N_2 and H_2 will be produced until equilibrium is achieved.
- No matter what the starting composition of reactants and products is, the equilibrium mixture contains the same relative concentrations of reactants and products.
  - Equilibrium can be reached from either direction.

[9] "Fritz Haber" from Further Readings
[10] "Equilibrium Constant" Activity from Instructor's Resource CD/DVD
[11] "An Elementary Discussion of Chemical Equilibrium" from Further Readings
[12] "Equilibrium and Le Châtelier's Principle" from Live Demonstrations
[13] "Chemical Equilibrium in the General Chemistry Course" from Further Readings
[14] "The Complexity of Teaching and Learning Chemical Equilibrium" from Further Readings
[15] "Equilibrium: A Teaching/Learning Activity" from Further Readings
[16] "Introducing Dynamic Equilibrium as an Explanatory Model" from Further Readings
[17] "Simulations for Teaching Chemical Equilibrium" from Further Readings

- We can write an expression for the relationship between the concentration of the reactants and products at equilibrium.
  - This expression is based on the **law of mass action**.
  - For a general reaction,

$$a\text{A} + b\text{B} \leftrightarrows d\text{D} + e\text{E}$$

  - The **equilibrium-constant expression** is given by:

$$K_c = \frac{[\text{D}^d][\text{E}]^e}{[\text{A}]^a[\text{B}]^b}$$

  - Where K_c is the **equilibrium constant**.
  - The subscript "c" indicates that molar concentrations were used to evaluate the constant.
  - Note that the equilibrium constant expression has products in the numerator and reactants in the denominator.

Evaluating K_c

- The value of K_c does not depend on initial concentrations of products or reactants.
  - Consider the reaction:

$$\text{N}_2\text{O}_4(g) \leftrightarrows 2\text{NO}_2(g)$$

  - The equilibrium constant is given by:

$$K_c = \frac{[\text{NO}_2]^2}{[\text{N}_2\text{O}_4]}$$

  - The value of this constant (at 100 °C) is 6.50 (regardless of the initial concentrations of $\text{N}_2\text{O}_4(g)$ or $\text{NO}_2(g)$.
- The equilibrium expression depends on stoichiometry.
  - It does not depend on the reaction mechanism.
  - The value of K_c varies with temperature.
- We generally omit the units of the equilibrium constant.

Equilibrium Constants in Terms of Pressure, K_p

- When the reactants and products are gases, we can write an equilibrium expression using partial pressures rather than molar concentrations.
- The equilibrium constant is K_p where "p" stands for pressure.
- For the reaction:

$$a\text{A} + b\text{B} \leftrightarrows d\text{D} + e\text{E}$$

$$K_p = \frac{(P_\text{D})^d (P_\text{E})^e}{(P_\text{A})^a (P_\text{B})^b}$$

- They can be interconverted using the ideal gas equation and our definition of molarity:
$$PV = nRT \quad \text{thus } P = (n/V)RT$$
- If we express volume in liters the quantity (n/V) is equivalent to molarity.
- Thus the partial pressure of a substance, A, is given as:
$$P_\text{A} = (n_\text{A}/V)RT = [\text{A}]RT$$
- We can use this to obtain a general expression relating K_c and K_p:
$$K_p = K_c(RT)^{\Delta n}$$
  - Where Δn = (moles of gaseous products) − (moles of gaseous reactants).
  - The numerical values of K_c and K_p will differ if $\Delta n = 0$.

Copyright © 2012 Pearson Education, Inc.

FORWARD REFERENCES
- Various equilibrium constants: K_a, K_b, K_w, K_{sp} will be used throughout Chapters 16 and 17, and later in select end-of-chapter problems in Chapters 19 and 20.
- K_p and K_c will be revisited in Chapter 19 (section 19.7).
- Haber process will be further discussed in Chapter 22 (sections 22.2 and 22.7).

Equilibrium Constants and Units

- Equilibrium constants are reported without units.
  - The equilibrium constant may be derived from thermodynamic measurements.
  - The constants are defined in terms of *activities* rather than concentrations or partial pressures.
  - The activity of a substance in an *ideal* mixture is the ratio of the concentration or pressure of the substance either to a reference concentration (1 *M*) or a reference pressure (1 atm).
    - The units in these ratios cancel, thus activities have no units.
    - The numerical value of the activity equals the concentration.
    - For pure solids and pure liquids, the activities equal 1.
  - What about "real" systems?
    - Here activities also have no units.
    - The activities are not exactly equal to concentration but we will ignore the differences.
    - *Thermodynamic equilibrium constants* derived from these activities also have no units.

15.3 Understanding and Working with Equilibrium Constants

The Magnitude of Equilibrium Constants

- The equilibrium constant, K, is the ratio of products to reactants.
  - Therefore, the larger K the more products are present at equilibrium.
  - Conversely, the smaller K the more reactants are present at equilibrium.
    - If $K \gg 1$, then products dominate at equilibrium and equilibrium *lies to the right*.
    - If $K \ll 1$, then reactants dominate at equilibrium and the equilibrium *lies to the left*.

The Direction of the Chemical Equation and K

- An equilibrium can be approached from either direction.
- Consider the reaction:

$$N_2O_4(g) \rightleftharpoons 2NO_2(g)$$

- The equilibrium constant for this reaction (at 100 °C) is:

$$K_c = \frac{[NO_2]^2}{[N_2O_4]} = 0.212$$

- However, when we write the equilibrium expression for the reverse reaction,

$$2NO_2(g) \rightleftharpoons N_2O_4(g)$$

- The equilibrium constant for this reaction (at 100 °C) is:

$$K_c = \frac{[N_2O_4]}{[NO_2]^2} = 4.72$$

- The equilibrium constant for a reaction in one direction is the reciprocal of the equilibrium constant of the reaction in the reverse direction.

Relating Chemical Equation Stoichiometry and Equilibrium Constants

- It is possible to calculate the equilibrium constant for a reaction if we know the equilibrium constants for other reactions that add up to give us the one we want.
  - This is similar to using Hess's law.

- The equilibrium constant of a reaction in the reverse direction is the inverse of the equilibrium constant of the reaction in the forward direction.
- The equilibrium constant of a reaction that has been multiplied by a number is the equilibrium constant raised to a power equal to that number.
- The equilibrium constant for a net reaction made up of two or more steps is the product of the equilibrium constants for the individual steps.

15.4 Heterogeneous Equilibria[18]

- Equilibria in which all reactants and products are present in the same phase are called **homogeneous equilibria**.
- Equilibria in which one or more reactants or products are present in a different phase are called **heterogeneous equilibria**.
- Consider the equilibrium established when solid lead(II) chloride dissolves in water to form a saturated solution:

$$PbCl_2(s) \leftrightarrows Pb^{2+}(aq) + 2Cl^-(aq)$$

  - Experimentally, the amount of Pb^{2+} and Cl^- does not depend on the amount of $PbCl_2$.
    - Why?
  - The concentration of a pure solid or pure liquid equals its density divided by its molar mass.
  - Neither density nor molar mass is a variable.
    - Thus the concentrations of solids and pure liquids are constant.
  - For the dissolution of $PbCl_2$:

$$K_c = [Pb^{2+}][Cl^-]^2$$

- If a pure solid or pure liquid is involved in a heterogeneous equilibrium, its concentration is not included in the equilibrium constant expression.
- Note: Although the *concentrations* of these species are not included in the equilibrium expression, they *do* participate in the reaction and *must* be present for an equilibrium to be established!
- Other common examples of heterogeneous equilibria include:
  - systems involving solids and gases.
    - Example: $CaCO_3(s) \leftrightarrows CaO(s) + CO_2(g)$

$$K_c = [CO_2] \text{ and } K_p = P_{CO_2}$$

  - systems where the solvent is involved as a reactant or product and the solutes are present at low concentrations.
    - Example: $H_2O(l) + CO_3^{2-}(aq) \leftrightarrows OH^-(aq) + HCO_3^-(aq)$

$$K_c = [OH^-][HCO_3^-] / [CO_3^{2-}]$$

    - Here the concentration of water is essentially constant and we can think of it as a pure liquid.

FORWARD REFERENCES
- Solubility equilibria will be discussed in detail in Chapter 17 (section 17.4).
- Exclusion of pure liquids and solids from equilibrium expressions will be revisited in Chapter 19.

15.5 Calculating Equilibrium Constants[19,20]

- Proceed as follows:

---

[18] "Carbon Dioxide" 3-D Model from Instructor's Resource CD/DVD
[19] "Using an Equilibrium Table" Activity from Instructor's Resource CD/DVD
[20] "Applying the Reaction Table Method for Chemical Reaction Problems (Stoichiometry and Equilibrium)" from Further Readings

- Tabulate initial and equilibrium concentrations (or partial pressures) for all species in the equilibrium.
- If an initial *and* an equilibrium concentration are given for a species, calculate the change in concentration.
- Use the coefficients in the balanced chemical equation to calculate the changes in concentration of all species.
- Deduce the equilibrium concentrations of all species.
- Use these to calculate the value of the equilibrium constant.

FORWARD REFERENCES
- Methods of finding equilibrium constants from thermodynamic or electrochemical will be discussed in Chapters 19 and 20, respectively.

15.6 Applications of Equilibrium Constants

Predicting the Direction of Reaction

- For a general reaction:

$$aA + bB \rightleftharpoons dD + eE$$

- We define Q, the **reaction quotient**, as:

$$Q = \frac{[D]^d [E]^e}{[A]^a [B]^b}$$

- Where [A], [B], [D], and [E] are molarities (for substances in solution) or partial pressures (for gases) at any given time.
- We can compare Q_c to K_c or Q_p to K_p:
  - If $Q = K$, then the system is at equilibrium.
  - If $Q < K$, then the forward reaction must occur to reach equilibrium.
  - If $Q > K$, then the reverse reaction must occur to reach equilibrium.
    - Products are consumed, reactants are formed.
    - Q decreases until it equals K.

Calculating Equilibrium Concentrations

- The same steps used to calculate equilibrium constants are used to calculate equilibrium concentrations.
- Generally, we do not have a number for the change in concentration.
  - Therefore, we need to assume that x mol/L of a species is produced (or used).
- The equilibrium concentrations are given as algebraic expressions.

FORWARD REFERENCES
- Q will be used in Chapter 19 (section 19.7) to determine Gibb's free energy change at nonstandard conditions.
- Q will be used in Chapter 20 (section 20.6) to determine cell potentials at nonstandard conditions (Nernst equation).

15.7 Le Châtelier's Principle[21,22,23,24,25]

- Consider the Haber process:

---

[21] Figure 15.9 from Transparency Pack
[22] "Formation of Water" Movie from Instructor's Resource CD/DVD
[23] "Nitrogen" 3-D Model from Instructor's Resource CD/DVD
[24] "Hydrogen" 3-D Model from Instructor's Resource CD/DVD
[25] "Ammonia" 3-D Model from Instructor's Resource CD/DVD

$$N_2(g) + 3H_2(g) \rightleftharpoons 2NH_3(g)$$

- As the pressure increases, the amount of ammonia present at equilibrium increases.
- As the temperature increases, the amount of ammonia at equilibrium decreases.
- Can this be predicted?
  - Yes! We can use Le Châtelier's principle to make qualitative predictions about how a system at equilibrium responds to various changes in external conditions.
    - Le Châtelier's principle: if a system at equilibrium is disturbed by a change in temperature, a change in pressure, or a change in the concentration of one or more components, the system will shift its equilibrium position in such a way as to counteract the effects of the disturbance.

Change in Reactant or Product Concentration[26,27,28,29,30,31,32]

- If a chemical system is at equilibrium and we add or remove a product or reactant, the reaction will shift so as to reestablish equilibrium.
  - For example, consider the Haber process again:

$$N_2(g) + 3H_2(g) \rightleftharpoons 2NH_3(g)$$

  - If H_2 is added while the system is at equilibrium, $Q < K$.
    - The system must respond to counteract the added H_2 (Le Châtelier's principle).
    - That is, the system must consume the H_2 and produce products until a new equilibrium is established.
      - Therefore, $[H_2]$ and $[N_2]$ will decrease and $[NH_3]$ will increase until $Q = K$.
- We can exploit this industrially.
  - Suppose that we wanted to optimize the amount of ammonia we formed from the Haber process.
  - We might flood the reaction vessel with reactants and continuously remove product.
  - The amount of ammonia produced is optimized because the product (NH_3) is continuously removed and the reactants (N_2 and H_2) are continuously being added.

Effects of Volume and Pressure Changes[33]

- Consider a system at equilibrium.
- If the equilibrium involves gaseous products or reactants, the concentration of these species will be changed if we change the volume of the container.
  - For example, if we decrease the volume of the container, the partial pressures of each gaseous species will increase.
  - Le Châtelier's principle predicts that if pressure is increased, the system will shift to counteract the increase.
    - That is, the system shifts to remove gases and decrease pressure.
    - An increase in pressure favors the direction that has fewer moles of gas.
- Consider the following system:

$$N_2O_4(g) \rightleftharpoons 2NO_2(g)$$

  - An increase in pressure (by decreasing the volume) favors the formation of colorless N_2O_4.

---

[26] "Amounts Tables as a Diagnostic Tool for Flawed Stoichiometric Reasoning" from Further Readings

[27] "Calculating Equilibrium Concentrations by Iteration: Recycle Your Approximations" from Further Readings

[28] "Man of Principle" from Further Readings

[29] Figure 15.10 from Transparency Pack

[30] "Chemical Equilibrium and Polynomial Equations: Beware of Roots" from Further Readings

[31] "Le Châtelier's Principle" from Further Readings

[32] "Effect of Concentration on Equilibrium: Cobalt Complex" from Live Demonstrations

[33] "Le Châtelier's Principle" Activity from Instructor's Resource CD/DVD

- The instant the pressure increases, the concentration of both gases increases and the system is not at equilibrium.
- The system changes to reduce the number moles of gas.
- A new equilibrium is established.
  - The mixture is lighter in color.
  - Some of the brown NO_2 has been converted into colorless $N_2O_4(g)$
- In a reaction with the same number of moles of gas in the products and reactants, changing the pressure has no effect on the equilibrium.
- In addition, no change will occur if we increase the total gas pressure by the addition of a gas that is not involved in the reaction.

Effect of Temperature Changes[34,35,36,37,38,39]

- The equilibrium constant is temperature dependent.
- How will a change in temperature alter a system at equilibrium?
  - It depends on the particular reaction.
  - For example, consider the endothermic reaction:
    $$Co(H_2O)_6^{2+}(aq) + 4Cl^-(aq) \rightleftarrows CoCl_4^{2-}(aq) + 6H_2O(l) \quad \Delta H > 0$$
  - $Co(H_2O)_6^{2+}$ is pale pink and $CoCl_4^{2-}$ is a deep blue.
  - At room temperature, an equilibrium mixture (light purple) is placed in a beaker of warm water.
    - The mixture turns deep blue.
    - This indicates a shift toward products (blue $CoCl_4^{2-}$).
    - This reaction is endothermic.
    - For an endothermic reaction ($\Delta H > 0$), heat can be considered as a reactant.
      - Thus, adding heat causes a shift in the forward direction.
  - The room-temperature equilibrium mixture is placed in a beaker of ice water.
    - The mixture turns bright pink.
    - This indicates a shift toward reactants (pink $Co(H_2O)_6^{2+}$).
    - In this case, by cooling the system we are removing a reactant (heat).
    - Thus, the reaction is shifted in the reverse reaction.
- A change in temperature causes a change in the value of K.
  - If we increase the temperature of an endothermic reaction, K increases.
  - If we increase the temperature of an exothermic reaction, K decreases.

The Effect of Catalysts

- A catalyst lowers the activation energy barrier for the reaction.
  - Therefore, a catalyst will decrease the amount of time needed to reach equilibrium.
  - A catalyst *does not* affect the composition of the equilibrium mixture.

FORWARD REFERENCES
  - Le Châtelier's principle versus percent ionization will be mentioned in Chapter 16 (section 16.6).
  - Le Châtelier's principle will be brought up in the common ion effect in Chapter 17 (sections 17.1 and 17.3).

---

[34] "Effect of Temperature Change on Equilibrium: Cobalt Complexes" from Live Demonstrations
[35] "Equilibrium in the Gas Phase" from Live Demonstrations
[36] "From Chicken Breath to the Killer Lakes of Cameroon: Uniting Seven Interesting Phenomena with a Single Chemical Underpinning" from Live Demonstrations
[37] "The Fizz Keeper, a Case Study in Chemical Education, Equilibrium, and Kinetics" from Further Readings
[38] "Temperature Dependence of Equilibrium" Animation from Instructor's Resource CD/DVD
[39] "Tetrachlorocobaltate(III)" 3-D Model from Instructor's Resource CD/DVD

- Le Châtelier's principle versus solubility will be discussed in Chapter 17 (section 17.5).
- Predictions of the equilibrium shifts will be made in Chapter 19 (section 19.7).
- Haber process will be further discussed in Chapter 22 (sections 22.2 and 22.7).

Further Readings:

1. Martin R. Feldman and Monica L. Tarver, "Fritz Haber," *J. Chem. Educ.*, Vol. 60, **1983**, 463–464.

2. Carl W. David, "An Elementary Discussion of Chemical Equilibrium," *J. Chem. Educ.*, Vol. 65, **1988**, 407–409.

3. Vladimir E. Fainzilberg and Stewart Karp, "Chemical Equilibrium in the General Chemistry Course," *J. Chem. Educ.*, Vol. 71, **1994**, 769–770.

4. Louise Tyson, David F. Treagust, and Robert B. Bucat, "The Complexity of Teaching and Learning Chemical Equilibrium," *J. Chem. Educ.*, Vol. 76, **1999**, 554–558.

5. Audrey H. Wilson, "Equilibrium: A Teaching/Learning Activity," *J. Chem. Educ.*, Vol. 75, **1998**, 1176–1177.

6. Jan H. Van Driel, Wobbe de Vos, and Nico Verloop, "Introducing Dynamic Equilibrium as an Explanatory Model," *J. Chem. Educ.*, Vol. 76, **1999**, 559–561.

7. Penelope A. Huddle, Margie W. White, and Fiona Rogers, "Simulations for Teaching Chemical Equilibrium," *J. Chem. Educ.*, Vol. 77, **2000**, 920–926.

8. Steven F. Watkins, "Applying the Reaction Table Method for Chemical Reaction Problems (Stoichiometry and Equilibrium)," *J. Chem. Educ.*, Vol. 80, **2003**, 658–661.

9. John Olmsted III, "Amounts Tables as a Diagnostic Tool for Flawed Stoichiometric Reasoning," *J. Chem. Educ.*, Vol. 76, **1999**, 52–54.

10. Michael Sutton, "Man of Principle," *Chemistry in Britain*, **June 2000**, 42–44.

11. William R. Smith and Ronald W. Missen, "Chemical Equilibrium and Polynomial Equations: Beware of Roots," *J. Chem. Educ.*, Vol. 66, **1989**, 489–490.

12. E. Weltin, "Calculating Equilibrium Concentrations by Iteration: Recycle Your Approximations," *J. Chem. Educ.*, Vol. 72, **1995**, 36–38.

13. Richard S. Treptow, "Le Châtelier's Principle," *J. Chem. Educ.*, Vol. 57, **1980**, 417–420.

14. Reed A. Howald, "The Fizz Keeper, a Case Study in Chemical Education, Equilibrium, and Kinetics," *J. Chem. Educ.*, Vol. 76, **1999**, 208–209.

Live Demonstrations:

1. Lee R. Summerlin and James L. Ealy, Jr., "Equilibrium in the Gas Phase," *Chemical Demonstrations, A Sourcebook for Teachers* (Washington: American Chemical Society, **1988**), pp. 85–86. Color changes in a mixture of NO_2 and N_2O_4 as a sealed tube of gas is heated or cooled are used to demonstrate Le Châtelier's principle.

2. Lee. R. Summerlin, and James. L. Ealy, Jr., "Effect of Temperature Change on Equilibrium: Cobalt Complex," *Chemical Demonstrations, A Sourcebook for Teachers, Volume 1* (Washington: American

Chemical Society, **1988**), pp. 79–80. An equilibrium system containing the dehydrated-hydrated cobalt complex is shifted in response to changes in temperature.

3. Lee. R. Summerlin, and James. L. Ealy, Jr., "Equilibrium and Le Châtelier's Principle," *Chemical Demonstrations, A Sourcebook for Teachers*, *Volume 1* (Washington: American Chemical Society, **1988**), pp. 77–78. An overhead projector demonstration of the effect of reactant concentration on equilibrium.

4. Lee. R. Summerlin, and James. L. Ealy, Jr., "Effect of Concentration on Equilibrium: Cobalt Complex," *Chemical Demonstrations, A Sourcebook for Teachers*, *Volume 1* (Washington: American Chemical Society, **1988**), pp. 81–82.

5. Ron DeLorenzo, "From Chicken Breath to the Killer Lakes of Cameroon: Uniting Seven Interesting Phenomena with a Single Chemical Underpinning," *J. Chem. Educ.*, Vol. 78, **2001**, 191–194. A collection of demonstrations dealing with equilibria associated with a sodium bicarbonate solution.

Chapter 16. Acid-Base Equilibria

Media Resources

Figures and Tables in Transparency Pack: **Section:**

Figure 16.3 Relative Strengths of Select Conjugate   16.2 Brønsted-Lowry Acids and Bases
    Acid-Base Pairs

Figure 16.5 H$^+$ Concentration of H$^+$ and pH Values   16.4 The pH Scale
    of Some Common Substances at 25 °C

Figure 16.7 pH Ranges for Common Acid-Base   16.4 The pH Scale
    Indicators

Table 16.2 Some Weak Acids in Water at 25 °C   16.6 Weak Acids

Table 16.3 Acid-Dissociation Constants of Some   16.6 Weak Acids
    Common Polyprotic Acids

Table 16.4 Some Weak Bases in Water at 25 °C   16.7 Weak Bases

Table 16.5 Some Conjugate Acid-Base Pairs   16.8 Relationship between K_a and K_b

Figure 16.18 Acidity of the Hypohalous Oxyacids   16.10 Acid-Base Behavior and Chemical Structure
    (YOH) as a Function of Electronegativity of Y

Activities: **Section:**

Conjugate Acids and Bases   16.2 Brønsted-Lowry Acids and Bases
K_w 16.3 The Autoionization of Water
pH Estimation   16.4 The pH Scale
Acids and Bases   16.4 The pH Scale
Equilibrium Constant   16.6 Weak Acids

Animations: **Section:**

Introduction to Aqueous Acids   16.5 Strong Acids and Bases
Introduction to Aqueous Bases   16.7 Weak Bases
Lewis Acid-Base Theory   16.11 Lewis Acids and Bases

Movies: **Section:**

Natural Indicators   16.4 The pH Scale

3-D Models: **Section:**

Oxalic Acid   Introduction
Water   16.2 Brønsted-Lowry Acids and Bases
Hydronium Ion   16.2 Brønsted-Lowry Acids and Bases
Hydrogen Chloride   16.2 Brønsted-Lowry Acids and Bases
Ammonia   16.2 Brønsted-Lowry Acids and Bases
Ammonium Ion   16.2 Brønsted-Lowry Acids and Bases
Hydroxide Ion   16.3 The Autoionization of Water
Dimethylamine   16.7 Weak Bases
Hydroxhylamine   16.7 Weak Bases
Formic Acid   16.6 Weak Acids
Methanol   16.6 Weak Acids
Hydrated Magnesium Cation   16.9 Acid-Base Properties of Salt Solutions
Hydrated Aluminum Cation   16.9 Acid-Base Properties of Salt Solutions
Deprotonated Hydrated Aluminum Cation   16.9 Acid-Base Properties of Salt Solutions
Hypoiodous Acid   16.10 Acid-Base Behavior and Chemical Structure

Phosphorus Pentachloride

16.11 Lewis Acids and Bases

Other Resources

Further Readings: **Section:**

Acids and Bases — 16.1 Acids and Bases: A Brief Review
The Origin of the Term 'Base' — 16.1 Acids and Bases: A Brief Review
The Brønsted-Lowry Acid-Base Concept — 16.2 Brønsted-Lowry Acids and Bases
Teaching Brønsted-Lowry Acid-Base Theory in a Direct Comprehensive Way — 16.2 Brønsted-Lowry Acids and Bases
An Analogy for the Leveling Effect in Acid-Base Chemistry — 16.2 Brønsted-Lowry Acids and Bases
Acid and Base Dissociation Constants of Water and Its Associated Ions — 16.2 Brønsted-Lowry Acids and Bases
Historical Development of the Hydrogen Ion Concept — 16.2 Brønsted-Lowry Acids and Bases
One-Hundred Years of pH — 16.4 The pH Scale
Do pH in Your Head — 16.4 The pH Scale
Teaching the Truth about pH — 16.4 The pH Scale
The pH Concept — 16.4 The pH Scale
Defining and Teaching pH — 16.4 The pH Scale
The Symbol for pH — 16.4 The pH Scale
Fruit Anthocyanins: Colorful Sensors of Molecular Milieu — 16.4 The pH Scale
Pictorial Analogies XI: Concentrations and Acidity of Solutions — 16.6 Weak Acids
Weak vs. Strong Acids and Bases: The Football Analogy — 16.6 Weak Acids
Factors That Influence Relative Acid Strength in Water: A Simple Model — 16.10 Acid-Base Behavior and Chemical Structure
The Relative Strength of Oxyacids and Its Application — 16.10 Acid-Base Behavior and Chemical Structure
The Correlation of Binary Acid Strengths with Molecular Properties in First-Year Chemistry — 16.10 Acid-Base Behavior and Chemical Structure
The Chemistry of Swimming Pool Maintenance — 16.10 Acid-Base Behavior and Chemical Structure
The Research Style of Gilbert N. Lewis: Acids and Bases — 16.11 Lewis Acids and Bases

Live Demonstrations: **Section:**

Food is Usually Acidic, Cleaners Are Usually Basic — 16.4 The pH Scale
Colorful Acid-Base Indicators — 16.4 The pH Scale
Rainbow Colors with Mixed Acid-Base Indicators — 16.4 The pH Scale
Colorful Effects of Hydrochloric Acid Dilution — 16.5 Strong Acids and Bases
Acid-Base Indicators Extracted from Plants — 16.5 Strong Acids and Bases
Disappearing Ink — 16.5 Strong Acids and Bases
Differences between Acid Strength and Concentration — 16.6 Weak Acids
Hydrolysis: Acidic and Basic Properties of Salts — 16.9 Acid-Base Properties of Salt Solutions
Effect of Molecular Structure on the Strength of Organic Acids and Bases in Aqueous Solutions — 16.10 Acid-Base Behavior and Chemical Structure

Chapter 16. Acid-Base Equilibria

Common Student Misconceptions
- Students often confuse a weak acid with a dilute acid.
- Students have problems with the numerical parts of this chapter. They should be strongly encouraged to do many problems on their own.
- Students often have difficulty using their calculators to take decimal logarithms and antilogarithms.
- Students confuse decimal (*log*) and natural (*ln*) logarithms.
- Students have a difficult time accepting that acids may be neutral as well as both positively and negatively charged species.
- Students tend to forget that $[H_3O^+][OH^-]$ is equal to 1.0×10^{-14} only at 25 °C.
- Students often wrestle with neutralization reactions producing solutions with pH different from 7.

Teaching Tips
- Determining pH of salts is often very conceptually and mathematically challenging. Solving and assigning many problems is needed to overcome these difficulties.
- Students should be made aware of the fact that terms such as *hydrogen ion, aqueous proton* – or simply *proton*, as well as *hydronium ion*, are often used interchangeably in the context of acid-base chemistry.
- Students should be reminded that water has both acidic and basic properties *depending* on what is mixed with it.
- Leveraging students' familiarity with Lewis Structures is useful in explaining relative strength of acids and reinforces ideas learned in Chapter 8.
- Remind students that, while strong acids and a vast majority of weak acids and weak bases are molecular substances, strong bases are ionic compounds.

Lecture Outline[1]

16.1 Acids and Bases: A Brief Review[2,3]
- Acids taste sour and cause certain dyes to change color.
- Bases taste bitter and feel soapy.
- Arrhenius concept of acids and bases:
    - An *acid* is a substance that, when dissolved in water, increases the concentration of H^+ ions.
        - Example: HCl is an acid.
    - An Arrhenius *base* is a substance that, when dissolved in water, increases the concentration of OH^- ions.
        - Example: NaOH is a base.
    - This definition is quite narrow in scope as it limits us to aqueous solutions.

16.2 Brønsted-Lowry Acids and Bases[4,5]
- We can use a broader, more general definition for acids and bases that is based on the fact that acid-base reactions involve proton transfers.

---

[1] "Oxalic Acid" 3-D Model from Instructor's Resource CD/DVD
[2] "Acids and Bases" from Further Readings
[3] "The Origin of the Term 'Base'" from Further Readings
[4] "The Brønsted-Lowry Acid-Base Concept" from Further Readings
[5] "Historical Development of the Hydrogen Ion Concept" from Further Readings

The H$^+$ Ion in Water[6,7]

- The H$^+$(aq) ion is simply a proton (nucleus of a hydrogen atom without its valence electron).
- In water, clusters of hydrated H$^+$(aq) ions form.
- The simplest cluster is H$_3$O$^+$(aq).
  - We call this a **hydronium ion**.
  - Larger clusters are also possible (such as H$_5$O$_2^+$ and H$_9$O$_4^+$).
- Generally, we use H$^+$(aq) and H$_3$O$^+$(aq) interchangeably.

Proton-Transfer Reactions[8,9,10,11]

- We will focus our attention on H$^+$(aq).
- According to the Arrhenius definitions, an acid increases [H$^+$] and a base increases [OH$^-$].
- Another definition of acids and bases was proposed by Brønsted and Lowry.
- In the Brønsted-Lowry system, a **Brønsted-Lowry acid** is a species that donates H$^+$ and a **Brønsted-Lowry base** is a species that accepts H$^+$.
  - Therefore, a Brønsted-Lowry base does not need to contain OH$^-$.
    - NH$_3$ is a Brønsted-Lowry base, but not an Arrhenius base.
- Consider NH$_3$(aq) + H$_2$O(l) $\rightleftarrows$ NH$_4^+$(aq) + OH$^-$(aq):
  - H$_2$O donates a proton to ammonia.
    - Therefore, water is acting as an acid.
  - NH$_3$ accepts a proton from water.
    - Therefore, ammonia is acting as a base.
    - An **amphiprotic** substance can behave either as an acid or as a base.
    - Thus, water is an example of an amphiprotic species.

Conjugate Acid-Base Pairs[12]

- Whatever is left of the acid after the proton is donated is called its conjugate base.
- Similarly, a conjugate acid is formed by adding a proton to the base.
- Consider HX(aq) + H$_2$O(l) $\rightleftarrows$ H$_3$O$^+$(aq) + X$^-$(aq):
  - HX and X$^-$ differ only in the presence or absence of a proton.
    - They are said to be a **conjugate acid-base pair**.
    - X$^-$ is called the **conjugate base**.
  - After HX (acid) loses its proton it is converted into X$^-$ (base).
    - Therefore HX and X$^-$ are a conjugate acid-base pair.
  - After H$_2$O (base) gains a proton it is converted into H$_3$O$^+$ (acid).
    - H$_3$O$^+$ is the **conjugate acid**.
    - Therefore, H$_2$O and H$_3$O$^+$ are a conjugate acid-base pair.

Relative Strengths of Acids and Bases[13,14]

- The stronger an acid is, the weaker its conjugate base will be.
- We can categorize acids and bases according to their behavior in water.
  - 1. *Strong acids* completely transfer their protons to water.

---

[6] "Water" 3-D Model from Instructor's Resource CD/DVD

[7] "Hydronium Ion" 3-D Model from Instructor's Resource CD/DVD

[8] "Teaching Brønsted-Lowry Acid-Base Theory in a Direct Comprehensive Way" from Further Readings

[9] "Hydrogen Chloride" 3-D Model from Instructor's Resource CD/DVD

[10] "Ammonia" 3-D Model from Instructor's Resource CD/DVD

[11] "Ammonium Ion" 3-D Model from Instructor's Resource CD/DVD

[12] Conjugate Acids and Bases" Activity from Instructor's Resource CD/DVD

[13] Figure 16.3 from Transparency Pack

[14] "An Analogy for the Leveling Effect in Acid-Base Chemistry" from Further Readings

- No undissociated molecules remain in solution.
- Their conjugate bases have negligible tendencies to become protonated.
  - An example is HCl.
- 2. *Weak acids* only partially dissociate in aqueous solution.
  - They exist in solution as a mixture of molecules and component ions.
  - Their conjugate bases show a slight tendency to abstract protons from water.
  - These conjugate bases are weak bases.
    - Example: Acetic acid is a weak acid; acetate ion (conjugate base) is a weak base.
- 3. *Substances with negligible acidity* do not transfer a proton to water.
  - An example is CH_4.
  - The conjugate base of a substance with negligible acidity is a strong base.
- In every acid-base reaction, the position of the equilibrium favors the transfer of a proton from the stronger acid to the stronger base.
  - H^+ is the strongest acid that can exist in equilibrium in aqueous solution.
  - OH^- is the strongest base that can exist in equilibrium in aqueous solution.
- Hydronium ions and hydroxide ions are the strongest possible acid and base, respectively, that can exist in aqueous solution.
  - Stronger acids react with water to produce hydronium ions and stronger bases react with water to form hydroxide ions.
  - This effect is known as the *leveling effect* of water.

FORWARD REFERENCES
- Acid-base neutralization reaction will be discussed in detail in Chapter 17 (sections 17.1-17.3).
- Acid rain will be discussed in Chapter 18 (section 18.2).
- Inverse relationship between conjugate acids and bases will be mentioned in Chapter 20 (section 20.4).
- Acid-base properties in proton-transfer reactions involving OH^-, H_2O, NH_3, etc. will be further discussed in Chapter 22 (section 22.1).

16.3 The Autoionization of Water[15,16]
- In pure water the following equilibrium is established:
$$2H_2O(l) \rightleftharpoons H_3O^+(aq) + OH^-(aq).$$
- This process is called the **autoionization** of water.

The Ion Product of Water[17]
- We can write an equilibrium constant expression for the autoionization of water.
- Because $H_2O(l)$ is a pure liquid, we exclude it from the expression:
$$K_c = [H_3O^+][OH^-] = K_w.$$

- **K_w is called the ion-product constant.**
  - At 25°C, the ion-product of water is:
$$1.0 \times 10^{-14} = K_w = [H_3O^+][OH^-].$$
- This applies to pure water as well as to aqueous solutions.
  - A solution is *neutral* if $[OH^-] = [H_3O^+]$.
  - If the $[H_3O^+] > [OH^-]$, the solution is *acidic*.
  - If the $[H_3O^+] < [OH^-]$, the solution is *basic*.

---

[15] "Acid and Base Dissociation Constants of Water and Its Associated Ions" from Further Readings
[16] "Hydroxide Ion" 3-D Model from Instructor's Resource CD/DVD
[17] "K_w" Activity from Instructor's Resource CD/DVD

FORWARD REFERENCES

- H$_2$O participating in acid-base reaction as a H$^+$ donor or acceptor will be mentioned in Chapter 18 (section 18.3).

16.4 The pH Scale[18,19,20,21,22,23,24,25,26,27]

- In most solutions, [H$^+$] is quite small.
- We express the [H$^+$] in terms of **pH**.

$$pH = -\log[H^+] = -\log[H_3O^+].$$

  - Note that this is a logarithmic scale.
  - Thus, a change in [H$^+$] by a factor of 10 causes the pH to change by 1 unit.
- Most pH values fall between 0 and 14.
  - In neutral solutions at 25 °C, pH = 7.00.
  - In acidic solutions, [H$^+$] > 1.0 × 10^{-7}, so pH < 7.00.
    - As the pH decreases, the acidity of the solution *increases*.
  - In basic solutions, [H$^+$] < 1.0 × 10^{-7}, so pH > 7.00.
    - As the pH increases, the basicity of the solution increases (acidity *decreases*).

pOH and Other "p" Scales

- We can use a similar system to describe the [OH$^-$].

$$pOH = -\log[OH^-].$$

- Recall that the value of K_w at 25 °C is 1.0 × 10^{-14}.
  - Thus, we can describe a relationship between pH and pOH:

$$-\log[H^+] + (-\log[OH^-]) = pH + pOH = -\log K_w = 14.00.$$

Measuring pH[28,29,30,31,32]

- The most accurate method to measure pH is to use a *pH meter*.
  - A pH meter consists of a pair of electrodes connected to a meter that measures small voltages.
  - A voltage that varies with pH is generated when the electrodes are placed in a solution.
  - This voltage is read by the meter, which is calibrated to display pH.
- Dyes that change color as pH changes are also useful.
  - They are called acid-base indicators.
  - Indicators are less precise than pH meters.
  - Many indicators do not have a sharp color change as a function of pH.
  - Most acid-base indicators can exist as either an acid or a base.
    - These two forms have different colors.

---

[18] "One-Hundred Years of pH" from Further Readings
[19] "Do pH in Your Head" from Further Readings
[20] "pH Estimation" Activity from Instructor's Resource CD/DVD
[21] "Teaching the Truth about pH" from Further Readings
[22] "The pH Concept" from Further Readings
[23] "Defining and Teaching pH" from Further Readings
[24] "The Symbol for pH" from Further Readings
[25] Figure 16.5 from Transparency Pack
[26] "Acids and Bases" Activity from Instructor's Resource CD/DVD
[27] "Food is Usually Acidic, Cleaners Are Usually Basic" from Live Demonstrations
[28] "Fruit Anthocyanins: Colorful Sensors of Molecular Milieu" from Further Readings
[29] Figure 16.7 from Transparency Pack
[30] "Colorful Acid-Base Indicators" from Live Demonstrations
[31] "Natural Indicators" Movie from Instructor's Resource CD/DVD
[32] "Rainbow Colors with Mixed Acid-Base Indicators" from Live Demonstrations

- The relative concentration of the two different forms is sensitive to the pH of the solution.
- Thus, if we know the pH at which the indicator turns color, we can use this color change to determine whether a solution has a higher or lower pH than this value.
- Some natural products can be used as indicators. (Tea is colorless in acid and brown in base; red cabbage extract is another natural indicator.)

FORWARD REFERENCES
- Buffer capacity and pH range will be discussed in Chapter 17 (section 17.2).
- The effect of pH on solubility of poorly soluble salts and hydroxides will be discussed in Chapter 17 (section 17.5).
- H_2O as a proton donor and acceptor will be mentioned in Chapter 18 in the discussion of the role of the oceans (section 18.3).
- In Chapter 20 (section 20.6), measuring cell potentials will be used to determine pH.

16.5 Strong Acids and Bases

Strong Acids[33,34,35]

- The most common strong acids are HCl, HBr, HI, HNO_3, $HClO_3$, $HClO_4$, and H_2SO_4.
- Strong acids are *strong electrolytes*.
  - All strong acids ionize completely in solution.
  - For example: nitric acid completely ionizes in water:
$$HNO_3(aq) + H_2O(l) \rightarrow H_3O^+(aq) + NO_3^-(aq).$$
    - Since H^+ and H_3O^+ are used interchangeably, we write:
$$HNO_3(aq) \rightarrow H^+(aq) + NO_3^-(aq).$$
      - Note that we do not use equilibrium arrows for this equation because the reaction lies entirely to the right.
- In solutions the strong acid is usually the only significant source of H^+.
  - Therefore, the pH of a solution of a monoprotic acid may usually be calculated directly from the initial molarity of the acid.
  - Caution: If the molarity of the acid is less than 10^{-6} M then the autoionization of water needs to be taken into account.

Strong Bases[36]

- The most common strong bases are ionic hydroxides of the alkali metals or the heavier alkaline earth metals (e.g., $NaOH$, KOH, and $Sr(OH)_2$ are all strong bases).
- Strong bases are strong electrolytes and dissociate completely in solution.
  - For example:
$$NaOH(aq) \rightarrow Na^+(aq) + OH^-(aq)$$
- The pOH (and thus the pH) of a strong base may be calculated using the initial molarity of the base.
- Not all bases contain the OH^- ion.
  - Ionic metal oxides, for example, are basic.
  - They are thus able to abstract a proton from water and generate OH^-.
$$O^{2-}(aq) + H_2O(l) \rightarrow 2OH^-(aq)$$

FORWARD REFERENCES
- Adding strong acids and bases to buffers will be discussed in detail in Chapter 17 (section 17.2).

---

[33] "Colorful Effects of Hydrochloric Acid Dilution" from Live Demonstrations
[34] "Acid-Base Indicators Extracted from Plants" from Live Demonstrations
[35] "Introduction to Aqueous Acids" Animation from Instructor's Resource CD/DVD
[36] "Disappearing Ink" from Live Demonstrations

- The use of strong acids and bases as titrants will be discussed in Chapter 17 (section 17.3).
- Basic oxides (also peroxides and superoxides) will be discussed in Chapter 22 (section 22. 5).

16.6 Weak Acids[37,38,39,40,41,42,43]

- Weak acids are only partially ionized in aqueous solution.
    - There is a mixture of ions and un-ionized acid in solution.
    - Therefore, weak acids are in equilibrium:
    $$HA(aq) + H_2O(l) \rightleftharpoons H_3O^+(aq) + A^-(aq)$$
    or
    $$HA(aq) \rightleftharpoons H^+(aq) + A^-(aq)$$
    - We can write an equilibrium constant expression for this dissociation:

$$K_a = \frac{[H_3O^+][A^-]}{[HA]} \text{ or } K_a = \frac{[H^+][A^-]}{[HA]}$$

    - K_a is called the **acid-dissociation constant**.
    - Note that the subscript "a" indicates that this is the equilibrium constant for the dissociation (ionization) of an acid.
    - Note that $[H_2O]$ is omitted from the K_a expression. (H_2O is a pure liquid.)
- The larger the K_a, the stronger the acid.
    - K_a is larger since there are more ions present at equilibrium relative to un-ionized molecules.
    - If $K_a \gg 1$, then the acid is completely ionized and the acid is a strong acid.

Calculating K_a from pH

- In order to find the value of K_a, we need to know all of the equilibrium concentrations.
    - The pH gives the equilibrium concentration of H^+.
    - Thus, to find K_a we use the pH to find the equilibrium concentration of H^+ and then use the stoichiometric coefficients of the balanced equation to help us determine the equilibrium concentration of the other species.
    - We then substitute these equilibrium concentrations into the equilibrium constant expression and solve for K_a.

Percent Ionization

- Another measure of acid strength is **percent ionization**.
    - For the reaction,
    $$HA(aq) \rightleftharpoons H^+(aq) + A^-(aq)$$

    $$\% \text{ ionization} = \frac{[H^+]_{equilibrium}}{[HA]_{initial}} \times 100\%$$

    - Percent ionization relates the *equilibrium* H^+ concentration, $[H^+]_{equilibrium}$, to the *initial* HA concentration, $[HA]_{initial}$.

---

[37] "Pictorial Analogies XI: Concentrations and Acidity of Solutions" from Further Readings
[38] Table 16.2 from Transparency Pack
[39] "Weak vs. Strong Acids and Bases: The Football Analogy" from Further Readings
[40] "Equilibrium Constant" Activity from Instructor's Resource CD/DVD
[41] "Differences between Acid Strength and Concentration" from Live Demonstrations
[42] "Formic Acid" 3-D Model from Instructor's Resource CD/DVD
[43] "Methanol" 3-D Model from Instructor's Resource CD/DVD

- The higher the percent ionization, the stronger the acid.
- However, we need to keep in mind that percent ionization of a weak acid decreases as the molarity of the solution increases.

Using K_a to Calculate pH

- Using K_a, we can calculate the concentration of H^+ (and hence the pH).
- Write the balanced chemical equation clearly showing the equilibrium.
- Write the equilibrium expression. Look up the value for K_a (in a table).
- Write down the initial and equilibrium concentrations for everything except pure water.
  - We usually assume that the equilibrium concentration of H^+ is x.
- Substitute into the equilibrium constant expression and solve.
  - Remember to convert x to pH if necessary.
- What do we do if we are faced with having to solve a quadratic equation in order to determine the value of x?
  - Often this cannot be avoided.
  - However, if the K_a value is quite small, we find that we can make a simplifying assumption.
    - Assume that x is negligible compared with the initial concentration of the acid.
    - This will simplify the calculation.
    - It is always necessary to check the validity of any assumption.
    - Once we have the value of x, check to see how large it is compared with the initial concentration.
    - If x is < 5% of the initial concentration, the assumption is probably a good one.
    - If x > 5% of the initial concentration, then it may be best to solve the quadratic equation or use successive approximations.
- Weak acids are only partially ionized.
- Percent ionization is another method used to assess acid strength.

Polyprotic Acids[44]

- **Polyprotic acids** have more than one ionizable proton.
- The protons are removed in successive steps.
  - Consider the weak acid, H_2SO_3 (sulfurous acid):

$$H_2SO_3(aq) \rightleftharpoons H^+(aq) + HSO_3^-(aq) \qquad K_{a1} = 1.7 \times 10^{-2}$$
$$HSO_3^-(aq) \rightleftharpoons H^+(aq) + SO_3^{2-}(aq) \qquad K_{a2} = 6.4 \times 10^{-8}$$

  - where K_{a1} is the dissociation constant for the first proton released, K_{a2} is for the second, etc..
- It is always easier to remove the first proton than the second proton in a polyprotic acid.
  - Therefore, $K_{a1} > K_{a2} > K_{a3}$, etc..
- The majority of the $H^+(aq)$ at equilibrium usually comes from the first ionization (i.e., the K_{a1} equilibrium).
  - If the successive K_a values differ by a factor of $\geq 10^3$, we can usually get a good approximation of the pH of a solution of a polyprotic acid by only considering the first ionization.

FORWARD REFERENCES

- The use of weak acids and bases as analytes in acid-base titrations will be discussed in Chapter 17 (section 17.3).
- Absorption of CO_2 by the oceans, and subsequent equilibria will be discussed in Chapter 18 (section 18.3).
- Weak acid (and base) ionization constants will be used in Chapter 19 to estimate $\Delta G°$ of ionization reactions.
- pH of electrolytes will be related to the cell potential in Chapter 20 (section 20.6).
- Weak acidic behavior of alcohols, incl. phenol, will be discussed in Chapter 24 (section 24.4).

---

[44] Table 16.3 from Transparency Pack

- The role of a triprotic H_3PO_4 in the formation of nucleic acids will be demonstrated in Chapter 24 (section 24.10).

16.7 Weak Bases[45,46,47,48]

- Weak bases remove protons from substances.
- There is an equilibrium between the base and the resulting ions:

$$\text{weak base} + H_2O(l) \rightleftharpoons \text{conjugate acid} + OH^-(aq)$$

  - Example:

$$NH_3(aq) + H_2O(l) \rightleftharpoons NH_4^+(aq) + OH^-(aq).$$

  - The **base-dissociation constant**, K_b, is defined as:

$$K_b = \frac{[NH_4^+][OH^-]}{[NH_3]}$$

    - The larger K_b, the stronger the base.

Types of Weak Bases

- Weak bases generally fall into one of two categories.
  - Neutral substances with a lone pair of electrons that can accept protons.
    - Most neutral weak bases contain nitrogen.
    - **Amines** are related to ammonia and have one or more N–H bonds replaced with N–C bonds (e.g., CH_3NH_2 is methylamine).
  - Anions of weak acids are also weak bases.
    - Example: ClO^- is the conjugate base of HClO (weak acid):

$$ClO^-(aq) + H_2O(l) \rightleftharpoons HClO(aq) + OH^-(aq) \qquad K_b = 3.33 \times 10^{-7}$$

FORWARD REFERENCES

- NH_3 as a weak base will be further mentioned in Chapter 22 (section 22.5).
- The fact that many organic compounds contain basic groups such as $-NH_2$, $-NHR$, and $-NR_2$ will be brought up in Chapter 24 (section 24.1).
- Amines, as weak bases, will be discussed in Chapter 24 (section 24.4).

16.8 Relationship Between K_a and K_b[49]

- We can quantify the relationship between the strength of an acid and the strength of its conjugate base.
- Consider the following equilibria:

$$NH_4^+(aq) \rightleftharpoons NH_3(aq) + H^+(aq)$$
$$NH_3(aq) + H_2O(l) \rightleftharpoons NH_4^+(aq) + OH^-(aq)$$

  - We can write equilibrium expressions for these reactions:

$$K_a = \frac{[NH_3][H^+]}{[NH_4^+]} \qquad K_b = \frac{[NH_4^+][OH^-]}{[NH_3]}$$

  - If we add these equations together:

$$NH_4^+(aq) \rightleftharpoons NH_3(aq) + H^+(aq)$$
$$NH_3(aq) + H_2O(l) \rightleftharpoons NH_4^+(aq) + OH^-(aq)$$

---

[45] "Introduction to Aqueous Bases" Animation from Instructor's Resource CD/DVD
[46] Table 16.4 from Transparency Pack
[47] "Dimethylamine" 3-D Model from Instructor's Resource CD/DVD
[48] "Hydroxylamine" 3-D Model from Instructor's Resource CD/DVD
[49] Table 16.5 from Transparency Pack

- The net reaction is the autoionization of water.
$$H_2O(l) \leftrightharpoons H^+(aq) + OH^-(aq)$$
- Recall that:
$$K_w = [H^+][OH^-]$$
- We can use this information to write an expression that relates the values of K_a, K_b, and K_w for a conjugate acid-base pair.

$$K_a K_b = \left(\frac{[NH_3][H^+]}{[NH_4^+]} \right) \left(\frac{[NH_4^+][OH^-]}{[NH_3]} \right) = [H^+][OH^-] = K_w$$

- The product of the acid-dissociation constant for an acid (K_a) and the base-dissociation constant for its conjugate base (K_b) equals the ion-product constant for water (K_w):
$$K_a \times K_b = K_w$$
- Alternatively, we can express this as:
$$pK_a + pK_b = pK_w = 14.00 \text{ (at 25 °C)}$$
- Thus, the larger K_a (and the smaller pK_a), the smaller K_b (and the larger pK_b).
- The stronger the acid, the weaker its conjugate base and vice versa.

16.9 Acid-Base Properties of Salt Solutions[50]

- Nearly all salts are strong electrolytes.
  - Therefore, salts in solution exist entirely of ions.
  - Acid-base properties of salts are a consequence of the reactions of their ions in solution.
- Many salt ions can react with water to form OH^- or H^+.
  - This process is called **hydrolysis**.

An Anion's Ability to React with Water

- Consider an anion, X^-, as the conjugate base of an acid.
  - Anions from weak acids are basic.
    - They will cause an increase in pH.
  - Anions from strong acids are neutral.
    - They do not cause a change in pH.
  - Anions with ionizable protons (e.g., HSO_3^-) are amphiprotic.
    - How they behave in water is determined by the relative magnitudes of K_a and K_b for the ion:
      - If $K_a > K_b$, the anion tends to decrease the pH.
      - If $K_b > K_a$, the anion tends to increase the pH.

A Cation's Ability to React with Water[51,52,53]

- Polyatomic cations that have one or more ionizable protons are conjugate acids of weak bases.
  - They tend to decrease pH.
- Many metal ions can cause a decrease in pH.
  - Metal cations of Group 1A and heavy alkaline earth metals are cations of strong bases and do not alter pH.
  - Metals with small, highly charged cations such as Fe^{3+} and Al^{3+} have K_a values comparable to values for familiar weak acids such as acetic acid.
    - The metal ions attract unshared electron pairs of water molecules and become hydrated.

---

[50] "Hydrolysis: Acidic and Basic Properties of Salts" from Live Demonstrations
[51] "Hydrated Magnesium Cation" 3-D Model from Instructor's Resource CD/DVD
[52] "Hydrated Aluminum Cation" 3-D Model from Instructor's Resource CD/DVD
[53] "Deprotonated Hydrated Aluminum Cation" 3-D Model from Instructor's Resource CD/DVD

- The larger the charge on the metal ion, the stronger the interaction between the ion and the oxygen of its hydrating water molecules.
- This weakens the O–H bonds in the water molecules and facilitates proton transfer from hydration water molecules to solvent water molecules.

Combined Effect of Cation and Anion in Solution

- The pH of a solution may be qualitatively predicted using the following guidelines:
  - Salts derived from a strong acid and a strong base are neutral.
    - Examples are NaCl and $Ba(NO_3)_2$.
  - Salts derived from a strong base and a weak acid are basic.
    - Examples are NaClO and $Ba(C_2H_3O_2)_2$.
  - Salts derived from a weak base (or a small cation with a charge of 2+ or greater) and a strong acid are acidic.
    - An example is NH_4NO_3 and $AlCl_3$.
  - Salts derived from a weak acid and a weak base can be either acidic or basic.
    - Equilibrium rules apply!
    - We need to compare K_a and K_b for hydrolysis of the anion and the cation.
    - For example, consider NH_4CN.
      - Both ions undergo significant hydrolysis.
      - Is the salt solution acidic or basic?
        - The K_a of NH_4^+ is smaller than the K_b of CN^-, so the solution should be basic.

16.10 Acid-Base Behavior and Chemical Structure[54]

Factors that Affect Acid Strength[55]

- Consider H–X.
- For this substance to be an acid:
  - The H–X bond must be polar with $H^{\delta+}$ and $X^{\delta-}$.
- In ionic hydrides, the bond polarity is reversed.
  - The H–X bond is polar with $H^{\delta-}$ and $X^{\delta+}$.
  - In this case, the substance is a base.
- Other important factors in determining acid strength include:
  - The strength of the bond.
    - The H–X bond must be weak enough to be broken.
  - The stability of the conjugate base, X^-.
    - The greater the stability of the conjugate base, the more acidic the molecule.

Binary Acids[56]

- The H–X bond strength is important in determining relative acid strength in any *group* in the periodic table.
  - The H–X bond strength tends to decrease as the element X increases in size.
  - Acid strength increases down a group; base strength decreases down a group.
- H–X bond polarity is important in determining relative acid strength in any *period* of the periodic table.

---

[54] "Effect of Molecular Structure on the Strength of Organic Acids and Bases in Aqueous Solutions" from Live Demonstrations
[55] "Factors that Influence Relative Acid Strength in Water: A Simple Model" from Further Readings
[56] "The Correlation of Binary Acid Strengths with Molecular Properties in First-Year Chemistry" from Further Readings

- Acid strength increases and base strength decreases from left to right across a period as the electronegativity of X increases.
- For example, consider the molecules HF and CH_4.
  - HF is a weak acid because the bond energy is high.
  - The electronegativity difference between C and H is so small that the polarity of C–H bond is negligible, and CH_4 is neither an acid nor a base.

Oxyacids[57,58,59,60]

- Many acids contain one or more O–H bonds.
  - Acids that contain OH groups (and often additional oxygen atoms) bound to the central atom are called **oxyacids.**
    - All oxyacids have the general structure Y–O–H.
- The strength of the acid depends on Y and the atoms attached to Y.
  - As the electronegativity of Y increases, so does the acidity of the substance.
    - The bond polarity increases and so does the stability of the conjugate base (usually an anion) increases.
- We can summarize how acid structure relates to the electronegativity of Y and the number of groups attached to Y:
  - For oxyacids with the same number of OH groups and the same number of oxygen atoms:
    - Acid strength increases with increasing electronegativity of the central atom, Y.
      - Example: HClO > HBrO > HIO
  - For oxyacids with the same central atom, Y:
    - Acid strength increases as the number of oxygen atoms attached to Y increases.
    - Example: $HClO_4$ > $HClO_3$ > $HClO_2$ > HClO

Carboxylic Acids

- There is a large class of acids that contain a –COOH group (a *carboxyl* group).
  - Acids that contain this group are called **carboxylic acids.**
    - Examples are acetic acid, benzoic acid, and formic acid.
- Why are these molecules acidic?
  - The additional oxygen atom on the carboxyl group increases the polarity of the O–H bond and stabilizes the conjugate base.
  - The conjugate base (*carboxylate anion*) exhibits resonance.
    - This gives it the ability to delocalize the negative charge over the carboxylate group, further increasing the stability of the conjugate base.
- The acid strength also increases as the number of electronegative groups in the acid increases.
  - For example, acetic acid is much weaker than trichloroacetic acid.

FORWARD REFERENCES

- Oxoacids and oxoanions containing halogens will be mentioned in Chapter 22 (section 22.4).
- Carboxylic acids will be discussed in Chapter 24 (section 24.4).
- Amphiprotic behavior of amino acids and zwitterions of amino acids will be discussed in Chapter 24 (section 24.7).
- The relative strength of acetic vs. pyruvic acids (with an additional carbonyl group) will be discussed in a sample integrative exercise in Chapter 24 (section 24.10).

---

[57] "The Relative Strength of Oxyacids and Its Application" from Further Readings
[58] Figure 16.18 from Transparency Pack
[59] "The Chemistry of Swimming Pool Maintenance" from Further Readings
[60] "Hypoiodous Acid" 3-D Model from Instructor's Resource CD/DVD

16.11 Lewis Acids and Bases[61,62,63]

- A Brønsted-Lowry acid is a proton donor.
- Focusing on electrons, a Brønsted-Lowry acid can be considered as an electron pair acceptor.
- Lewis proposed a new definition of acids and bases that emphasizes the shared electron pair.
  - A **Lewis acid** is an electron pair acceptor.
  - A **Lewis base** is an electron pair donor.
    - Note that Lewis acids and bases do not need to contain protons.
    - Therefore, the Lewis definition is the most general definition of acids and bases.
- What types of compounds can act as Lewis acids?
  - Lewis acids generally have an incomplete octet (e.g., BF_3).
  - Transition-metal ions are generally Lewis acids.
  - Lewis acids must have a vacant orbital (into which the electron pairs can be donated).
  - Compounds with multiple bonds can act as Lewis acids.
    - For example, consider the reaction:
$$H_2O(l) + CO_2(g) \rightarrow H_2CO_3(aq)$$
    - Water acts as the electron pair donor and carbon dioxide as the electron pair acceptor in this reaction.
    - Overall, the water (Lewis base) has donated a pair of electrons to the CO_2 (Lewis acid).
- The Lewis concept may be used to explain the acidic properties of many metal ions.
- Metal ions are positively charged and attract water molecules (via the lone pairs on the oxygen atom of water).
  - This interaction is called *hydration*.
- Hydrated metal ions act as acids.
  - For example:
$$Fe(H_2O)_6^{3+}(aq) \rightleftharpoons Fe(H_2O)_5(OH)^{2+}(aq) + H^+(aq) \qquad K_a = 2 \times 10^{-3}.$$
- In general:
  - the higher the charge is, the stronger the $M–OH_2$ interaction.
  - the smaller the metal ion is, the more acidic the ion.
    - Thus, the pH increases as the size of the ion increases (e.g., Ca^{2+} vs. Zn^{2+}) and as the charge increases (e.g., Na^+ vs. Ca^{2+} and Zn^{2+} vs. Al^{3+}).

FORWARD REFERENCES
- Lewis bases and Crystal Field Theory will be discussed in Chapter 23 (section 23.6).

---

[61] "The Research Style of Gilbert N. Lewis: Acids and Bases" from Further Readings
[62] "Lewis Acid-Base Theory" Animation from Instructor's Resource CD/DVD
[63] "Phosphorus Pentachloride" 3-D Model from Instructor's Resource CD/DVD

Further Readings:

1. Doris Kolb, "Acids and Bases," *J. Chem. Educ.*, Vol. 55, **1978**, 459–464.

2. William B. Jensen, "The Origin of the Term 'Base'," *J. Chem. Educ.*, Vol. 83, **2006**, 1130.

3. George B. Kauffman, "The Brønsted-Lowry Acid-Base Concept," *J. Chem. Educ.*, Vol. 65, **1988**, 28–31.

4. Carl E. Moore, Bruno Jaselskis, and Jan Florian, "Historical Development of the Hydrogen Ion Concept," *J. Chem. Educ.*, Vol. 87, **2010**, 922–923.

5. Jamie L. Adcock, "Teaching Brønsted-Lowry Acid–Base Theory in a Direct Comprehensive Way," *J. Chem. Educ.*, Vol. 78, **2001**, 1495–1496.

6. A. M. de Lange and J. H. Potgieter, "Acid and Base Dissociation Constants of Water and Its Associated Ions," *J. Chem. Educ.*, Vol. 68, **1991**, 304–305.

7. F. Axtell Kramer, "An Analogy for the Leveling Effect in Acid-Base Chemistry," *J. Chem. Educ.*, Vol. 63, **1986**, 275.

8. Joseph F. Lomax, "Kinetic Classroom: Acid-Base and Redox Demonstrations with Student Movement," *J. Chem. Educ.*, Vol. 71, **1994**, 428–430.

9. Rollie J. Myers, "One-Hundred Years of pH," *J. Chem. Educ.*, Vol. 87, **2010**, 30–32.

10. Addison Ault, "Do pH in Your Head," *J. Chem. Educ.*, Vol. 76, **1999**, 936–938.

11. Stephen J. Hawkes, "Teaching the Truth about pH," *J. Chem. Educ.*, Vol. 71, **1994**, 747–749.

12. Doris Kolb, "The pH Concept," *J. Chem. Educ.*, Vol. 56, **1979**, 49–53.

13. Richard F. Burton, "Defining and Teaching pH," *J. Chem. Educ.*, Vol. 84, **2007**, 1129.

14. William B. Jensen, "The Symbol for pH," *J. Chem. Educ.*, Vol. 81, **2004**, 21.

15. Robert D. Curtright, James A. Rynearson, and John Markwell, "Fruit Anthocyanins: Colorful Sensors of Molecular Milieu," *J. Chem. Educ.*, Vol. 71, **1994**, 682–684.

16. John J. Fortman, "Pictorial Analogies XI: Concentrations and Acidity of Solutions," *J. Chem. Educ.*, Vol. 71, **1994**, 430–432.

17. Todd P. Silverstein, "Weak vs. Strong Acids and Bases: The Football Analogy," *J. Chem. Educ.*, Vol. 77, **2000**, 849–850.

18. Michael J. Moran, "Factors That Influence Relative Acid Strength in Water: A Simple Model," *J. Chem. Educ.*, Vol. 83, **2006**, 800–803.

19. Manus Monroe and Karl Abrams, "The Relative Strength of Oxyacids and Its Application," *J. Chem. Educ.*, Vol. 62, **1985**, 41–43.

20. Travis D. Fridgen, "The Correlation of Binary Acid Strengths with Molecular Properties in First-Year Chemistry," *J. Chem. Educ.*, Vol. 85, **2008**, 1200–1221.

21. Carl Salter and David L. Langhus, "The Chemistry of Swimming Pool Maintenance," ," *J. Chem. Educ.*, Vol. 84, **2007**, 1124–1128.

22. Glen T. Seaborg, "The Research Style of Gilbert N. Lewis: Acids and Bases," *J. Chem. Educ.*, Vol. 61, **1984**, 93–100.

Live Demonstrations:

1. Bassam Z. Shakhashiri, "Acid-Base Indicators Extracted from Plants," *Chemical Demonstrations: A Handbook for Teachers of Chemistry, Volume 3* (Madison: The University of Wisconsin Press, **1989**), pp. 50–57. A wide range of plant materials is used as sources of acid-base indicators. Included in this group is an old favorite: red cabbage.

2. Bassam Z. Shakhashiri, "Differences between Acid Strength and Concentration," *Chemical Demonstrations: A Handbook for Teachers of Chemistry, Volume 3* (Madison: The University of Wisconsin Press, **1989**), pp. 136–139. The strength of three acids (acetic, hydrochloric, and sulfuric) is compared by reaction with sodium hydroxide. A companion procedure, involving base strength, is also included.

3. Lee. R. Summerlin, Christie L. Borgford, and Julie B. Ealy, "Disappearing Ink," *Chemical Demonstrations, A Sourcebook for Teachers, Volume 2* (Washington: American Chemical Society, **1988**), p. 176. "Disappearing ink" is made from thymolphthalein indicator and dilute sodium hydroxide.

4. Bassam Z. Shakhashiri, "Colorful Acid-Base Indicators," *Chemical Demonstrations: A Handbook for Teachers of Chemistry, Volume 3* (Madison: The University of Wisconsin Press, **1989**), pp. 33–40.

5. Bassam Z. Shakhashiri, "Hydrolysis: Acidic and Basic Properties of Salts," *Chemical Demonstrations: A Handbook for Teachers of Chemistry, Volume 3* (Madison: The University of Wisconsin Press, **1989**), pp. 103–108.

6. Bassam Z. Shakhashiri, "Effect of Molecular Structure on the Strength of Organic Acids and Bases in Aqueous Solutions," *Chemical Demonstrations: A Handbook for Teachers of Chemistry, Volume 3* (Madison: The University of Wisconsin Press, **1989**), pp. 158–161.

7. Bassam Z. Shakhashiri, "Food Is Usually Acidic, Cleaners Are Usually Basic," *Chemical Demonstrations: A Handbook for Teachers of Chemistry, Volume 3* (Madison: The University of Wisconsin Press, **1989**), pp. 65–69.

8. Bassam Z. Shakhashiri, "Rainbow Colors with Mixed Acid-Base Indicators," *Chemical Demonstrations: A Handbook for Teachers of Chemistry, Volume 3* (Madison: The University of Wisconsin Press, **1989**), pp. 41–46.

9. Lee R. Summerlin, Christie L. Borgford, and July B. Ealy, "Colorful Effects of Hydrochloric Acid Dilution," *Chemical Demonstrations, A Sourcebook for Teachers, Volume 2* (Washington: American Chemical Society, **1988**), pp. 177–178.

Chapter 17. Additional Aspects of Aqueous Equilibria

Media Resources

Figures and Tables in Transparency Pack:	**Section:**
Figure 17.2 Buffer Action	17.2 Buffered Solutions
Figure 17.3 Calculating the pH of a Buffer After Addition of Acid or Base	17.2 Buffered Solutions
Figure 17.7 Titration of a Strong Acid with a Strong Base	17.3 Acid-Base Titrations
Figure 17.8 Titration of a Weak Acid with a Strong Base	17.3 Acid-Base Titrations
Figure 17.10 Procedure for Calculating pH when a Weak Acid Is Partially Neutralized by a Strong Base	17.3 Acid-Base Titrations
Figure 17.11 A Set of Curves Showing the Effect of Acid Strength on the Characteristics of the Titration Curve when a Weak Acid Is Titrated by a Strong Base	17.3 Acid-Base Titrations
Figure 17.12 Titration Curve for a Diprotic Acid	17.3 Acid-Base Titrations
Figure 17.15 Good and Poor Indicators of a Weak Base with a Strong Acid	17.3 Acid-Base Titrations
Figure 17.16 Procedure for Converting between Solubility and K_{sp}	17.4 Solubility Equilibria
Figure 17.23 Qualitative Analysis	17.7 Qualitative Analysis for Metallic Elements

Activities:	**Section:**
Calculating pH Using Henderson-Hasselbalch Equation	17.2 Buffered Solutions
Buffer pH	17.2 Buffered Solutions
Buffer pH Calculation	17.2 Buffered Solutions
Acid-Base Titration	17.3 Acid-Base Titrations
Titration Calculation	17.3 Acid-Base Titrations
Solubility Product Constant	17.4 Solubility Equilibria
Selective Precipitation of Ions	17.6 Precipitation and Separation of Ions
Qualitative Analysis	17.7 Qualitative Analysis for Metallic Elements

Animations:	**Section:**
Common-Ion Effect	17.1 The Common-Ion Effect
Acid-Base Titration	17.3 Acid-Base Titrations
Dissolution of $Mg(OH)_2$ by Acid	17.5 Factors That Affect Solubility

Movies:	**Section:**
Precipitation Reactions	17.5 Factors That Affect Solubility
Flame Tests for Metals	17.7 Qualitative Analysis for Metallic Elements

3-D Models:	**Section:**
Acetic Acid	17.1 The Common-Ion Effect
Hydroxide Ion	17.3 Acid-Base Titrations
Phosphorous Acid	17.3 Acid-Base Titrations
Ammonia	17.5 Factors That Affect Solubility
Diamminosilver Cation	17.5 Factors That Affect Solubility
Hydrated Aluminum Cation	17.5 Factors That Affect Solubility

Other Resources

Further Readings:	**Section:**
A Good Idea Leads to a Better Buffer	17.2 Buffered Solutions
Phosphate Buffers and Telephone Poles—A Useful Analogy with Limitations	17.2 Buffered Solutions
The Henderson-Hasselbalch Equation: Its History and Limitations	17.2 Buffered Solutions
One-Hundred Years of pH	17.2 Buffered Solutions
Blood-Chemistry Tutorials: Teaching Biological Applications of General Chemistry Material	17.2 Buffered Solutions
Acid-Base Indicators: A New Look at an Old Topic	17.3 Acid-Base Titrations
Edible Acid-Base Indicators	17.3 Acid-Base Titrations
Predicting Acid-Base Titration Curves without Calculations	17.3 Acid-Base Titrations
The Murky Pool	17.4 Solubility Equilibria
The K_{sp}-Solubility Conundrum	17.4 Solubility Equilibria
The Useless Tea Kettle	17.4 Solubility Equilibria
Assessing Students' Conceptual Understanding of Solubility Equilibrium	17.4 Solubility Equilibria
What Should We Teach Beginners about Solubility and Solubility Products?	17.4 Solubility Equilibria
Chemical Aspects of Dentistry	17.5 Factors That Affect Solubility
Dentifrice Fluoride	17.5 Factors That Affect Solubility
Fluorine Compounds and Dental Health: Applications of General Chemistry Topics	17.5 Factors That Affect Solubility
Acid-Base Chemistry of the Aluminum Ion in Aqueous Solution	17.5 Factors That Affect Solubility
Complexometric Titrations: Competition of Complexing Agents in the Determination of Water Hardness with EDTA	17.5 Factors That Affect Solubility
Major Sources of Difficulty in Students' Understanding of Basic Inorganic Qualitative Analysis	17.7 Qualitative Analysis for Metallic Elements
Swimming Pools, Hot Rods, and Qualitative Analysis	17.7 Qualitative Analysis for Metallic Elements

Live Demonstrations:	**Section:**
The Common Ion Effect: Second Demonstration	17.1 The Common-Ion Effect
Effect of Acetate Ion on the Acidity of Acetic Acid: The Common-Ion Effect	17.1 The Common-Ion Effect
The Common-Ion Effect: Ammonium Hydroxide and Ammonium Acetate	17.1 The Common-Ion Effect

Buffering Action and Capacity	17.2 Buffered Solutions
Buffering Action of Alka-Seltzer	17.2 Buffered Solutions
Equilibrium: The Dissociation of Acetic Acid	17.2 Buffered Solutions
Determination of Neutralizing Capacity of Antacids	17.2 Buffered Solutions
Teas as Natural Indicators	17.3 Acid-Base Titrations
Solubility of Some Silver Compounds	17.4 Solubility Equilibria
Silver Ion Solubilities: Red and White Precipitates	17.4 Solubility Equilibria
Red and White Precipitates in Sodium Silicate	17.4 Solubility Equilibria
Fizzing and Foaming: Reactions of Acids with Carbonates	17.5 Factors That Affect Solubility
Milk of Magnesia versus Acid	17.5 Factors That Affect Solubility
Colorful Complex Ions in Ammonia	17.5 Factors That Affect Solubility
Green and Blue Copper Complexes	17.5 Factors That Affect Solubility
Acidic and Basic Properties of Oxides	17.5 Factors That Affect Solubility

Chapter 17. Additional Aspects of Aqueous Equilibria

Common Student Misconceptions

- Students often believe that the pH at the equivalence point for any titration is 7.00; in other words, students often think that neutralization always results in the formation of a *neutral* solution.
- Students often think that titration is a new type of a reaction, rather than an experimental technique.
- Students tend to find buffers particularly difficult to understand.
- Students often forget to consider volume changes that occur when two solutions are mixed (this will have an effect on the concentration of the species present).
- The approximate nature of the Henderson-Hasselbalch equation in a majority of applications is often lost on students.
- Students tend to confuse K_{sp} and solubility.
- Students often struggle with the concept of competing or subsequent equilibria when considering factors affecting solubility of ionic compounds.
- Students often confuse amphiprotic and amphoteric substances.

Teaching Tips

- Students should review Le Châtelier's principle, pH of salts, and solubility rules prior to starting this chapter.
- The common ion effect can be introduced as an example of how Le Châtelier's principle works.
- In terms of problem-solving skills, this is probably the most difficult chapter for most students.
- The latter sections of this chapter offer an opportunity for a review of inorganic nomenclature.

Lecture Outline

17.1 The Common Ion Effect[1,2,3,4,5]

- The dissociation of a weak electrolyte is decreased by the addition of a strong electrolyte that has an ion in common with the weak electrolyte.
- For example, consider the ionization of a weak acid, acetic acid.

$$HC_2H_3O_2(aq) \rightleftharpoons H^+(aq) + C_2H_3O_2^-(aq)$$

  - If we add additional $C_2H_3O_2^-$ ions, from the addition of a strong electrolyte, (e.g., $NaC_2H_3O_2$) the equilibrium is shifted to the left.
  - This causes a reduction in the $[H^+]$ and a decrease in the percent ionization of the acetic acid.
  - By adding the sodium acetate, we have disturbed the acetic acid equilibrium.
  - In effect, we have added a product of this equilibrium (i.e., the acetate ion).
    - This phenomenon is called the **common-ion effect**.
      - The extent of ionization of a weak electrolyte is decreased by adding to the solution a strong electrolyte that has an ion *in common* with the weak electrolyte.
- Common ion equilibrium problems are solved following the same pattern as other equilibrium problems.
  - However, the initial concentration of the common ion (from the salt) must be considered.

---

[1] "The Common-Ion Effect: Second Demonstration" from Live Demonstrations
[2] "Common-Ion Effect" Animation from Instructor's Resource CD/DVD
[3] "Effect of Acetate Ion on the Acidity of Acetic Acid: The Common-Ion Effect" from Live Demonstrations
[4] "The Common-Ion Effect: Ammonium Hydroxide and Ammonium Acetate" from Live Demonstrations
[5] "Acetic Acid" 3-D Model from Instructor's Resource CD/DVD

17. 2 Buffered Solutions

- A **buffered solution**, or **buffer**, is a solution that resists a drastic change in pH upon addition of small amounts of strong acid or strong base.

Composition and Action of Buffered Solutions[6,7,8,9,10,11]

- A buffer consists of a mixture of a weak acid (HX) and its conjugate base (X⁻).

$$HX(aq) \rightleftharpoons H^+(aq) + X^-(aq)$$

- Thus, a buffer contains both:
  - an acidic species (to neutralize OH⁻) and
  - a basic species (to neutralize H⁺).
- When a small amount of OH⁻ is added to the buffer, the OH⁻ reacts with HX to produce X⁻ and water.
  - But the [HX]/[X⁻] ratio remains more or less constant, so the pH is not significantly changed.
- When a small amount of H⁺ is added to the buffer, X⁻ is consumed to produce HX.
  - Once again, the [HX]/[X⁻] ratio is more or less constant, so the pH does not change significantly.

Calculating the pH of a Buffer[12,13,14,15]

- The pH of the buffer is related to K_a and to the relative concentrations of the acid and base.
- We can derive an equation that shows the relationship between conjugate acid-base concentrations, pH and K_a.
- By definition:

$$K_a = \frac{[H^+][X^-]}{[HX]}$$

- Rearranging, we get:

$$[H^+] = K_a \frac{[HX]}{[X^-]}$$

- If we take the negative natural logarithm of each side of the equation, we get:

$$-\log[H^+] = -\log K_a - \log \frac{[HX]}{[X^-]}$$

- By definition:

$$pH = pK_a - \log \frac{[HX]}{[X^-]}$$

---

[6] "A Good Idea Leads to a Better Buffer" from Further Readings

[7] "Phosphate Buffers and Telephone Poles—A Useful Analogy with Limitations" from Further Readings

[8] "Buffering Action and Capacity" from Live Demonstrations

[9] "Buffering Action of Alka-Seltzer" from Live Demonstrations

[10] Figure 17.2 from Transparency Pack

[11] "Equilibrium: The Dissociation of Acetic Acid" from Live Demonstrations

[12] "The Henderson-Hasselbalch Equation: Its History and Limitations" from Further Readings

[13] "Calculating pH Using Henderson-Hasselbalch Equation" Activity from Instructor's Resource CD/DVD

[14] "One-Hundred Years of pH" from Further Readings

[15] "Buffer pH" Activity from Instructor's Resource CD/DVD

- An alternate form of this equation is:

$$pH = pK_a + \log\frac{[X^-]}{[HX]} = pK_a + \log\frac{[base]}{[acid]}$$

- The above equation is the **Henderson-Hasselbalch equation**.
  - Note that this equation uses the equilibrium concentrations of the acid and conjugate base.
  - However, if K_a is sufficiently small (i.e., if the equilibrium concentration of the undissociated acid is close to the initial concentration), then we can use the initial values of the acid and base concentrations in order to get a good estimate of the pH.

Buffer Capacity and pH Range[16]

- **Buffer capacity** is the amount of acid or base that can be neutralized by the buffer before there is a significant change in pH.
- Buffer capacity depends on the concentrations of the components of the buffer.
  - The greater the concentrations of the conjugate acid-base pair, the greater the buffer capacity.
- The **pH range** of a buffer is the pH range over which it is an effective buffer.
  - The pH range of a buffer is generally within one pH unit of the pK_a of the buffering agent.

Addition of Strong Acids or Bases to Buffers[17,18,19]

- Keep in mind that reactions between strong acids and weak bases proceed essentially to completion.
- The same is true for reactions between strong bases and weak acids.
  - If we do not exceed the buffering capacity of the buffer, then the added strong acid or base is completely consumed by reaction with the buffer.
- We can break the calculation into two parts.
  - A *stoichiometric* calculation.
    - The addition of a strong acid or base results in a neutralization reaction:
    $$X^- + H_3O^+ \rightarrow HX + H_2O$$
    $$HX + OH^- \rightarrow X^- + H_2O$$
    - By knowing how much H_3O^+ or OH^- was added, we know how much HX or X^- was formed.
  - An *equilibrium* calculation.
    - With the concentrations of HX and X^- (taking into account the change in volume of the solution) we can calculate the pH from the Henderson-Hasselbalch equation:

17.3 Acid-Base Titrations[20,21]

- In an acid-base titration:
  - a solution of base of known concentration is added to an acid (or an acid of known concentration is added to a base).
  - acid-base indicators, or pH meters, are used to signal the equivalence point.
    - The *equivalence point* is the point at which stoichiometrically equivalent quantities of acid and base have been added.
  - The plot of pH versus volume during a titration is called a **pH titration curve**.

---

[16] "Determination of the Neutralizing Capacity of Antacids" from Live Demonstrations
[17] "Buffer pH Calculation" Activity from Instructor's Resource CD/DVD
[18] Figure 17.3 from Transparency Pack
[19] "Blood-Chemistry Tutorials: Teaching Biological Applications of General Chemistry Material" from Further Readings
[20] "Acid-Base Titration" Animation from Instructor's Resource CD/DVD
[21] "Hydroxide Ion" 3-D Model from Instructor's Resource CD/DVD

Strong Acid–Strong Base Titrations[22,23,24,25,26,27]

- Consider adding a strong base (e.g., NaOH) to a solution of a strong acid (e.g., HCl).
- We can divide the titration curve into four regions.
    - 1. *Initial pH* (before any base is added)
        - The pH is given by the strong acid solution.
        - Therefore, pH < 7.
    - 2. *Between the initial pH and the equivalence point.*
        - When base is added, before the equivalence point, the pH is given by the amount of strong acid in excess.
        - Therefore, pH < 7.
    - 3. *At the equivalence point.*
        - The amount of base added is stoichiometrically equivalent to the amount of acid originally present.
        - The cation of a strong base and the anion of a strong acid do not undergo hydrolysis.
        - Therefore, pH = 7.00.
    - 4. *After the equivalence point.*
        - The pH is determined by the excess base in the solution.
        - Therefore, pH > 7.
- The shape of a strong base-strong acid titration curve is very similar to a strong acid-strong base titration curve.
    - Initially, the strong base is in excess, so the pH > 7.
    - As acid is added, the pH decreases but is still greater than 7.
    - At the equivalence point, the pH is given by the salt solution (i.e., pH = 7).
    - After the equivalence point, the pH is given by the strong acid in excess, so pH is less than 7.

Weak Acid-Strong Base Titration[28,29,30,31]

- Consider the titration of acetic acid, $HC_2H_3O_2$, with NaOH.
- Again, we divide the titration into four general regions:
    - 1. *Before any base is added.*
        - The solution contains only weak acid.
        - Therefore, pH is given by the equilibrium calculation.
    - 2. *Between the initial pH and the equivalence point.*
        - As strong base is added it consumes a stoichiometric quantity of weak acid:
        $$HC_2H_3O_2(aq) + OH^-(aq) \rightarrow C_2H_3O_2^-(aq) + H_2O(l)$$
        - However, there is an excess of acetic acid.
        - Therefore, we have a mixture of weak acid and its conjugate base.
            - Thus, the composition of the mixture is that of a buffer.
            - The pH is given by the buffer calculation.

---

[22] "Acid-Base Indicators: A New Look at an Old Topic" from Further Readings
[23] "Teas as Natural Indicators" from Live Demonstrations
[24] "Acid-Base Titration" Activity from Instructor's Resource CD/DVD
[25] "Edible Acid-Base Indicators" from Further Readings
[26] "Predicting Acid-Base Titration Curves without Calculations" from Further Readings
[27] Figure 17.7 from Transparency Pack
[28] Figure 17.8 from Transparency Pack
[29] "Titration Calculation" Activity from Instructor's Resource CD/DVD
[30] Figure 17.10 from Transparency Pack
[31] Figure 17.11 from Transparency Pack

- First the amount of $C_2H_3O_2^-$ generated is calculated, as well as the amount of $HC_2H_3O_2$ consumed (stoichiometry).
  - Then the pH is calculated using equilibrium conditions (Henderson-Hasselbalch equation).
- 3. *At the equivalence point*, all the acetic acid has been consumed and all the NaOH has been consumed.
  - However, $C_2H_3O_2^-$ has been generated.
  - Therefore, the pH depends on the $C_2H_3O_2^-$ concentration.
  - The pH > 7 at the equivalence point.
  - More importantly, the pH of the equivalence point is NOT equal to 7 for a weak acid-strong base titration.
- 4. *After the equivalence point.*
  - the pH is given by the concentration of the excess strong base.
- The pH curve for a weak acid-strong base titration differs significantly from that of a strong acid-strong base titration.
  - For a strong acid-strong base titration:
    - the pH begins at less than 7 and gradually increases as base is added.
    - Near the equivalence point, the pH increases dramatically.
  - For a weak acid-strong base titration:
    - the initial pH rise is steeper than in the strong acid-strong base case.
    - However, then there is a leveling off due to buffer effects.
    - The middle section of the titration curve is not as steep for a weak acid-strong base titration.
  - The shape of the two curves after the equivalence point is the same because pH is determined by the strong base in excess.
  - The pH at the equivalence point differs also.
    - The pH is 7.00 for the strong acid-strong base equivalence point due to the formation of a neutral salt.
    - The pH is > 7.00 for the weak acid-strong base equivalence point due to the formation of a basic salt.

Titrations of Polyprotic Acids[32,33]

- In polyprotic acids, the ionizable protons dissociate in a series of steps.
  - Therefore, in a titration there are *n* equivalence points corresponding to each ionizable proton.
- In the titration of H_3PO_4 with NaOH there are three equivalence points:
  - one for the formation of $H_2PO_4^-$,
  - one for the formation of HPO_4^{2-}, and
  - one for the formation of PO_4^{3-}.

Titrating with an Acid-Base Indicator[34]

- How can we analyze the titration (i.e., how will we know when we are at the equivalence point)?
  - We often use a pH indicator.
    - The indicator chosen should begin and end its color change anywhere on the rapid-rise portion of the titration curve.
    - The *end point* in a titration is the point where the indicator changes color.
      - It represents a close approximation of the equivalence point.
  - Consider adding a strong base (e.g., NaOH) to a solution of a strong acid (e.g., HCl).
    - We know the pH at the equivalence point is 7.00.

---

[32] Figure 17.12 from Transparency Pack
[33] "Phosphorous Acid" 3-D Model from Instructor's Resource CD/DVD
[34] Figure 17.15 from Transparency Pack

- The pH changes rapidly only over the pH range from about pH 11 to 3.
- To detect the equivalence point, we use an indicator that changes color somewhere close to the pH at the equivalence point.
- Usually, we use phenolphthalein, which changes color between pH 8.3 and 10.0.
  - Methyl red is a poor choice as it changes color between pH 4.2 and 6.0, before the equivalence point is reached.
- In acid, phenolphthalein is colorless.
- As NaOH is added, there is a slight pink color at the addition point.
- When the flask is swirled and the reagents mixed, the pink color disappears.
- At the end point, the solution is light pink.
- If more base is added, the solution turns darker pink.
- The equivalence point in a titration is the point at which the acid and base are present in stoichiometrically equivalent quantities.
  - Consider adding a strong acid (e.g., HCl) to a solution of a weak base (e.g., NH_3).
  - We know the pH at the equivalence point is 5.28.
  - Here methyl red is a good choice while phenolphthalein would be a poor choice for indicator.

FORWARD REFERENCES
- Redox titrations will be briefly mentioned in Chapter 20 (section 20.2).
- Oxyacids of phosphorus will be discussed in more detail in Chapter 22 (section 22.8).

17.4 Solubility Equilibria[35,36,37]

The Solubility-Product Constant, K_{sp}[38,39,40,41,42,43]

- Consider a saturated solution of $BaSO_4$ in contact with solid $BaSO_4$.
  - We can write an equilibrium expression for the dissolving of the slightly soluble solid.

$$BaSO_4(s) \leftrightarrows Ba^{2+}(aq) + SO_4^{2-}(aq)$$

  - Because $BaSO_4(s)$ is a pure solid, the equilibrium expression depends only on the concentration of the ions.
  - K_{sp} is the equilibrium constant for the equilibrium between an ionic solid solute and its saturated aqueous solution.
    - K_{sp} is called the **solubility-product constant**, or the **solubility product**.
    - K_{sp} for $BaSO_4$ is:

$$K_{sp} = [Ba^{2+}][SO_4^{2-}]$$

- In general, the solubility product is equal to the product of the molar concentration of ions raised to powers corresponding to their stoichiometric coefficients.

Solubility and K_{sp}[44]

- *Solubility* is the amount of substance that dissolves to form a saturated solution.
  - This is often expressed as *grams of solute* that will dissolve *per liter of solution*.
- *Molar solubility* is the *number of moles of solute* that dissolve to form *a liter of saturated solution*.

---

[35] "Solubility of Some Silver Compounds" from Live Demonstrations
[36] "Red and White Precipitates in Sodium Silicate" from Live Demonstrations
[37] "The Murky Pool" from Further Readings
[38] "The K_{sp}-Solubility Conundrum" from Further Readings
[39] "Silver Ion Solubilities: Red and White Precipitates" from Live Demonstrations
[40] "The Useless Tea Kettle" from Further Readings
[41] "Assessing Students' Conceptual Understanding of Solubility Equilibrium" from Further Readings
[42] "Solubility Product Constant" Activity from Instructor's Resource CD/DVD
[43] "What Should We Teach Beginners about Solubility and Solubility Products?" from Further Readings
[44] Figure 17.16 from Transparency Pack

- We can use the solubility to find K_{sp} and vice versa.
  - To convert solubility to K_{sp}:
    - Convert solubility into molar solubility (via molar mass).
    - Convert molar solubility into the molar concentration of ions at equilibrium (equilibrium calculation).
    - Use the equilibrium concentration of ions in the K_{sp} expression.
  - To convert K_{sp} to solubility:
    - Write the K_{sp} expression.
    - Let x = the molar solubility of the salt.
    - Use the stoichiometry of the reaction to express the concentration of each species in terms of x.
    - Substitute these concentrations into the equilibrium expression and solve for x.
    - This calculation works best for salts whose ions have low charges.

FORWARD REFERENCES
- The role of acid-base and solubility reactions in tying the ocean to the atmosphere and the global climate will be discussed in Chapter 18 (sections 18.3 and 18.4).
- Water softening to remove hardness ions will be discussed in Chapter 18 (section 18.4).
- Calculations involving K_{sp} versus ΔG_{rxn}° will be performed in Chapter 19 (section 19.7).

17.5 Factors That Affect Solubility
- Three factors that have a significant impact on solubility are:
  - The presence of a common ion,
  - The pH of the solution, and
  - The presence of complexing agents.
    - *Amphoterism* is related to the effects of both pH and complexing agents.

Common-Ion Effect
- The solubility of a slightly soluble salt is decreased when a common ion is added.
  - This is an application of Le Châtelier's principle.
- Consider the solubility of CaF_2:

$$CaF_2(s) \leftrightarrows Ca^{2+}(aq) + 2F^-(aq)$$

- If more F^- is added (i.e., by the addition of NaF), the equilibrium shifts to the left to offset the increase.
  - Therefore, $CaF_2(s)$ is formed and precipitation occurs.
    - As NaF is added to the system, the solubility of CaF_2 decreases.
- In general, the solubility of a slightly soluble salt is decreased by the presence of a second salt that produces a common ion.

Solubility and pH[45,46,47]
- Again, we apply Le Châtelier's principle:

$$Mg(OH)_2(s) \leftrightarrows Mg^{2+}(aq) + 2OH^-(aq)$$

- If OH^- is removed, then the equilibrium shifts toward the right and $Mg(OH)_2$ dissolves.
- OH^- can be removed by adding a strong acid:

$$OH^-(aq) + H^+(aq) \leftrightarrows H_2O(aq)$$

- As pH decreases, $[H^+]$ increases and the solubility of $Mg(OH)_2$ increases.
- Another example:

---

[45] "Dissolution of $Mg(OH)_2$ by Acid" Animation from Instructor's Resource CD/DVD
[46] "Fizzing and Foaming: Reactions of Acids with Carbonates" from Live Demonstrations
[47] "Milk of Magnesia versus Acid" from Live Demonstrations

$$PbF_2(s) \rightleftharpoons Pb^{2+}(aq) + 2F^-(aq)$$

- If the F^- is removed, then the equilibrium shifts towards the right and PbF_2 dissolves.
- F^- can be removed by adding a strong acid:

$$F^-(aq) + H^+(aq) \rightleftharpoons HF(aq)$$

- As pH decreases, $[H^+]$ increases and solubility of PbF_2 increases.
- The effect of pH on solubility can be dramatic.
- The effect is most significant if one or both ions involved are at least somewhat acidic or basic.
- In general:
  - The solubility of slightly soluble salts containing basic ions increases as pH decreases.
  - The more basic the anion is, the greater the effect.

Formation of Complex Ions[48,49,50,51,52,53,54,55,56]

- Recall that metal ions may act as Lewis acids in aqueous solution (water may act as the Lewis base).
  - Such an interaction may have a significant impact on metal salt solubility.
  - For example, AgCl has a very low solubility.
    - K_{sp} for AgCl $= 1.8 \times 10^{-10}$
    - However, the solubility is greatly increased if ammonia is added.
      - Why?
- Consider the formation of $Ag(NH_3)_2^+$:

$$Ag^+(aq) + 2NH_3(aq) \rightleftharpoons Ag(NH_3)_2^+(aq)$$

- The $Ag(NH_3)_2^+$ is called a **complex ion**.
- NH_3 (the attached Lewis base) is called a *ligand*.
- The equilibrium constant for the reaction is called the **formation constant**, K_f:

$$K_f = \frac{\left[Ag(NH_3)_2^+ \right]}{[Ag^+][NH_3]^2} = 1.7 \times 10^7$$

- Consider the addition of ammonia to AgCl (white salt):

$$AgCl(s) \rightleftharpoons Ag^+(aq) + Cl^-(aq)$$

$$Ag^+(aq) + 2NH_3(aq) \rightleftharpoons Ag(NH_3)_2^+(aq)$$

- The overall reaction is:

$$AgCl(s) + 2NH_3(aq) \rightleftharpoons Ag(NH_3)_2^+(aq) + Cl^-(aq)$$

- Effectively, the $Ag^+(aq)$ has been removed from solution.
- By Le Châtelier's principle, the forward reaction (the dissolving of AgCl) is favored.

---

[48] "Chemical Aspects of Dentistry" from Further Readings

[49] "Dentifrice Fluoride" from Further Readings

[50] "Fluorine Compounds and Dental Health: Applications of General Chemistry Topics" from Further Readings

[51] "Colorful Complex Ions in Ammonia" from Live Demonstrations

[52] "Green and Blue Copper Complexes" from Live Demonstrations

[53] "Complexometric Titrations: Competition of Complexing Agents in the Determination of Water Hardness with EDTA" from Further Readings

[54] "Ammonia" 3-D Model from Instructor's Resource CD/DVD

[55] "Diamminosilver Cation" 3-D Model from Instructor's Resource CD/DVD

[56] "Hydrated Aluminum Cation" 3-D Model from Instructor's Resource CD/DVD

Amphoterism[57,58,59]

- Substances that are capable of acting either as an acid or a base are **amphoteric**.
    - The term is similar to one discussed earlier: *amphiprotic*, which relates more generally to any species that can either gain or lose a proton.
- **Amphoteric metal oxides and hydroxides** will dissolve in either a strong acid or a strong base.
    - Examples are hydroxides and oxides of Al^{3+}, Cr^{3+}, Zn^{2+}, and Sn^{2+}.
    - The hydroxides generally form complex ions with several hydroxide ligands attached to the metal:

$$Al(OH)_3(s) + OH^-(aq) \rightleftharpoons Al(OH)_4^-(aq)$$

- Hydrated metal ions act as weak acids.
    - As strong base is added, protons are removed:

$$Al(H_2O)_6^{3+}(aq) + OH^-(aq) \rightleftharpoons Al(H_2O)_5(OH)^{2+}(aq) + H_2O(l)$$

$$Al(H_2O)_5(OH)^{2+}(aq) + OH^-(aq) \rightleftharpoons Al(H_2O)_4(OH)_2^+(aq) + H_2O(l)$$

$$Al(H_2O)_4(OH)_2^+(aq) + OH^-(aq) \rightleftharpoons Al(H_2O)_3(OH)_3(s) + H_2O(l)$$

$$Al(H_2O)_3(OH)_3(s) + OH^-(aq) \rightleftharpoons Al(H_2O)_2(OH)_4^-(aq) + H_2O(l)$$

- The addition of an acid reverses these reactions.

FORWARD REFERENCES

- Chelating agents will be further mentioned in Chapters 23 (section 23.3, respectively).
- Amphoteric oxides of transition metals will be mentioned in Chapter 22 (section 22.5).
- The formation of stable cyanide complexes with transition metals will be brought up in Chapter 22 (section 22.10).
- Chemistry of coordination compounds, including hemoglobin and chlorophyll, will be discussed detail throughout Chapter 23.

17.6 Precipitation and Separation of Ions

- Consider the following:

$$BaSO_4(s) \rightleftharpoons Ba^{2+}(aq) + SO_4^{2-}(aq)$$

- At any instant in time, $Q = [Ba^{2+}][SO_4^{2-}]$.
    - If $Q > K_{sp}$, precipitation occurs until $Q = K_{sp}$.
    - If $Q = K_{sp}$ equilibrium exists (saturated solution).
    - If $Q < K_{sp}$, solid dissolves until $Q = K_{sp}$.

Selective Precipitation of Ions[60]

- Ions can be separated from each other based on the solubilities of their salts.
    - Example: If HCl is added to a solution containing Ag^+ and Cu^{2+}, the silver precipitates (K_{sp} for AgCl is 1.8×10^{-10}) while the Cu^{2+} remains in solution.
        - Removal of one metal ion from a solution is called *selective precipitation*.
    - The sulfide ion is often used to separate metal ions.
        - Example: Consider a mixture of $Zn^{2+}(aq)$ and $Cu^{2+}(aq)$.
            - CuS ($K_{sp} = 6 \times 10^{-37}$) is less soluble than ZnS ($K_{sp} = 2 \times 10^{-25}$).
            - Thus, CuS will be removed from solution before ZnS.
            - As H_2S is bubbled through the acidified green solution, black CuS forms.
            - When the precipitate is removed, a colorless solution containing $Zn^{2+}(aq)$ remains.

---

[57] "Precipitation Reactions" Movie from Instructor's Resource CD/DVD

[58] "Acid-Base Chemistry of the Aluminum Ion in Aqueous Solution" from Further Readings

[59] "Acidic and Basic Properties of Oxides" from Live Demonstrations

[60] "Selective Precipitation of Ions" Activity from Instructor's Resource CD/DVD

- When more H_2S is added to the solution, a second precipitate of white ZnS forms.

17.7 Qualitative Analysis for Metallic Elements[61,62,63,64,65]

- **Quantitative analysis** is designed to determine how much metal ion is present.
- **Qualitative analysis** is designed to detect the presence of metal ions.
  - Typical qualitative analysis of a metal ion mixture involves:
    - 1. separation of ions into five major groups on the basis of their differential solubilities.
      - insoluble chlorides
      - acid-insoluble sulfides
      - base-insoluble sulfides and hydroxides
      - insoluble phosphates
      - alkali metals and ammonium ion
    - 2. separation of individual ions within each group by selectively dissolving members of the group.
    - 3. specific tests to determine whether a particular ion is present or absent.

---

[61] "Major Sources of Difficulty in Students' Understanding of Basic Inorganic Qualitative Analysis" from Further Readings
[62] Figure 17.23 from Transparency Pack
[63] "Qualitative Analysis" Activity from Instructor's Resource CD/DVD
[64] "Swimming Pools, Hot Rods, and Qualitative Analysis" from Further Readings
[65] "Flame Tests for Metals" Movie from Instructor's Resource CD/DVD

Further Readings:

1. Charles L. Bering, "A Good Idea Leads to a Better Buffer," *J. Chem. Educ.*, Vol. 64, **1987**, 803–805.

2. Edwin S. Gould, "Phosphate Buffers and Telephone Poles—A Useful Analogy with Limitations," *J. Chem. Educ.*, Vol. 76, **1999**, 1511.

3. Henry N. Po and N. M. Senozan, "The Henderson-Hasselbalch Equation: Its History and Limitations," *J. Chem. Educ.*, Vol. 78, **2001**, 1499–1503.

4. Rollie J. Myers, "One-Hundred Years of pH," *J. Chem. Educ.*, Vol. 87, **2010**, 30–32.

5. Rachel E. Casidey, Dewey Holten, Richard Krathen, and Regina F. Frey, "Blood-Chemistry Tutorials: Teaching Biological Applications of General Chemistry Material," *J. Chem. Educ.*, Vol. 78, **2001**, 1210–1214. The relationship between oxygen transport, iron transport, blood buffering, kidney dialysis, and general topics is discussed.

6. Ara S. Kooser, Judith L. Jenkins, and Lawrence E. Welch, "Acid-Base Indicators: A New Look at an Old Topic," *J. Chem. Educ.*, Vol. 78, **2001**, 1504–1506.

7. Robert C. Mebane and Thomas R. Rybolt, "Edible Acid-Base Indicators," *J. Chem. Educ.*, Vol. 62, **1985**, 285.

8. Dennis Barnum, "Predicting Acid-Base Titration Curves without Calculations," *J. Chem. Educ.*, Vol. 76, **1999**, 938–942.

9. Robert Perkins, "The Useless Tea Kettle," *J. Chem. Educ.*, Vol. 61, **1984**, 383.

10. Roy W. Clark and Judith M. Bonicamp, "The K_{sp}-Solubility Conundrum," *J. Chem. Educ.*, Vol. 75, **1998**, 1182–1185.

11. Robert Perkins, "The Murky Pool," *J. Chem. Educ.*, Vol. 61, **1984**, 383–384.

12. Andres Raviolo, "Assessing Students' Conceptual Understanding of Solubility Equilibrium," *J. Chem. Educ.*, Vol. 78, **2001**, 629–631.

13. Stephen J. Hawkes, "What Should We Teach Beginners about Solubility and Solubility Products?" *J. Chem. Educ.*, Vol. 75, **1998**, 1179–1181.

14. Murry Helfman, "Chemical Aspects of Dentistry," *J. Chem. Educ.*, Vol. 59, **1982**, 666–668.

15. Philip E. Rakita, "Dentifice Fluoride," *J. Chem. Educ.*, Vol. 81, **2004**, 677–680.

16. Gabriel Pinto, "Fluorine Compounds and Dental Health: Applications of General Chemistry Topics," *J. Chem. Educ.*, Vol. 86, **2009**, 185–187.

17. Edward Koubek, Cole McWherter, and George L. Gilbert, "Acid-Base Chemistry of the Aluminum Ion in Aqueous Solution," *J. Chem. Educ.*, Vol. 75, **1998**, 60.

18. Kim Chwee, Daniel Tan, Ngoh Khang Goh, Lian Sai Chai, and David F. Teagust, "Major Sources of Difficulty in Students' Understanding of Basic Inorganic Qualitative Analysis," *J. Chem. Educ.*, Vol. 81, **2004**, 725–732.

19. M. Cecilia Yappert and Donald B. DuPre, "Complexometric Titrations: Competition of Complexing Agents in the Determination of Water Hardness with EDTA," *J. Chem. Educ.*, Vol. 74, **1997**, 1422–1423.

20. Dale D. Clyde, "Swimming Pools, Hot Rods, and Qualitative Analysis," *J. Chem. Educ.*, Vol. 65, **1988**, 911–913.

Live Demonstrations:

1. Lee. R. Summerlin, and James. L. Ealy, Jr., "The Common Ion Effect: Second Demonstration," *Chemical Demonstrations, A Sourcebook for Teachers, Volume 1* (Washington: American Chemical Society, **1988**), pp. 93–94. The reaction of calcium carbonate and acetic acid is used to demonstrate the common ion effect.

2. Bassam Z. Shakhashiri, "Effect of Acetate Ion on the Acidity of Acetic Acid: The Common Ion Effect," *Chemical Demonstrations: A Handbook for Teachers of Chemistry, Volume 3* (Madison: The University of Wisconsin Press, **1989**), pp. 155–157.

3. Lee. R. Summerlin, and James. L. Ealy, Jr., "The Common Ion-Effect: Ammonium Hydroxide and Ammonium Acetate," *Chemical Demonstrations, A Sourcebook for Teachers, Volume 1* (Washington: American Chemical Society, **1988**), p. 95.

4. Bassam Z. Shakhashiri, "Buffering Action and Capacity," *Chemical Demonstrations: A Handbook for Teachers of Chemistry, Volume 3* (Madison: The University of Wisconsin Press, **1989**), pp. 173–185.

5. Bassam Z. Shakhashiri, "Buffering Action of Alka-Seltzer," *Chemical Demonstrations: A Handbook for Teachers of Chemistry, Volume 3* (Madison: The University of Wisconsin Press, **1989**), pp. 186–187.

6. Lee. R. Summerlin, Christie L. Borgford, and Julie B. Ealy, "Equilibrium: The Dissociation of Acetic Acid," *Chemical Demonstrations, A Sourcebook for Teachers, Volume 2* (Washington: American Chemical Society, **1988**), pp.160–161. Changes in indicator color upon addition of base or acetate to acetic acid are explored.

7. Bassam Z. Shakhashiri, "Determination of Neutralizing Capacity of Antacids," *Chemical Demonstrations: A Handbook for Teachers of Chemistry, Volume 3* (Madison: The University of Wisconsin Press, **1989**), pp. 162–166.

8. Dianne N. Epp, "Teas as Natural Indicators," *J. Chem. Educ.*, Vol. 70, **1993**, 326. The use of teas as natural acid-base indicators is demonstrated.

9. Lee. R. Summerlin, Christie L. Borgford, and Julie B. Ealy, "Solubility of Some Silver Compounds," *Chemical Demonstrations, A Sourcebook for Teachers, Volume 2* (Washington: American Chemical Society, **1988**), pp. 83–85. The solubility of a series of silver salts and complexes is explored in this colorful demonstration.

10. Lee R. Summerlin, Christie L Borgford, and Julie B. Ealy, "Silver Ion Solubilities: Red and White Precipitates," *Chemical Demonstrations, A Sourcebook for Teachers, Volume 2* (Washington: American Chemical Society, **1988**), pp. 124–125. This is an effective introduction to equilibrium; the relative solubilities of silver chromate and silver chloride are investigated.

11. Bassam Z. Shakhashiri, "Fizzing and Foaming: Reactions of Acids with Carbonates," *Chemical Demonstrations: A Handbook for Teachers of Chemistry, Volume 3* (Madison: The University of Wisconsin Press, **1989**), pp. 96–99.

12. Lee. R. Summerlin, Christie L. Borgford, and Julie B. Ealy, "Milk of Magnesia versus Acid," *Chemical Demonstrations, A Sourcebook for Teachers, Volume 2* (Washington: American Chemical Society, **1988**), p. 173. An antacid, milk of magnesia, is mixed with acid in this demonstration.

13. Lee. R. Summerlin, Christie L. Borgford, and Julie B. Ealy, " Colorful Complex Ions in Ammonia," *Chemical Demonstrations, A Sourcebook for Teachers, Volume 2* (Washington: American Chemical Society, **1988**), pp. 75–76. Ammine complexes of copper and cobalt are prepared in this demonstration.

14. Lee. R. Summerlin, Christie L. Borgford, and Julie B. Ealy, " Green and Blue Copper Complexes," *Chemical Demonstrations, A Sourcebook for Teachers, Volume 2* (Washington: American Chemical Society, **1988**), pp.71–72. Three copper complexes are prepared in this demonstration.

15. Bassam Z. Shakhashiri, "Acidic and Basic Properties of Oxides," *Chemical Demonstrations: A Handbook for Teachers of Chemistry, Volume 3* (Madison: The University of Wisconsin Press, **1989**), pp. 109–113.

16. Lee R. Summerlin, Christie L. Borgford, and Julie B. Ealy, "Red and White Precipitates in Sodium Silicate," *Chemical Demonstrations: A Sourcebook for Teachers, Volume 2* (Washington: American Chemical Society **1988**), p. 131.

Chapter 18. Chemistry of the Environment

Media Resources

Figures and Tables in Transparency Pack:	**Section:**
Figure 18.1 Temperature and Pressure in the Atmosphere Vary as a Function of Altitude Above Sea Level	18.1 Earth's Atmosphere
Figure 18.6 Ozone Present in the Southern Hemisphere, Sept. 24, 2006	18.2 Human Activities and Earth's Atmosphere
Figure 18.9 One Method for Removing SO_2 from Combusted Fuel	18.2 Human Activities and Earth's Atmosphere
Figure 18.11 Earth's Thermal Balance	18.2 Human Activities and Earth's Atmosphere
Figure 18.12 Portions of the Infrared Radiation Emitted by Earth's Surface That Are Absorbed Atmospheric CO_2 and H_2O	18.2 Human Activities and Earth's Atmosphere
Figure 18.13 Rising CO_2 Levels	18.2 Human Activities and Earth's Atmosphere
Table 18.5 Ionic Constituents of Seawater Present in Concentrations Greater than 0.001 g/kg (1 ppm)	18.3 Earth's Water
Figure 18.20 Common Steps in Treating Water for a Public Water System	18.4 Human Activities and Earth's Water

Animations:	**Section:**
Stratospheric Ozone	18.1 Earth's Atmosphere
CFCs and Stratospheric Ozone	18.2 Human Activities and Earth's Atmosphere
Catalytic Destruction of Stratospheric Ozone	18.2 Human Activities and Earth's Atmosphere

Movies:	**Section:**
Carbon Dioxide Behaves as an Acid in Water	18.2 Human Activities and Earth's Atmosphere

3-D Models:	**Section:**
Nitrogen	18.1 Earth's Atmosphere
Oxygen	18.1 Earth's Atmosphere
Carbon Dioxide	18.1 Earth's Atmosphere
Heme (with bound O_2)	18.2 Human Activities and Earth's Atmosphere
Water	18.3 Earth's Water

Other Resources

Further Readings:	**Section:**
Introducing Atmospheric Reactions: A Systematic Approach for Students	18.1 Earth's Atmosphere
Thermal Physics (and Some Chemistry) of the Atmosphere	18.1 Earth's Atmosphere
'Holes' in Student Understanding: Addressing Prevalent Misconceptions Regarding Atmospheric Environmental Chemistry	18.1 Earth's Atmosphere

Chemists Celebrate Earth Day 2009: Air—The Sky's the Limit. JCE Resources for Chemistry and the Atmosphere: An Update   18.1 Earth's Atmosphere

Outdoor Carbon Monoxide: Risk to Millions   18.1 Earth's Atmosphere

Carbon Monoxide Poisoning. Some Surprising Aspects of the Equilibrium between Hemoglobin, Carbon Monoxide, and Oxygen   18.1 Earth's Atmosphere

Understanding Ozone   18.2 Human Activities and Earth's Atmosphere

Ozone Depletion: 20 Years after the Alarm   18.2 Human Activities and Earth's Atmosphere

News from Online: Stratospheric Chemistry   18.2 Human Activities and Earth's Atmosphere

Local and Regional Ozone: A Student Study Project   18.2 Human Activities and Earth's Atmosphere

Acid Rain Effects on Stone Monuments   18.2 Human Activities and Earth's Atmosphere

Atmospheric Dust and Acid Rain   18.2 Human Activities and Earth's Atmosphere

Getting to 'Clean Coal'   18.2 Human Activities and Earth's Atmosphere

Climate Change   18.2 Human Activities and Earth's Atmosphere

Water in the Atmosphere   18.2 Human Activities and Earth's Atmosphere

Using the Relationship between Vehicle Fuel Consumption and CO_2 Emissions to Illustrate Chemical Principles   18.2 Human Activities and Earth's Atmosphere

The Expiration of Respiration: Oxygen–The Missing Ingredient in Many Bodies of Water   18.4 Human Activities and Earth's Water

A Discovery-Based Experiment Illustrating How Iron Metal Is Used to Remediate Contaminated Groundwater   18.4 Human Activities and Earth's Water

The Water Softener–A Relevant, Unifying Example of Many Common Chemical Principles and Calculations   18.4 Human Activities and Earth's Water

Carbon Footprint Calculations: An Application of Chemical Principles   18.5 Green Chemistry

Green Chemistry Gets Greener   18.5 Green Chemistry

Topics in Green Chemistry   18.5 Green Chemistry

Some Exercises Reflecting Green Chemistry Concepts   18.5 Green Chemistry

JCE Resources for Chemistry and Recycling   18.5 Green Chemistry

Live Demonstrations: **Section:**

Acid-Neutralizing Capacity of Lake Beds   18.4 Human Activities and Earth's Water

Going Green: Lecture Assignments and Lab Experiences for the College Curriculum   18.5 Green Chemistry

Chapter 18. Chemistry of the Environment

Common Student Misconceptions

- Students often confuse the toxicity of ozone in the troposphere and the beneficial effects of ozone in the stratosphere.
- Students often think that ozone depletion causes global warming.
- Students often equate greenhouse effect with global warming; they are linked, but not the same.

Teaching Tips

- This chapter gives an excellent opportunity to review Dalton's law of partial pressure, Planck's law calculations, ionization energy, equilibrium, reaction mechanisms, and some acid-base chemistry.

Lecture Outline

18.1 Earth's Atmosphere[1,2]

- The temperature of the atmosphere varies with altitude.
- The atmosphere is divided into four regions based on the temperature profile.
    - The **troposphere** (below an altitude of 12 km)
        - The temperature decreases from 290 K to 215 K as altitude increases.
        - This region is where we spend most of our time.
        - The boundaries between regions are given the suffix *-pause*.
            - The area at the boundary of the troposphere is the *tropopause*.
        - 75% of the mass of the atmosphere is within the troposphere.
    - The **stratosphere** (10 km – 50 km)
        - The temperature increases from 215 K to 275 K.
    - The **mesosphere** (50 km – 85 km)
        - The temperature decreases (275 K to 190 K).
    - The **thermosphere** (>85 km)
        - The temperature increases.
    - There is only slow mixing of gases between regions in the atmosphere.
- The variation of pressure with altitude is simple; pressure decreases as altitude increases.
    - The pressure at sea level is 760 torr; the pressure at 200 km is 1×10^{-6} torr.

Composition of the Atmosphere[3,4,5,6,7,8,9,10]

- The composition of the atmosphere is not uniform.

---

[1] "Introducing Atmospheric Reactions: A Systematic Approach for Students" from Further Readings
[2] Figure 18.1 from Transparency Pack
[3] "Thermal Physics (and Some Chemistry) of the Atmosphere" from Further Readings
[4] " 'Holes' in Student Understanding: Addressing Prevalent Misconceptions Regarding Atmospheric Environmental Chemistry" from Further Readings
[5] "Chemists Celebrate Earth Day 2009: Air—The Sky's the Limit. JCE Resources for Chemistry and the Atmosphere: An Update" from Further Readings
[6] "Outdoor Carbon Monoxide: Risk to Millions" from Further Readings
[7] "Carbon Monoxide Poisoning. Some Surprising Aspects of the Equilibrium between Hemoglobin, Carbon Monoxide, and Oxygen" from Further Readings
[8] "Nitrogen" 3-D Model from Instructor's Resource CD/DVD
[9] "Oxygen" 3-D Model from Instructor's Resource CD/DVD
[10] "Carbon Dioxide" 3-D Model from Instructor's Resource CD/DVD

- Temperature and pressure vary over a wide range with altitude.
- Gases in the atmosphere are bombarded by radiation and energetic particles from the sun.
- Gravity also plays a role.
  - Lighter molecules and atoms are found at higher altitudes.
- Two major components of the atmosphere are nitrogen, N_2, and oxygen, O_2.
  - N_2 and O_2 make up approximately 99% of the atmosphere.
  - CO_2 and noble gases make up most of the remainder of the atmosphere.
  - The concentration of gases in the atmosphere is given in parts per million (ppm).
    - The definition of ppm in this instance is on a per volume basis.
    - 1 ppm = 1 part by volume per million volumes of the whole.
  - The concentration in ppm is equal to the mole fraction times 10^6.
  - Thus, the concentrations of N_2 and O_2 are 7.8×10^5 and 2.1×10^5, respectively.
  - These two components differ significantly with respect to reactivity.
    - The O=O and N≡N bonds are very strong, however, the O=O bond is much weaker than the N≡N bond.
    - Therefore, O_2 is significantly more reactive than N_2.

Photochemical Reactions in the Atmosphere

- Recall:

$$E = h\nu = hc/\lambda$$

- Thus, the higher the frequency, the shorter the wavelength and the higher the energy of radiation.
- For a chemical reaction induced by radiation to occur, the photons must have sufficient energy to break the required bonds, and the molecules must absorb the photons.
- **Photodissociation** is the rupture of a chemical bond induced by absorption of a photon by a molecule.
  - No ions are formed.
  - Bond cleavage leaves half the bonding electrons with each of the two atoms forming two neutral particles.
- In the upper atmosphere, photodissociation causes the formation of oxygen atoms:

$$O_2(g) + h\nu \rightarrow 2O(g)$$

  - The minimum energy required to induce this depends on the dissociation energy of O_2 (495 kJ/mol).
  - The longest wavelength of light that causes the formation of oxygen atoms is 242 nm.
- In 1924, electrons were discovered in the upper atmosphere.
  - Therefore, cations must be present in the upper atmosphere.
- **Photoionization** is the ionization of molecules (and atoms) caused by radiation.
  - The molecule absorbs energy, causing the loss of an electron.
  - Thus, the photon must have sufficient energy to remove an electron when it is absorbed by a molecule.
  - Wavelengths of light that cause photoionization and photodissociation are absorbed by the upper atmosphere.
    - This filters them out and prevents them from reaching the Earth.

Ozone in the Upper Atmosphere[11]

- Ozone absorbs photons with wavelengths between 240 and 310 nm.
- Most of the ozone is present in the stratosphere; 90% of it is found at 10–50 km.
- Between altitudes of 30 and 90 km. photodissociation of oxygen is possible:

$$O_2(g) + h\nu \rightarrow 2O(g)$$

  - Here the concentration of O_2 is greater than that of O.

---

[11] "Stratospheric Ozone" Animation from Instructor's Resource CD/DVD

- The oxygen atoms can collide with oxygen molecules to form ozone with excess energy, O_3^*:
$$O(g) + O_2(g) \rightarrow O_3^*(g)$$
- The excited ozone (O_3^*) can lose energy by decomposing to oxygen atoms and oxygen molecules (the reverse reaction) or by transferring the energy to M (usually N_2 or O_2):
$$O(g) + O_2(g) \rightarrow O_3^*(g)$$
$$O_3^*(g) + M(g) \rightarrow O_3(g) + M^*(g)$$
- Why does maximum ozone formation occur in the stratosphere?
  - The formation of ozone in the atmosphere depends on the presence of $O(g)$.
    - At low altitudes, the radiation with sufficient energy to form $O(g)$ has been absorbed.
  - The release of energy from O_3^* depends on collisions that generally occur at lower altitudes.
    - The concentration of molecules is generally greater at lower altitudes, thus more frequent collisions occur.
  - Combining these factors results in maximum ozone formation in the stratosphere.
- The *ozone shield* in the stratosphere protects plant and animal life on Earth's surface from being bombarded with high-energy radiation.

18.2 Human Activities and Earth's Atmosphere

The Ozone Layer and Its Depletion[12,13,14,15,16,17,18,19]

- 1970: Cratzen demonstrated that naturally occurring nitrogen oxides can catalytically degrade ozone.
- 1974: Rowland and Molina demonstrated that chlorine atoms from **chlorofluorocarbons** (CFCs) deplete the ozone layer.
  - Rowland and Molina were awarded the Nobel prize in 1995.
  - CFCs such as $CFCl_3$ (Freon-11) and CF_2Cl_2 (Freon-12) were commonly used as propellants in spray cans, as refrigerants, and in the plastics industry.
  - CFCs are relatively insoluble in water.
  - Thus, they are not removed from the atmosphere by rain.
  - Their lack of chemical reactivity allows them to survive in the atmosphere and diffuse into the stratosphere.
- In the stratosphere, CFCs undergo photochemical rupture of a C–Cl bond:
$$CF_2Cl_2(g) + h\nu \rightarrow CF_2Cl(g) + Cl(g) \quad \text{(optimal at 30 km)}$$
  - The free chlorine atoms subsequently react with ozone:
$$Cl(g) + O_3(g) \rightarrow ClO(g) + O_2(g)$$
    - Rate = $k[Cl][O_3]$, $k = 7.2 \times 10^9\ M^{-1}s^{-1}$ at 298 K.
  - In addition, the ClO generated may produce Cl as well:
$$2ClO(g) \rightarrow O_2(g) + 2Cl(g)$$
  - These chlorine atoms can react with more ozone.
  - The overall reaction is:
$$2O_3(g) \rightarrow 3O_2(g)$$
- The use and production of CFCs was completely banned as of 1996 (by 100 nations).
  - Hydrofluorocarbons are the main alternatives to hydrofluorocarbons.

---

[12] "Understanding Ozone" from Further Readings
[13] Figure 18.6 from Transparency Pack
[14] "Ozone Depletion: 20 Years after the Alarm" from Further Readings
[15] "News from Online: Stratospheric Chemistry" from Further Readings
[16] "Local and Regional Ozone: A Student Study Project" from Further Readings
[17] "CFCs and Stratospheric Ozone" Animation from Instructor's Resource CD/DVD
[18] "Catalytic Destruction of Stratospheric Ozone" Animation from Instructor's Resource CD/DVD
[19] "Heme (with bound O_2)" 3-D Model from Instructor's Resource CD/DVD

Sulfur Compounds and Acid Rain[20,21,22,23,24]

- Sulfur dioxide, SO_2, is produced by natural events (volcanic gases, bacterial action, forest fires).
  - The major source is linked to human activities such as the combustion of sulfur-containing fuels.
    - Combustion of coal accounts for approximately 65% of the SO_2 released in the United States.
  - The amount of SO_2 produced depends on the sulfur content of the coal or oil, which varies with the source of the coal or oil.
  - The SO_2 can be oxidized to SO_3, which dissolves in water to produce sulfuric acid (a component of **acid rain**):
$$SO_3(g) + H_2O(l) \rightarrow H_2SO_4(aq)$$
- Nitrogen oxides also contribute to acid rain by forming nitric acid.
- Normal rainwater has a pH of about 5.6 (due to the H_2CO_3 produced from CO_2).
  - Acid rain has a pH around 4, whereas the pH of natural waters containing living organisms is between 6.5 and 8.5.
  - Natural waters with a pH below 4 cannot sustain life.
    - All vertebrates, most invertebrates, and many microorganisms cannot survive at such a low pH conditions.
- The acids in acid rain are problematic.
  - They react with metals and promote corrosion.
  - They react with carbonates (such as the calcium carbonate in marble and limestone).
- How can we reduce the amount of SO_2 produced from fuel combustion?
  - It is too expensive to remove sulfur from oil and coal prior to its use.
    - Therefore, the SO_2 is removed from fuel on combustion.
  - SO_2 is commonly removed from the gases formed by the combustion of fuels (oil and coal) as follows:
    - Powdered limestone decomposes into CaO in the furnace of a power plant.
    - CaO reacts with SO_2 to form $CaSO_3$ in the furnace.
    - $CaSO_3$ and unreacted SO_2 are passed into a scrubber (purification chamber) where the SO_2 is converted to $CaSO_3$ by jets of CaO.
    - $CaSO_3$ is precipitated into a watery slurry and is removed.

Nitrogen Oxides and Photochemical Smog

- **Photochemical smog** is the result of photochemical reactions on pollutants.
  - Oxides of nitrogen are the primary components of smog.
- In car engines, NO forms as follows:
$$2NO(g) + O_2(g) \rightarrow 2NO_2(g) \qquad \Delta H = -113.1 \text{ kJ}$$
  - In air NO is rapidly oxidized:
$$NO_2(g) + h\nu \rightarrow NO(g) + O(g)$$
  - Light with a wavelength of 393 nm causes photodissociation of NO_2:
$$NO_2(g) + h\nu \rightarrow NO(g) + O(g)$$
  - The O can react with O_2 to form O_3, which is the key component of smog:
$$O(g) + O_2(g) + M(g) \rightarrow O_3(g) + M^*(g)$$
  - In the troposphere ozone is undesirable because it is toxic and reactive.
- A further pollutant is emitted by automobiles: unburned hydrocarbons.
- Catalytic converters reduce the level of NO_x and hydrocarbon emissions.

[20] Figure 18.9 from Transparency Pack
[21] "Acid Rain Effects on Stone Monuments" from Further Readings
[22] "Atmospheric Dust and Acid Rain" from Further Readings
[23] "Getting to 'Clean Coal'" from Further Readings
[24] "Carbon Dioxide Behaves as an Acid in Water" Movie from Instructor's Resource CD/DVD

Greenhouse Gases: Water Vapor, Carbon Dioxide, and Climate[25,26,27,28,29,30]

- There is a thermal balance between the Earth and its surroundings.
- Therefore, radiation is emitted from the Earth at the same rate as it is absorbed by the Earth.
- The troposphere is transparent to visible light.
- However, the troposphere is not transparent to IR radiation (heat).
- Therefore, the troposphere insulates the Earth, making it appear colder from the outside than it is on the surface.
- CO_2 and H_2O absorb IR radiation escaping from the Earth's surface.
  - The effect of CO_2, H_2O, and other gases on Earth's temperature is called the *greenhouse effect*.
  - The gases themselves are called *greenhouse gases*.
- At night, the Earth emits radiation.
  - Water vapor plays a major role in maintaining atmospheric temperature at night.
  - CO_2 also plays a role in maintaining surface temperature.
- The carbon dioxide level on Earth has been increasing over the years.
  - Much of the increase is due to the combustion of fuels.
  - We speculate that the increased CO_2 concentration is resulting in a gradual warming of the Earth's surface.
  - Between 2050 and 2100, the CO_2 concentration is expected to be twice the present level.
  - This will result in a global temperature increase of 1-3 °C. (Assuming that we continue to use fossil fuels in the present manner.)

FORWARD REFERENCES
- Other methods of energy production, such as direct methanol fuel cells, will be discussed in Chapter 20 (section 20.7).
- Chemistry of halides will be covered in detail in Chapter 22 (section 22.4).
- Chemistry of oxygen and the depletion of stratospheric ozone will be discussed in Ch. 22 (section 22.5).
- Polluting nature of ozone in the lower atmosphere will be mentioned in Ch. 22 (section 22.5).
- Chemistry of sulfur and the "unclean" fuels leading to air pollution will be discussed in Ch. 22 (section 22.6).
- Chemistry of nitrogen and nitrogen oxides will be discussed in Ch. 22 (section 22.7).

18.3 The Earth's Water

- 72% of the Earth's surface is covered with water.
- Water plays an important role in our environment.
- The properties of water are important.
  - Water exhibits extensive H-bonding (thus, water has a high melting point, a high boiling point, and a high heat capacity).
  - Water is highly polar and can dissolve many ionic and polar-covalent substances.
  - Water may participate in many reactions (e.g., acid-base, redox).

The Global Water Cycle

- All water on Earth is connected in a global water cycle.

---

[25] Figure 18.11 from Transparency Pack
[26] Figure 18.12 from Transparency Pack
[27] "Climate Change" from Further Readings
[28] Figure 18.13 from Transparency Pack
[29] "Water in the Atmosphere" from Further Readings
[30] "Using the Relationship between Vehicle Fuel Consumption and CO_2 Emissions to Illustrate Chemical Principles" from Further Readings

- Water is warmed by the sun.
- Liquid water in the oceans evaporates into the atmosphere as water vapor.
- The water vapor condenses into water droplets.
- Water falls to the ground as water, snow, or rain.

Saltwater: Earth's Oceans and Seas[31]

- The volume of oceans in the world is 1.35×10^9 km^3.
- The oceans contain 97.2% of Earth's water.
- The remainder is primarily in ice caps/glaciers (2.1%) and freshwater sources (0.6%).
- The **salinity** of seawater is defined as the mass (in grams) of dry salts present in 1 kg seawater.
    - Seawater has an average salinity of about 35.
- Most elements in seawater are only present in low concentration.
    - Only NaCl, bromine, and magnesium are currently obtained from seawater in commercially important amounts.

Freshwater and Groundwater

- *Freshwater* : natural waters that have low concentrations of dissolved salts and solids.
    - Includes waters of lakes, rivers, ponds, and streams.
- An adult needs about 2 L of water a day for drinking.
- In the United States, the average person uses about 300 L of freshwater per day.
- Industry uses even more freshwater than this (e.g., about 10^5 L of water is used to make 1000 kg of steel).
- Freshwater is only a small fraction of the total water on Earth.
    - Its source is evaporation of ocean water.
    - The water accumulates as water vapor in the atmosphere.
    - It returns to Earth as rain or snow.
    - After rain and snow falls, the water flows into rivers and dams.
    - As the water flows over the Earth, it dissolves many substances.
    - Freshwater usually contains some ions (Na^+, K^+, Mg^{2+}, Ca^{2+}, Fe^{2+}, Cl^-, SO_4^{2-}, and HCO_3^-) and dissolved gases (O_2, N_2, and CO_2).
- *Groundwater*: accounts for about 20% of the world's freshwater.
    - Groundwater resides in *aquifers (layers of porous rock that holds water).*
        - The chemical composition of groundwater is influenced by the nature of the rock.

18.4 Human Activities and Earth's Water

Dissolved Oxygen and Water Quality[32,33]

- Water fully saturated with air at 1 atm and 20°C has 9 ppm of O_2 dissolved in it.
- Cold-water fish require about 5 ppm of dissolved oxygen for life.
- Aerobic bacteria consume oxygen to oxidize **biodegradable** organic material.
    - Biodegradable materials are *oxygen-demanding wastes.*
    - Examples are sewage, industrial waste from food-processing plants and paper mills, and effluent from meat packing plants.
    - Aerobic bacteria oxidize organic material into CO_2, HCO_3^-, H_2O, NO_3^-, SO_4^{2-}, and phosphates.
- These oxidation reactions may deplete the dissolved oxygen so that aerobic bacteria can no longer survive.

---

[31] Table 18.5 from Transparency Pack
[32] "Acid-Neutralizing Capacity of Lake Beds" from Live Demonstrations
[33] "The Expiration of Respiration: Oxygen—The Missing Ingredient in Many Bodies of Water" from Further Readings

- Anaerobic bacteria then complete the decomposition process forming CH_4, NH_3, H_2S, PH_3, and other foul-smelling products.
- Nitrogen- and phosphorous-containing compounds may simulate excessive growth of aquatic plants.
- *Eutrophication* is the increase in dead and decaying plant matter resulting from excessive plant growth.

Water Purification: Desalination

- Seawater has a salt concentration too high for drinking.
  - Water used for drinking should contain less than 500 ppm dissolved salts (United States municipal water).
- **Desalination** is the removal of salts from seawater or brackish water.
- Common methods for isolation of drinking water include *distillation* (small scale) and **reverse osmosis** (used commercially; small and large scale).
  - Recall that osmosis involves the transport of solvent molecules across a semipermeable membrane.
  - In reverse osmosis, pressure is applied to cause the solvent to move from the more concentrated solution to the more dilute solution.
    - Seawater is introduced under pressure and water passes through the hollow fibers of semipermeable membranes.
    - The water is thus separated from the ions.

Water Purification: Municipal Treatment[34,35]

- There are five steps:
  - Coarse filtration
    - This occurs as water is taken from a lake, river, or reservoir and passed through a screen.
  - Sedimentation
    - Water is allowed to stand so that solid particles (e.g., sand) can settle out.
    - To remove small components (like bacteria), CaO and $Al_2(SO_4)_3$ are added.
      - They cause a gelatinous precipitate of $Al(OH)_3$ to form and settle slowly.
      - As the $Al(OH)_3$ settles, it carries small particles with it.
  - Sand filtration
    - Water is filtered through a sand bed to remove $Al(OH)_3$ and anything it trapped in it.
  - Aeration
    - Air hastens the oxidation of any organic material that may be present.
  - Sterilization using chlorine or ozone to kill bacteria, viruses, and other microorganisms.
    - Both chlorine and ozone are known to generate toxic byproducts.
      - Chlorination of water produces toxic byproducts called *trihalomethanes* (THMs).
        - Some THMs are suspected carcinogens while others interfere with the endocrine system.
      - Ozone may oxidize aqueous bromide, producing bromate ion, another species with cancer-causing potential
      - There are currently no completely satisfactory alternatives to chlorination or ozonation.

---

[34] "A Discovery-Based Experiment Illustrating How Iron Metal Is Used to Remediate Contaminated Groundwater" from Further Readings
[35] Figure 18.20 from Transparency Pack

Water Softening[36]

- Water containing a high concentration of Ca^{2+} and Mg^{2+} and other divalent cations is called **hard water**.
- The presence of these ions may cause the water to be unsuitable for some uses.
  - For example, soaps form an insoluble soap "scum" and water in water heaters forms a deposit (*scale*) via reactions involving the divalent cations.
  - These ions can be removed by a process called *water softening*.
    - Municipal water supplies utilize the **lime-soda process** for large-scale water softening.
      - Water is treated with CaO (lime) and soda ash (Na_2CO_3).
      - They cause the Ca^{2+} and Mg^{2+} to precipitate as $CaCO_3$ and $Mg(OH)_2$.
    - **Ion exchange** is often used for household water softening.
      - The divalent cations are removed and replaced with sodium ions.
      - The sodium ions do not form precipitates.

FORWARD REFERENCES

- The role of water in redox reactions will be discussed throughout Chapter 20.
- Teflon will be mentioned in Chapter 22 (section 22.4).
- Lead chemistry, lead poisoning, and chelating agents will be mentioned in Chapter 23.
- Organic compounds such as ethylene, benzene, and toluene will be discussed in Chapter 24.
- Sodium hypochlorite and chlorine use in water treatment will be further discussed in Chapter 22 (section 22.4).
- The environmental impact of the use of phosphates in fertilizers and detergents will be discussed in Chapter 22 (section 22.8).
- Water hardness will be further discussed in Chapters 22 and 23.

18.5 Green Chemistry[37,38,39,40,41,42]

- 12 basic principles of **green chemistry**: an initiative that promotes the design and application of chemical products and processes that are compatible with human health and that preserve the environment:
  - **1. Prevention**
  - **2. Atom Economy**
  - **3. Less Hazardous Chemical Syntheses**
  - **4. Designing Safer Chemicals**
  - **5. Safer Solvents and Auxiliaries**
  - **6. Design for Energy Efficiency**
  - **7. Use of Renewable Feedstocks**
  - **8. Reduce Derivatives**
  - **9. Catalysis**
  - **10. Design for Degradation**
  - **11. Real-Time Analysis for Pollution Prevention**
  - **12. Inherently Safer Chemistry for Accident Prevention**

---

[36] "The Water Softener–A Relevant, Unifying Example of Many Common Chemical Principles and Calculations" from Further Readings

[37] "Carbon Footprint Calculations: An Application of Chemical Principles" from Further Readings

[38] "Green Chemistry Gets Greener" from Further Readings

[39] "Topics in Green Chemistry" from Further Readings

[40] "Some Exercises Reflecting Green Chemistry Concepts" from Further Readings

[41] "JCE Resources for Chemistry and Recycling" from Further Readings

[42] "Going Green: Lecture Assignments and Lab Experiences for the College Curriculum" from Live Demonstrations

Supercritical Solvents

- The release of toxic volatile solvents to the atmosphere must be avoided.
  - Alternative environmentally friendly methods need to be developed.
  - Examples are:
    - the use of nontoxic supercritical fluids (e.g., CO_2) to replace toxic conventional solvents (e.g., chlorofluorocarbons) in the production of Teflon™.
    - the use of supercritical water in the synthesis of plastics.
- Substitution of an environmentally friendly reagent in place of a particularly toxic reagent should be encouraged.

Greener Reagents and Processes

- Earth-friendly alternatives are being developed for many processes important to modern society.
  - Where possible, synthetic routes are adjusted to result in a high level of 'atom economy":
    - A high percentage of the atoms from the starting materials end up in the product.

Further Readings:

1. N. Colin Baird, "Introducing Atmospheric Reactions: A Systematic Approach for Students," *J. Chem. Educ.*, Vol. 72, **1995**, 153–157.

2. Stephen K. Lower, "Thermal Physics (and Some Chemistry) of the Atmosphere," *J. Chem. Educ.*, Vol. 75, **1998**, 837–840.

3. Sara C. Kerr and Kenneth A. Walz, " 'Holes' in Student Understanding: Addressing Prevalent Misconceptions Regarding Atmospheric Environmental Chemistry," *J. Chem. Educ.*, Vol. 84, **2007**, 1693–1696.

4. Erica K. Jacobsen, "Chemists Celebrate Earth Day 2009: Air—The Sky's the Limit. JCE Resources for Chemistry and the Atmosphere: An Update," *J. Chem. Educ.*, Vol. 86, **2009**, 158–160.

5. Janet Raloff, "Outdoor Carbon Monoxide: Risk to Millions," *Science News*, **October 14, 1995**, 247.

6. N. M. Senozan and J. A Devore, "Carbon Monoxide Poisoning. Some Surprising Aspects of the Equilibrium between Hemoglobin, Carbon Monoxide, and Oxygen," *J. Chem. Educ.*, Vol. 73, **1996**, 767–770.

7. F. Sherwood Rowland and Mario J. Molina, "Ozone Depletion: 20 Years after the Alarm," *Chemical and Engineering News*, **August 15, 1994**, 8–15.

8. Lynn Diener, "News from Online: Stratospheric Chemistry," *J. Chem. Educ.*, Vol. 86, **2009**, 153–155.

9. Muhammad Hanif, "Understanding Ozone," *The Science Teacher*, **December 1995**, 20–23.

10. Otto Klemm, "Local and Regional Ozone: A Student Study Project," *J. Chem. Educ.*, Vol. 78, **2001**, 1641–1646.

11. Lars O. Hedin and Gene E. Likens, "Atmospheric Dust and Acid Rain," *Scientific American*, **December 1996**, 88–92.

12. Jeff Johnson, "Getting to 'Clean Coal'," *Chemical and Engineering News*, **February 23, 2004**, 20–44.

13. A. Elena Charola, "Acid Rain Effects on Stone Monuments," *J. Chem. Educ.*, Vol. 64, **1987**, 436–437.

14. Tina Adler, "The Expiration of Respiration: Oxygen—The Missing Ingredient in Many Bodies of Water," *Science News*, **February 10, 1996**, 88–89.

15. Barbara A. Balko and Paul G Tratnyek, "A Discovery-Based Experiment Illustrating How Iron Metal Is Used to Remediate Contaminated Groundwater," *J. Chem. Educ.*, Vol. 78, **2001**, 1661–1663.

16. Richard S. Treptow, "Carbon Footprint Calculations: An Application of Chemical Principles," *J. Chem. Educ.*, Vol. 87, **2010**, 168–171.

17. Maria T. Oliver-Hoyo and Gabriel Pinto, "Using the Relationship between Vehicle Fuel Consumption and CO_2 Emissions to Illustrate Chemical Principles," *J. Chem. Educ.*, Vol. 85, **2008**, 218–220.

18. Joel M. Kauffman, "Water in the Atmosphere," *J. Chem. Educ.*, Vol. 81, **2004**, 1229–1230.

19. John E. Fulkrod, "The Water Softener—A Relevant, Unifying Example of Many Common Chemical Principles and Calculations," *J. Chem. Educ.*, Vol. 62, **1985**, 529.

20. Mary M. Kirchhoff, "Topics in Green Chemistry," *J. Chem. Educ.*, Vol. 78, **2001**, 1577.

21. Stephan K. Ritter, "Green Chemistry Gets Greener," *Chemical and Engineering News*, **May 20, 2002**, 38–42.

22. Bette Hileman, "Climate Change," *Chemical and Engineering News*, **December 15, 2003**, 27–37.

23. Yu-min Song, Yong-Cheng Want, and Zhi-Yuan Geng, "Some Exercises Reflecting Green Chemistry Concepts," *J. Chem. Educ.*, Vol. 81, **2004**, 691–692.

24. Erica K. Jacobsen, "JCE Resources for Chemistry and Recycling," *J. Chem. Educ.*, Vol. 84, **2007**, 212–213. An annotated bibliography of JCE articles with recycling and/or green chemistry themes.

Live Demonstrations:

1. Bassam Z. Shakhashiri, "Acid-Neutralizing Capacity of Lake Beds," *Chemical Demonstrations: A Handbook for Teachers of Chemistry, Volume 3* (Madison: The University of Wisconsin Press, **1989**), pp. 125–127.

2. Julie A. Haack, James E. Hutchison, Mary M. Kirchhoff, and Irvin J. Levy, "Going Green: Lecture Assignments and Lab Experiences for the College Curriculum," *J. Chem. Educ.*, Vol. 82, **2004**, 974–976. This report includes a listing of various green chemistry experiments from the *Journal of Chemical Education* as well as suggestions for ways to incorporate green chemistry principles into the curriculum.

Chapter 19. Chemical Thermodynamics

Media Resources

Figures and Tables in Transparency Pack:	Section:
Figure 19.4 Reversible Flow of Heat	19.1 Spontaneous Processes
Figure 19.5 An Irreversible Process	19.1 Spontaneous Processes
Figure 19.6 Possible Arrangements of Two Gas Molecules in Two Flasks	19.3 Molecular Interpretation of Entropy
Figure 19.8 Vibrational and Rotational Motions in a Water Molecule	19.3 Molecular Interpretation of Entropy
Figure 19.10 Entropy Changes When an Ionic Solid Dissolves in Water	19.3 Molecular Interpretation of Entropy
Figure 19.13 Entropy Increases with Increasing Temperature	19.3 Molecular Interpretation of Entropy
Table 19.1 Standard Molar Entropies of Selected Substances at 298 K	19.4 Entropy Changes in Chemical Reactions
Figure 19.16 Potential Energy and Free Energy	19.5 Gibbs Free Energy
Figure 19.17 Free Energy and Approaching Equilibrium	19.5 Gibbs Free Energy

Activities:	Section:
Molecular Motions	19.3 Molecular Interpretation of Entropy
Mixing of Gases	19.3 Molecular Interpretation of Entropy
Temperature Dependence of Entropy	19.3 Molecular Interpretation of Entropy
Estimation of Entropy Changes	19.4 Entropy Changes in Chemical Reactions
Free Energy and Reaction Mixture	19.5 Gibbs Free Energy
Gibbs Free Energy	19.6 Free Energy and Temperature
Free Energy and Chemical Equilibrium	19.7 Free Energy and the Equilibrium Constant

Animations:	Section:
Air Bags	19.1 Spontaneous Processes

Movies:	Section:
Formation of Water	19.5 Gibbs Free Energy

3-D Models:	Section:
Oxygen	19.1 Spontaneous Processes
Ice	19.1 Spontaneous Processes
Water	19.3 Molecular Interpretation of Entropy
Methane	19.4 Entropy Changes in Chemical Reactions
Ethane	19.4 Entropy Changes in Chemical Reactions
Propane	19.4 Entropy Changes in Chemical Reactions
Hydrogen	19.5 Gibbs Free Energy
Nitrogen	19.5 Gibbs Free Energy
Ammonia	19.5 Gibbs Free Energy
Sodium Chloride (1 × 1 Unit Cell)	19.7 Free Energy and the Equilibrium Constant

Other Resources

Further Readings:	**Section:**
Demystifying Introductory Chemistry. Part 4: An Approach to Reaction Thermodynamics through Enthalpies, Entropies, and Free Energies of Atomization	19.1 Spontaneous Processes
A Model of Thermal Equilibrium: A Tool for the Introduction of Thermodynamics	19.1 Spontaneous Processes
Thermodynamics and Spontaneity	19.1 Spontaneous Processes
Teaching Entropy Analysis in the First-Year High School Course and Beyond	19.2 Entropy and the Second Law of Thermodynamics
Visualizing Entropy	19.2 Entropy and the Second Law of Thermodynamics
Another Face of Entropy	19.2 Entropy and the Second Law of Thermodynamics
Pictorial Analogies III: Heat Flow, Thermodynamics, and Entropy	19.2 Entropy and the Second Law of Thermodynamics
Order, Chaos, and All That!	19.2 Entropy and the Second Law of Thermodynamics
Entropy: Conceptual Disorder	19.2 Entropy and the Second Law of Thermodynamics
Spontaneous Assembly of Soda Straws	19.2 Entropy and the Second Law of Thermodynamics
Give Them Money: The Boltzmann Game, a Classroom or Laboratory Activity Modeling Entropy Changes and the Distribution of Energy in Chemical Systems	19.3 Molecular Interpretation of Energy
The Boltzmann Distribution	19.3 Molecular Interpretation of Energy
Derivation of the Second Law of Thermodynamics from Boltzmann's Distribution Law	19.3 Molecular Interpretation of Energy
Periodic Trends for the Entropy of Elements	19.4 Entropy Changes in Chemical Reactions
J. Willard Gibbs (1839–1903): A Modern Genius	19.5 Gibbs Free Energy
Josiah Willard Gibbs and Wilhelm Ostwald: A Contrast in Scientific Style	19.5 Gibbs Free Energy
The Free-Energy Prediction and the Principle of Le Châtelier	19.7 Free Energy and the Equilibrium Constant
The Conversion of Chemical Energy. Part 2: Biochemical Examples	19.7 Free Energy and the Equilibrium Constant

Live Demonstrations:	**Section:**
Entropy, Disorder, and Freezing	19.2 Entropy and the Second Law of Thermodynamics
A Chemical Hand Warmer	19.2 Entropy and the Second Law of Thermodynamics

Chapter 19. Chemical Thermodynamics

Common Student Misconceptions

- Students often believe that a spontaneous process should occur very quickly. They do not appreciate the difference between kinetics and thermodynamics.
- Students have a problem distinguishing between absolute thermodynamic quantities and the change in thermodynamic quantities.
- Students often cannot tell the difference between heat and temperature.
- Students often think that only exothermic reactions can be spontaneous.
- Students often forget about the system's surroundings when evaluating changes in thermodynamic quantities, such as entropy.
- Students often do not pay attention to the states of matter (g, l, s) of substances in Appendix C.
- Students often include the temperature of 298 K as part of the standard conditions.

Teaching Tips

- Equation 19.15 is valid only when $\Delta H°$ and $\Delta S°$ do not significantly change with temperature and pressure.
- When $\Delta G°$ is negative, reactions are said to be *exergonic*; when $\Delta G°$ is positive, reactions are said to be *endergonic*.
- Students usually benefit from reviewing logarithms and graphs from Appendix A prior to starting this chapter.

Lecture Outline

19.1 Spontaneous Processes[1,2,3,4]

- *Chemical thermodynamics* is concerned with energy relationships in chemical reactions.
  - We consider enthalpy.
  - We also consider *entropy* in the reaction.
- Recall the first law of thermodynamics: energy is conserved.
$$\Delta E = q + w$$
  - where ΔE is the change in internal energy, q is the heat absorbed by the system from the surroundings, and w is the work done.
- Any process that occurs without outside intervention is a **spontaneous** process.
  - When two eggs are dropped, they spontaneously break.
  - The reverse reaction (two eggs leaping into your hand with their shells back intact) is not spontaneous.
  - We can conclude that a spontaneous process has a direction.
- A process that is spontaneous in one direction is *nonspontaneous* in the opposite direction.
- Temperature may also affect the spontaneity of a process.

---

[1] "Air Bags" Animation from Instructor's Resource CD/DVD
[2] "Demystifying Introductory Chemistry. Part 4: An Approach to Reaction Thermodynamics through Enthalpies, Entropies, and Free Energies of Atomization" from Further Readings
[3] "A Model of Thermal Equilibrium: A Tool for the Introduction of Thermodynamics" from Further Readings
[4] "Thermodynamics and Spontaneity" from Further Readings

Seeking a Criterion for Spontaneity

- To understand why some processes are spontaneous we must look at the ways in which the state of a system might change.
    - Temperature, internal energy, and enthalpy are state functions.
    - Heat transferred between a system and the surroundings, as well as work done on or by a system, are *not* state functions.

Reversible and Irreversible Processes[5,6,7,8]

- A **reversible process** is one that can go back and forth between states along the same path.
    - The reverse process restores the system to its original state.
    - The path taken back to the original state is *exactly* the reverse of the forward process.
    - There is no net change in the system or the surroundings when this cycle is completed.
    - Completely reversible processes are too slow to be attained in practice.
- Consider the interconversion of ice and water at 1 atm, 0 °C.
    - Ice and water are in equilibrium.
    - We now add heat to the system from the surroundings.
        - We melt 1 mole of ice to form 1 mole of liquid water.
            - $q = \Delta H_{fus}$
    - To return to the original state, we reverse the procedure.
        - We remove the same amount of heat from the system to the surroundings.
- An **irreversible process** cannot be reversed to restore the system and surroundings back to their original state.
    - A different path (with different values of q and w) must be taken.
- Consider a gas in a cylinder with a piston.
    - Remove the partition, and the gas expands to fill the space.
    - No P-V work is done on the surroundings.
        - $w = 0$
    - Now use the piston to compress the gas back to the original state.
    - The surroundings must do work on the system.
        - $w > 0$
    - A different path is required to get the system back to its original state.
        - Note that the surroundings are NOT returned to their original conditions.
- For a system at equilibrium, reactants and products can interconvert *reversibly*.
- For a spontaneous process, the path between reactants and products is *irreversible*.
- Consider the expansion of an ideal gas.
- Consider an initial state: two 1-liter flasks connected by a closed stopcock.
    - One flask is evacuated and the other contains 1 atm of gas.
    - We open the stopcock while maintaining the system at constant temperature.
    - Initial state: an ideal gas confined to a cylinder kept at constant temperature in a water bath.
    - The process is **isothermal** at constant temperature.
    - $\Delta E = 0$ for an isothermal process.
    - Thus, $q = -w$.
- Allow the gas to expand from V_1 to V_2.
- Pressure decreases from P_1 to P_2.
    - The final state: two flasks connected by an open stopcock.

---

[5] Figure 19.4 from Transparency Pack
[6] Figure 19.5 from Transparency Pack
[7] "Ice" 3-D Model from Instructor's Resource CD/DVD
[8] "Oxygen" 3-D Model from Instructor's Resource CD/DVD

- • Each flask contains gas at 0.5 atm.
  - • Therefore, the gas does no work and heat is not transferred.
- • Why does the gas expand?
  - • Why is the process spontaneous?
  - • Why is the reverse process nonspontaneous?
  - • When the gas molecules spread out into the 2 liter system there is an increase in the *randomness* or *disorder*.
  - • Processes in which the disorder or entropy of the system increases tend to be spontaneous.

19.2 Entropy and the Second Law of Thermodynamics[9,10,11,12,13,14,15]

Entropy Change

- • **Entropy**, S, is a thermodynamic term that reflects the disorder, or randomness, of the system.
  - • The more disordered, or random, the system is, the larger the value of S.
- • Entropy is a state function.
  - • It is independent of path.
  - • For a system, $\Delta S = S_{final} - S_{initial}$.
- • If $\Delta S > 0$ the randomness increases, if $\Delta S < 0$ the order increases.
- • Suppose a system changes reversibly between state 1 and state 2.
  - • Then, the change in entropy is given by:

$$\Delta S = \frac{q_{rev}}{T}$$

  - • Where q_{rev} is the amount of heat added reversibly to the system.
    - • The subscript "rev" reminds us that the path between states is reversible.
    - • Example: A phase change occurs at constant temperature with the reversible addition of heat.

ΔS for Phase Changes

- • Phase changes (such as melting a substance at its melting point) are isothermal processes.

$$\Delta S_{fusion} = \frac{q_{rev}}{T} = \frac{\Delta H_{fusion}}{T}$$

The Second Law of Thermodynamics[16]

- • The **second law of thermodynamics**:
  - • any irreversible process results in an increase in total entropy while any reversible process results in no overall change in entropy.
  - • This explains why spontaneous processes have a direction.
- • In any spontaneous process, the entropy of the universe increases.
- • The change in entropy of the universe is the sum of the change in entropy of the system and the change in entropy of the surroundings.

$$\Delta S_{univ} = \Delta S_{system} + \Delta S_{surroundings}$$

[9] "Teaching Entropy Analysis in the First-Year High School Course and Beyond" from Further Readings
[10] "Visualizing Entropy" from Further Readings
[11] "Another Face of Entropy" from Further Readings
[12] "Pictorial Analogies III: Heat Flow, Thermodynamics, and Entropy" from Further Readings
[13] "Order, Chaos, and All That!" from Further Readings
[14] "Entropy: Conceptual Disorder" from Further Readings
[15] "Entropy, Disorder, and Freezing" from Live Demonstrations
[16] "Spontaneous Assembly of Soda Straws" from Further Readings

- For a reversible process:

$$\Delta S_{univ} = \Delta S_{system} + \Delta S_{surroundings} = 0$$

- For a spontaneous process (i.e., irreversible):

$$\Delta S_{univ} = \Delta S_{system} + \Delta S_{surroundings} > 0$$

  - Entropy is not conserved: ΔS_{univ} is continually increasing.
- Note that the second law states that the entropy of the universe must increase in a spontaneous process.
  - It is possible for the entropy of a system to decrease as long as the entropy of the surroundings increases.

19.3 Molecular Interpretation of Entropy

Expansion of a Gas at the Molecular Level[17]

- Gas expansion into a vacuum is a spontaneous process.
- Consider two flasks connected by a stopcock.
  - Track the movement of two gas molecules as they move around.
    - Before opening the stopcock: both molecules are confined to the left flask.
    - After opening the stopcock: the molecules move randomly throughout the entire apparatus.
    - Since the molecular motion is random, all four of the arrangements are equally likely.
      - The probability of finding both molecules in the left flask is $(1/2)^2$.
    - What if we had three molecules?
      - The probability of finding all three in the same flask is $(1/2)^3$.
    - What if we had a *mole* of gas molecules?
      - The probability is now $(1/2)^N$ where N is 6.02×10^{23}!
      - There is essentially zero likelihood that all of the gas molecules will be in the same flask at the same time.
      - When the gas spreads throughout the system, any given molecule can be in either flask rather than confined to the left flask.
      - The arrangement is more random or disordered than when the molecules are all confined to the left flask.

Boltzmann's Equation and Microstates[18,19,20,21,22]

- *Statistical thermodynamics* is a field that uses statistics and probability to link the microscopic and macroscopic worlds.
  - Entropy may be connected to the behavior of atoms and molecules.
  - Envision a **microstate**: a snapshot of the positions and speeds of all molecules in a sample of a particular macroscopic state at a given point in time.
  - Consider a molecule of ideal gas at a given temperature and volume.
    - A microstate is a single possible arrangement of the positions and kinetic energies of the gas molecules.
    - Other snapshots are possible (different microstates).
- Each thermodynamic state has a characteristic number of microstates (W).

---

[17] Figure 19.6 from Transparency Pack

[18] "Derivation of the Second Law of Thermodynamics from Botlzmann's Distribution Law" from Further Readings

[19] "Give Them Money: The Boltzmann Game, a Classroom or Laboratory Activity Modeling Entropy Changes and the Distribution of Energy in Chemical Systems" from Further Readings

[20] "The Boltzmann Distribution" from Further Readings

[21] Figure 19.8 from Transparency Pack

[22] "Mixing of Gases" Activity from Instructor's Resource CD/DVD

- The Boltzmann equation shows how entropy (S) relates to W.
  $$S = k \ln W, \text{ where } k \text{ is Boltzmann's constant } (1.38 \times 10^{-23} \text{ J/K}).$$
- Entropy is thus a measure of how many microstates are associated with a particular macroscopic state.
- Any change in the system that increases the number of microstates gives a positive value of ΔS and vice versa.
  - In general, the number of microstates will increase with an increase in volume, an increase in temperature, or an increase in the number of molecules because any of these changes increases the possible positions and energies of the molecules.

Molecular Motions and Energy[23,24]

- When a substance is heated, the motion of its molecule increases.
  - The higher the temperature, the faster the molecules move.
  - Hotter systems have *broader distribution* of molecular speeds.
  - Consider a sample of ideal gas.
    - The molecules move around the container.
    - They also show three kinds of more complex motion:
      - **translational motion**
        - The moving of a molecule from one point in space to another.
      - **vibrational motion**
        - The shortening and lengthening of bonds, including the change in bond angles.
      - **rotational motion**
        - The spinning of a molecule about some axis.
  - Energy is required to get a molecule to translate, vibrate, or rotate.
    - These forms of motion are ways molecules can store energy (*motional energy*).
    - The more energy stored in translation, vibration, and rotation, the greater the entropy.
- In general:
  - The number of microstates possible for a system increases with an increase in volume, temperature, or the number of molecules.
  - Each of these changes increases the possible positions and kinetic energies of the molecules in the system.

Making Qualitative Predictions About ΔS[25]

- In most cases, an increase in the number of microstates (and thus entropy) parallels an increase in:
  - temperature
  - volume
  - number of independently moving particles.
- Consider the melting of ice.
  - In ice, the molecules are held rigidly in a lattice.
  - When it melts, the molecules will have more freedom to move (increases the number of degrees of freedom).
  - The molecules are more randomly distributed.
- Consider a KCl crystal dissolving in water.
  - The solid KCl has ions in a highly ordered arrangement.
  - When the crystal dissolves, the ions have more freedom.
  - They are more randomly distributed.
  - However, now the water molecules are more ordered.

---

[23] "Molecular Motions" Activity from Instructor's Resource CD/DVD

[24] "Water" 3-D Model from Instructor's Resource CD/DVD

[25] Figure 19.10 from Transparency Pack

- Some must be used to hydrate the ions.
  - Thus this example involves both ordering and disordering.
  - The disordering usually predominates (for most salts).
- Consider the reaction of $NO(g)$ with $O_2(g)$ to form $NO_2(g)$:

$$2NO(g) + O_2(g) \rightarrow 2NO_2(g)$$

  - The total number of gas molecules decreases.
    - Therefore, the entropy decreases.
  - How can we relate changes in entropy to changes at the molecular level?
    - Formation of the new N-O bonds "tie up" more of the atoms in the products than in the reactants.
    - The *degrees of freedom* associated with the atoms have changed.
    - The greater the freedom of movement and degrees of freedom, the greater the entropy of the system.
  - Individual molecules have degrees of freedom associated with motions within the molecule.
- In general, entropy will increase when:
  - liquids or solutions are formed from solids,
  - gases are formed from solids or liquids, or
  - the number of gas molecules increases.

The Third Law of Thermodynamics[26,27]

- In a perfect crystal at 0 K there is no translation, rotation, or vibration of molecules.
  - Therefore, this is a state of perfect order.
  - **Third law of thermodynamics**: The entropy of a perfect pure crystal at 0 K is zero.
- Entropy will increase as we increase the temperature of the perfect crystal.
  - Molecules gain vibrational motion.
  - The degrees of freedom increase.
- As we heat a substance from absolute zero, the entropy must increase.
- The entropy changes dramatically at a phase change.
  - When a solid melts, the molecules and atoms have a large increase in freedom of movement.
  - Boiling corresponds to a much greater change in entropy than melting.

19.4 Entropy Changes in Chemical Reactions[28,29,30,31,32,33]

- Absolute entropy can be determined from complicated measurements.
  - Values are based on a reference point of zero for a perfect crystalline solid at 0K (the 3rd law).
- **Standard molar entropy, $S°$** is the molar entropy of a substance in its standard state.
  - Similar in concept to $\Delta H°$.
  - Units: J/mol-K.
    - Note that the units of ΔH are kJ/mol.
- Some observations about $S°$ values:
  - Standard molar entropies of elements are not zero.
  - $S°_{gas} > S°_{liquid}$ or $S°_{solid}$.
  - $S°$ tends to increase with increasing molar mass of the substance.

---

[26] "Temperature Dependence of Entropy" Activity from Instructor's Resource CD/DVD
[27] Figure 19.13 from Transparency Pack
[28] Table 19.1 from Transparency Pack
[29] "Periodic Trends for the Entropy of Elements" from Further Readings
[30] "Estimation of Entropy Changes" Activity from Instructor's Resource CD/DVD
[31] "Methane" 3-D Model from Instructor's Resource CD/DVD
[32] "Ethane" 3-D Model from Instructor's Resource CD/DVD
[33] "Propane" 3-D Model from Instructor's Resource CD/DVD

- $S°$ tends to increase with the number of atoms in the formula of the substance.
- For a chemical reaction that produces n products from m reactants:

$$\Delta S° = \sum nS°(\text{products}) - \sum mS°(\text{reactants})$$

- Example: Consider the reaction:

$$N_2(g) + 3H_2(g) \rightarrow 2NH_3(g)$$
$$\Delta S° = 2S°(NH_3) - [S°(N_2) + 3S°(H_2)]$$

Entropy Changes in the Surroundings

- For an isothermal process,
  - $$\Delta S_{surr} = \frac{q_{sys}}{T}$$
- For a reaction at constant pressure,
  - $q_{sys} = \Delta H$
- Example: consider the reaction:

$$N_2(g) + 3H_2(g) \rightarrow 2NH_3(g)$$

- The entropy gained by the surroundings is greater than the entropy lost by the system.
- This is the sign of a spontaneous reaction: the overall entropy change of the universe is positive.
- $\Delta S_{univ} > 0$

19.5 Gibbs Free Energy[34,35,36,37,38,39,40,41,42]

- For a spontaneous reaction the entropy of the universe must increase.
- Reactions with large negative ΔH values *tend* to be spontaneous.
- How can we use ΔS and ΔH to predict whether a reaction is spontaneous?
- The **Gibbs free energy, (free energy)**, G, of a state is:
$$G = H - TS$$
  - Free energy is a state function.
  - For a process occurring at constant temperature, the free energy change is:
$$\Delta G = \Delta H - T\Delta S$$
- Recall:
  - $\Delta S_{univ} = \Delta S_{sys} + \Delta S_{surr} = \Delta S_{sys} + [-\Delta H_{sys} / T]$
    - Thus,
      - $-T\Delta S_{univ} = \Delta H_{sys} - T\Delta S_{sys}$
- The sign of ΔG is important in predicting the spontaneity of the reaction at T, p = constant.
  - If $\Delta G < 0$ then the forward reaction is spontaneous.
  - If $\Delta G = 0$ then the reaction is at equilibrium and no net reaction will occur.
  - If $\Delta G > 0$ then the forward reaction is not spontaneous.
    - However, the reverse reaction is spontaneous.
    - If $\Delta G > 0$, work must be supplied from the surroundings to drive the reaction.

---

[34] "Josiah Willard Gibbs and Wilhelm Ostwald: A Contrast in Scientific Style" from Further Readings
[35] "J. Willard Gibbs (1839–1903): A Modern Genius" from Further Readings
[36] Figure 19.16 from Transparency Pack
[37] Figure 19.17 from Transparency Pack
[38] "Free Energy and Reaction Mixture" Activity from Instructor's Resource CD/DVD
[39] "Formation of Water" Movie from Instructor's Resource CD/DVD
[40] "Hydrogen" 3-D Model from Instructor's Resource CD/DVD
[41] "Nitrogen" 3-D Model from Instructor's Resource CD/DVD
[42] "Ammonia" 3-D Model from Instructor's Resource CD/DVD

- The equilibrium position in a spontaneous process is given by the minimum free energy available to the system.
  - The free energy decreases until it reaches this minimum value.

Standard Free-Energy Changes

- We can tabulate **standard free energies of formation**, $\Delta G°_f$.
  - Standard states are pure solid, pure liquid, 1 atm (gas), 1 M concentration (solution), and $\Delta G°_f = 0$ for elements.
    - We most often use 25 °C (or 298 K) as the temperature.
  - The standard free-energy change for a process is given by:

$$\Delta G° = \sum n\Delta G°_f \left(\text{products}\right) - \sum m\Delta G°_f \left(\text{reactants}\right)$$

  - The quantity $\Delta G°$ for a reaction tells us whether a mixture of substances will spontaneously react to produce more reactants ($\Delta G° > 0$) or products ($\Delta G° < 0$).

FORWARD REFERENCES
- Standard conditions (Table 19.3) will be brought up throughout Chapter 20.
- ΔG as a measure of reaction spontaneity will be linked to the cell potential in Chapter 20 (section 20.5).
- Entropy of the chelate effect will be further discussed in Chapter 23 (section 23.3).

19.6 Free Energy and Temperature[43]

- The sign of ΔG tells us if the reaction is spontaneous, at a given temperature and pressure condition.
- Focus on $\Delta G = \Delta H - T\Delta S$.
  - If $\Delta H < 0$ and $-T\Delta S < 0$:
    - ΔG will always be < 0.
    - Thus the reaction will be spontaneous.
  - If $\Delta H > 0$ and $-T\Delta S > 0$:
    - ΔG will always be > 0.
    - Thus, the reaction will not be spontaneous.
  - If ΔH and $-T\Delta S$ have different signs:
    - The sign of ΔG will depend on the sign and magnitudes of the other terms.
    - Temperature will be an important factor.
  - For example, consider the following reaction:
$$H_2O(s) \rightarrow H_2O(l) \qquad \Delta H > 0, \Delta S > 0$$
    - At a temperature less than 0 °C:
      - $\Delta H > T\Delta S$
      - $\Delta G > 0$
      - The melting of ice is not spontaneous when the temperature is less than 0 °C.
    - At a temperature greater than 0 °C:
      - $\Delta H < T\Delta S$
      - $\Delta G < 0$
      - The melting of ice is spontaneous when the temperature is greater than 0 °C.
    - At 0 °C:
      - $\Delta H = T\Delta S$
      - $\Delta G = 0$
      - Ice and water are in equilibrium at 0 °C.
- Note that we have assumed that both $\Delta H°$ and $\Delta S°$ were independent of temperature; they aren't, but the changes are negligible.
- Even though a reaction has a negative ΔG, it may occur too slowly to be observed.

---

[43] "Gibbs Free Energy" Activity from Instructor's Resource CD/DVD

- Thermodynamics gives us the direction of a spontaneous process; it does not give us the rate of the process.

19.7 Free Energy and the Equilibrium Constant[44,45,46,47]

Free Energy Under Nonstandard Conditions

- Recall that $\Delta G°$ and K_{eq} (equilibrium constant) apply to *standard conditions*.
- Recall that ΔG and Q (equilibrium quotient) apply to *any conditions*.
- It is useful to determine whether substances will react under specific conditions:

$$\Delta G = \Delta G° + RT\ln Q$$

Relationship Between $\Delta G°$ and K

- At equilibrium, $Q = K_{eq}$ and $\Delta G = 0$, so:

$$\Delta G = \Delta G° + RT\ln Q$$
$$0 = \Delta G° + RT\ln K$$
$$\therefore \Delta G° = - RT\ln K$$

Thus we see a relationship between free energy and the equilibrium constant:

$$K = e^{-\Delta G° / RT}$$

- From the above we can conclude:
  - If $\Delta G° < 0$, then $K > 1$.
  - If $\Delta G° = 0$, then $K = 1$.
  - If $\Delta G° > 0$, then $K < 1$.

Driving Nonspontaneous Reactions

- If $\Delta G > 0$, work must be supplied from the surroundings to drive the reaction.
- Biological systems often use one *spontaneous* reaction to drive another *nonspontaneous* reaction.
  - These reactions are *coupled reactions*.
- The energy required to drive most nonspontaneous reactions comes from the metabolism of foods.
  - Example: Consider the oxidation of glucose:

$$C_6H_{12}O_6(s) + 6O_2(g) \rightarrow 6CO_2(g) + 6H_2O(l) \qquad \Delta G° = -2880 \text{ kJ}.$$

  - The free energy released by glucose oxidation is used to convert low energy adenosine diphosphate (ADP) and inorganic phosphate into high energy adenosine triphosphate (ATP).
- When ATP is converted back to ADP the energy released may be used to "drive" other reactions.

FORWARD REFERENCES

- Units of Gibb's free energy change in calculations linking ΔG with the cell potential will be discussed in Chapter 20 (section 20.5).
- Gibb's free energy change will be used to derive the Nernst equation in Chapter 20 (section 20.6).
- Equation 19.17 will be used in Chapter 22 (section 22.5) to calculate the equilibrium constant for reactions involving oxygen.
- Energy released by ATP→ADP reaction can be used to perform mechanical work in muscle contraction and drive biochemical reactions (Chapter 22, section 22.8).

---

[44] "The Free Energy Prediction and the Principle of Le Châtelier" from Further Readings
[45] "Free Energy and Chemical Equilibrium" Activity from Instructor's Resource CD/DVD
[46] "The Conversion of Chemical Energy. Part 2: Biochemical Examples" from Further Readings
[47] "Sodium Chloride (1 × 1 Unit Cell)" 3-D Model from Instructor's Resource CD/DVD

Further Readings:

1. James N. Spencer, Richard S. Moog, and Ronald J. Gillespie, "Demystifying Introductory Chemistry. Part 4: An Approach to Reaction Thermodynamics through Enthalpies, Entropies, and Free Energies of Atomization," *J. Chem. Educ.*, Vol. 73, **1996**, 631–636.

2. Raymond S. Ochs, "Thermodynamics and Spontaneity," *J. Chem. Educ.*, Vol. 73, **1996**, 952–954.

3. Ruth Ben-Zvi, Judith Silberstein, and Rachel Mamiok, "A Model of Thermal Equilibrium: A Tool for the Introduction of Thermodynamics," *J. Chem. Educ.*, Vol. 70, **1993**, 31–34.

4. Thomas H. Bindel, "Teaching Entropy Analysis in the First-Year High School Course and Beyond," *J. Chem. Educ.*, Vol. 81, **2004**, 1585–1594.

5. Joseph H. Lechner, "Visualizing Entropy," *J. Chem. Educ.*, Vol. 76, **1999**, 1382–1387.

6. Peter Weiss, "Another Face of Entropy," *Science News*, Vol. 154, **August 15, 1998**, 108–109.

7. John J. Fortman, "Pictorial Analogies III: Heat Flow, Thermodynamics, and Entropy," *J. Chem. Educ.*, Vol. 70, **1993**, 102–103.

8. L. Glasser, "Order, Chaos, and All That!" *J. Chem. Educ.*, Vol. 66, **1989**, 997–1001.

9. John P. Lowe, "Entropy: Conceptual Disorder," *J. Chem. Educ.*, Vol. 65, **1988**, 403–406.

10. D. J. Campbell, E. R. Freidinger, J. M. Hastings, and M. K. Querns, "Spontaneous Assembly of Soda Straws," *J. Chem. Educ.*, Vol. 17, **2002**, 201–202.

11. Robert M. Hanson and Bridget Michalek, "Give Them Money: The Boltzmann Game, a Classroom or Laboratory Activity Modeling Entropy Changes and the Distribution of Energy in Chemical Systems," *J. Chem. Educ.*, Vol. 83, **2006**, 581–588.

12. P. G. Nelson, "Derivation of the Second Law of Thermodynamics from Boltzmann's Distribution Law," *J. Chem. Educ.*, Vol. 65, **1989**, 390–393.

13. Douglas K. Russell, "The Boltzmann Distribution," *J. Chem. Educ.*, Vol. 73, **1996**, 299–300.

14. Travis Thoms, "Periodic Trends for the Entropy of Elements," *J. Chem. Educ.*, Vol. 72, **1995**, 16.

15. Sidney Rosen, "J. Willard Gibbs (1839–1903): A Modern Genius," *J. Chem. Educ.*, Vol. 60, **1983**, 593–594.

16. Robert J. Deltete and David L. Thorsell, "Josiah Willard Gibbs and Wilhelm Ostwald: A Contrast in Scientific Style," *J. Chem. Educ.*, Vol. 73, **1996**, 289–295.

17. Zheng Xianmin, "The Free Energy Prediction and the Principle of Le Châtelier," *J. Chem. Educ.*, Vol. 66, **1989**, 401–402.

18. Donald J. Wink, "The Conversion of Chemical Energy. Part 2: Biochemical Examples," *J. Chem. Educ.*, Vol. 69, **1992**, 264–267.

Live Demonstrations:

1. Lee R. Summerlin, Christie L. Borgford, and Julie B. Ealy, "A Chemical Hand Warmer," *Chemical Demonstrations: A Sourcebook for Teachers, Volume 2* (Washington: American Chemical Society, **1988**), pp. 99–100.

2. Brian B. Laird, "Entropy, Disorder, and Freezing," *J. Chem. Educ.*, Vol. 76, **1999**, 1388–1390.

Chapter 20. Electrochemistry

Media Resources

Figures and Tables in Transparency Pack:	**Section:**
Figure 20.5 A Voltaic Cell that Uses a Salt Bridge to Complete the Electrical Circuit	20.3 Voltaic Cells
Figure 20.9 A Voltaic Cell Using a Standard Hydrogen Electrode (SHE)	20.4 Cell Potentials Under Standard Conditions
Table 20.1 Standard Reduction Potentials in Water at 25 °C	20.4 Cell Potentials Under Standard Conditions
Figure 20.12 Relative Strengths of Oxidizing and Reducing Agents	20.4 Cell Potentials Under Standard Conditions
Figure 20.19 A 12-V Automotive Lead-Acid Battery	20.7 Batteries and Fuel Cells
Figure 20.22 Corrosion of Iron in Contact with Water	20.8 Corrosion
Figure 20.23 Cathodic Protection of Iron in Contact with Zinc	20.8 Corrosion
Figure 20.25 Electrolysis of Molten Sodium Chloride	20.9 Electrolysis
Figure 20.27 Relationship Between Charge and Amount of Reactant and Product in Electrolysis Reactions	20.9 Electrolysis

Activities:	**Section:**
Balancing Redox Equations in Acid	20.2 Balancing Redox Equations
Balancing Redox Equations in Base	20.2 Balancing Redox Equations
Nernst Equation	20.6 Cell Potentials Under Nonstandard Conditions
Batteries	20.7 Batteries and Fuel Cells
Electrolysis	20.9 Electrolysis
Electrolysis Calculation Example	20.9 Electrolysis
Prevention of Corrosion	20.8 Corrosion

Animations:	**Section:**
Oxidation-Reduction Reactions—Part I	20.1 Oxidation States and Oxidation Reduction Reactions
Oxidation-Reduction Reactions—Part II	20.1 Oxidation States and Oxidation Reduction Reactions
Voltaic Cells I: The Copper-Zinc Cell	20.3 Voltaic Cells
Voltaic Cells II: The Zinc-Hydrogen Cell	20.4 Cell Potentials Under Standard Conditions
Standard Reduction Potential	20.4 Cell Potentials Under Standard Conditions

Movies:	**Section:**
Redox Chemistry of Iron and Copper	20.3 Voltaic Cells
Formation of Silver Crystals	20.3 Voltaic Cells
Electroplating	20.9 Electrolysis

3-D Models:
Hydronium Ion
Hydrogen

Section:
20.2 Balancing Redox Equations
20.7 Batteries and Fuel Cells

Other Resources

Further Readings:	**Section:**
Redox Balancing without Puzzling	20.2 Balancing Redox Equations
Ask the Historian: Balancing Redox Equations	20.2 Balancing Redox Equations
Common Student Misconceptions in Electrochemistry: Galvanic, Electrolytic and Concentration Cells"	20.3 Voltaic Cells
Alleviating the Common Confusion Caused by Polarity in Electrochemistry	20.3 Voltaic Cells
Electrochemical Errors	20.3 Voltaic Cells
Dental Filling Discomforts Illustrate Electrochemical Potentials of Metals	20.3 Voltaic Cells
Using a Teaching Model to Correct Known Misconceptions in Electrochemistry	20.3 Voltaic Cells
Using the Biological Cell in Teaching Electrochemistry	20.6 Cell Potentials Under Nonstandard Conditions
Batteries: Full Speed Ahead	20.7 Batteries and Fuel Cells
Structure and Content of Some Primary Batteries	20.7 Batteries and Fuel Cells
Time to Recharge	20.7 Batteries and Fuel Cells
Lithium Batteries: A Practical Application of Chemical Principles	20.7 Batteries and Fuel Cells
Batteries, from Cradle to Grave	20.7 Batteries and Fuel Cells
Vehicle of Change	20.7 Batteries and Fuel Cells
Evaluation of Corrosion Susceptibility of a Metal: Student Corrosion Experiment II	20.8 Corrosion

Live Demonstrations:	**Section:**
Visible Oxidation-Reduction in Electrochemical Cells	20.3 Voltaic Cells
Activity Series for Some Metals	20.5 Free Energy and Redox Reactions
An Activity Series: Zinc, Copper, and Silver Half Cells	20.5 Free Energy and Redox Reactions
Making a Simple Battery: The Gerber Cell	20.7 Batteries and Fuel Cells
Electrolytic Cells in Series: A Red, White, and Blue Electrolysis	20.9 Electrolysis
Floating Pennies	20.9 Electrolysis
Electroplating Copper	20.9 Electrolysis

Chapter 20. Electrochemistry

Common Student Misconceptions
- Students often think that *oxidation* must necessarily mean *adding oxygen*.
- Students often have trouble balancing redox equations.
- Students often think that pure polar solvents, such as water, conduct electricity.
- Students commonly think that electrons flow through the salt-bridge (or the porous barrier) and through solutions.
- Students often do not consider water as a participant in the redox reactions.
- Students often think that, since individual electrode potentials cannot be measured, there are no processes taking place when a metal is immersed in an electrolyte.
- Many students think that a measured potential for a galvanic cell cannot be negative; it can, in which case one can re-connect the leads of the voltmeter to the opposite electrodes and obtain a positive reading.
- Students often think that cell potentials are independent of concentrations (and pressures) of ions (and gases) in the electrochemical reaction.
- Students find it difficult to understand that electrochemical potentials are relative in nature.
- Students often do not realize that electrochemical processes can be viewed as reversible; this allows us to make a connection between $E°_{cell}$, $\Delta G°$, and K.

Teaching Tips
- Students should be encouraged to review section 4.4.
- Many authors have suggested mnemonics for oxidation and reduction. One of the most common is "*LEO goes GER*," for lose electrons = oxidation and gain electrons = reduction.
- One of the most frequent errors students make when balancing redox reactions by the method of half-reactions is to incorrectly count up the charges on each side of the reaction.

Lecture Outline

20.1 Oxidation States and Oxidation-Reduction Reactions[1,2]
- Chemical reactions in which the oxidation state of one or more substances change are called **oxidation-reduction reactions** (*redox reactions*).
  - Recall:
    - Oxidation involves loss of electrons (OIL).
    - Reduction involves gain of electrons (RIG).
  - Also:
    - Oxidation involves an *increase* of an oxidation number.
    - Reduction involves a *decrease* of an oxidation number.
- **Electrochemistry** is the branch of chemistry that deals with relationships between electricity and chemical reactions.
- Consider the spontaneous reaction that occurs when Zn is added to HCl.
$$Zn(s) + 2H^+(aq) \rightarrow Zn^{2+}(aq) + H_2(g)$$
  - The oxidation numbers of Zn and H^+ have changed.
    - The oxidation number of Zn has increased from 0 to +2.

---

[1] "Oxidation-Reduction Reactions—Part I" Animation from Instructor's Resource CD/DVD
[2] "Oxidation-Reduction Reactions—Part II" Animation from Instructor's Resource CD/DVD

- The oxidation number of H has decreased from +1 to 0.
  - Therefore, Zn is oxidized to Zn^{2+}, while H^+ is reduced to H_2.
- H^+ causes Zn to be oxidized.
  - Thus, H^+ is the **oxidizing agent**, or **oxidant**.
- Zn causes H^+ to be reduced.
  - Thus, Zn is the **reducing agent**, or **reductant**.
- Note that the reducing agent is oxidized and the oxidizing agent is reduced.

FORWARD REFERENCES
- Oxidation numbers of transition metals will be covered again in Chapters 23 (section 23.1) for metal complexes.

20.2 Balancing Redox Equations[3,4]

- Recall the *law of conservation of mass*: The amount of each element present at the beginning of the reaction must be present at the end.
- *Conservation of charge*: Electrons are not lost in a chemical reaction.
- Some redox equations may be easily balanced by inspection.
  - However, for many redox reactions we need to look carefully at the transfer of electrons.

Half-Reactions

- **Half-reactions** are a convenient way of separating oxidation and reduction reactions.
- Consider the reaction:
$$Sn^{2+}(aq) + 2Fe^{3+}(aq) \rightarrow Sn^{4+}(aq) + 2Fe^{2+}(aq)$$
- The oxidation half-reaction is:
$$Sn^{2+}(aq) \rightarrow Sn^{4+}(aq) + 2e^-$$
  - Note that electrons are a product here.
- The reduction half-reaction is:
$$2Fe^{3+}(aq) + 2e^- \rightarrow 2Fe^{2+}(aq)$$
  - Note that electrons are a reactant here. These are the same two electrons as in the oxidation half-reaction above.

Balancing Equations by the Method of Half-Reactions[5,6]

- Consider the titration of an acidic solution of $Na_2C_2O_4$ (sodium oxalate, colorless) with $KMnO_4$ (deep purple).
  - MnO_4^- is reduced to Mn^{2+} (pale pink), while the $C_2O_4^{2-}$ is oxidized to CO_2.
  - The equivalence point is indicated by the presence of a pale pink color.
  - If more $KMnO_4$ is added, the solution turns purple due to the excess $KMnO_4$.
- What is the balanced chemical equation for this reaction?
- We can determine this using the method of half-reactions:
  - Write down the two incomplete half reactions.
$$MnO_4^-(aq) \rightarrow Mn^{2+}(aq)$$
$$C_2O_4^{2-}(aq) \rightarrow CO_2(g)$$
  - Balance each half reaction.
    - First, balance elements other than H and O.
$$MnO_4^-(aq) \rightarrow Mn^{2+}(aq)$$
$$C_2O_4^{2-}(aq) \rightarrow 2CO_2(g)$$
  - Then balance O by adding water.

[3] "Redox Balancing without Puzzling" from Further Readings
[4] "Ask the Historian: Balancing Redox Equations" from Further Readings
[5] "Balancing Redox Equations in Acid" Activity from Instructor's Resource CD/DVD
[6] "Hydronium Ion" 3-D Model from Instructor's Resource CD/DVD

$$MnO_4^- (aq) \rightarrow Mn^{2+}(aq) + 4H_2O(l)$$
$$C_2O_4^{2-} (aq) \rightarrow 2CO_2(g)$$

- Then balance H by adding H^+.

$$8H^+(aq) + MnO_4^- (aq) \rightarrow Mn^{2+}(aq) + 4H_2O(l)$$
$$C_2O_4^{2-} (aq) \rightarrow 2CO_2(g)$$

- Finish by balancing charge by adding electrons.
    - This is an easy place to make an error!
        - For the permanganate half-reaction, note that there is a charge of 7+ on the left and 2+ on the right.
        - Therefore, 5 electrons need to be added to the left:

$$5e^- + 8H^+(aq) + MnO_4^- (aq) \rightarrow Mn^{2+}(aq) + 4H_2O(l)$$

        - In the oxalate half-reaction, there is a 2– charge on the left and a 0 charge on the right, so we need to add two electrons to the products:

$$C_2O_4^{2-} (aq) \rightarrow 2CO_2(g) + 2e^-$$

- Multiply each half-reaction to make the number of electrons equal.
    - To balance the 5 electrons for permanganate and 2 electrons for oxalate, we need 10 electrons for both.
        - Multiplying gives:

$$10e^- + 16H^+(aq) + 2MnO_4^- (aq) \rightarrow 2Mn^{2+}(aq) + 8H_2O(l)$$
$$5C_2O_4^{2-} (aq) \rightarrow 10CO_2(g) + 10e^-$$

- Now add the reactions and simplify.

$$16H^+(aq) + 2MnO_4^- (aq) + 5C_2O_4^{2-} (aq) \rightarrow 2Mn^{2+}(aq) + 8H_2O(l) + 10CO_2(g)$$

- The equation is now balanced!
- Note that all of the electrons have cancelled out!

Balancing Equations for Reactions Occurring in Basic Solution[7]
- The same method as above is used, but OH^- is added to "neutralize" the H^+ used.
- The equation must again be simplified by canceling like terms on both sides of the equation.

FORWARD REFERENCES
- Redox reactions involving transition metals will be covered in Chapter 23 (section 23.1).

20.3 Voltaic Cells[8,9,10,11,12,13,14,15,16,17]

- The energy released in a spontaneous redox reaction may be used to perform electrical work.
- **Voltaic**, or **galvanic cells**, are devices in which electron transfer occurs via an external circuit.
- Voltaic cells utilize spontaneous reactions.
- If a strip of Zn is placed in a solution of $CuSO_4$, Cu is deposited on the Zn and the Zn dissolves by forming Zn^{2+}.

---

[7] "Balancing Redox Equations in Base" Activity from Instructor's Resource CD/DVD
[8] "Common Student Misconceptions in Electrochemistry: Galvanic, Electrolytic and Concentration Cells" from Further Readings
[9] "Alleviating the Common Confusion Caused by Polarity in Electrochemistry" from Further Readings
[10] "Voltaic Cells I: The Copper-Zinc Cell" Animation from Instructor's Resource CD/DVD
[11] "Visible Oxidation-Reduction in Electrochemical Cells" from Live Demonstrations
[12] "Redox Chemistry of Iron and Copper" Movie from Instructor's Resource CD/DVD
[13] "Formation of Silver Crystals" Movie from Instructor's Resource CD/DVD
[14] Figure 20.5 from Transparency Pack
[15] "Electrochemical Errors" from Further Readings
[16] "Dental Filling Discomforts Illustrate Electrochemical Potentials of Metals" from Further Readings
[17] "Using a Teaching Model to Correct Known Misconceptions in Electrochemistry" from Further Readings

$$Zn(s) + Cu^{2+}(aq) \rightarrow Zn^{2+}(aq) + Cu(s)$$

- Zn is spontaneously oxidized to Zn^{2+} by Cu^{2+}.
- The Cu^{2+} is spontaneously reduced to Cu^0 by Zn.
- The entire process is spontaneous.
- Each of the two compartments of a voltaic cell is called a *half-cell*.
- This voltaic cells consists of:
  - The two solid metals are the *electrodes* (cathode and anode).
  - An oxidation half-reaction:
    $$Zn(s) \rightarrow Zn^{2+}(aq) + 2e^-$$
    - Oxidation takes place at the **anode**.
  - A reduction half-reaction:
    $$Cu^{2+}(aq) + 2e^- \rightarrow Cu(s)$$
    - Reduction takes place at the **cathode**.
  - As oxidation occurs, Zn is converted to Zn^{2+} and $2e^-$.
    - The electrons flow toward the cathode where they are used in the reduction reaction.
  - We expect the Zn electrode to lose mass and the Cu electrode to gain mass.
- Electrons flow from the anode to the cathode.
  - Therefore, the anode is negative and the cathode is positive.
  - Electrons cannot flow through the solution; they have to be transported through an external wire.
- Anions and cations move through a porous barrier,, or a *salt bridge*.
  - A salt bridge is filled with a saturated solution of an electrolyte and is used to maintain the electrical neutrality of the solutions in both half-cells.
    - Cations from the salt bridge electrolyte move towards the cathode to neutralize the excess of negatively charged ions
      (Cathode: $Cu^{2+} + 2e^- \rightarrow Cu$, so the counter ion of Cu, e.g., NO_3^-, is in excess).
    - Anions from the salt bridge electrolyte move towards the anode to neutralize the excess Zn^{2+} ions formed by oxidation.

20.4 Cell Potentials Under Standard Conditions

- The flow of electrons from anode to cathode is spontaneous.
  - What is the "driving force"?
- Electrons flow from anode to cathode because the cathode has a lower electrical potential energy than the anode.
  - *Potential difference* is the difference in electrical potential.
  - The potential difference is measured in volts.
  - One volt (V) is the potential difference required to impart one joule (J) of energy to a charge of one coulomb (C):
    $$1V = 1\frac{J}{C}$$
  - **Electromotive force (emf)** is the force required to push electrons through the external circuit.
    - **Cell potential:** E_{cell} is the emf of a cell.
      - This is known as the *cell voltage*.
      - E_{cell} is > 0 for a spontaneous reaction.
- For $1M$ solutions or 1 atm pressure for gases at 25°C (standard conditions), the **standard emf (standard cell potential)** is called $E°_{cell}$.
  - For example, for the reaction:
    $$Zn(s) + Cu^{2+}(aq) \rightarrow Zn^{2+}(aq) + Cu(s)$$
    - $E°_{cell} = +1.10$ V

Standard Reduction Potentials[18,19,20,21]

- We can conveniently tabulate electrochemical data.
- **Standard reduction potentials**, $E°_{red}$ are measured relative to a standard.
- The emf of a cell can be calculated from standard reduction potentials:
$$E°_{cell} = E°_{red}(cathode) - E°_{red}(anode)$$
- We use the following half-reaction as our standard:
$$2H^+ (aq, 1M) + 2e^- \rightarrow H_2(g, 1 \text{ atm}) \qquad E°_{cell} = 0 \text{ V}.$$
    - This electrode is called a **standard hydrogen electrode** (SHE) or the normal hydrogen electrode (NHE).
    - The SHE is *assigned* a standard reduction potential of zero.
- Consider the half-reaction:
$$Zn(s) \rightarrow Zn^{2+}(aq) + 2e^-$$
    - We can *measure* $E°_{cell}$ relative to the SHE (cathode):
        - It consists of a Pt electrode in a tube placed in $1 \ M \ H^+$ solution.
        - H_2 is bubbled through the tube.
$$E°_{cell} = E°_{red}(cathode) - E°_{red}(anode)$$
$$0.76 \text{ V} = 0 \text{ V} - E°_{red}(anode).$$
        - Therefore, $E°_{red}(anode) = -0.76$ V.
- Standard reduction potentials must be written as reduction reactions:
$$Zn^{2+}(aq, 1M) + 2e^- \rightarrow Zn(s) \qquad E°_{red} = -0.76 \text{ V}.$$
    - Since $E°_{red} = -0.76$ V, we conclude that the *reduction* of Zn^{2+} in the presence of the SHE is *not* spontaneous.
        - However, the *oxidation* of Zn with the SHE *is* spontaneous.
- The standard reduction potential is an intensive property.
    - Therefore, changing the stoichiometric coefficient does not affect $E°_{red}$.
$$2Zn^{2+}(aq) + 4e^- \rightarrow 2Zn(s) \qquad E°_{red} = -0.76 \text{ V}$$
- Reactions with $E°_{red} > 0$ are spontaneous reductions relative to the SHE.
    - Reactions with $E°_{red} < 0$ are spontaneous oxidations relative to the SHE.
    - The larger the difference between $E°_{red}$ values, the larger $E°_{cell}$.
- The more positive the value of $E°_{red}$, the greater the driving force for reduction.

Strengths of Oxidizing and Reducing Agents[22]

- Consider a table of standard reduction potentials.
- We can use this table to determine the relative strengths of reducing (and oxidizing) agents.
    - The more positive the $E°_{red}$, the stronger the oxidizing agent (written in the table as a reactant).
    - The more negative the $E°_{red}$, the stronger the reducing agent (written as a product in the table).
    - We can use this to predict if one reactant can spontaneously oxidize another.
        - For example:
            - F_2 can oxidize H_2 or Li.
            - Ni^{2+} can oxidize Al(s).
    - We can use this table to predict if one reactant can spontaneously reduce another.
        - For example:
            - Li can reduce F_2.

---

[18] "Voltaic Cells II: The Zinc-Hydrogen Cell" Animation from Instructor's Resource CD/DVD
[19] Table 20.1 from Transparency Pack
[20] Figure 20.9 from Transparency Pack
[21] "Standard Reduction Potential" Animation from Instructor's Resource CD/DVD
[22] Figure 20.12 from Transparency Pack

20.5 Free Energy and Redox Reactions[23,24]

- For any electrochemical process
$$E° = E°_{red}(\text{reduction process}) - E°_{red}(\text{oxidation process}).$$
    - A positive $E°$ indicates a spontaneous process (galvanic cell).
    - A negative $E°$ indicates a nonspontaneous process.
- The above equation is used to understand the activity series of metals.
    - Consider the reaction of nickel with silver ion:
$$Ni(s) + 2Ag^+(aq) \rightarrow Ni^{2+}(aq) + 2Ag(s)$$
    - The standard cell potential is:
$$E° = E°_{red}(Ag^+/Ag) - E°_{red}(Ni^{2+}/Ni)$$
$$= (0.80 \text{ V}) - (-0.28 \text{ V}) = 1.08 \text{ V}$$
    - This value indicates that the reaction is spontaneous.

EMF, Free Energy and the Equilibrium Constant

- We can show that:
$$\Delta G = -nFE$$
    - where ΔG is the change in free energy, n is the number of moles of electrons transferred, F is **Faraday's constant**, and E is the emf of the cell.
- We define F as:
$$1F = 96,500 \frac{C}{\text{mol } e^-} = 96,500 \frac{J}{(V)(\text{mol } e^-)}$$
    - Since n and F are positive, if $\Delta G < 0$ then $E > 0$, and the reaction will be spontaneous.
    - When the reactants and products are in their standard states:
$$\Delta G° = -nFE°$$
- Since $\Delta G°$ is related to the equilibrium constant, K, we can relate $E°$ to K:
$$E° = \frac{\Delta G°}{-nF} = \frac{-RT\ln K}{-nF} = \frac{RT}{nF}\ln K$$

Electrical Work

- Free energy is a measure of the maximum amount of useful work that can be obtained from a system.
    - We know:
$$\Delta G = w_{max}$$
    - and:
$$\Delta G = -nFE$$
    - thus:
$$w_{max} = -nFE$$
    - If E_{cell} is positive, w_{max} will be negative.
        - Work is done *by* the system *on* the surroundings.
- The emf can be thought of as being a measure of the driving force for a redox process.
    - In an electrolytic cell an external source of energy is required to force the reaction to proceed.
$$w = nFE_{external}$$
    - In order to drive the nonspontaneous reaction, the external emf must be greater than E_{cell}.
    - From physics we know that work is measured in units of watts:
$$1 \text{ W} = 1 \text{ J/s}$$
    - Electric utilities use units of kilowatt-hours: $kWh = 3.6 \times 10^6 \text{ J}$.

---

[23] "Activity Series for Some Metals" from *Live Demonstrations*
[24] "An Activity Series: Zinc, Copper, and Silver Half Cells" from *Live Demonstrations*

20.6 Cell Potentials Under Nonstandard Conditions

- A voltaic cell is functional until $E = 0$ at which point equilibrium has been reached.
  - The cell is then "dead."
- The point at which $E = 0$ is determined by the concentrations of the species involved in the redox reaction.

The Nernst Equation[25]

- We can calculate the cell potential under nonstandard conditions.
- Recall that:

$$\Delta G = \Delta G° + RT \ln Q$$

- We can substitute in our expression for the free energy change:

$$-nFE = -nFE° + RT \ln Q$$

- Rearranging, we get the **Nernst equation**:

$$E = E° - \frac{RT}{nF} \ln Q$$

or

- Note that there is a change from natural logarithm to log base 10.

$$E = E° - \frac{2.303RT}{nF} \log Q$$

- The Nernst equation can be simplified by collecting all the constants together and using a temperature of 298 K:

$$E = E° - \frac{0.0592}{n} \log Q$$

- Example: If we have the reaction:

$$Zn(s) + Cu^{2+}(aq) \rightarrow Zn^{2+}(aq) + Cu(s)$$

  - If $[Cu^{2+}] = 5.0\ M$ and $[Zn^{2+}] = 0.050 M$:

$$E_{cell} = 1.10\,V - \frac{0.0592}{2} \log \frac{0.050}{5.0} = 1.16\,V$$

Concentration Cells[26]

- A **concentration cell** is one whose emf is generated solely because of a concentration difference.
- Example: Consider a cell with two compartments, each with a Ni(s) electrode but with different concentrations of $Ni^{2+}(aq)$.
  - One cell has $[Ni^{2+}] = 1.0\ M$ and the other has $[Ni^{2+}] = 0.001\ M$.
  - The standard cell potential is zero.
  - But this cell is operating under nonstandard conditions!
  - The driving force is the difference in Ni^{2+} concentrations.
    - Anode (dilute Ni^{2+}):

$$Ni(s) \rightarrow Ni^{2+}(aq) + 2e^-$$

    - Cathode (concentrated Ni^{2+}):

$$Ni^{2+}(aq) + 2e^- \rightarrow Ni(s)$$

- Using the Nernst equation we can calculate a cell potential of +0.0888 V for this concentration cell.

---

[25] "Nernst Equation" Activity from Instructor's Resource CD/DVD
[26] "Using the Biological Cell in Teaching Electrochemistry" from Further Readings

20.7 Batteries and Fuel Cells[27,28,29,30,31,32]

- A **battery** is a portable, self-contained electrochemical power source consisting of one or more voltaic cells.
  - *Primary* cells: cannot be recharged.
  - *Secondary* cells: can be recharged from an external power source after its voltage has dropped.

Lead-Acid Battery[33]

- A 12 V car battery consists of six cathode/anode pairs each producing 2 V.
- Cathode: PbO_2 on a metal grid in sulfuric acid:
$$PbO_2(s) + HSO_4^-(aq) + 3H^+(aq) + 2e^- \rightarrow PbSO_4(s) + 2H_2O(l)$$
- Anode: Pb:
$$Pb(s) + HSO_4^-(aq) \rightarrow PbSO_4(s) + H^+(aq) + 2e^-$$
- The overall electrochemical reaction is
$$PbO_2(s) + Pb(s) + 2HSO_4^-(aq) + 2H^+(aq) \rightarrow 2PbSO_4(s) + 2H_2O(l)$$
- The standard cell potential for this reaction is:
$$E°_{cell} = E°_{red}(\text{cathode}) - E°_{red}(\text{anode})$$
$$= (+1.685 \text{ V}) - (-0.356 \text{ V}) = +2.041 \text{ V}$$
- Wood or glass-fiber spacers are used to prevent the electrodes from touching.
- An advantage of these cells is that they can be recharged.
  - An external source of energy is used to reverse the process.

Alkaline Battery

- The most common nonrechargeable battery is the alkaline battery.
- Powdered zinc metal is immobilized in a gel in contact with a concentrated solution of KOH.
- Thus, these batteries are *alkaline*.
- The reaction at the anode is:
$$Zn(s) + 2OH^-(aq) \rightarrow Zn(OH)_2(aq) + 2e^-$$
- The reaction at the cathode is the reduction of MnO_2:
$$2MnO_2(s) + 2H_2O(l) + 2e^- \rightarrow 2MnO(OH)(s) + 2OH^-(aq)$$
- The cell potential of these batteries is 1.55 V at room temperature.

Nickel-Cadmium, Nickel-Metal-Hydride, and Lithium-Ion Batteries[34]

- A common rechargeable battery is the nickel-cadmium (NiCad) battery.
  - The reaction at the cathode is:
$$2NiO(OH)(s) + 2H_2O(l) + 2e^- \rightarrow 2Ni(OH)_2(s) + 2OH^-(aq)$$
  - The reaction at the anode is:
$$Cd(s) + 2OH^-(aq) \rightarrow Cd(OH)_2(s) + 2e^-$$
  - The cell potential of this battery is about 1.30 V at room temperature.
  - Cadmium is a toxic heavy metal.
    - There are environmental concerns to be addressed regarding the disposal of such batteries.
- Other rechargeable batteries have been developed.

---

[27] "Batteries: Full Speed Ahead" from Further Readings

[28] "Structure and Content of Some Primary Batteries" from Further Readings

[29] "Making a Simple Battery: The Gerber Cell" from Live Demonstrations

[30] "Batteries" Activity from Instructor's Resource CD/DVD

[31] "Time to Recharge" from Further Readings

[32] "Batteries, from Cradle to Grave" from Further Readings

[33] Figure 20.19 from Transparency Pack

[34] "Lithium Batteries: A Practical Application of Chemical Principles" from Further Readings

- NiMH batteries (nickel-metal-hydride).
- Li-ion batteries (lithium-ion batteries).

Hydrogen Fuel Cells[35,36]

- Direct production of electricity from fuels occurs in a **fuel** cell.
- An example is a hydrogen fuel cell.
  - At the cathode:

$$2H_2O(l) + O_2(g) + 4e^- \rightarrow 4OH^-(aq)$$

  - At the anode:

$$2H_2(g) + 4OH^-(aq) \rightarrow 4H_2O(l) + 4e^-$$

- This cell is known as a PEM fuel cell (proton exchange membrane).
- The anode and cathode are separated by a polymer membrane that is permeable to protons but not electrons; it acts as a salt bridge.

FORWARD REFERENCES
- Hydrogen economy will be further mentioned in Chapter 22 (section 22.2).

20.8 Corrosion

- An example of an undesirable redox reaction is the **corrosion** of metals.
- Metal is attacked by a substance in the environment and converted to an unwanted compound.

Corrosion of Iron (Rusting)[37,38]

- Consider the rusting of iron:
  - Since $E^\circ_{red}(Fe^{2+}) < E^\circ_{red}(O_2)$, iron can be oxidized by oxygen.
  - Cathode: $O_2(g) + 4H^+(aq) + 4e^- \rightarrow 2H_2O(l)$ $E^\circ_{red} = 1.23$ V.
  - Anode: $Fe(s) \rightarrow Fe^{2+}(aq) + 2e^-$ $E^\circ_{red} = -0.44$ V.
- Dissolved oxygen in water usually causes the oxidation of iron.
- The Fe^{2+} initially formed can be further oxidized to Fe^{3+}, which forms rust, $Fe_2O_3 \cdot xH_2O(s)$.
- Oxidation occurs at the site with the greatest concentration of O_2.
- Other factors are the pH, presence of salts, stress on the iron, and contact with other metals.

Preventing Corrosion of Iron[39,40]

- Corrosion can be prevented by coating the iron with paint or another metal.
  - This prevents oxygen and water from reacting at the surface of the iron.
  - *Galvanized iron* is coated with a thin layer of zinc.
  - Zinc protects the iron since Zn is the anode and Fe is the cathode:
$$Zn^{2+}(aq) + 2e^- \rightarrow Zn(s) \qquad E^\circ_{red} = -0.76 \text{ V}$$
$$Fe^{2+}(aq) + 2e^- \rightarrow Fe(s) \qquad E^\circ_{red} = -0.44 \text{ V}$$
  - The standard reduction potentials indicate that Zn is easier to oxidize than Fe.
  - This process is **cathodic protection** (the *sacrificial anode* is destroyed).
- We can use something similar to protect underground pipelines.
  - Often, Mg is used as a sacrificial anode:
$$Mg^{2+}(aq) + 2e^- \rightarrow Mg(s) \qquad E^\circ_{red} = -2.37 \text{ V}$$
$$Fe^{2+}(aq) + 2e^- \rightarrow Fe(s) \qquad E^\circ_{red} = -0.44 \text{ V}$$

---

[35] "Vehicle of Change" from Further Readings
[36] "Hydrogen" 3-D Model from Instructor's Resource CD/DVD
[37] "Evaluation of Corrosion Susceptibility of a Metal: Student Corrosion Experiment II" from Further Readings
[38] Figure 20.22 from Transparency Pack
[39] Figure 20.23 from Transparency Pack
[40] "Prevention of Corrosion" Activity from Instructor's Resource CD/DVD

20.9 Electrolysis[41,42,43,44,45]

- **Electrolysis reactions** are nonspontaneous reactions that require an external current in order to force the reaction to proceed.
  - They take place in **electrolytic cells**.
- In voltaic and electrolytic cells, reduction occurs at the cathode and oxidation occurs at the anode.
  - However, in electrolytic cells, electrons are forced to flow from the anode to the cathode.
  - In **electrolytic cells,** the anode is positive and the cathode is negative.
    - In voltaic cells, the anode is negative and the cathode is positive.
- Example: The decomposition of molten NaCl.
  - Cathode: $2Na^+(l) + 2e^- \rightarrow 2Na(l)$
  - Anode: $2Cl^-(l) \rightarrow Cl_2(g) + 2e^-$.
  - Industrially, electrolysis is used to produce metals like Al.
- Electrolysis of high-melting ionic substances requires very high temperatures.
  - Do we get the same products if we electrolyze an aqueous solution of the salt?
  - Water complicates the issue!
  - Example: Consider the electrolysis of NaF(aq):

$$Na^+(aq) + e^- \rightarrow Na(s) \qquad E^\circ_{red} = -2.71 \text{ V}$$
$$2H_2O(l) + 2e^- \rightarrow H_2(g) + 2OH^-(aq) \qquad E^\circ_{red} = -0.83 \text{ V}$$

  - Thus, water is more easily reduced than the sodium ion.

$$2F^-(aq) \rightarrow F_2(g) + 2e^- \qquad E^\circ_{red} = +2.87 \text{ V}$$
$$2H_2O(l) \rightarrow O_2(g) + 4H^+(aq) + 4e^- \qquad E^\circ_{red} = +1.23 \text{ V}$$

  - Thus, it is easier to oxidize water than the fluoride ion.
- Electrolysis does not always involve *inert* electrodes.
  - *Active* electrodes are electrodes that take part in electrolysis.
    - An example is *electroplating*.
      - Consider an active Ni electrode and another metallic electrode (steel) placed in an aqueous solution of $NiSO_4$:
      - Anode (nickel strip): $Ni(s) \rightarrow Ni^{2+}(aq) + 2e^-$
      - Cathode (steel strip): $Ni^{2+}(aq) + 2e^- \rightarrow Ni(s)$
      - Ni plates on the inert electrode.
      - Electroplating is important in protecting objects from corrosion.

Quantitative Aspects of Electrolysis[46,47,48]

- We want to know how much material we obtain with electrolysis.
- Consider the reduction of Cu^{2+} to Cu.

$$Cu^{2+}(aq) + 2e^- \rightarrow Cu(s).$$

- 2 moles of electrons will plate 1 mol of Cu.
- The charge of one mol of electrons is 96,500 C (1 *F*).
  - A *coulomb* is the amount of charge passing a point in one second when the current is one ampere.
- The amount of Cu can be calculated from the current (*amperes*) and time required to plate.

$$Coulombs = amperes \times seconds$$

---

[41] "Electroplating" Movie from Instructor's Resource CD/DVD
[42] "Electrolytic Cells in Series: A Red, White, and Blue Electrolysis" from Live Demonstrations
[43] "Electroplating Copper" from Live Demonstrations
[44] Figure 20.25 from Transparency Pack
[45] "Floating Pennies" from Live Demonstrations
[46] "Electrolysis" Activity from Instructor's Resource CD/DVD
[47] "Electrolysis Calculation Example" Activity from Instructor's Resource CD/DVD
[48] Figure 20.27 from Transparency Pack

Further Readings:

1. Marten J. ten Hoor, "Redox Balancing without Puzzling," *J. Chem. Educ.*, Vol. 74, **1997**, 1376–1368.

2. William B. Jensen, "Ask the Historian: Balancing Redox Equations," *J. Chem. Educ.*, Vol. 86, **2009**, 681–682.

3. Michael J. Sanger and Thomas J. Greenbowe, "Common Student Misconceptions in Electrochemistry: Galvanic, Electrolytic and Concentration Cells," *J. Res. Sci. Teach.*, Vol. 34, **1997**, 377–398.

4. P. J. Moran and E. Gileadi, "Alleviating the Common Confusion Caused by Polarity in Electrochemistry," *J. Chem. Educ.*, Vol. 66, **1989**, 912.

5. Ron DeLorenzo, "Electrochemical Errors," *J. Chem. Educ.*, Vol. 62, **1985**, 424–425.

6. Richard S. Treptow, "Dental Filling Discomforts Illustrate Electrochemical Potentials of Metals," *J. Chem. Educ.*, Vol. 55, **1978**, 189.

7. Penelope Ann Huddle, Margaret Dawn White, and Fiona Rogers, "Using a Teaching Model to Correct Known Misconceptions in Electrochemistry," *J. Chem. Educ.*, Vol. 77, **2000**, 104–110.

8. Eva Gankiewicz Merkel, "Using the Biological Cell in Teaching Electrochemistry," *J. Chem. Educ.*, Vol. 71, **1994**, 240.

9. Gerald Ondrey, Charlene Crabb, and Takeshi Kamiya, "Batteries: Full Speed Ahead," *Chemical Engineering*, Vol. 106(2), **1999**, 47–51. This is an article comparing many of the new up-and-coming batteries with older conventional batteries.

10. Michael J. Smith and Colin A. Vincent, "Structure and Content of Some Primary Batteries," *J. Chem. Educ.*, Vol. 78, **2001**, 519–521.

11. Robert Armstrong and Alastair Robertson, "Time to Recharge," *Chemistry in Britain*, **February 2002**, 38–41.

12. Richard S. Treptow, "Lithium Batteries: A Practical Application of Chemical Principles," *J. Chem. Educ.*, Vol. *80,* **2003**, 1015–1020.

13. Michael J. Smith and Fiona M. Gray, "Batteries, from Cradle to Grave," *J. Chem. Educ.*, Vol. 87, **2010**, 162–167.

14. Lawrence D. Burns, J. Byron McCormick, and Christopher E. Borroni-Bird, "Vehicle of Change," *Scientific American*, **October 2002**, 64–73. This is an article about hydrogen fuel cells.

15. A. I. Onuchukwu, "Evaluation of Corrosion Susceptibility of a Metal: Student Corrosion Experiment II," *J. Chem. Educ.*, Vol. 65, **1988**, 934.

Live Demonstrations:

1. Lee R. Summerlin, Christie L. Borgford, and Julie B. Ealy, "Visible Oxidation-Reduction in Electrochemical Cells," *Chemical Demonstrations, A Sourcebook for Teachers, Volume 2* (Washington: American Chemical Society, **1988**), pp. 202–203. This is a nice visual demonstrations of basic operation of electrochemical cells.

2. Bassam Z. Shakhashiri, "An Activity Series: Zinc, Copper, and Silver Half Cells," *Chemical Demonstrations: A Handbook for Teachers of Chemistry, Volume 4* (Madison: The University of Wisconsin Press, **1992**), pp. 101–106.

3. Lee. R. Summerlin and James. L. Ealy, Jr., "Activity Series for Some Metals," *Chemical Demonstrations, A Sourcebook for Teachers, Volume 1* (Washington: American Chemical Society, **1988**), p. 150. This overhead projector demonstration employs hydrogen gas formation.

4. Lee R. Summerlin, Christie L. Borgford, and Julie B. Ealy, "Making a Simple Battery: The Gerber Cell," *Chemical Demonstrations, A Sourcebook for Teachers, Volume 2* (Washington: American Chemical Society, **1988**), pp. 115–116. $Mg/CuSO_4$ and a baby food jar are used to construct a simple electrochemical cell.

5. Lee. R. Summerlin, Christie L. Borgford, and Julie B. Ealy, "Floating Pennies," *Chemical Demonstrations, A Sourcebook for Teachers, Volume 2* (Washington: American Chemical Society, **1988**), p. 63. The zinc core of copper-coated pennies reacts with acid to form pennies that float in this demonstration.

6. Lee. R. Summerlin, Christie L. Borgford, and Julie B. Ealy, "Electroplating Copper," *Chemical Demonstrations, A Sourcebook for Teachers, Volume 2* (Washington: American Chemical Society, **1988**), pp. 199–200. A stainless steel spoon is electroplated with copper in this demonstration.

7. Bassam Z. Shakhashiri, "Electrolytic Cells in Series: A Red, White, and Blue Electrolysis," *Chemical Demonstrations, A Handbook for Teachers of Chemistry, Volume 4* (Wisconsin: The University of Wisconsin Press, **1992**), pp. 170–173. Electrolysis in a series of beakers results in color changes in pH indicators.

Chapter 21. Nuclear Chemistry

Media Resources

Figures and Tables in Transparency Pack:

	Section:
Figure 21.2 Stable and Radioactive Isotopes as a Function of Numbers of Neutrons and Protons in a Nucleus	21.2 Patterns of Nuclear Stability
Figure 21.3 Nuclear Disintegration Series for Uranium-238	21.2 Patterns of Nuclear Stability
Figure 21.12 Nuclear Binding Energies	21.6 Energy Changes in Nuclear Reactions
Figure 21.15 Subcritical, Critical and Supercritical Fission	21.7 Nuclear Power: Fission
Figure 21.19 Basic Design of a Pressurized Water Reactor Nuclear Power Plant	21.7 Nuclear Power: Fission

Activities:

	Section:
Uranium-238 Decay Series	21.2 Patterns of Nuclear Stability
Radioactive Decay	21.4 Rates of Radioactive Decay

Animations:

	Section:
Separation of Alpha, Beta, and Gamma Rays	21.1 Radioactivity
First-Order Process	21.4 Rates of Radioactive Decay

Other Resources

Further Readings:

	Section:
Radioactivity in the Classroom	21.1 Radioactivity
Identifying Students' Misconceptions about Nuclear Chemistry	21.1 Radioactivity
Nuclear Chemistry: State of the Art for Teachers	21.1 Radioactivity
Radioactivity: A Natural Phenomenon	21.1 Radioactivity
Beta Decay Diagram	21.1 Radioactivity
Scientists Honor Centennial of the Discovery of Radioactivity	21.1 Radioactivity
Radioactivity in Everyday Life	21.1 Radioactivity
Teaching Nuclear Science: A Cosmological Approach	21.1 Radioactivity
Teaching Aids for Nuclear Chemistry	21.2 Patterns of Nuclear Stability
Chemistry of the Heaviest Elements—One Atom at a Time	21.2 Patterns of Nuclear Stability
Modeling Nuclear Decay: A Point of Integration between Chemistry and Mathematics	21.3 Nuclear Transmutations
Heavy Stuff	21.3 Nuclear Transmutations
Nucleogenesis! A Game with Natural Rules for Teaching Nuclear Synthesis and Decay	21.4 Rates of Radioactive Decay
Archaeological Dating	21.4 Rates of Radioactive Decay
Radioactive Dating: A Method for Geochronology	21.4 Rates of Radioactive Decay

California Earthquakes: Predicting the Next Big One Using Radiocarbon Dating — 21.4 Rates of Radioactive Decay

Searching for Real Time — 21.4 Rates of Radioactive Decay
How Radioactive Is your Banana? — 21.5 Detection of Radioactivity
Development and Proliferation of Radioimmunoassay Technology — 21.5 Detection of Radioactivity

Radioactivity in the Service of Many — 21.5 Detection of Radioactivity
Positron Emission Tomography Merges Chemistry with Biological Imaging — 21.5 Detection of Radioactivity

PET Practice — 21.5 Detection of Radioactivity
Visualizing the Mind — 21.5 Detection of Radioactivity
Nuclear Medicine and Positron Emission Tomography: An Overview — 21.5 Detection of Radioactivity

Special Agents — 21.5 Detection of Radioactivity
The Role of Chemistry in Positron Emission Tomography — 21.5 Detection of Radioactivity

Enriching Uranium — 21.7 Nuclear Power: Fission
Nuclear Power for the Future — 21.7 Nuclear Power: Fission
Lise Meitner and the Discovery of Nuclear Fission — 21.7 Nuclear Power: Fission
Aspects of Nuclear Waste Disposal of Use in Teaching Basic Chemistry — 21.7 Nuclear Power: Fission

Fusion—A Potential Power Source — 21.8 Nuclear Power: Fusion
Uranium to Electricity: The Chemistry of the Nuclear Fuel Cycle — 21.8 Nuclear Power: Fusion

How Much Radon Is Too Much? — 21.9 Radiation in the Environment and Living Systems

Chapter 21. Nuclear Chemistry

Common Student Misconceptions

- Initially, many students think that atoms of one element cannot be transformed into atoms of another element.
- Students often think that all radiation is man-made and harmful.
- Many students think that radioactivity is a man-made phenomenon.
- Students often think that the rate of radioactive decay depends on external conditions, such as T or p.
- Students often think that all isotopes of uranium are radioactive.

Teaching Tips

- This is new territory for students who have not taken advanced courses in physics.
- Radioactive decay processes are invariably first-order and therefore obey the rate law $\ln N_t/N_0 = -kt$ and the half-life expression $t_{1/2} = 0.693/k$, where k is the characteristic rate constant. Discussions of radionuclide half-lives may thus benefit from a short review of first-order kinetics from Chapter 14.

Lecture Outline

21.1 Radioactivity[1,2]

- **Nuclear reactions** involve changes in the atomic nuclei.
  - *Nuclear chemistry* is the study of nuclear reactions (their uses in chemistry and their impact on biological systems).
- When nuclei change spontaneously, emitting energy, they are said to be radioactive.
- Nuclear chemistry is the study of nuclear reactions and their uses and effects on biological systems.
- **Nucleons** are particles in the nucleus:
  - p^+: *proton*
  - n^0: *neutron*
  - *Atomic number* is the number of p^+.
  - *Mass number* is the number of $p^+ + n^0$.
    - The mass number is the total number of nucleons in the nucleus.
- *Isotopes* have the same number of p^+ but different numbers of n^0.
  - Different isotopes of the same element are distinguished by their mass numbers.
  - Different isotopes have different natural abundances.
  - Different isotopes of an element may be written using the name followed by the mass numbers:
    - Example: uranium-234
    They may also be written in a manner that shows the mass number as a superscript and the atomic number as a subscript:
    $$^{234}_{92}U$$
- **A *nuclide* is a nucleus containing a specified number of protons and neutrons.**
  - A **radionuclide** is a radioactive nucleus.
  - Atoms containing these nuclei are called **radioisotopes**.

---

[1] "Radioactivity in the Classroom" from Further Readings
[2] "Identifying Students' Misconceptions about Nuclear Chemistry" from Further Readings

Nuclear Equations[3,4]

- Most nuclei are stable.
  - Radionuclides are unstable and spontaneously emit particles and/or electromagnetic radiation.
  - Example: Uranium-238 is radioactive.
    - It emits **alpha (α) particles**.
    - These are helium-4 particles.
      - A stream of these particles is called *alpha radiation*.
- When a nucleus spontaneously decomposes in this manner, we say it has decayed (*radioactive decay*).
  - *Nuclear equations* are used to represent this process.
    - In nuclear equations, the total number of nucleons is conserved.
    - We can represent the uranium-238 decay by the following nuclear equation:

$$^{238}_{92}U \rightarrow ^{234}_{90}Th + ^{4}_{2}He$$

    - The total number of protons and neutrons before a nuclear reaction must be the same as the total number of nucleons after the reaction.
    - If alpha particles are involved in the reaction, it may be described as **alpha decay**.

Types of Radioactive Decay[5,6,7,8,9]

- There are three types of radiation which we will consider:

  - α-Radiation is the loss of $^{4}_{2}He$ (**alpha particles**) from the nucleus.

  - β-Radiation is the loss of an electron from the nucleus.
    - These high-speed electrons are called **beta (β) particles**.
      - Example; iodine-131 undergoes decay by **beta emission**.
  - **Gamma (γ)-Radiation** is the loss of high-energy photons from the nucleus.
- Nucleons can undergo two other types of decay:
  - **positron emission**
    - A positron is a particle with the same mass as an electron but with the opposite sign.
  - **electron capture**
    - The nucleus captures an electron from the electron cloud surrounding the nucleus.
- Representations:
  - In nuclear chemistry, to ensure the conservation of nucleons we write all particles with their atomic and mass numbers: $^{4}_{2}He$ and $^{4}_{2}\alpha$ represent α-radiation.

- Nucleons can undergo decay. For example:

  - (β-emission) $\quad ^{1}_{0}n \rightarrow ^{1}_{1}p + ^{0}_{-1}e$

  - (electron capture) $\quad ^{1}_{1}p + ^{0}_{-1}e \rightarrow ^{1}_{0}n$

---

[3] "Nuclear Chemistry: State of the Art for Teachers" from Further Readings
[4] "Radioactivity: A Natural Phenomenon" from Further Readings
[5] "Beta Decay Diagram" from Further Readings
[6] "Separation of Alpha, Beta, and Gamma Rays" Animation from Instructor's Resource CD/DVD
[7] "Scientists Honor Centennial of the Discovery of Radioactivity" from Further Readings
[8] "Radioactivity in Everyday Life" from Further Readings
[9] "Teaching Nuclear Science: A Cosmological Approach" from Further Readings

21.2 Patterns of Nuclear Stability[10]

Neutron-to-Proton Ratio[11]

- The proton has high mass and high charge.
- Therefore, the proton-proton repulsion is large.
- In the nucleus the protons are very close to each other.
- The cohesive forces in the nucleus are called *strong nuclear forces*.
  - Neutrons are involved with the strong nuclear force.
- As more protons are added (the nucleus gets heavier) the proton-proton repulsion gets larger.
  - Therefore, the heavier the nucleus, the more neutrons are required for stability.
- The *belt of stability* is the portion of a graph of (number of protons) vs. (number of neutrons) that contains all stable nuclei.
  - All nuclei with 84 or more protons are radioactive.
  - Nuclei above the belt of stability undergo β-emission.
    - When an $^{0}_{-1}e$ is lost; the number of neutrons decreases and the number of protons increases.
  - Nuclei below the belt of stability undergo β^{+}-emission or electron capture.
    - This results in the number of neutrons increasing and the number of protons decreasing.
  - Nuclei with atomic numbers greater than 83 usually undergo α-emission.
    - The number of protons and neutrons decreases (in steps of 2).

Radioactive Series[12,13]

- A nucleus usually undergoes more than one transition on its path to stability.
- The series of nuclear reactions that accompany this path is the **radioactive series**, or the **nuclear disintegration series**.

Further Observations[14]

- **Magic numbers** are 2, 8, 20, 28, 50, or 82 protons or 2, 8, 20, 28, 50, 82, or 126 neutrons.
  - Nuclei with a "magic number" of nucleons are more stable than nuclei that do not have the magic number of nucleons.
  - The magic numbers correspond to filled, closed-shell nucleon configurations.
- Nuclei with even numbers of protons and neutrons are more stable than nuclei with any odd numbers of nucleons.
  - The *shell model* of the nucleus rationalizes these observations.
    - The shell model of the nucleus is similar to the shell model for the atom.
  - Pairs of protons and neutrons in the nucleus are analogous to pairs of electrons in the atom.

21.3 Nuclear Transmutations[15]

- **Nuclear transmutations** are nuclear reactions resulting from the collisions between nuclei or between a nucleus and a neutron.
- For example, nuclear transmutations can occur using high-velocity α-particles:

$$^{14}_{7}N + ^{4}_{2}He \rightarrow ^{17}_{8}O + ^{1}_{1}H$$

---

[10] "Teaching Aids for Nuclear Chemistry" from Further Readings
[11] Figure 21.2 from Transparency Pack
[12] "Uranium-238 Decay Series" Activity from Instructor's Resource CD/DVD
[13] Figure 21.3 from Transparency Pack
[14] "Chemistry of the Heaviest Elements—One Atom at a Time" from Further Readings
[15] "Modeling Nuclear Decay: A Point of Integration between Chemistry and Mathematics" from Further Readings

Accelerating Charged Particles

- To overcome electrostatic forces, charged particles need to be accelerated before they react.
  - **Particle accelerators** (atom smashers, cyclotrons, synchnotrons) are used to accelerate particles using strong magnetic and electrostatic fields.
    - The Relativistic Heavy Ion Collider (RHIC) at Brookhaven National laboratory, the Tevatron at Fermilab and the Large Hadron Collider (LHC) are the largest particle accelerators in the world.

Reactions Involving Neutrons

- Most synthetic isotopes used in medicine and research are made using neutrons as projectiles.
- An example is the preparation of cobalt-60 for use in cancer radiation therapy.

Transuranium Elements[16]

- **Transuranium elements** follow uranium in the periodic table.

21.4 Rates of Radioactive Decay[17,18,19]

- Radioactive decay is a first-order process.
- Each isotope has a characteristic **half-life**.
  - Half-lives are not affected by temperature, pressure or chemical composition.
  - Natural radioisotopes tend to have longer half-lives than synthetic radioisotopes.
  - Half-lives range from fractions of a second to millions of years.
  - Naturally occurring radioisotopes can be used to determine the age of a sample.
    - This process is radiometric dating.

Radiometric Dating[20,21]

- The half-life of any particular nuclide is constant.
  - Thus, half –life may be used as a nuclear clock to determine the age of objects.
  - Dating of objects based on their isotopes and isotope abundances is called *radiometric dating*.
- Carbon-14 (^{14}C) is used to determine the ages of organic compounds by radiometric dating.
- For ^{14}C to be detected, the object must be less than 50,000 years old.
  - We assume that the ratio of ^{12}C to ^{14}C has been constant over time.
  - The half-life of ^{14}C is 5,715 years.
  - ^{14}C undergoes decay to ^{14}N via β-decay:

$$^{14}_{6}C \rightarrow ^{14}_{7}N + ^{0}_{-1}e$$

- Other dating methods are also used.
  - Uranium-lead dating has been used to estimate the age of the Earth at approximately 4.0-4.5 billion years.

Calculations Based on Half-life[22,23]

- Radioactive decay is a first-order process:

---

[16] "Heavy Stuff" from Further Readings
[17] "Nucleogenesis! A Game with Natural Rules for Teaching Nuclear Synthesis and Decay" from Further Readings
[18] "First-Order Process" Animation from Instructor's Resource CD/DVD
[19] "Radioactive Decay" Activity from Instructor's Resource CD/DVD
[20] "Archaeological Dating" from Further Readings
[21] "Radioactive Dating: A Method for Geochronology" from Further Readings
[22] "California Earthquakes: Predicting the Next Big One Using Radiocarbon Dating" from Further Readings
[23] "Searching for Real Time" from Further Readings

$$\text{Rate} = kN$$

- If the activity of a sample at time = t is N_t, and the activity at time = 0 is N_0, then:

$$\ln\frac{N_t}{N_0} = -kt$$

- The half-life of the sample is given by:

$$t_{\frac{1}{2}} = \frac{0.693}{k}$$

- In radioactive decay the constant, k, is called the *decay constant*.
- The rate of decay is called **activity** (disintegrations per unit time).
- There are several units used to express activity or radioactivity.
  - The **becquerel** (Bq) is the SI unit of radioactivity.
    - 1 Bq = 1 disintegration per second (dps).
  - The **Curie** (Ci) is an older, but still very widely used, unit of activity.
    - 1 Ci = 3.7×10^{10} disintegrations per second.

21.5 Detection of Radioactivity[24,25]

- Matter is ionized by radiation.
- A Geiger counter determines the amount of ionization by detecting an electric current.
  - A thin window is penetrated by the radiation and causes the ionization of Ar gas.
  - The ionized gas carries a charge, so current is produced.
    - The current pulse generated when the radiation enters is amplified and counted.
- Other methods are also used to detect radioactivity.
- One common method employs an instrument called a scintillation counter.
  - A substance called a *phosphor* is allowed to interact with radiation.
  - Light is produced when radiation strikes a suitable phosphor.
  - This light is detected and used to quantify the amount of radiation.

Radiotracers[26,27,28,29,30,31,32]

- Photosynthesis has been studied using ^{14}C:

$$6\,^{14}CO_2 + 6H_2O \xrightarrow[\text{chlorophyll}]{\text{sunlight}} {}^{14}C_6H_{12}O_6 + 6O_2$$

- The carbon dioxide is said to be ^{14}C labeled.
- The presence of ^{14}C in the intermediates or products of photosynthesis can be determined.
  - ^{14}C is detected as it moves from carbon dioxide to ultimately become incorporated into glucose.
    - Thus the path of the carbon atoms may be *traced*.
    - **Radiotracers** are used to follow an element through a chemical reaction.

---

[24] "How Radioactive Is Your Banana?" from Further Readings
[25] "Development and Proliferation of Radioimmunoassay Technology" from Further Readings
[26] "Radioactivity in the Service of Many" from Further Readings
[27] "Positron Emission Tomography Merges Chemistry with Biological Imaging" from Further Readings
[28] "PET Practice" from Further Readings
[29] "Visualizing the Mind" from Further Readings
[30] "Nuclear Medicine and Positron Emission Tomography: An Overview" from Further Readings
[31] "Special Agents" from Further Readings
[32] "The Role of Chemistry in Positron Emission Tomography" from Further Readings

21.6 Energy Changes in Nuclear Reactions

- Einstein showed that mass and energy are proportional:
$$E = mc^2$$
  - If a system loses mass, it loses energy (exothermic).
  - If a system gains mass, it gains energy (endothermic).
- Since c^2 is a large number, small changes in mass cause large changes in energy.
- Mass and energy changes in nuclear reactions are much greater than in chemical reactions.
- Consider:
$$^{238}_{92}U \rightarrow {}^{234}_{90}Th + {}^{4}_{2}He$$

- For 1 mol of $^{238}_{92}U$, the masses are:
$$238.0003 \text{ g} \rightarrow 233.9942 \text{ g} + 4.0015 \text{ g}.$$
  - The change in mass during the reaction is:
$$233.9942 \text{ g} + 4.0015 \text{ g} - 238.0003 \text{ g} = -0.0046 \text{ g}$$
  - The process is exothermic because the system has lost mass.

$$\Delta E = \Delta(mc^2) = c^2(\Delta m)$$

$$\Delta E = (2.9979 \times 10^8 \text{ m/s})^2 (-0.0046 \text{ g})\left(\frac{1 \text{ kg}}{1000 \text{ g}}\right)$$

$$\Delta E = -4.1 \times 10^{11} \frac{\text{kg m}^2}{\text{s}^2} = -4.1 \times 10^{11} \text{ J}$$

- To calculate the energy change per mole of ^{238}U:

Nuclear Binding Energies[33]

- The mass of a nucleus is less than the mass of its nucleons.
  - **Mass defect** is the difference between the mass of a nucleus and the masses of its nucleons.
  - **Nuclear binding energy** is the energy required to separate a nucleus into its nucleons.
  - Since $E = mc^2$, the binding energy is related to the mass defect.
- The larger the binding energy, the more likely a nucleus is to decompose.
- Heavy nuclei gain stability by splitting into smaller nuclei.
  - They give off energy if fragmented into two mid-sized nuclei.
  - This reaction is called **fission**.
- Very light nuclei are combined or fused together to form more massive nuclei.
  - Energy is released from this nuclear **fusion**.

21.7 Nuclear Power: Fission[34,35]

- Nuclear power plants and most forms of nuclear weapons utilize nuclear fission.
- Splitting of heavy nuclei is exothermic for large mass numbers.
- Consider a neutron bombarding a ^{235}U nucleus.
  - The heavy ^{235}U nucleus can split in several different ways such as:
$$^{1}_{0}n + {}^{235}_{92}U \rightarrow {}^{142}_{56}Ba + {}^{91}_{36}Kr + 3{}^{1}_{0}n$$
  - For every ^{235}U fission, an average of 2.4 neutrons are produced.

---

[33] Figure 21.12 from Transparency Pack
[34] "Enriching Uranium" from Further Readings
[35] Figure 21.15 from Transparency Pack

- Each neutron produced can cause the fission of another ^{235}U nucleus.
  - The number of fissions and the resulting energy increase rapidly.
  - Reactions that multiply this way are called **chain reactions**.
- Without controls, an explosion results.
  - Consider the fission of a nucleus that results in the production of neutrons.
  - Each neutron can cause another fission.
  - Eventually, a chain reaction forms.
  - A minimum mass of fissionable material is required for a chain reaction (or neutrons will escape before they can cause another fission).
    - This is called a **critical mass**.
  - When enough material is present for a chain reaction, we have a critical mass.
  - If the mass is lower than the critical mass (subcritical mass), the neutrons escape and a chain reaction does not occur.
  - At the critical mass, one neutron from each fission is effective in causing another fission.
  - Any mass over the critical mass is called **supercritical mass**.
- Critical mass for ^{235}U is about 1 kg.

Nuclear Reactors[36,37,38,39]

- Use fission as a power source.
- Use a subcritical mass of ^{235}U (^{238}U is enriched with about 3% ^{235}U).
- *Fuel elements* contain enriched $^{235}UO_2$ pellets are encased in Zr or stainless steel tubes.
- *Control rods* are composed of Cd or B, which absorb neutrons.
  - They help to regulate the flux of neutrons.
- *Moderators* are inserted to slow down the neutrons to make them more easily captured.
- A *containment shell* surrounds the reactor as an added safety precaution.
- Heat produced in the reactor core is removed by a *primary coolant.*
  - Water acts as both moderator and primary coolant in a *pressurized water reactor.*
- Much of the heat is transferred to a *secondary coolant.*
  - The secondary coolant is converted to high-pressure steam and is used to drive a turbine to generate electricity.
- About 2/3 of commercial reactors are pressurized water reactors.
  - Variations on the basic design include:
    - *Boiling water reactors*: generates steam by boiling the primary coolant (no secondary coolant is needed).
    - *Heavy water reactor*: used D_2O as moderator and primary coolant.
    - *Gas-cooled reactors*: used a gas such as CO_2 as primary coolant and graphite as moderator.
    - *High-temperature pebble-bed reactor*: not yet in commercial use.

Nuclear Waste

- Fission products accumulate as a reactor operates.
  - These reduce the reactor efficiency.
  - Commercial reactors are stopped periodically to replace or reprocess the fuel elements.
  - Transportation of the radioactive fuel rods using the nation's roads has met intense opposition.
  - Spent rods are stored at the reactor sites but the fuel is reprocessed outside of the country.
- Storage and disposal of radioactive wastes from such reactions is not a simple problem.
  - The fission products are extremely radioactive.

---

[36] Figure 21.19 from Transparency Pack
[37] "Nuclear Power for the Future" from Further Readings
[38] "Lise Meitner and the Discovery of Nuclear Fission" from Further Readings
[39] "Aspects of Nuclear Waste Disposal of Use in Teaching Basic Chemistry" from Further Readings

- The potential for environmental contamination by long-lived isotopes is a serious consideration.
- *Fast breeder reactors* may represent a method of getting more power out of existing uranium sources and potentially reducing radioactive waste.
- The material separated from the uranium and plutonium during reprocessing is less radioactive than waste from other reactors.

21.8 Nuclear Power: Fusion[40,41]

- Light nuclei can fuse to form heavier nuclei.
  - Most reactions in the Sun are fusion reactions.
- Fusion products are not usually radioactive, so fusion is a good energy source.
- Also, the hydrogen required for the reaction can easily be supplied by seawater.
  - However, high energies are required to overcome repulsion between nuclei before the reaction can occur.
  - High energies are achieved by high temperatures, the reactions are known as **thermonuclear reactions**.
- Fusion of tritium and deuterium requires a temperature of about 40,000,000 K:

$$\,_1^2\text{H} + \,_1^3\text{H} \rightarrow \,_2^4\text{He} + \,_0^1\text{n}$$

  - These temperatures can be achieved in a nuclear bomb, or a *tokamak*.
  - A tokamak is a magnetic bottle; strong magnetic fields contain a high-temperature plasma, so the plasma does not come into contact with the walls. (No known material can survive the temperatures required for fusion.)
  - To date, temperatures of about 100,000,000 K have been achieved in a tokamak.
- Research continues.

FORWARD REFERENCES
- Hydrogen as a fuel used by the Sun and other stars to produce energy will be mentioned in Chapter 22 (section 22.2).

21.9 Radiation in the Environment and Living Systems

- **Ionizing radiation** involves ionization that occurs when radiation removes an electron from an atom or molecule.
  - This is generally more harmful to biological systems than **nonionizing radiation**.
    - Radiation absorbed by tissue causes excitation (nonionizing radiation) or ionization (ionizing radiation).
- Most ionizing radiation interacts with water in tissues to form H_2O^+.
  - The H_2O^+ ions react with water to produce H_3O^+ and OH.
  - OH has one unpaired electron.
    - It is called the *hydroxy radical*.
    - The unpaired electron is shown by writing the species with a single dot: •*OH*
    - This is an example of a **free radical**, a substance with unpaired electrons.
    - Free radicals generally undergo chain reactions.
    - They are capable of causing substantial damage in biological tissues.
- The penetrating power of radiation is a function of the mass of the radiation.
  - Therefore, γ-radiation (zero mass) penetrates much further than β-radiation, which penetrates much further than α-radiation.

Radiation Doses
- Absorbed radiation is measured in:

---

[40] "Fusion—A Potential Power Source" from Further Readings
[41] "Uranium to Electricity: The Chemistry of the Nuclear Fuel Cycle" from Further Readings

- **Gray**: 1 Gy is the SI unit for absorption of 1 J of energy per kg of tissue.
- **Rad** is the *r*adiation *a*bsorbed *d*ose.
  - One rad is the absorption of 10^{-2} J of radiation per kg of tissue.
  - The rad is the unit most often used in medicine.
- One gray is equivalent to 100 rads.
- Because not all forms of radiation have the same effect, we correct for the differences using the RBE (*relative biological effectiveness*).
  - The RBE is about 1 for β- and γ-radiation and 10 for α-radiation.
  - A **rem** (*r*oentgen *e*quivalent for *m*an) = (rads) x (RBE).
  - The SI unit for effective dosage is the Sievert (1 Sv = 1 Gy = 100 rem).
    - The rem is the unit of radiation damage usually used in medicine.
- The average annual exposure to all natural sources of ionizing radiation (*background radiation*) is about 360 mrem.

Radon[42]

- The nucleus is $^{222}_{86}$Rn which is a decay product of $^{238}_{92}$U

- Radon exposure accounts for more than half of the 360 mrem annual exposure to ionizing radiation.
- Rn is a noble gas; it is extremely stable.
  - Therefore, it is inhaled and exhaled without any chemical reactions occurring.

  - The half-life of $^{222}_{86}$Rn is 3.82 days.

  - It decays as follows:
  $$^{222}_{86}\text{Rn} \rightarrow ^{218}_{84}\text{Po} + ^{4}_{2}\text{He}$$
- The α-particles produced have a high RBE.
  - Therefore, inhaled Rn is thought to be a cause of lung cancer.

- The situation is complicated because $^{218}_{84}$Po has a short half-life (3.11 min) also:
  $$^{218}_{84}\text{Po} \rightarrow ^{214}_{82}\text{Pb} + ^{4}_{2}\text{He}$$

  - The $^{218}_{84}$Po gets trapped in the lungs, where it continually produces α-particles.

- The EPA recommends $^{222}_{86}$Rn levels in homes be kept below 4 pCi per liter of air.

  - Radon testing kits are readily available in many areas of the country.

FORWARD REFERENCES
  - Group 8A elements will be the subject of section 22.3 in Chapter 22.

---

[42] "How Much Radon Is Too Much?" from Further Readings

Further Readings:

1. Enrique A. Hughes and Anita Zalts, "Radioactivity in the Classroom," *J. Chem. Educ.*, Vol. 77, **2000**, 613–614.

2. Canan Nakiboglu and Berna Bülbül Tekin, "Identifying Students' Misconceptions about Nuclear Chemistry," *J. Chem. Educ.*, Vol. 83, **2006**, 1712–1718.

3. "Nuclear Chemistry: State of the Art for Teachers," a series of articles in the **October 1994** issue of the *Journal of Chemical Education*. Articles include a *J. Chem. Educ.* bibliography list.

4. C. Ronneau, "Radioactivity: A Natural Phenomenon," *J. Chem. Educ.*, Vol. 67, **1990**, 736–737.

5. Robert Suder, "Beta Decay Diagram," *J. Chem. Educ.*, Vol. 66, **1989**, 231.

6. Stu Borman, "Scientists Honor Centennial of The Discovery of Radioactivity," *Chemical and Engineering News*, **April 29, 1996**, 55–65.

7. S. G. Hutchinson and F. I. Hutchinson, "Radioactivity in Everyday Life," *J. Chem. Educ.*, Vol. 74, **1997**, 501–505.

8. V. E. Viola, "Teaching Nuclear Science: A Cosmological Approach," *J. Chem. Educ.*, Vol. 71, **1994**, 840–944.

9. Charles H. Atwood, "Teaching Aids for Nuclear Chemistry," *J. Chem. Educ.*, Vol. 71, **1994**, 845–847.

10. Darleane C. Hoffman and Diana M. Lee, "Chemistry of the Heaviest Elements–One Atom at a Time," *J. Chem. Educ.*, Vol. 76, **1999**, 332–347.

11. Kent J. Crippen and Robert D. Curtright, "Modeling Nuclear Decay: A Point of Integration between Chemistry and Mathematics," *J. Chem. Educ.*, Vol. 75, **1998**, 1434–1436.

12. Bill Gelletly, "Heavy Stuff," *Chemistry in Britain*, **March 2000**, 40–43. An article about heavy atom synthesis.

13. Donald J. Olbris and Judith Herzfeld, "Nucleogenesis! A Game with Natural Rules for Teaching Nuclear Synthesis and Decay," *J. Chem. Educ.*, Vol. 76, **1999**, 349–352.

14. M. W. Rowe, "Archaeological Dating," *J. Chem. Educ.*, Vol. 63, **1986**, 16–20.

15. M. W. Rowe, "Radioactive Dating: A Method for Geochronology," *J. Chem. Educ.*, Vol. 62, **1985**, 580–584.

16. Ron DeLorenzo, "California Earthquakes: Predicting the Next Big One Using Radiocarbon Dating," *J. Chem. Educ.*, Vol. 57, **1980**, 601.

17. Richard Corfield, "Searching for Real Time," *Chemistry in Britain*, **January 2002**, 22–26. An article about radiometric dating methods.

18. David W. Ball, "How Radioactive Is Your Banana?," *J. Chem. Educ.*, Vol. 81, **2004**, 1440.

19. Rosalyn S. Yalow, "Development and Proliferation of Radioimmunoassay Technology," *J. Chem. Educ.*, Vol. 76, **1999**, 767–768.

20. Rosalyn S. Yalow, "Radioactivity in the Service of Many," *J. Chem. Educ.*, Vol. 59, **1982**, 735–738.

21. Mairin B. Brennan, "Positron Emission Tomography Merges Chemistry with Biological Imaging," *Chemical and Engineering News*, **February 19, 1996**, 26–33.

22. Emma Davies, "PET Practice," *Chemistry in Britain*, **April 2003**, 31–33.

23. Marcus E. Raichle, "Visualizing the Mind," *Scientific American*, **April 1994**, 64.

24. Timothy J. McCarthy, Sally W. Schwarz, and Michael J. Welch, "Nuclear Medicine and Positron Emission Tomography: An Overview," *J. Chem. Educ.*, Vol. 71, **1994**, 830–836.

25. Helen Carmichael, "Special Agents," *Chemistry in Britain*, Vol. 34(8), **August 1998**, 30–33. An introduction to contrast agents for medical imaging.

26. Anthony L. Feliu, "The Role of Chemistry in Positron Emission Tomography," *J. Chem. Educ.*, Vol. 65, **1988**, 655–660.

27. David Fishlock, "Enriching Uranium," *Chemistry World*, **June 2004**, 46–49.

28. Michael Freemantle, "Nuclear Power for the Future," *Chem. Eng. News*, **September 13, 2004**, 31–35.

29. Ruth Lewin Sime, "Lise Meitner and the Discovery of Nuclear Fission," *J. Chem. Educ.*, Vol. 66, **1989**, 373–378. This issue of *Journal of Chemical Education* includes several papers on radiochemistry.

30. Gregory R. Choppin, "Aspects of Nuclear Waste Disposal of Use in Teaching Basic Chemistry," *J. Chem. Educ.*, Vol. 71, **1994**, 826–829.

31. Torkil H. Jensen, "Fusion-A Potential Power Source," *J. Chem. Educ.*, Vol. 71, **1994**, 820–823.

32. Frank A. Settle, "Uranium to Electricity: The Chemistry of the Nuclear Fuel Cycle," *J. Chem. Educ.*, Vol. 86, **2009**, 316–323.

33. Charles H. Atwood, "How Much Radon Is Too Much?" *J. Chem. Educ.*, Vol. 69, **1992**, 351–355.

Chapter 22. Chemistry of the Nonmetals

Media Resources

Figures and Tables in Transparency Pack:
Figure 22.1 Trends in Elemental Properties
Table 22.1 Properties of Xenon Compounds
Table 22.2 Some Properties of the Halogens
Table 22.5 Some Properties of the Group 6A
    Elements
Table 22.6 Oxidation States of Nitrogen
Table 22.7 Properties of the Group 5A Elements

Table 22.8 Some Properties of the Group 4A
    Elements
Figure 22.34 Silicate Chains and Sheets

Section:
22.1 Periodic Trends and Chemical Reactions
22.3 Group 8A: The Noble Gases
22.4 Group 7A: The Halogens
22.6 The Other Group 6A Elements: S, Se, Te,
    and Po
22.7 Nitrogen
22.8 The Other Group 5A Elements: P, As, Sb,
    and Bi
22.10 The Other Group 4A Elements: Si, Ge, Sn,
    and Pb
22.10 The Other Group 4A Elements: Si, Ge, Sn,
    and Pb

Activities:
Carbon-Silicon Orbital Overlap

Section:
22.1 Periodic Trends and Chemical Reactions

Animations:
Periodic Trends: Acid-Base Behavior of Oxides

Sections:
22.5 Oxygen

Movies:
Formation of Water
Physical Properties of the Halogens
Nitrogen Dioxide and Dinitrogen Tetroxide
Carbon Dioxide Behaves as an Acid in Water

Section:
22.2 Hydrogen
22.4 Group 7A: The Halogens
22.7 Nitrogen
22.9 Carbon

3-D Models:
Carbon Dioxide
Teflon
Ozone
Hydrogen Peroxide
Water
Sulfate Ion

Hydrazine
Dinitrogen Trioxide
Dinitrogen Tetroxide
Nitrogen Dioxide
Phosphorus

Tetraphosphorus Hexoxide

Tetraphosphorus Decoxide

Phosphoric Acid

Section:
22.1 Periodic Trends and Chemical Reactions
22.4 Group 7A: The Halogens
22.5 Oxygen
22.5 Oxygen
22.5 Oxygen
22.6 The Other Group 6A Elements: S, Se, Te,
    and Po
22.7 Nitrogen
22.7 Nitrogen
22.7 Nitrogen
22.7 Nitrogen
22.8 The Other Group 5A Elements: P, As, Sb,
    and Bi
22.8 The Other Group 5A Elements: P, As, Sb,
    and Bi
22.8 The Other Group 5A Elements: P, As, Sb,
    and Bi
22.8 The Other Group 5A Elements: P, As, Sb,
    and Bi

Phosphorous Acid

Disilicate Anion ($Si_2O_7^{6-}$)

Single-Chain Silicate

Silicate Tetrahedron

Diborane

22.8 The Other Group 5A Elements: P, As, Sb, and Bi

22.10 The Other Group 4A Elements: Si, Ge, Sn, and Pb

22.10 The Other Group 4A Elements: Si, Ge, Sn, and Pb

22.10 The Other Group 4A Elements: Si, Ge, Sn, and Pb

22.11 Boron

Other Resources

Further Readings:
What's the Use? Hydrogen
Electronegativities of the Noble Gases
Discovery and Early Uses of Iodine
Dentifrice Fluoride
Joseph Priestley, Preeminent Amateur Chemist
The Discovery of Oxygen and other Priestley Matters
The Three Forms of Molecular Oxygen
An Acidity Scale for Binary Oxides
Herman Frasch, Sulfur King

Some History of Nitrates
Bad Rap of Nitrate?
Biological Roles of Nitric Oxide
The Discovery of Nitroglycerine: Its Preparation and Therapeutic Utility
Arsenic: Not So Evil After All?

Keeping the Fire Cold

Arsenic in Drinking Water—A Global Environmental Problem
Glass-Sand + Imagination

Glass Doesn't Flow and Doesn't Crystallize, and It Isn't a Liquid
The Origin of Pyrex

Boron Clusters Come of Age

Section:
22.2 Hydrogen
22.3 Group 8A: The Noble Gases
22.4 Group 7A: The Halogens
22.4 Group 7A: The Halogens
22.5 Oxygen
22.5 Oxygen
22.5 Oxygen
22.5 Oxygen
22.6 The Other Group 6A Elements: S, Se, Te, and Po

22.7 Nitrogen
22.7 Nitrogen
22.7 Nitrogen
22.7 Nitrogen

22.8 The Other Group 5A Elements: P, As, Sb, and Bi
22.8 The Other Group 5A Elements: P, As, Sb, and Bi
22.8 The Other Group 5A Elements: P, As, Sb, and Bi
22.10 The Other Group 4A Elements: Si, Ge, Sn, and Pb

22.10 The Other Group 4A Elements: Si, Ge, Sn, and Pb
22.10 The Other Group 4A Elements: Si, Ge, Sn, and Pb

22.11 Boron

Live Demonstrations:
Making Hydrogen Gas from an Acid and a Base
An Overhead Demonstration of Some Descriptive Chemistry of the Halogens and Le Châtelier's Principle
Preparation of Chlorine Gas from Laundry Bleach
Demonstrating a Lack of Reactivity Using a Teflon-Coated Pan
Combining Volume of Oxygen with Sulfur
Plastic Sulfur

Section:
22.2 Hydrogen
22.4 Group 7A: The Halogens

22.4 Group 7A: The Halogens
22.4 Group 7A: The Halogens

22.5 Oxygen
22.6 The Other Group 6A Elements: S, Se, Te, and Po

Chapter 22. Chemistry of the Nonmetals

Common Student Misconceptions:
- Students often find detailed discussions of descriptive chemistry to be difficult to digest.
- Students often think that all nonmetals are gaseous.

Teaching Tips:
- Videos and similar visual aids are useful in helping students learn the descriptive chemistry in this chapter.
- Students need to be encouraged to look for periodic trends in everything.
- Students should explore connections between the causes (e.g. electron configurations) and effects (e.g. properties, types of compounds formed) of these main group elements.
- Parts of this chapter could be incorporated into lectures on chapters 2, 4, 7, 8, and 9 as illustrations of the concepts discussed in these chapters.

Lecture Outline

22.1 Periodic Trends and Chemical Reactions[1,2,3]
- We divide the periodic table into metals, nonmetals, and metalloids.
- Nonmetals occupy the upper right portion of the periodic table.
  - H is a special case.
- Electronegativity is important when determining whether an element is a metal.
- Nonmetals tend to have higher electronegativities than metals.
  - Thus, reactions of metals and nonmetals often yield ionic compounds.
  - Compounds formed between nonmetals tend to be molecular.
- As we move down a group, the type of bonding changes.
  - Elements in the third period and below have accessible d orbitals that can participate in bonding.
    - Therefore, the octet rule can be broken for elements in the third period and below.
  - The first member of a group can form π bonds more readily than subsequent members.
    - This is due in part to the difference in atomic size.
    - Compare the elemental forms of carbon and silicon
      - Carbon has 5 major crystalline allotropes: diamond, graphite, buckminsterfullerene, graphene, and carbon nanotubes).
        - Diamond is a covalent-network solid with C-C sigma bonds but not pi bonds.
        - Graphite, buckminsterfullerene, graphene and carbon nanotubes have pi bonds from sideways overlap of orbitals
      - Elemental silicon exists only as a diamond-like covalent-network solid with sigma bonds.
        - It exhibits no form that is analogous to the other carbon allotropes.
  - We see significant differences in the dioxides of carbon and silicon.
    - Si is much larger than C, and the $3p$ orbitals are much larger than the $2p$ orbitals, so the overlap between $3p$ orbitals to form a π_{3p} bond is less effective than for a π_{2p} bond.
    - Since the Si–Si π bond is much weaker than the C–C π bond, Si tends to form σ bonds.
      - Example: at room temperature, CO_2 is a molecular gas with O=C=O bonds.
      - At room temperature, SiO_2 is a network solid with Si–O bonds.

---

[1] Figure 22.1 from Transparency Pack
[2] "Carbon-Silicon Orbital Overlap" Activity from Instructor's Resource CD/DVD
[3] "Carbon Dioxide" 3-D Model from Instructor's Resource CD/DVD

Chemical Reactions

- In this chapter we focus on reactions involving O_2 (oxidation or combustion) and H_2O (especially proton transfer).
- Combustion reactions with O_2 usually form H_2O (with H–containing compounds), CO or CO_2 (with C–containing compounds), and N_2 or NO (with N–containing compounds).
- Water, nitrogen, and CO_2 are thermodynamically stable because of the large bond energies for the H–O, N≡N, and C=O bonds.
- Examples:

$$2CH_3OH(l) + 3O_2(g) \rightarrow 2CO_2(g) + 4H_2O(l)$$
$$4CH_3NH_2(g) + 9O_2(g) \rightarrow 4CO_2(g) + H_2O(l) + 2N_2(g)$$

- In proton-transfer reactions, the weaker the Brønsted-Lowry acid is, the stronger the conjugate base.

FORWARD REFERENCES

- Corresponding physical properties of metals will be discussed in Chapter 23 (section 23.1).

22.2 Hydrogen

Isotopes of Hydrogen

- There are three isotopes of hydrogen: **protium** $\left(^1_1H\right)$, **deuterium** $\left(^2_1H\right)$, and **tritium** $\left(^2_1H\right)$.

  - Protium is the most abundant of these isotopes.
  - Deuterium (D) is about 0.0156% of naturally occurring H.
    - D_2O is also known as *heavy water*.
    - Deuteration (replacement of H for D) results in changes in the kinetics of reactions.
      - This phenomenon is called the *kinetic isotope effect*.
  - Tritium (T) is radioactive with a half-life of 12.3 yr.
- Deuterium and tritium are substituted for H in compounds in order to provide a molecular marker. Such compounds are said to be "labeled" (e.g., D_2O).

Properties of Hydrogen

- Hydrogen is unique.
- Hydrogen has a $1s^1$ electron configuration, so it is placed above Li in the periodic table.
  - However, H is significantly less reactive than the alkali metals.
- Hydrogen can gain an electron to form the *hydride ion* (H⁻), which has a He electron configuration.
  - Therefore, H could be placed above the halogens.
  - However, the electron affinity of H is lower than that of any halogen.
- Elemental hydrogen is a colorless, odorless diatomic gas at room temperature.
  - H_2 is sometimes referred to as *dihydrogen*, but is more commonly called either *molecular hydrogen* or simply hydrogen.
- Since H_2 is nonpolar and has only two electrons, its intermolecular forces are weak (boiling point –253 °C, melting point –250 °C).
- The H–H bond enthalpy is high (436 kJ/mol).
  - Therefore, reactions with hydrogen are slow at room temperature.
    - Often the molecules must be activated with heat, irradiation, or a catalyst.
- Hydrogen forms strong covalent bonds with many elements.
- When hydrogen is ignited in air, an explosion results:

$$2H_2(g) + O_2(g) \rightarrow 2H_2O(l) \qquad \Delta H = -571.7 \text{ kJ}$$

Production of Hydrogen[4]

- In the laboratory, hydrogen is usually prepared by the reduction of an acid.

---

[4] "Making Hydrogen Gas from an Acid and a Base" from Live Demonstrations

- For example, Zn is added to an acidic solution and hydrogen bubbles form.
- The hydrogen bubbles out of solution and is collected in a flask.
- The collection flask is usually filled with water, so the volume of hydrogen collected is the volume of water displaced.

$$Zn(s) + 2H^+(aq) \rightarrow Zn^{2+}(aq) + H_2(g)$$

- Hydrogen can be prepared in larger quantities by the reduction of methane in the presence of steam at 1100 °C:

$$CH_4(g) + H_2O(g) \rightarrow CO(g) + 3H_2(g)$$
$$CO(g) + H_2O(g) \rightarrow CO_2(g) + H_2(g)$$

- Alternatively,
  - hydrogen gas can be prepared by reacting carbon with steam at high temperatures to make *water gas* (a mixture of H_2 and CO).
  - H_2 is a by-product of the electrolysis of NaCl(*aq*):

$$2NaCl(aq) + 2H_2O(l) \rightarrow H_2(g) + Cl_2(g) + 2NaOH(aq)$$

Uses of Hydrogen

- About two-thirds of the 2×10^8 kg of hydrogen produced in the United States is used for ammonia production via the Haber process.
- Hydrogen is used to manufacture methanol:

$$CO(g) + 2H_2(g) \rightarrow CH_3OH(g)$$

Binary Hydrogen Compounds[5,6]

- Three types of binary hydrogen compounds are formed:
  - **ionic hydrides** (e.g., LiH)
    - contain H and alkali metals or heavier alkaline earth metals.
    - H^- is very reactive and basic.
      - Example: $H^-(aq) + H_2O(aq) \rightarrow H_2(g) + OH^-(aq)$
    - They are generally stored in an environment free from water and air.
  - **metallic hydrides** (e.g., TiH_2)
    - contain transition metals and H.
    - *Interstitial* hydrides can be made with less than stoichiometric amounts of H.
  - An example is $TiH_{1.8}$.
  - **molecular hydrides** (e.g., CH_4)
    - Contain nonmetals or semimetals and H.
    - The thermal stability of molecular hydrides (measured by $\Delta G°_f$) decreases as we go down a group and increases from left to right across a period.

22.3 Group 8A: The Noble Gases[7,8]

- The noble gases are all gases at room temperature.
  - He is the most important noble gas.
    - Liquid helium is used as a coolant.
    - It has the lowest boiling point of any substance.
  - Ar is the most abundant noble gas.

Noble-Gas Compounds

- The noble gases are very unreactive.

---

[5] "What's the Use? Hydrogen" from Further Readings
[6] "Formation of Water" Movie from Instructor's Resource CD/DVD
[7] "Electronegativities of the Noble Gases" from Further Readings
[8] Table 22.1 from Transparency Pack

- All noble gases have high ionization energies.
- The heavier noble gases react more readily than the lighter ones.
- The first compounds of noble gases were prepared by Neil Bartlett in 1962.
  - He prepared xenon fluorides.
- Oxygen-containing compounds are formed when the fluorides react with water.
$$XeF_6(s) + 3H_2O(l) \rightarrow XeO_3(aq) + 6HF(aq)$$
- Another known noble gas compound is KrF_2.
  - It decomposes to its elements at $-10\ °C$.

22.4 Group 7A: The Halogens
- The outer electron configurations are ns^2np^5.
- All halogens have large electron affinities.
  - They achieve a noble-gas configuration by gaining one electron.
  - Their most common oxidation state is -1, but oxidation states of $+1$, $+3$, $+5$, and $+7$ are possible.
- In the positive oxidation states, halogens are good oxidizing agents.
- Chlorine, bromine, and iodine are found as halides in seawater and salt deposits.
- Fluorine occurs in several minerals (e.g., fluorspar, CaF_2).
- All isotopes of At are radioactive.

Properties and Preparation of the Halogens[9,10,11,12]
- The properties of the halogens vary regularly with their atomic number.
- Each halogen is the most electronegative element in its row.
- Halogens exist as diatomic molecules.
  - In solids and liquids, the molecules are held together by weak London-dispersion forces.
  - Iodine has the highest melting point and the strongest intermolecular forces.
  - At room temperature, I_2 is a solid, Br_2 is a liquid, and Cl_2 and F_2 are gases.
- The bond enthalpy of F_2 is low.
  - Hence, fluorine is very reactive.
  - The reduction potential of fluorine is very high.
  - Water is oxidized more readily than fluorine, so F_2 cannot be prepared by electrolysis of a salt solution.
$$F_2(aq) + H_2O(l) \rightarrow 2HF(aq) + \tfrac{1}{2}O_2(g) \qquad E° = +1.80V$$
- Cl_2 is produced by electrolysis of $NaCl(l)$ or $NaCl(aq)$.

Uses of the Halogens[13,14,15,16]
- Fluorine is an important industrial chemical.
  - It is used to make fluorocarbons [used as lubricants and plastics (Teflon)].
- Chlorine is used in plastics (PVC), dichloroethane, and other organic chemicals; it is also used as a bleaching agent in the paper and textile industries.
  - NaClO is the active ingredient in bleach.
- NaBr is used in photography.

---

[9] Table 22.2 from Transparency Pack
[10] "An Overhead Demonstration of Some Descriptive Chemistry of the Halogens and Le Châtelier's Principle" from Live Demonstrations
[11] "Discovery and Early Uses of Iodine" from Further Readings
[12] "Physical Properties of the Halogens" Movie from Instructor's Resource CD/DVD
[13] "Demonstrating a Lack of Reactivity Using a Teflon-Coated Pan" from Live Demonstrations
[14] "Preparation of Chlorine Gas from Laundry Bleach" from Live Demonstrations
[15] "Dentifrice Fluoride" from Further Readings
[16] "Teflon" 3-D Model from Instructor's Resource CD/DVD

- Iodine is a necessary nutrient.
  - It is used by the body in the synthesis of thyroid hormone.
  - Lack of iodine in the diet results in a thyroid condition called *goiter*.

The Hydrogen Halides

- All halogens form diatomic molecules with hydrogen.
- Most hydrogen halides are prepared by treating a salt with a strong nonvolatile acid.
  - For example, we can utilize sulfuric acid in such a reaction to form HF or HCl:
  $$CaF_2(s) + H_2SO_4(l) \rightarrow 2HF(g) + CaSO_4(s)$$
  $$NaCl(s) + H_2SO_4(l) \rightarrow HCl(g) + NaHSO_4(s)$$
  - These reactions cannot be used to prepare HBr or HI.
- Hydrogen halides form hydrohalic acid solutions when dissolved in water.
- HF(*aq*) also reacts with **silica** (SiO_2) to form hexafluorosilicic acid:
  $$SiO_2(s) + 6HF(aq) \rightarrow H_2SiF_6(aq) + 2H_2O(l)$$
- HF must be stored in wax or plastic containers because it will react with the silicates in glass.

Interhalogen Compounds

- Diatomic molecules containing two different halogens are called **interhalogen compounds.**
- Most higher interhalogen compounds have Cl, Br, or I as the central atom surrounded by 3, 5, or 7 F atoms.
  - The larger the halogen, the more interhalogen compounds it can form.
  - The compound ICl_3 is unique.
    - The large size of the I atom allows it to accommodate the three Cl atoms.
    - No other halogen is large enough to accommodate three Cl atoms.
- Interhalogen compounds are very reactive; they are powerful oxidizing agents.

Oxyacids and Oxyanions

- Acid strength increases as the oxidation state of the halogen increases.
- All are strong oxidizing agents.
- They are generally unstable and decompose readily.
  - The oxyanions are more stable than oxyacids.
- Oxyacids and oxyanions of chlorine include:
  - hypochlorite salts (used in bleaches and disinfectants)
  - perchlorates (particularly unstable when heated in the presence of organic material)
    - Ammonium perchlorate is a potent oxidizer.
    - In the presence of powdered aluminum, NH_4ClO_4 is used to launch the space shuttle.
    - Each launch uses 700 tons of ammonium perchlorate.

FORWARD REFERENCES
  - The role of chlorides in the coordination chemistry of transition metals will be tabulated in Chapter 23 (section 23.1).

22.5 Oxygen

Properties of Oxygen[17,18]

- Oxygen has two allotropes: O_2 (*dioxygen*) and O_3 (*ozone*).
- O_2 is a colorless, odorless gas at room temperature.
  - The electron configuration is $[He]2s^2 2p^4$, which means the dominant oxidation state is –2.
  - It can complete an octet by gaining two e^- to form an oxide anion (O^{2-}) or by sharing $2e^-$.

---

[17] "Joseph Priestley, Preeminent Amateur Chemist" from Further Readings
[18] "The Discovery of Oxygen and Other Priestley Matters" from Further Readings

- In covalent compounds, it forms either two single bonds or a double bond.
- The O=O bond is strong (bond enthalpy 495 kJ/mol).

Production of Oxygen

- Laboratory preparation of oxygen often involves the catalytic decomposition of $KClO_3$ in the presence of MnO_2:

$$2KClO_3(s) \rightarrow 2KCl(s) + 3O_2(g)$$

- Atmospheric oxygen is replenished by photosynthesis.

Uses of Oxygen

- Oxygen is one of the most widely used oxidizing agents.
  - More than half of the oxygen produced is used in the steel industry to remove impurities.
- Oxygen is also used in medicine.
  - It is used with acetylene, C_2H_2 for oxyacetylene welding:

$$2C_2H_2(g) + 5O_2(g) \rightarrow 4CO_2(g) + 2H_2O(g) \qquad \Delta H° = -2510 \text{ kJ}$$

Ozone[19]

- Ozone is a pale blue poisonous gas.
- Ozone dissociates to form oxygen:

$$O_3(g) \rightarrow O_2(g) + O(g) \qquad \Delta H° = 105 \text{ kJ}.$$

- Ozone is a stronger oxidizing agent than oxygen:

$$O_3(g) + 2H^+(aq) + 2e^- \rightarrow O_2(g) + H_2O(l) \qquad E° = 2.07 \text{ V}$$
$$O_2(g) + 4H^+(aq) + 4e^- \rightarrow 2H_2O(l) \qquad E° = 1.23 \text{ V}$$

- Ozone can be made by passing an electric current through dry O_2:

$$3O_2(g) \rightarrow 2O_3(g) \qquad \Delta H° = 285 \text{ kJ}$$

- Ozone is used to kill bacteria and to prepare pharmaceuticals and lubricants.
- Ozone is an important component of the atmosphere.
  - In the upper atmosphere, ozone forms a shield to screen out harmful radiation.
  - In the lower atmosphere, ozone is considered an air pollutant.

Oxides[20,21,22,23,24]

- Oxygen is the second most electronegative element.
- *Oxides* are compounds with oxygen in the –2 oxidation state.
- Nonmetal oxides are covalent.
  - Most metal oxides combine with water to give oxyacids.
  - Oxides that react with water to form acids are called **acidic anhydrides**, or **acidic oxides**.
    - Anhydride means without water.
  - Example:

$$SO_2(g) + H_2O(l) \rightarrow H_2SO_3(aq)$$

- Metal oxides are ionic.
  - Oxides that react with water to form hydroxides are called **basic anhydrides**, or **basic oxides**.
  - Example: BaO in water produces $Ba(OH)_2$.

$$BaO(s) + H_2O(l) \rightarrow Ba(OH)_2(aq)$$

- Oxides that exhibit both acidic and basic properties are said to be *amphoteric* (e.g., Cr_2O_3).

---

[19] "Ozone" 3-D Model from Instructor's Resource CD/DVD
[20] "Combining Volume of Oxygen with Sulfur" from Live Demonstrations
[21] "Periodic Trends: Acid-Base Behavior of Oxides" Animation from Instructor's Resource CD/DVD
[22] "Three Forms of Molecular Oxygen" from Further Readings
[23] "An Acidity Scale for Binary Oxides" from Further Readings
[24] "Water" 3-D Model from Instructor's Resource CD/DVD

Peroxides and Superoxides[25]

- *Peroxides* have an O–O bond and O in the –1 oxidation state.
  - An example is hydrogen peroxide (H_2O_2).
- *Superoxides* have an O–O bond and O in an oxidation state of $-\frac{1}{2}$.
  - The superoxide ion is O_2^-.
  - Superoxides usually form with very active metals (KO_2, RbO_2 and CsO_2).
- Uses of superoxides:
  - Superoxides generate oxygen gas when dissolved in water.
  - This process is used in oxygen masks used in rescue work.
- Properties and uses of peroxides
  - Hydrogen peroxide is unstable and decomposes into water and oxygen:
    $$2H_2O_2(l) \rightarrow 2H_2O(l) + O_2(g) \qquad \Delta H° = -196.1 \text{ kJ}.$$
    - This is an example of a ***disproportionation reaction*** in which an element is simultaneously oxidized and reduced.
    - In dilute aqueous solution it is used as a mild antiseptic.
  - Peroxide is a by-product of some cellular metabolic processes.
    - These peroxides are reactive and potentially damaging to tissues.
    - Cells contain enzymes (peroxidases, catalase) that convert peroxides into less harmful species.
    - Peroxides are formed when active metals such as Na or Ca react with O_2 (i.e., to form metallic peroxides such as Na_2O_2, CaO_2).

FORWARD REFERENCES
- Several oxide minerals of transition metals will be tabulated in Chapter 23 (section 23.1).

22.6 The Other Group 6A Elements: S, Se, Te, and Po

General Characteristics of Group 6A Elements

- The outermost electron configuration is ns^2np^4.
- The dominant oxidation state is –2 (ns^2np^6).
- Other observed oxidation states are up to +6 (e.g., SF_6, SeF_6, TeF_6).
- There is a regular change in properties with increasing atomic number.

Occurrences and Production of S, Se, and Te[26,27]

- Sulfur, selenium, and tellurium can all be mined from the earth.
- S occurs widely as sulfates and in sulfide minerals.
  - Its presence in coal and petroleum poses an environmental problem when these fuels are burned.
- Se and Te occur in rare minerals (Cu_2Se, $PbSe$, Ag_2Se, Cu_2Te, $PbTe$, Ag_2Te, and Au_2Te) and are minor constituents in sulfide ores (usually of Cu, Fe, Ni, and Pb).

Properties and Uses of Sulfur, Selenium, and Tellurium

- Sulfur is yellow, tasteless, and almost odorless.
  - Sulfur is insoluble in water.
  - Sulfur exists in allotropes (rhombic S_8 rings, plastic sulfur).
  - Sulfur is used in the manufacture of sulfuric acid and in vulcanizing rubber.
- Se and Te both form helical chains of atoms in crystals.
  - There is some sharing of electron pairs between chains.
  - Se is used in photoelectric cells, photocopiers, and light meters.

---

[25] "Hydrogen Peroxide" 3-D Model from Instructor's Resource CD/DVD

[26] "Plastic Sulfur" from Live Demonstrations

[27] Table 22.5 from Transparency Pack

- Its electrical conductivity is poor in the dark and increases greatly when exposed to light.

Sulfides[28]

- S is in the –2 oxidation state in *sulfides*.
- Many metals are found in the form of sulfides in ores.
  - Examples are PbS (galena) and HgS (cinnabar).
- S in *pyrites* is in the –1 oxidation state, S_2^{2-}.
  - FeS_2 is iron pyrite, often called "fool's gold."
- Hydrogen sulfide (used for qualitative analysis of certain metals) is prepared by treating iron(II) sulfide with dilute acid:

$$FeS(s) + 2H^+(aq) \rightarrow H_2S(aq) + Fe^{2+}(aq)$$

- Hydrogen sulfide is responsible for the odor of rotten eggs and is quite toxic.

Oxides, Oxyacids, and Oxyanions of Sulfur[29]

- SO_2 is produced when sulfur is combusted in air.
- SO_2 in water produces sulfurous acid, H_2SO_3, a weak diprotic acid.
- SO_2 is toxic to fungi and is used to sterilize dried fruit and wine.
  - Na_2SO_3 and $NaHSO_3$ are used as preservatives.
    - Many people are allergic to these agents and must avoid foods treated with them.
- When sulfur burns in air, both SO_2 (major product) and SO_3 are formed.
- The oxidation of SO_2 to SO_3 requires a catalyst (usually V_2O_5 or Pt).
- SO_3 is used to produce H_2SO_4:

$$SO_3(g) + H_2SO_4(l) \rightarrow H_2S_2O_7(l) \text{ [pyrosulfuric acid]}$$
$$H_2S_2O_7(l) + H_2O(l) \rightarrow 2H_2SO_4(l)$$

- Commercially, sulfuric acid is 98% H_2SO_4.
- Sulfuric acid is a powerful dehydrating agent, a strong acid, and a moderate oxidizing agent.
- In aqueous solutions of H_2SO_4 only the first proton is completely ionized:

$$H_2SO_4(aq) \rightarrow HSO_4^-(aq) + H^+(aq)$$

- Bisulfate (HSO_4^-) salts are important components of "dry acids" used in toilet bowl cleaners and in adjusting the pH of swimming pools and hot tubs.
- The sulfite ion, SO_3^{2-}, and the *thio*sulfate ion, $S_2O_3^{2-}$, are other important sulfur-containing ions:

$$8SO_3^{2-}(aq) + S_8(s) \rightarrow 8S_2O_3^{2-}(aq)$$

FORWARD REFERENCES

- Several sulfide minerals of transition metals will be tabulated in Chapter 23 (section 23.1).

22.7 Nitrogen

Properties of Nitrogen[30]

- It is a colorless, odorless, tasteless gas composed of N_2 molecules.
- It is unreactive because of the strong triple bond.
- Exception: Burning Mg or Li in air (78% nitrogen) forms nitrides:

$$3Mg(s) + N_2(g) \rightarrow Mg_3N_2(s)$$
$$6Li(s) + N_2(g) \rightarrow 2Li_3N(s)$$

- N^{3-} is a strong Brønsted-Lowry base (forms NH_3 in water):

$$Mg_3N_2(s) + 6H_2O(l) \rightarrow 2NH_3(aq) + 3Mg(OH)_2(s)$$

- Nitrogen exhibits all formal oxidation states from –3 to +5.

---

[28] "Herman Frasch, Sulfur King" from Further Readings
[29] "Sulfate Ion" 3-D Model from Instructor's Resource CD/DVD
[30] Table 22.6 from Transparency Pack

- The most common oxidation states are +5, 0, and –3 (nitrogen has an $[He]2s^2 2p^3$ electron configuration).

Production and Uses of Nitrogen

- N_2 is produced by fractional distillation of air.
- Nitrogen is used as an inert gas to exclude oxygen from packaged foods and in the manufacture of chemicals, fabrication of metals, and production of electronics.
- Liquid nitrogen is an important coolant.
- The largest use of N_2 is in the manufacture of nitrogen-containing fertilizers to provide a source of *fixed* nitrogen.
  - Nitrogen is fixed by forming NH_3 (Haber Process).
  - NH_3 is converted into other useful chemicals.

Hydrogen Compounds of Nitrogen[31]

- *Ammonia* is one of the most important compounds of nitrogen.
  - Ammonia is a colorless toxic gas with an irritating aroma.
  - In the laboratory, ammonia is produced by the reaction between NaOH and an ammonium salt:
  $$NH_4Cl(aq) + NaOH(aq) \rightarrow NH_3(g) + H_2O(l) + NaCl(aq)$$
  - Commercially, ammonia is prepared by the Haber process.
  $$N_2(g) + 3H_2(g) \rightarrow 2NH_3(g)$$
- *Hydrazine* contains an N–N single bond (N_2H_4).
  - Hydrazine (poisonous) is prepared by the reaction of ammonia and hypochlorite:
  $$2NH_3(aq) + OCl^-(aq) \rightarrow N_2H_4(aq) + Cl^-(aq) + H_2O(l)$$
  - Poisonous chloramine, NH_2Cl, is an intermediate in the reaction.
    - It bubbles out of solution when household ammonia and bleach are mixed.
  - Pure hydrazine is an oily liquid that explodes on heating.
    - Hydrazine and related compounds are used as a component of rocket fuels.

Oxides and Oxyacids of Nitrogen[32,33,34,35,36,37,38,39]

- There are three common oxides of nitrogen:
  - N_2O (*nitrous oxide*).
    - This is also known as laughing gas and is used as an anesthetic.
  - NO (*nitric oxide*).
    - This is a toxic, colorless gas; it is an important neurotransmitter.
  - NO_2 (*nitrogen dioxide*).
    - This is a poisonous yellowish-brown gas, which is major constituent of smog.
- Some of the reactions used in their preparation include:
  $$NH_4NO_3(s) \rightarrow N_2O(g) + 2H_2O(g)$$
  $$3Cu(s) + 2NO_3^-(aq) + 8H^+(aq) \rightarrow 3Cu^{2+}(aq) + 2NO(g) + 4H_2O(l)$$
- The **Ostwald process** is the commercial route to HNO_3.
  - It takes place in 3 steps:

---

[31] "Hydrazine" 3-D Model from Instructor's Resource CD/DVD
[32] "Some History of Nitrates" from Further Readings
[33] "Nitrogen Dioxide and Dinitrogen Tetroxide" Movie from Instructor's Resource CD/DVD
[34] "Dinitrogen Trioxide" 3-D Model from Instructor's Resource CD/DVD
[35] "Dinitrogen Tetroxide" 3-D Model from Instructor's Resource CD/DVD
[36] "Nitrogen Dioxide" 3-D Model from Instructor's Resource CD/DVD
[37] "The Discovery of Nitroglycerine: Its Preparation and Therapeutic Utility" from Further Readings
[38] "Bad Rap of Nitrate" from Further Readings
[39] "Biological Roles of Nitric Acid" from Further Readings

- oxidation of NH_3 by oxygen to form NO (usually using a Pt catalyst).
$$4NH_3(g) + 5O_2(g) \rightarrow 4NO(g) + 6H_2O(g)$$
- oxidation of NO by oxygen to form NO_2 (unreacted NO is recycled).
- NO_2 dissolution in water to form nitric acid.
- The common oxyacids of nitrogen are HNO_3 (*nitric*) and HNO_2 (*nitrous*).
  - Nitric acid is a strong acid and a powerful oxidizing agent.
    - Concentrated nitric acid will oxidize most metals (exceptions are Au, Pt, Rh and Ir):
    $$NO_3^-(aq) + 4H^+(aq) + 3e^- \rightarrow NO(g) + 2H_2O(l) \qquad E° = 0.96V$$
  - Nitric acid is used to manufacture fertilizers (NH_4NO_3), drugs, plastics, and explosives [such as nitroglycerin and TNT (trinitrotoulene)].
  - Nitrous acid (weak, $K_a = 4.5 \times 10^{-4}$) is not stable and disproportionates into NO and HNO_3.

FORWARD REFERENCES
- Ammonia complexes of cobalt will be discussed in Chapter 23 (section 23.2).

22.8 The Other Group 5A Elements: P, As, Sb, and Bi

General Characteristics of the Group 5A Elements[40,41,42,43]

- The outermost shell electron configuration is ns^2np^3.
- The most common oxidation state is –3. Other common oxidation states are –1, +1, +3, and +5.
- The variation in atomic properties is very striking.
  - This group contains all three types of elements: metallic, nonmetallic, and semimetallic.
  - Size and metallic character increase with increasing atomic number within the group.
- The X–X bond enthalpies are difficult to measure.

Occurrence, Isolation, and Properties of Phosphorus[44]

- Occurs mainly in phosphorus minerals [e.g., phosphate rock, $Ca_3(PO_4)_2$].
- Elemental P_4 is produced by reduction:
$$2\ Ca_3(PO_4)_2(s) + 6SiO_2(s) + 10C(s) \rightarrow P_4(g) + 6CaSiO_3(l) + 10CO(g).$$
- There are two allotropes of phosphorus: red and white.
  - P_4 is white phosphorus.
    - All P–P–P bond angles are 60° (small), therefore, the molecule is strained and unstable.
    - White phosphorus is poisonous and highly reactive (spontaneously reacts with oxygen in air).
      - Therefore, white phosphorus is stored under water.
- If white phosphorus is heated to 400 °C in the absence of air, it converts into red phosphorus.
  - Red phosphorus is the more stable allotrope and is not usually stored under water.

Phosphorus Halides

- Phosphorus forms a variety of compounds with halogens with the tri- and pentahalides being the most important.
- The most important is PCl_3 which is used in soap, detergent, plastic, and insecticide production.
- Preparation of phosphorus halides involves direct oxidation of elemental phosphorous with elemental halogen.
  - For example:
$$2P(s) + 3Cl_2(g) \rightarrow 2PCl_3(l)$$
  - In the presence of excess chlorine:

---

[40] "Arsenic: Not So Evil After All?" from Further Readings
[41] Table 22.7 from Transparency Pack
[42] "Arsenic in Drinking Water—A Global Environmental Problem" from Further Readings
[43] "Phosphorus" 3-D Model from Instructor's Resource CD/DVD
[44] "Keeping the Fire Cold" from Further Readings

$$PCl_3(l) + Cl_2(g) \leftrightarrows PCl_5(s)$$

- In the presence of water hydrolysis occurs readily:

$$PBr_3(g) + 3H_2O(l) \rightarrow H_3PO_3(aq) + 3HBr(aq)$$
$$PCl_5(l) + 4H_2O(l) \rightarrow H_3PO_4(aq) + 5HCl(aq)$$

Oxy Compounds of Phosphorus[45,46,47,48]

- Oxygen-containing phosphorus compounds are extremely important.
    - Phosphorus(III) oxide, P_4O_6 is made by reacting white phosphorus with a limited supply of oxygen.
    - Phosphorus(V) oxide, P_4O_{10} is made by reacting phosphorus with excess oxygen.
    - Phosphorus(III) oxide, P_4O_6 produces phosphorous acid, H_3PO_3 in water.
- The oxides of phosphorus are acidic.
    - H_3PO_3 is a weak *di*protic acid (the H attached to P is not acidic).
    - Phosphorus(V) oxide, P_4O_{10} produces phosphoric acid, H_3PO_4.
        - H_3PO_4 is a weak *tri*protic acid.
        - P_4O_{10} is used as a drying agent because of its affinity for water.
- Phosphoric and phosphorous acids undergo condensation reactions.
    - A condensation reaction is one in which two or more molecules combine to form a larger molecule with the elimination of a smaller molecule.
    - For example:

$$nH_3PO_4 \rightarrow (HPO_3)_n + nH_2O$$

- Phosphoric acid and its salts are used in detergents (as $Na_5P_3O_{10}$) and fertilizers (from mined phosphate rock).
- Phosphorus compounds are important in biological systems [e.g., RNA, DNA, and adenosine triphosphate (ATP)].

FORWARD REFERENCES
- Phosphate groups in RNA and DNA will be discussed in Chapter 24 (section 24.10).

22.9 Carbon

Elemental Forms of Carbon

- Carbon constitutes about 0.027% of the Earth's crust.
- Carbon is the main constituent of living matter.
- The study of carbon compounds (*organic compounds*) is called *organic chemistry*.
- There are five allotropic forms of carbon: two of these are graphite and diamond:
    - *graphite* (soft, slippery, and black),
    - *diamond* (clear, hard, and forms a covalent network),
- Microcrystalline and amorphous forms of C include:
    - **carbon black**, formed when hydrocarbons are heated in a very limited supply of oxygen:

$$CH_4(g) + O_2(g) \rightarrow C(s) + 2H_2O(g)$$

    - Carbon black is used as a pigment in black inks and automobile tires.
    - **charcoal**, formed by heating wood in the absence of air.
        - Activated charcoal is used to remove odors and impurities from air and water.

Oxides of Carbon

- Carbon forms two principal oxides: CO and CO_2.

---

[45] "Tetraphosphorus Hexoxide" 3-D Model from Instructor's Resource CD/DVD
[46] "Tetraphosphorus Decoxide" 3-D Model from Instructor's Resource CD/DVD
[47] "Phosphoric Acid" 3-D Model from Instructor's Resource CD/DVD
[48] "Phosphorous Acid" 3-D Model from Instructor's Resource CD/DVD

- CO (*carbon monoxide*) is formed when carbon or hydrocarbons are burned in a limited supply of oxygen.

$$2C(s) + O_2(g) \rightarrow 2CO(g)$$

  - CO is very toxic (binds irreversibly to hemoglobin, interfering with oxygen transport).
    - It is odorless, colorless, and tasteless.
  - CO also has a lone pair of electrons on C, which is unusual.
  - CO is a good Lewis base and forms metal carbonyls with transition metals.
    - For example, $Ni(CO)_4$ forms readily when Ni is warmed in CO.
  - CO can be used as a fuel:

$$2CO(g) + O_2(g) \rightarrow 2CO_2(g) \qquad \Delta H° = -566 \text{ kJ}$$

  - CO is a good reducing agent

$$Fe_3O_4(s) + 4CO(g) \rightarrow 3Fe(s) + 4CO_2(g)$$

- CO_2 (*carbon dioxide*) is produced when organic compounds are burned in excess oxygen:

$$C_2H_5OH(l) + 3O_2(g) \rightarrow 2CO_2(g) + 3H_2O(g)$$

  - CO_2 is produced by either heating carbonates or treating them with acids:

$$CaCO_3(s) \rightarrow CO_2(g) + CaO(s)$$
$$CO_3^{2-}(aq) + 2H^+(aq) \rightarrow CO_2(g) + H_2O(l)$$

  - Fermentation of sugar to produce alcohol also produces CO_2:

$$C_6H_{12}O_6(aq) \rightarrow 2C_2H_5OH(aq) + 2CO_2(g)$$

- Some of the major uses of CO_2 are in refrigeration (using Dry Ice™), in the carbonation of beverages, and in the production of both *washing soda* ($Na_2CO_3 \cdot 10H_2O$) and *baking soda* ($NaHCO_3$).

Carbonic Acid and Carbonates[49]

- When CO_2 dissolves in water (moderately soluble) a diprotic acid, carbonic acid, forms:

$$CO_2(aq) + H_2O(l) \leftrightarrows H_2CO_3(aq)$$

- Carbonic acid is responsible for giving carbonated beverages a sharp acidic taste.
- Two salts of carbonic acid may be obtained by neutralization.
  - Partial neutralization of H_2CO_3 gives hydrogen carbonates (bicarbonates): HCO_3^-.
    - Aqueous solutions of bicarbonates are weakly basic.
  - Full neutralization gives carbonates: CO_3^{2-}.
    - Aqueous solutions of carbonates are more strongly basic.
- Many minerals contain CO_3^{2-}.
- Example: Calcite ($CaCO_3$) is the principal mineral in limestone, marble, etc..
- $CaCO_3$ reacts readily with acid:

$$CaCO_3(s) + 2H^+(aq) \leftrightarrows Ca^{2+}(aq) + CO_2(g) + H_2O(l)$$

- At elevated temperatures, $CaCO_3$ decomposes:

$$CaCO_3(s) \rightarrow CaO(s) + CO_2(g)$$

  - This reaction is the commercial source of *lime*, CaO.
  - CaO reacts with water and CO_2 to form $CaCO_3$, which binds the sand in mortar:

$$CaO(s) + H_2O(l) \leftrightarrows Ca^{2+}(aq) + 2OH^-(aq)$$
$$Ca^{2+}(aq) + 2OH^-(aq) + CO_2(aq) \rightarrow CaCO_3(s) + H_2O(l)$$

Carbides

- **Carbides** are binary compounds of C and metals, metalloids, and certain nonmetals.
- There are three types of carbides:
  - *Ionic carbides* (formed by active metals)
    - Most contain the *acetylide* ion, C_2^{2-}.
      - An example is CaC_2.

---

[49] "Carbon Dioxide Behaves as an Acid in Water" Movie from Instructor's Resource CD/DVD

- CaC$_2$ is used in the formation of acetylene:
$$CaC_2(s) + 2H_2O(l) \rightarrow Ca(OH)_2(aq) + C_2H_2(g)$$
- *Interstitial carbides* are formed by many transition metals.
  - An example is tungsten carbide.
  - The carbon atoms occupy the spaces or interstices between metal atoms.
- *Covalent carbides* are formed by B and Si.
  - SiC is also called Carborundum. It is nearly as hard as diamond.

Other Inorganic Compounds of Carbon

- Two interesting inorganic compounds of carbon are HCN and CS$_2$.
  - HCN (hydrogen cyanide) is an extremely toxic gas.
    - HCN is produced by reacting a salt, (e.g., NaCN) with acid.
    - Cyanides are used in the manufacture of plastics like nylon and Orlon.
    - CN$^-$ forms very stable complexes with transition metals.
    - One cause of its toxicity is its ability to combine with the iron(III) of a key enzyme in respiration (cytochrome oxidase).
  - CS$_2$ is an important solvent for waxes and greases.
    - CS$_2$ vapor is very toxic, colorless, and highly flammable.

FORWARD REFERENCES
- Chemistry of carbon will be discussed in detail throughout Chapter 24.

22.10 The Other Group 4A Elements: Si, Ge, Sn, and Pb

General Characteristics of Group 4A Elements[50]

- The outermost electron configuration is ns^2np^2.
- The electronegativities are low.
- Carbon has a coordination number of 4, the other members have higher coordination numbers.
  - Carbides (C^{4-}) are rare.
  - C–C bonds are very strong, so C shows the unusual ability to bond to itself to form long chains.
- The dominant oxidation state for Ge, Sn, and Pb is +2.
- Because the Si–O bond is stronger than the Si–Si bond, Si tends to form oxides (silicates).

Occurrence and Preparation of Silicon

- Si is the second most abundant element in the Earth's crust.
- Elemental Si is prepared by reducing SiO$_2$:
$$SiO_2(l) + 2C(s) \rightarrow Si(l) + 2CO(g)$$
- Silicon has many important uses in the electronics industry.
  - Wafers of Si are cut from cylindrical Si crystals.
  - Si must be extremely pure when used as a semiconductor.
  - Impure Si is converted to SiCl$_4$ (with Cl$_2$), distilled, and then reduced to pure Si:
$$SiCl_4(g) + 2H_2(g) \rightarrow Si(s) + 4HCl(g)$$
  - The Si is then further purified by zone refining.
    - *Zone refining* is used to produce ultrapure Si.
    - The silicon crystal is placed inside a tube with an inert atmosphere.
    - A heating coil is slowly moved down the Si.
    - As the coil melts the Si, any impurities dissolve and move down with the heating coil.
    - At the bottom of the crystal, the portion of Si containing all the impurities is cut off and discarded.
    - The remaining crystal is ultrapure.

---

[50] Table 22.8 from Transparency Pack

Silicates[51,52,53,54]

- More than 90% of the Earth's crust is composed of compounds of Si and O.
- The most common oxidation state of Si is +4.
- **Silicates** are compounds in which Si has four O atoms surrounding it in a tetrahedral arrangement.
  - Other minerals like zircon, $ZrSiO_4$ have a similar structure.
  - The silicate tetrahedra are building blocks for more complicated structures.
  - If two SiO_4^{4-} (*orthosilicate* ions) link together, one O atom is shared.
    - This structure is the *disilicate* ion, $Si_2O_7^{6-}$.
    - The mineral *thortveitite* ($Sc_2Si_2O_7$) contains disilicate ions.
- Many silicate tetrahedra can link together to form sheets, chains, or three-dimensional structures.
  - Consider a structure with two vertices linked to two other tetrahedra.
  - A single-strand silicate chain can form with a $Si_2O_6^{4-}$ repeating unit.
    - An example is *enstatite* ($MgSiO_3$).
  - Consider a structure with two vertices linked to three other tetrahedra.
    - A two-dimensional sheet results.
  - The mineral *talc* [talcum powder, $Mg_3(Si_2O_5)_2(OH)_2$] results.
- Many minerals are based on silicates.
  - Some are useful as clays, ceramics, and other materials.
  - Others have harmful effects on human health:
    - *Asbestos* is a general term applied to a group of fibrous silicate minerals.
      - They form chains or sheets of silicates.
      - The sheets in asbestos are formed into rolls.
      - The rolls make the asbestos fibrous.
      - The fibers can be woven into cloth (fireproof clothing).
        - Asbestos represents a significant health risk and has been linked to diseases such as lung cancer.
  - Three-dimensional silicate forms quartz.

Glass[55,56,57]

- Glasses result when silicates are heated (Si–O bonds are broken) and then rapidly cooled.
  - The Si–O bonds are re-formed before the atoms are able to organize into an ordered arrangement.
  - The amorphous solid is called quartz glass or silica glass.
- Additives are used to lower the melting point of the SiO_2.
  - **Glass** in windows and bottles is called *soda-lime glass* (CaO and Na_2O are used as additives).
    - The CaO and Na_2O are formed from limestone ($CaCO_3$) and soda ash (Na_2CO_3) when these inexpensive materials are heated.
- Other properties of glass may be altered by additives.
  - CoO produces blue cobalt glass.
  - K_2O produces a harder glass than glass made with Na_2O.
  - PbO produces lead crystal glass (high refractive index).
  - B_2O_3 is used to make Pyrex® and Kimax®.
    - Pyrex® and Kimax® glassware has a very high melting point and resists thermal shock.

---

[51] Figure 22.34 from Transparency Pack
[52] "Silicate Tetrahedron" 3-D Model from Instructor's Resource CD/DVD
[53] "Disilicate Anion ($Si_2O_7^{6-}$)" 3-D Model from Instructor's Resource CD/DVD
[54] "Single-Chain Silicate" 3-D Model from Instructor's Resource CD/DVD
[55] "Glass-Sand + Imagination" from Further Readings
[56] "Glass Doesn't Flow and Doesn't Crystallize and It Isn't a Liquid" from Further Readings
[57] "The Origin of Pyrex" from Further Readings

Silicones

- Silicones consist of O–Si–O chains with Si–R (R is an organic group such as CH_3) bonds filling the Si valency.
- Silicones can be oils or rubber-like materials depending on chain length and degree of cross-linking.
- Silicones are used in lubricants, car polishes, sealants, gaskets, and for waterproofing fabrics.

22.11 Boron[58,59]

- **Boranes** are compounds of boron and hydrogen.
- BH_3 is the simplest borane.
  - It reacts with itself to form *diborane*, B_2H_6.
    - Hydrogen appears to form two bonds.
      - These are called *bridging hydrogens*.
  - Diborane is very reactive:
$$B_2H_6(g) + 3O_2(g) \rightarrow B_2O_3(s) + 3H_2O(g) \qquad \Delta H^\circ = -2030 \text{ kJ.}$$
  - Some boranes such as pentaborane (B_5H_9), are reactive while some are stable in air at room temperature (e.g., decaborane: $B_{10}H_{14}$).
- Boron and hydrogen form a series of anions called *borane anions* such as BH_4^-.
  - They are used as reducing agents.
  - Sodium borohydride, $NaBH_4$, is used very commonly in organic chemistry.
- Boric oxide, B_2O_3, is the only important boron oxide.
  - It is the anhydride form of boric acid, H_3BO_3, a weak acid ($K_a = 5.8 \times 10^{-10}$).
  - Boric acid is used as an eyewash.
    - Heating causes a dehydration of boric acid, yielding a diprotic acid called tetraboric acid:
$$4H_3BO_3(s) \rightarrow H_2B_4O_7(s) + 5H_2O(g)$$
  - The hydrated sodium salt is called borax.
    - Solutions of borax are alkaline.
    - It is widely used as a cleaning agent.

---

[58] "Boron Clusters Come of Age" from Further Readings
[59] "Diborane" 3-D Model from Instructor's Resource CD/DVD

Further Readings:

1. Alton Banks, "What's the Use? Hydrogen," *J. Chem. Educ.*, Vol. 66, **1989**, 801. Each of the "What's the Use?" articles, written by Alton Banks, focuses on the uses of a specific element. See volumes 66 **(1989)**, 67 **(1990)**, 68 **(1991)** and 69 **(1992)** for other elements!

2. Terry L. Meek, "Electronegativities of the Noble Gases," *J. Chem. Educ.*, Vol. 72, **1995**, 17–18.

3. Louis Rosenfeld, "Discovery and Early Uses of Iodine," *J. Chem. Educ.*, Vol. 77, **2000**, 984–987.

4. Philip E. Rakita, "Dentifrice Fluoride," *J. Chem. Educ.*, Vol. 81, **2004**, 677–680.

5. Foil A. Miller, "Joseph Priestley, Preeminent Amateur Chemist," *J. Chem. Educ.*, Vol. 64, **1987**, 745–747.

6. Kathryn R. Williams, "The Discovery of Oxygen and other Priestley Matters," *J. Chem. Educ.,* Vol. 80, **2003**, 1129–1131.

7. Michael Laing, "The Three Forms of Molecular Oxygen," *J. Chem. Educ.*, Vol. 66, **1989**, 453–454.

8. Derek W. Smith, "An Acidity Scale for Binary Oxides," *J. Chem. Educ.*, Vol. 64, **1987**, 480–481.

9. Miriam C. Nagel, "Herman Frasch, Sulfur King," *J. Chem. Educ.*, Vol. 58, **1981**, 60–61.

10. Dennis W. Barnum, "Some History of Nitrates," *J. Chem. Educ.*, Vol. 80, **2003**, 1393–1396.

11. J. R. Minkel, "Bad Rap of Nitrate?", *Scientific American*, **September 2004**, 20.

12. David S. Bredt and Solomon, H. Snyder, "Biological Roles of Nitric Oxide", *Scientific American*, **May 1992**, 68–72.

13. Natalie I. Foster and Ned D. Heindel, "The Discovery of Nitroglycerine: Its Preparation and Therapeutic Utility," *J. Chem. Educ.*, Vol 58, **1981**, 364–365.

14. Annette Lykknes and Lise Kvittinger, "Arsenic: Not So Evil After All?" *J. Chem. Educ.*, Vol. 80, **2003**, 497–500.

15. Terence P. Lee, "Keeping the Fire Cold," *Chemistry in Britain*, **January 1996**, 41–45. An article on the importance of phosphorous.

16. Joanna Shaofen Wang and Chien M. Wai, "Arsenic in Drinking Water–A Global Environmental Problem," *J. Chem. Educ.*, Vol. 81, **2004**, 207–213.

17. Kenneth E. Kolb and Doris K. Kolb, "Glass-Sand + Imagination," *J. Chem. Educ.*, Vol. 77, **2000**, 812–816.

18. Stephen J. Hawkes, "Glass Doesn't Flow and Doesn't Crystallize and It Isn't a Liquid," *J. Chem. Educ.*, Vol. 77, **2000**, 846–848.

19. William B. Jensen, "The Origin of Pyrex," *J. Chem. Educ.*, Vol. 83, **2006**, 692–693.

20. Russell N. Grimes, "Boron Clusters Come of Age," *J. Chem. Educ.*, Vol. 81, **2004**, 658–672.

Live Demonstrations:

1. Lee R. Summerlin, Christie L. Borgford, and Julie B. Ealy, "Making Hydrogen Gas from an Acid and a Base," *Chemical Demonstrations, A Sourcebook for Teachers, Volume 2* (Washington: American Chemical Society, **1987**), pp. 33–34. Gas-generating reactions are carried out in two flasks fitted with balloons; the balloons inflate as they collect the hydrogen gas generated.

2. Robert C. Hansen, "An Overhead Demonstration of Some Descriptive Chemistry of the Halogens and Le Châtelier's Principle," *J. Chem. Educ.*, Vol. 65, **1988**, 264–265.

3. Lee R. Summerlin and James L. Ealy, Jr., "Preparation of Chlorine Gas from Laundry Bleach," *Chemical Demonstrations, A Sourcebook for Teachers,* (Washington: American Chemical Society, **1985**), p. 13. The bleaching effect of chlorine is shown in this reaction; chlorine gas is prepared by reaction of laundry bleach with hydrochloric acid.

4. Thomas G. Richmond and Paul F. Kraus, "Demonstrating a Lack of Reactivity Using a Teflon-Coated Pan," *J. Chem. Educ.*, Vol. 72, **1995**, 731. A short demonstration of the wonders of Teflon.

5. Bassam Z. Shakhashiri, "Combining Volume of Oxygen with Sulfur," *Chemical Demonstrations: A Handbook for Teachers of Chemistry, Volume 2* (Madison: The University of Wisconsin Press, **1985**), pp. 190–192. A demonstration of the production of SO_2, rather than SO_3, upon combustion of sulfur in O_2.

6. Lee R. Summerlin, Christie L. Borgford, and Julie B. Ealy, "Plastic Sulfur," *Chemical Demonstrations, A Sourcebook for Teachers, Volume 2* (Washington: American Chemical Society, **1987**), p. 53. Plastic sulfur is formed by pouring heated yellow sulfur into a beaker of water.

Chapter 23. Transition Metals and Coordination Chemistry

Media Resources

Figures and Tables in Transparency Pack:

	Section:
Figure 23.1 The Position of the Transition Metals In the Periodic Table	23.1 The Transition Metals
Figure 23.4 Nonzero Oxidation States of the Period 4 Transition Metals	23.1 The Transition Metals
Figure 23.5 The Relative Orientation of Electron Spins in Various Types of Compounds	23.1 The Transition Metals
Figure 23.7 *Cis* and *Trans* Isomers of $[Co(NH_3)_4Cl_2]^+$	23.2 Transition Metal Complexes
Figure 23.9 In Complexes Having Coordination Number 4, the Molecular Geometry Can Be Tetrahedral or Square Planar	23.2 Transition Metal Complexes
Figure 23.11 The $[Co(en)_3]^{3+}$ Ion	23.3 Common Ligands in Coordination Chemistry
Figure 23.12 The $EDTA^{4-}$ Ligand and the Complex Ion $[CoEDTA]^-$	23.3 Common Ligands in Coordination Chemistry
Figure 23.14 Myoglobin	23.3 Common Ligands in Coordination Chemistry
Figure 23.15 Coordination Sphere of the Hemes in Oxymyoglobin and Oxyhemoglobin	23.3 Common Ligands in Coordination Chemistry
Figure 23.16 The Absorption of Sunlight by Chlorophyll	23.3 Common Ligands in Coordination Chemistry
Table 23.5 Some Common Ligands and Their Names	23.4 Nomenclature and Isomerism in Coordination Chemistry
Figure 23.19 Forms of Isomerism in Coordination Compounds	23.4 Nomenclature and Isomerism in Coordination Chemistry
Figure 23.22 Optical Isomerism	23.4 Nomenclature and Isomerism in Coordination Chemistry
Figure 23.23 Using Polarized Light to Detect Optical Activity	23.4 Nomenclature and Isomerism in Coordination Chemistry
Figure 23.24 The Color of a Coordination Complex Changes with the Ligand Changes	23.5 Color and Magnetism in Coordination Chemistry
Figure 23.26 The Color of $[Ti(H_2O)_6]^{3+}$	23.5 Color and Magnetism in Coordination Chemistry
Figure 23.28 Energies of *d* Orbitals in a Free Metal Ion, a Spherically Symmetric Crystal Field, and an Octahedral Crystal Field	23.6 Crystal-Field Theory
Figure 23.30 Effect of Ligand on Crystal-Field Splitting	23.6 Crystal-Field Theory
Figure 23.36 Ligand-to-Metal Charge Transfer Transition in MnO_4^-	23.6 Crystal-Field Theory

Activities:

	Section:
Geometries of MLn Complexes	23.2 Transition Metal Complexes
Color Wheel	23.5 Color and Magnetism in Coordination Chemistry

Crystal Field Theory: Chromium Complexes
Octahedral vs. Square Planar

23.6 Crystal-Field Theory
23.6 Crystal-Field Theory

Animations:
Isomerism

Chirality

Optical Activity

Section:
23.4 Nomenclature and Isomerism in Coordination Chemistry
23.4 Nomenclature and Isomerism in Coordination Chemistry
23.4 Nomenclature and Isomerism in Coordination Chemistry

3-D Models:
cis-tetraamminedichlorocobalt(III)
trans-tetraamminedichlorocobalt(III)
Ethylenediamminecobalt(III)
Ethylenediamminetetraacetatecobalt(III)
Oxymyoglobin
Deoxymyoglobin
Heme (with bound O_2)
cis-diamminedichloroplatinum(II) (cisplatin)

trans-diamminedichloroplatinum(II) (transplatin)

D-trisethylenediamminecobalt(III)

L-trisethylenediamminecobalt(III)

Section:
23.2 Transition Metal Complexes
23.2 Transition Metal Complexes
23.3 Common Ligands in Coordination Chemistry
23.3 Common Ligands in Coordination Chemistry
23.3 Common Ligands in Coordination Chemistry
23.3 Common Ligands in Coordination Chemistry
23.3 Common Ligands in Coordination Chemistry
23.4 Nomenclature and Isomerism in Coordination Chemistry
23.4 Nomenclature and Isomerism in Coordination Chemistry
23.4 Nomenclature and Isomerism in Coordination Chemistry
23.4 Nomenclature and Isomerism in Coordination Chemistry

Other Resources

Further Readings:
Trends in Ionization Energy of Transition-Metal Elements
A Stability Ruler for Metal-Ion Complexes
The Concept of Oxidation States in Metal Complexes
Some Linguistic Detail on Chelation
Selecting and Using Chelating Agents
EDTA-Type Chelating Agents in Everyday Consumer Products: Some Medicinal and Personal Care Products
Toxicity of Heavy Metals and Biological Defense: Principles and Applications in Bioinorganic Chemistry, Part VII
The Biochemistry of Some Iron Porphyrin Complexes
Hemoglobin: Its Occurrence, Structure, and Adaptation
Iron as Nutrient and Poison
Blood-Chemistry Tutorials: Teaching Biological Applications of General Chemistry Material
The Chemical Pigments of Plants

Section:
23.1 The Transition Metals

23.2 Transition Metal Complexes
23.2 Transition Metal Complexes
23.3 Common Ligands in Coordination Chemistry
23.3 Common Ligands in Coordination Chemistry
23.3 Common Ligands in Coordination Chemistry

23.3 Common Ligands in Coordination Chemistry

23.3 Common Ligands in Coordination Chemistry

23.3 Common Ligands in Coordination Chemistry

23.3 Common Ligands in Coordination Chemistry
23.3 Common Ligands in Coordination Chemistry

23.3 Common Ligands in Coordination Chemistry

Iron Deficiency
Introducing Stereochemistry to Non-science Majors

Mirror-Image Molecules: New Techniques Promise
    More Potent Drugs and Pesticides
Pictorial Analogies VIII: Types of Formulas
    and Structural Isomers
Chiral Drugs

A 1- and 2-Dimensional Introduction to
    Stereochemistry
Color Classification of Coordination Compounds

Hope Springs Eternal

23.3 Common Ligands in Coordination Chemistry
23.4 Nomenclature and Isomerism in Coordination
    Chemistry
23.4 Nomenclature and Isomerism in Coordination
    Chemistry
23.4 Nomenclature and Isomerism in Coordination

23.4 Nomenclature and Isomerism in Coordination
    Chemistry
23.4 Nomenclature and Isomerism in Coordination
    Chemistry
23.5 Color and Magnetism in Coordination
    Chemistry
23.5 Color and Magnetism in Coordination
    Chemistry

Live Demonstrations:

The Copper Mirror
Metals in Metal Salts: A Copper Mirror
    Demonstration
Cobalt Complexes: Changing Coordination
    Numbers
Changing Coordination Numbers: Nickel
    Complexes
Separating Metallic Iron from Cereal
A Colorful Look at the Chelate Effect
Precipitates and Complexes of Copper (II)
Demonstration of Enantiomer Specificity of
    Proteins and Drugs
Green and Blue Copper Complexes

Copper Sulfate: Blue to White

Section:
23.2 Transition Metal Complexes
23.2 Transition Metal Complexes

23.2 Transition Metal Complexes

23.2 Transition Metal Complexes

23.3 Common Ligands in Coordination Chemistry
23.3 Common Ligands in Coordination Chemistry
23.3 Common Ligands in Coordination Chemistry
23.4 Nomenclature and Isomerism in Coordination
    Chemistry
23.5 Color and Magnetism in Coordination
    Chemistry
23.5 Color and Magnetism in Coordination
    Chemistry

Chapter 23. Transition Metals and Coordination Chemistry

Common Student Misconceptions

- Students have difficulty naming coordination complexes.
- Students often think that chirality is only possible for organic compounds.
- Students often think that metals ions, M^{n+}(aq) and their aqueous complex ions should have similar physical and chemical properties.

Teaching Tips

- Students should be encouraged to review Chapters 2, 6, 7, 9, 11, 17 and 19 prior to covering this chapter.

Lecture Outline

23.1 The Transition Metals[1]

- Transition metals occupy the *d* block of the periodic table.
- Most metals are found in nature in the form of solid inorganic compounds called **minerals**.
  - Names of minerals are based on the location of their discovery, the person who discovered them, or some characteristic of the mineral.
    - For example, some minerals are named after their colors
  - The oxidation state of transition metals in minerals are commonly +1, +2 or +3.
    - Various chemical processes are required to reduce the metal to the 0 oxidation state.
- **Metallurgy** is the science and technology of extracting metals from natural sources and preparing them for practical use.
- There are five important steps:
  - mining (getting the ore out of the ground)
  - concentrating (preparing it for further treatment)
    - Differences in the chemical and physical properties of the mineral of interest and the undesired material, called *gangue*, are used to separate these components.
    - Example: Iron can be separated from gangue in finely ground magnetite by using a magnet to attract the iron.
  - reduction (to obtain the free metal in the 0 oxidation state)
  - purifying or refining (to obtain the pure metal)
  - mixing with other metals (to form an *alloy*)
    - Alloys are metallic materials composed of two or more elements.

Physical Properties[2]

- The physical properties of transition metals can be classified into two groups: atomic properties (e.g., atomic radius, ionization energy) and bulk properties (e.g., density, melting point).
- Most of the trends in bulk properties are less smooth than the atomic properties.
- The atomic trends tend to be smooth for the transition metals.
- The trends in atomic properties of the transition metals can be exemplified with atomic radii.
  - Atomic radius decreases and reaches a minimum around group 8B (Fe, Co, Ni) and then increases for groups 1 and 2.
  - This trend is again understood in terms of effective nuclear charge.

---

[1] Figure 23.1 from Transparency Pack
[2] "Trends in Ionization Energy of Transition-Metal Elements" from Further Readings

- The increase in size of the Cu and Zn triads is rationalized in terms of the completely filled d orbital.
  - In general, atomic size increases down a group.
- An important exception: Hf has almost the same radius as Zr (group 4B); we would expect Hf to be larger than Zr.
  - Between La and Hf the $4f$ shell fills (lanthanides).
  - As $4f$ orbitals fill, the effective nuclear charge increases and the lanthanides contract smoothly.
  - The **lanthanide contraction** balances the increase in size we anticipate between Hf and Zr.
  - The second and third series are usually about the same size, with the first series being smaller.
  - Second and third series metals are very similar in their properties (e.g., Hf and Zr are always found together in ores and are very difficult to separate).

Electron Configurations and Oxidation States[3]

- Even though the $(n-1)d$ orbital is filled after the ns orbital, electrons are lost from the orbital with the highest n first.
- That is, transition metals lose s electrons before the d electrons.
  - Example: Fe: $[Ar]3d^6 4s^2$ Fe^{2+}: $[Ar]3d^6$.
- d electrons are responsible for some important properties:
  - Transition metals have more than one oxidation state.
  - Transition-metal compounds are colored.
  - Transition-metal compounds have magnetic properties.
- Note that all oxidation states for metals are positive.
  - The +2 oxidation state is common because it corresponds to the loss of both s electrons.
    - An exception is in Sc where the +3 oxidation state is isoelectronic with Ar.
  - The maximum oxidation state for the first transition series is +7 for Mn.
  - For the second and third series, the maximum oxidation state is +8 for Ru and Os (RuO_4 and OsO_4).

Magnetism[4]

- Magnetism provides important bonding information.
- Electron spin generates a magnetic field with a *magnetic moment*.
- There are several types of magnetic behavior:
  - *diamagnetic* (no atoms or ions with magnetic moments)
    - When two spins are opposite, the magnetic fields cancel (diamagnetic).
    - Diamagnetic substances are weakly repelled by external magnetic fields.
  - *paramagnetic* (magnetic moments not aligned outside a magnetic field)
    - When spins are unpaired, the magnetic fields do not cancel (paramagnetic).
    - Generally, the unpaired electrons in a solid are not influenced by adjacent unpaired electrons.
      - That is, the magnetic moments are randomly oriented.
    - When paramagnetic materials are placed in a magnetic field, the electrons become aligned.
  - **ferromagnetic** (coupled magnetic centers aligned in a common direction)
    - Ferromagnetism is a special case of paramagnetism where the magnetic moments are permanently aligned (e.g., Fe, Co, and Ni).
    - Ferromagnetic oxides are used in magnetic recording tape (e.g., CrO_2 and Fe_3O_4).
  - Two additional types of magnetism involve ordered arrangements of unpaired electrons.
    - **Antiferromagnetism** (the unpaired electrons on a given atom align so that their spins are oriented in the opposite direction as the spins on neighboring atoms).
    - **Ferrimagnetism** (has characteristics of both a ferromagnet and an antiferromagnet).

---

[3] Figure 23.4 from Transparency Pack
[4] Figure 23.5 from Transparency Pack

- All magnetically ordered materials become paramagnetic when heated above a critical temperature.
  - *Curie temperature* (T_c): critical temperature for ferromagnets and ferrimagnets.
  - *Néel temperature* (T_n): critical temperature for antiferromagnets.

FORWARD REFERENCES
- Nickel used as a heterogeneous catalyst in hydrogenation of alkenes will be mentioned in Chapter 24 (section 24.3).
- Transition metals as catalysts in carbonylation reactions will be mentioned in Chapter 24 (section 24.4).
- Metal oxides used as catalysts in formation of methanol will be mentioned in Chapter 24 (section 24.4).

23.2 Transition-Metal Complexes[5,6,7]

- **Metal complexes** (or *complexes*) have a metal ion (which can have a 0 oxidation state) bonded to a number of molecules or ions.
  - If the complex has a net electrical charge, it is called a *complex ion.*
- Compounds that contain complexes are known as **coordination compounds.**
- Most coordination compounds are metal compounds formed by Lewis acid-base interactions involving transition metal ions.
  - The molecules or ions surrounding the metal ion in a complex are called **ligands**.
    - The ligands act as Lewis bases.
      - Ligands are usually either anions or polar molecules.
      - They have at least one unshared pair of valence electrons.
    - The metal ion functions as a Lewis acid (electron-pair acceptor).
      - The ligands are said to *coordinate* to the metal.

The Development of Coordination Chemistry: Werner's Theory[8,9,10,11]

- Alfred Werner proposed:
  - Metal ions exhibit a primary and secondary valence.
    - Primary valence: The oxidation state of the metal.
    - Secondary valence: The number of atoms directly bonded to the metal ion.
      - This is the **coordination number.**
  - The central metal and ligands bound to it are the **coordination sphere** of the complex.
    - Example: $[Co(NH_3)_6]Cl_3$
      - Co^{3+} is the metal ion.
      - NH_3 groups are ligands.
  - When Cl^- is part of the coordination sphere, it is tightly bound and not released when the complex is dissolved in water.
    - Example: $[Co(NH_3)_5Cl]Cl_2$
- Different arrangements of ligands are possible.
  - Example: There are two ways to arrange the ligands in $[Co(NH_3)_4Cl_2]^+$.
    - In *cis*-$[Co(NH_3)_4Cl_2]^+$:
      - the chloride ligands occupy adjacent vertices of the octahedral arrangement.
    - In *trans*-$[Co(NH_3)_4Cl_2]^+$.

---

[5] "A Stability Ruler for Metal Ion Complexes" from Further Readings
[6] "The Copper Mirror" from Live Demonstrations
[7] "Metals in Metal Salts: A Copper Mirror Demonstration" from Live Demonstrations
[8] Figure 23.7 from Transparency Pack
[9] "The Concept of Oxidation States in Metal Complexes" from Further Readings
[10] "*cis*-tetraamminedichlorocobalt(III)" 3-D Model from Instructor's Resource CD/DVD
[11] "*trans*-tetraamminedichlorocobalt(III)" 3-D Model from Instructor's Resource CD/DVD

- the chlorides are opposite each other.

The Metal-Ligand Bond

- The metal-ligand bond is an interaction between:
  - a Lewis acid (the metal ion with its empty valence orbitals) and
  - a Lewis base (the ligand with its unshared pairs of electrons).
- Ligands can alter the properties of the metal.
  - Complexes display physical and chemical properties different from those of the metal ion or the ligands.
  - For example, consider the properties of Ag^+ and a complex involving Ag^+ and CN^-:

$$Ag^+(aq) + e^- \rightarrow Ag(s) \qquad\qquad E^\circ = +0.799 \text{ V}$$
$$[Ag(CN)_2]^-(aq) + e^- \rightarrow Ag(s) + 2CN^-(aq) \qquad\qquad E^\circ = -0.31 \text{ V}$$

Charges, Coordination Numbers, and Geometries[12,13,14,15]

- The charge on a complex ion equals the sum of the charge on the metal plus the charges on the ligands.
- In a complex the **donor atom** is the atom bonded directly to the metal.
- The coordination number is the number of ligands attached to the metal.
  - The most common coordination numbers are 4 and 6.
  - Some metal ions have a constant coordination number (e.g., Cr^{3+} and Co^{3+} have coordination numbers of 6).
  - The size of the metal ion and the size of the ligand affect the coordination number (e.g., iron(III) can coordinate to six fluorides but only to four chlorides; thus $[FeF_6]^{3-}$ and $[FeCl_4]^-$ are stable).
  - The amount of charge transferred from ligand to metal affects the coordination number.
    - The greater the transfer of negative charge to the metal, the lower the coordination number tends to be.
    - For example, $[Ni(NH_3)_6]^{2+}$ and $[Ni(CN)_4]^{2-}$ are both stable.
- Four-coordinate complexes have two common geometries: tetrahedral and square planar.
  - Square-planar complexes are commonly seen for d^8 metal ions such as Pt^{2+} and Au^{3+}.
- Six-coordinate complexes are usually octahedral.

23.3 Common Ligands in Coordination Chemistry[16,17,18,19,20]

- **A donor atom is the ligand atom that binds to the central metal ion in a coordination complex.**
- **Monodentate ligands** bind through one donor atom only.
  - Therefore, they can occupy only one coordination site.
- **Some ligands bind through two or more donor atoms simultaneously.**
  - **Bidentate ligands bind through two donor atoms.**
  - **Polydentate** ligands (or **chelating agents**) have three or more donor atoms.
  - **Bidentate and polydentate species have multiple donor atoms** that can simultaneously coordinate to the metal ion.
    - They can thus occupy more than one coordination site.

---

[12] "Cobalt Complexes: Changing Coordination Numbers" from Live Demonstrations
[13] Figure 23.9 from Transparency Pack
[14] "Geometries of MLn Complexes" Activity from Instructor's Resource CD/DVD
[15] "Changing Coordination Numbers; Nickel Complexes" from Live Demonstrations
[16] Figure 23.11 from Transparency Pack
[17] Figure 23.12 from Transparency Pack
[18] "Some Linguistic Detail on Chelation" from Further Readings
[19] "Selecting and Using Chelating Agents" from Further Readings
[20] "Ethylenediamminecobalt(III)" 3-D Model from Instructor's Resource CD/DVD

- Because bidentate and polydentate ligands grasp the metal between two or more donor atoms and are called **chelating agents**.
  - Example: *ethylenediamine* ($H_2NCH_2CH_2NH_2$)
    - The abbreviation for ethylenediamine is "en."
    - There are two nitrogen atoms that can act as ligands.
    - They are far enough apart on the molecule that it can wrap around a metal ion.
    - The molecule can simultaneously coordinate to two sites on the metal ion.
    - Ethylenediamine is thus an example of a bidentate ligand.
    - The octahedral $[Co(en)_3]^{3+}$ is a typical "en" complex.
- Chelating agents form more stable complexes than do monodentate ligands.
  - Examples:

$$[Ni(H_2O)_6]^{2+}(aq) + 6NH_3 \rightleftharpoons [Ni(NH_3)_6]^{2+}(aq) + 6H_2O(l) \quad K_f = 1.2 \times 10^9$$
$$[Ni(H_2O)_6]^{2+}(aq) + 3en \rightleftharpoons [Ni(en)_3]^{2+}(aq) + 6H_2O(l) \quad K_f = 6.8 \times 10^{17}$$

  - The **chelate effect** refers to the larger formation constants for polydentate ligands as compared with corresponding monodentate ligands.
- Chelating agents are sometimes referred to as *sequestering agents*.
  - In medicine, sequestering agents are used to selectively remove toxic metal ions (e.g., Hg^{2+} and Pb^{2+}) while leaving biologically important metals.
- One very important chelating agent is ethylenediaminetetraacetate ($EDTA^{4-}$).
  - EDTA occupies six coordination sites; for example, $[CoEDTA]^-$ is an octahedral Co^{3+} complex.
  - Both N atoms and O atoms coordinate to the metal.
  - EDTA is used in consumer products to complex the metal ions that would otherwise catalyze unwanted decomposition reactions.

Metals and Chelates in Living Systems[21,22,23,24,25,26,27,28,29,30,31,32,33,34,35,36,37]

- Ten of the twenty-nine elements required for human life are transition metals (V, Cr, Mn, Fe, Co, Cu, Zn, Mo, Cd, and Ni).
- Many natural chelates coordinate to the *porphine* molecule.
  - Porphine forms a tetradentate ligand with the loss of the two protons bound to its nitrogen atoms.
  - A **porphyrin** is a metal complex derived from porphine.

---

[21] "EDTA-Type Chelating Agents in Everyday Consumer Products: Some Medicinal and Personal Care Products" from Further Readings
[22] "Toxicity of Heavy Metals and Biological Defense: Principles and Applications in Bioinorganic Chemistry, Part VII" from Further Readings
[23] "Heme (with bound O_2)" 3-D Model from Instructor's Resource CD/DVD
[24] "Oxymyoglobin" 3-D Model from Instructor's Resource CD/DVD
[25] "Deoxymyoglobin" 3-D Model from Instructor's Resource CD/DVD
[26] Figure 23.14 from Transparency Pack
[27] "The Biochemistry of Some Iron Porphyrin Complexes" from Further Readings
[28] "Hemoglobin: Its Occurrence, Structure, and Adaptation" from Further Readings
[29] Figure 23.15 from Transparency Pack
[30] Figure 23.16 from Transparency Pack
[31] "Iron as a Nutrient and Poison" from Further Readings
[32] "Blood-Chemistry Tutorials: Teaching Biological Applications of General Chemistry Material" from Further Readings
[33] "The Chemical Pigments of Plants" from Further Readings
[34] "Iron Deficiency" from Further Readings
[35] "Separating Metallic Iron from Cereal" from Live Demonstrations
[36] "A Colorful Look at the Chelate Effect" from Live Demonstrations
[37] "Ethylenediamminetetraacetatecobalt(III)" 3-D Model from Instructor's Resource CD/DVD

- Two important porphyrins are heme (which contains Fe^{2+}) and chlorophyll (which contains Mg^{2+}).
- Two important heme-containing molecules are myoglobin and hemoglobin.
  - These proteins are important oxygen-binding proteins.
  - Myoglobin is *globular protein* (it folds into a compact, roughly spherical shape) found in muscle tissue, while hemoglobin is made of four heme-containing subunits (each is similar to myoglobin); it is found in red blood cells.
    - In each case the heme iron is coordinated to six ligands.
      - Four of these are nitrogen atoms of the porphyrin ring.
      - One ligand is a nitrogen atom that is part of one of the amino acids of the protein.
    - The sixth coordination site around the iron is occupied by either O_2 or water.
      - Other ligands, such as CO, can also serve as the sixth ligand.
        - CO is poisonous due to its ability to bind very tightly to hemoglobin.
        - The binding constant for CO is 210 times greater than that for O_2.
- A different metal complex is important in the process of **photosynthesis**.
  - Photosynthesis is the conversion of CO_2 and water to glucose and oxygen in plants in the presence of light.
  - The synthesis of one mole of sugar requires the absorption and utilization of 48 moles of photons.
  - **Chlorophylls** are porphyrins that contain Mg(II). Photons of light are absorbed by chlorophyll-containing pigments in plant leaves.
    - Chlorophyll *a* is the most abundant chlorophyll.
    - The other chlorophylls differ in the structure of the side chains.
    - Mg^{2+} is in the center of the porphyrin-like ring.
    - The alternating or *conjugated* double bonds give chlorophyll its ability to absorb light strongly in the visible part of the spectrum.
    - Chlorophyll absorbs red light (655 nm) and blue light (430 nm), and transmits green light.
    - The absorbed energy is ultimately used to drive the endothermic reaction:
$$6CO_2 + 6H_2O \rightarrow C_6H_{12}O_6 + 6O_2$$
  - Plant photosynthesis sustains life on Earth.

FORWARD REFERENCES
- Photosynthesis will be covered in Chapter 24 (section 24.6).
- Tertiary structure of myoglobin will be mentioned in Chapter 24 (section 24.7).

23.4 Nomenclature and Isomerism in Coordination Chemistry[38]

- We can name complexes in a systematic manner using some simple nomenclature rules.
  - For salts, the name of the cation is given before the name of the anion.
    - Example: In $[Co(NH_3)_5Cl]Cl_2$ we name $[Co(NH_3)_5Cl]^{2+}$ before Cl^-.
  - Within a complex ion or molecule, the ligands are named (in alphabetical order) before the metal.
    - Example: $[Co(NH_3)_5Cl]^{2+}$ is pentaamminechlorocobalt(III).
    - Note that the *penta* portion indicates the number of NH_3 groups and is therefore not considered in alphabetizing the ligands.
  - The names of anionic ligands end in *o*, and for neutral ligands the name of the molecule is used.
    - Example: Cl^- is *chloro* and CN^- is *cyano*.
    - Exceptions are H_2O (aqua) and NH_3 (ammine).
  - Greek prefixes are used to indicate the number of ligands (di-, tri-, tetra-, penta-, and hexa-).
    - Exception: If the ligand name already has a Greek prefix.
      - Then enclose the name of the ligand in parentheses and use bis-, tris-, tetrakis-, pentakis-, and hexakis-.

---

[38] "Isomerism" Animation from Instructor's Resource CD/DVD

- Example [Co(en)$_3$]Cl$_3$ is tris(ethylenediamine)cobalt(III) chloride.
- If the complex is an anion, the name ends in -ate.
  - For example, [CoCl$_4$]$^{2-}$ is the tetrachlorocobaltate(II) ion.
- The oxidation state of the metal is given in Roman numerals in parenthesis after the name of the metal.
- Two compounds with the same formula but different arrangements of atoms are called **isomers**.
- There are two kinds of isomers:
  - **Structural isomers** have different bonds.
  - **Stereoisomers** have the same bonds but different spatial arrangements of the bonds.

Structural Isomerism[39,40]

- Two examples of structural isomerism in coordination chemistry are:
  - **linkage isomerism**
    - *Linkage isomers*: A ligand is capable of coordinating to a metal in two different ways.
    - Example: Nitrite can coordinate via a nitrogen or an oxygen atom.
      - If the nitrogen atom is the donor atom, the ligand is called *nitro*.
      - If the oxygen atom is the donor atom, the ligand is called *nitrito*.
    - The ligand thiocyanate (SCN$^-$) is also capable of being involved in linkage isomerism.
  - **coordination-sphere isomerism**
    - *Coordination-sphere isomers* differ in the ligands that are directly bound to the metal.
    - Example: CrCl$_3$(H$_2$O)$_6$ exists in three different forms:
      - [Cr(H$_2$O)$_6$]Cl$_3$
      - [Cr(H$_2$O)$_5$Cl]Cl$_2$·H$_2$O
      - [Cr(H$_2$O)$_4$Cl$_2$]Cl·2H$_2$O

Stereoisomerism[41,42,43,44,45,46,47,48,49,50,51,52,53]

- Stereoisomers have the same connectivity but different spatial arrangements of atoms.
- Two types of stereoisomerism are:
  - **geometric isomerism**
    - In *geometric isomerism* the arrangement of the atoms is different although the same bonds are present.
    - Examples are *cis* and *trans* isomers.
      - Consider square planar [Pt(NH$_3$)$_2$Cl$_2$].
        - The two NH$_3$ ligands can either be 90° apart or 180° apart.

---

[39] Figure 23.19 from Transparency Pack
[40] "Pictorial Analogies VIII: Types of Formulas and Structural Isomers" from Further Readings
[41] "Introducing Stereochemistry to Non-science Majors" from Further Readings
[42] Figure 23.22 from Transparency Pack
[43] "Chirality" Animation from Instructor's Resource CD/DVD
[44] "Chiral Drugs" from Further Readings
[45] "Optical Activity" Animation from Instructor's Resource CD/DVD
[46] Figure 23.23 from Transparency Pack
[47] "Mirror–Image Molecules: New Techniques Promise More Potent Drugs and Pesticides" from Further Readings
[48] "A 1- and 2-Dimensional Introduction to Stereochemistry" from Further Readings
[49] "Demonstration of Enantiomer Specificity of Proteins and Drugs" from Live Demonstrations
[50] "*cis*-diamminedichloroplatinum(II) (cisplatin)" 3-D Model from Instructor's Resource CD/DVD
[51] "*trans*-diamminedichloroplatinum(II) (transplatin)" 3-D Model from Instructor's Resource CD/DVD
[52] "D-trisethylenediamminecobalt(III)" 3-D Model from Instructor's Resource CD/DVD
[53] "L-trisethylenediamminecobalt(III)" 3-D Model from Instructor's Resource CD/DVD

- Therefore, the spatial arrangement of the atoms is different.
- In the *cis* isomer, the two NH_3 groups are adjacent.
  - The *cis* isomer (cisplatin) is used in chemotherapy.
- In the *trans* isomer, the two NH_3 groups are across from each other.
- It is possible to find *cis* and *trans* isomers in octahedral complexes.
  - For example, *cis*-$[Co(NH_3)_4Cl_2]^+$ is violet.
  - The *trans*-$[Co(NH_3)_4Cl_2]^+$ isomer is green.
  - The two isomers also have different solubilities.
- **optical isomerism**
  - *Optical isomers* are nonsuperimposable mirror images.
  - These are referred to as **enantiomers**.
  - Complexes that exist as enantiomers are **chiral**.
    - Chiral species are molecules or ions that cannot be superimposed on their mirror image.
  - Most physical and chemical properties of enantiomers are identical.
    - Therefore, enantiomers are very difficult to separate.
  - Optical isomers are differentiated from each other by their interaction with plane-polarized light.
    - Enantiomers are capable of rotating the plane of polarized light.
    - Horizontally polarized light is passed through an optically active solution.
    - As the light emerges from the solution, the plane of polarity has changed.
    - The mirror image of an enantiomer will rotate the plane of polarized light by the same amount in the opposite direction.
    - **Dextrorotatory** solutions rotate the plane of polarized light to the right.
      - This isomer is called the *dextro* or *d* isomer.
    - **Levorotatory** solutions rotate the plane of polarized light to the left.
      - This isomer is called the *levo* or *l* isomer.
- Chiral molecules are said to be **optically active** because of their effect on light.
  - **Racemic** mixtures contain equal amounts of *l* and *d* isomers.
    - They have no overall effect on the plane of polarized light.
- The 2001 Nobel Prize in Chemistry was awarded to W. S. Knowles and K. B. Sharpless of the United States and R. Noyori of Japan for work on the catalysis of chiral reactions.

FORWARD REFERENCES
- Arrangement of groups in geometric isomers will be covered in Chapter 24 (section 24.3)
- Chirality of organic compounds, enantiomers, and rotation of the light will be discussed in detail in Chapter 24 (section 24.5).

23.5 Color and Magnetism in Coordination Chemistry

Color[54,55,56,57,58,59,60]

- The color of a complex depends on the metal, the ligands present, and the oxidation state of the metal.
  - For example, pale blue $[Cu(H_2O)_6]^{2+}$ can be converted into dark blue $[Cu(NH_3)_6]^{2+}$ by adding $NH_3(aq)$.
- A partially filled *d* orbital is usually required for a complex to be colored.

---

[54] "Color Classification of Coordination Compounds" from Further Readings
[55] "Green and Blue Copper Complexes" from Live Demonstrations
[56] "Copper Sulfate: Blue to White" from Live Demonstrations
[57] "Color Wheel" Activity from Instructor's Resource CD/DVD
[58] "Hope Springs Eternal" from Further Readings
[59] Figure 23.24 from Transparency Pack
[60] Figure 23.26 from Transparency Pack

- Thus, ions with completely empty (e.g., Al^{3+} or Ti^{4+}) or completely filled (e.g., Zn^{2+}) d subshells are usually colorless.
- Colored compounds absorb visible light.
  - The color perceived is the sum of the light reflected or transmitted by the complex.
    - An object will have a particular color if it reflects or transmits that color or if it absorbs light of the **complementary** color.
      - An object appears black if it absorbs all wavelengths of light.
      - An object appears white or colorless if it absorbs no visible light.
- A plot of the amount of absorbed light versus wavelength is called the **absorption spectrum**.

Magnetism of Coordination Compounds

- Many transition-metal complexes are paramagnetic (i.e., they have unpaired electrons).
- Consider a d^6 metal ion:
  - Compounds of $[Co(NH_3)_6]^{3+}$ have no unpaired electrons, but compounds of $[CoF_6]^{3-}$ have four unpaired electrons per metal ion.
- We need to develop a bonding theory to account for both color and magnetism in transition metal complexes.

23.6 Crystal-Field Theory[61,62]

- **Crystal-field theory** describes bonding in transition-metal complexes.
- The formation of a complex is a Lewis acid-base reaction.
  - Both electrons in the bond come from the ligand and are donated into an empty hybridized orbital on the metal.
  - Charge is donated from the ligand to the metal.
- An assumption in crystal-field theory is that the interaction between ligand and metal is electrostatic.
  - Orbitals that point directly at the ligands have their energies raised more than those that point between the ligands.
  - The complex metal ion has a lower energy than the separated metal and ligands.
  - However, repulsion occurs between the ligands and the d electrons of the metal.
- In an octahedral field, the five d orbitals do not have the same energy: three degenerate orbitals have a lower energy than two degenerate orbitals.
  - We assume an octahedral array of negative charges placed around the metal ion (which is positive).
    - The d_{z2} and d_{x2-y2} orbitals lie on the same axes as negative charges.
      - Therefore, there is a large, unfavorable interaction between the ligand and these orbitals.
      - These orbitals form the degenerate high-energy pair of energy levels.
    - The d_{xy}, d_{yz} and d_{xz} orbitals are oriented between the negative charges.
      - Therefore, there is a smaller repulsion between ligands and these orbitals.
      - These orbitals form the degenerate low-energy set of energy levels.
    - The energy gap between these two sets of d orbitals is labeled Δ.
      - Δ is referred to as the *crystal-field splitting energy*.
- For example, consider the $[Ti(H_2O)_6]^{3+}$ complex.
  - Ti^{3+} is a d^1 metal ion.
  - Therefore, the one electron is in a low energy orbital.
  - For Ti^{3+}, the gap between energy levels, Δ, is of the order of the wavelength of visible light.
  - As the $[Ti(H_2O)_6]^{3+}$ complex absorbs visible light the electron is promoted to a higher energy level.

---

[61] Figure 23.28 from Transparency Pack
[62] Figure 23.30 from Transparency Pack

- This transition is called a **d-d transition** because it involves exciting an electron from one set of d orbitals to the other.
  - Because there is only one d, electron, there is only one possible absorption line for this molecule.
  - The color of a complex depends on the magnitude of Δ, which, in turn, depends on the metal and the type of ligand.
    - $[Ti(H_2O)_6]^{3+}$ is purple, $[Fe(H_2O)_6]^{3+}$ is light violet, $[Cr(H_2O)_6]^{3+}$ is violet, and $Cr(NH_3)_6]^{3+}$ is yellow.
- A **spectrochemical series** is a listing of ligands in order of their ability to increase Δ:
$$Cl^- < F^- < H_2O < NH_3 < en < NO_2^- \text{ (N-bonded)} < CN^-$$
  - *Weak-field ligands* lie on the low-Δ end of the spectrochemical series.
  - *Strong-field ligands* lie on the high-Δ end of the spectrochemical series.
  - Example: When the ligand coordinated to Cr^{3+} is changed from the weak-field ligand F^- to the strong-field ligand CN^-, Δ increases and the color of the complex changes from green (in $[CrF_6]^{3+}$) to yellow (in $[Cr(CN)_6]^{3-}$).

Electron Configurations in Octahedral Complexes[63]

- Recall that when transition metals form cations, s electrons are lost first.
  - Thus, Ti^{3+} is a d^1 ion, V^{3+} is a d^2 ion, and Cr^{3+} is a d^3 ion.
- If one to three electrons add to the d orbitals in an octahedral complex ion, Hund's rule applies.
  - The first three electrons go into different d orbitals with their spins parallel.
- We have a choice for the placement of the fourth electron:
  - If it goes into a higher-energy orbital, then there is an energy cost (Δ).
  - If it goes into a lower-energy orbital, there is a different energy cost (called the **spin-pairing energy** due to pairing with the electron already present).
    - Weak-field ligands tend to favor adding electrons to the higher-energy orbitals (**high-spin complexes**) because Δ is less than the spin-pairing energy.
    - Strong-field ligands tend to favor adding electrons to lower-energy orbitals (**low-spin complexes**) because Δ is greater than the spin-pairing energy.

Tetrahedral and Square Planar Complexes[64,65]

- By using the same arguments as for the octahedral case, we can derive the relative orbital energies for d orbitals in a tetrahedral field.
  - The splitting of the d orbitals is the opposite of that observed for an octahedral field.
  - Because there are only four ligands, Δ for a tetrahedral field is smaller than Δ for an octahedral field.
  - This causes all tetrahedral complexes to be high-spin.
- Square-planar complexes can be thought of as follows: Start with an octahedral complex and remove two ligands along the z-axis.
  - As a consequence the four planar ligands are drawn in towards the metal.
  - Most d^8 metal ions form square-planar complexes.
  - The majority of complexes are low-spin (i.e., diamagnetic).
  - Examples: Pd^{2+}, Pt^{2+}, Ir^+, and Au^{3+}.

---

[63] "Crystal Field Theory: Chromium Complexes" Activity from Instructor's Resource CD/DVD
[64] "Octahedral vs. Square Planar" Activity from Instructor's Resource CD/DVD
[65] Figure 23.36 from Transparency Pack

Further Readings:

1. Paul S. Matsumoto, "Trends in Ionization Energy of Transition-Metal Elements," *J. Chem. Educ.*, Vol. 82, **2005**, 1660–1661.

2. R. Bruce Martin, "A Stability Ruler for Metal Ion Complexes," *J. Chem. Educ.*, Vol. 64, **1987**, 402.

3. Dirk Steinborn, "The Concept of Oxidation States in Metal Complexes," *J. Chem. Educ.*, Vol. 81, **2004**, 1148–1154.

4. Daniel T. Haworth, "Some Linguistic Detail on Chelation," *J. Chem. Educ.*, Vol. 75, **1998**, 47.

5. Mark Conway, Smallwood Holoman, Ladell Jones, Ray Leenhouts, and Gerald Williamson, "Selecting and Using Chelating Agents," *Chemical Engineering*, Vol. 106(3), **March 1999**, 86–90.

6. J. Roger Hart, "EDTA-Type Chelating Agents in Everyday Consumer Products: Some Medicinal and Personal Care Products," *J. Chem. Educ.*, Vol. 61, **1984**, 1060–1061.

7. Ei-Ichiro Ochiai, "Toxicity of Heavy Metals and Biological Defense: Principles and Applications in Bioinorganic Chemistry, Part VII," *J. Chem. Educ.*, Vol. 72, **1995**, 479–484.

8. Colin J. Rix, "The Biochemistry of Some Iron Porphyrin Complexes," *J. Chem. Educ.*, Vol. 59, **1982**, 389–392.

9. N. M. Senozan and R. L. Hunt, "Hemoglobin: Its Occurrence, Structure, and Adaptation," *J. Chem. Educ.*, Vol. 59, **1982**, 173–178.

10. N. M. Senozan and M. P. Christiano, "Iron as Nutrient and Poison," *J. Chem. Educ.*, Vol. 74, **1997**, 1060–1063.

11. Rachel E. Casiday, Dewey Holten, Richard Krathen, and Regina F. Frey, "Blood-Chemistry Tutorials: Teaching Biological Applications of General Chemistry Material," *J. Chem. Educ.*, Vol. 78, **2001**, 1210–1214. The relationship between oxygen transport, iron transport, blood buffering, kidney dialysis and general chemistry topics is discussed.

12. Joy Alkema and Spencer L. Seager, "The Chemical Pigments of Plants," *J. Chem. Educ.*, Vol. 59, **1982**, 183–186.

13. Nevin S. Scrimshaw, "Iron Deficiency," *Scientific American*, **October 1991**, 46–52.

14. John J. Fortman, "Pictorial Analogies VIII: Types of Formulas and Structural Isomers," *J. Chem. Educ.*, Vol. 70, **1993**, 755.

15. Hannia Lujan-Upton, "Introducing Stereochemistry to Non-science Majors," *J. Chem. Educ.*, Vol. 78, **2001**, 475–477.

16. Karen F. Schmidt, "Mirror–Image Molecules: New Techniques Promise More Potent Drugs and Pesticides," *Science News*, **May 29, 1993**, 348–350.

17. Stephen C. Stinson, "Chiral Drugs," *Chemical and Engineering News*, **September 19, 1994**, 38–57.

18. Robert E. Gawley, "Chirality Made Simple: A 1- and 2-Dimensional Introduction to Stereochemistry," *J. Chem. Educ.*, Vol. 82, **2005**, 1009–1012.

19. Laurence Poncini and Franz L. Wimmer, "Color Classification of Coordination Compounds," *J. Chem. Educ.*, Vol. 64, **1987**, 1001–1002.

20. Anthony Butler and Rossyln Nicholson, "Hope Springs Eternal," *Chemistry in Britain*, Vol. 34, **December 1998**, 34–36. A brief article investigating the color of the Hope diamond and other colored gems.

Live Demonstrations:

1. Lee R. Summerlin, Christie L. Borgford, and Julie B. Ealy, "The Copper Mirror," *Chemical Demonstrations, A Sourcebook for Teachers,* Vol. 2 (Washington: American Chemical Society, 1988), pp. 187–188.

2. Robert D. Pike, "Metals in Metal Salts: A Copper Mirror Demonstration," *J. Chem. Educ.*, Vol. 87, **2010**, 1062–1063.

3. Lee R. Summerlin and James L. Ealy, Jr., "Cobalt Complexes: Changing Coordination Numbers," *Chemical Demonstrations, A Sourcebook for Teachers,* (Washington: American Chemical Society, 1988), pp. 41–42. The coordination number of cobalt in cobalt chloride solutions is changed as the solutions are mixed with varying amounts of ethanol.

4. Lee R. Summerlin, Christie L. Borgford, and Julie B. Ealy, "Changing Coordination Numbers: Nickel Complexes," *Chemical Demonstrations, A Sourcebook for Teachers, Volume 2* (Washington: American Chemical Society, **1987**), pp. 73–74.

5. Lee. R. Summerlin,, Christie L. Borgford, and Julie B. Ealy, "Separating Metallic Iron from Cereal," *Chemical Demonstrations, A Sourcebook for Teachers, Volume 2* (Washington: American Chemical Society, **1988**), p. 62. Iron is removed from fortified cereal in this simple demonstration.

6. Donald C. Bowman, "A Colorful Look at the Chelate Effect," *J. Chem. Educ.*, Vol. 83, **2006**, 1158–1160. A set of overhead projector demonstrations.

7. Gretchen L. Anderson and Shallee T. Page, "Demonstration of Enantiomer Specificity of Proteins and Drugs," *J. Chem. Educ.*, Vol. 81, **2004**, 971–974.

8. Bassam Z. Shakhashiri, "Precipitates and Complexes of Copper (II)," *Chemical Demonstrations: A Handbook for Teachers of Chemistry, Volume 1* (Madison: The University of Wisconsin Press, **1983**), pp. 318–323. The sequential addition of various agents to beakers of $CuSO_4$ or $Cu(NO_3)_2$ yields a variety of colored copper complexes and precipitates.

9. Lee. R. Summerlin, Christie L. Borgford, and Julie B. Ealy, "Green and Blue Copper Complexes," *Chemical Demonstrations, A Sourcebook for Teachers, Volume 2* (Washington: American Chemical Society, **1988**), pp.71–72. Three copper complexes are prepared in this demonstration.

10. Lee. R. Summerlin,, Christie L. Borgford, and Julie B. Ealy, "Copper Sulfate: Blue to White," *Chemical Demonstrations, A Sourcebook for Teachers, Volume 2* (Washington: American Chemical Society, **1988**), pp. 69–70. An exploration of color change associated with the dehydration of copper sulfate.

Chapter 24. The Chemistry of Life: Organic and Biological Chemistry

Media Resources

Figures and Tables in Transparency Pack:

	Section:
Figure 24.1 Carbon Geometries	24.1 General Characteristics of Organic Molecules
Table 24.1 The Four Hydrocarbon Types	24.2 Introduction to Hydrocarbons
Figure 24.3 Bonds about Carbon in Methane	24.2 Introduction to Hydrocarbons
Figure 24.4 Rotation about a C–C Bond Occurs Easily and Rapidly in All Alkanes	24.2 Introduction to Hydrocarbons
Table 24.4 Condensed Structural Formulas and Common Names for Several Alkyl Groups	24.2 Introduction to Hydrocarbons
Figure 24.8 Geometric Isomers Exist Because Rotation about a Carbon-Carbon Double Bond Requires Too Much Energy	24.3 Alkenes, Alkynes, and Aromatic Hydrocarbons
Figure 24.15 The Two Enantiomeric Forms of 2-Bromopentane	24.5 Chirality in Organic Chemistry
Figure 24.18 The 20 Amino Acids Found in the Human Body	24.7 Proteins
Figure 24.20 The Structure of Proteins	24.7 Proteins
Figure 24.21 Linear Structure of the Carbohydrates Glucose and Fructose	24.8 Carbohydrates
Figure 24.22 Cyclic Glucose Has an α Form and a β Form	24.8 Carbohydrates
Figure 24.24 Structures of Starch and Cellulose	24.8 Carbohydrates
Figure 24.28 A Nucleotide	24.10 Nucleic Acids
Figure 24.31 Hydrogen Bonding Between Complementary Bases	24.10 Nucleic Acids

Activities:

	Section:
Boiling Point	24.2 Introduction to Hydrocarbons
Condensed Structural Formula	24.2 Introduction to Hydrocarbons
Nomenclature of Alkanes	24.2 Introduction to Hydrocarbons
Addition Reactions of Alkenes	24.3 Alkenes, Alkynes, and Aromatic Hydrocarbons

Animations:

	Section:
Surface Reaction-Hydrogenation	24.3 Alkenes, Alkynes, and Aromatic Hydrocarbons
Chirality	24.5 Chirality in Organic Chemistry
Optical Activity	24.5 Chirality in Organic Chemistry
Proteins and Amino Acids	24.7 Proteins

Movies:

	Section:
Testing for Unsaturated Hydrocarbons with Bromine	24.3 Alkenes, Alkynes, and Aromatic Hydrocarbons

3-D Models:

Section:

Methane — 24.1 General Characteristics of Organic Molecules
Acetonitrile — 24.1 General Characteristics of Organic Molecules
Glucose — 24.1 General Characteristics of Organic Molecules
Sodium Stearate — 24.1 General Characteristics of Organic Molecules
Ethane — 24.2 Introduction to Hydrocarbons
Chloromethane — 24.2 Introduction to Hydrocarbons
Ethene (ethylene) — 24.2 Introduction to Hydrocarbons
Ethyne (acetylene) — 24.2 Introduction to Hydrocarbons
Benzene — 24.2 Introduction to Hydrocarbons
Propane — 24.2 Introduction to Hydrocarbons
Butane — 24.2 Introduction to Hydrocarbons
Methylpropane (isobutane) — 24.2 Introduction to Hydrocarbons
Pentane — 24.2 Introduction to Hydrocarbons
Neopentane (dimethylpropane) — 24.2 Introduction to Hydrocarbons
Trans-2-butene — 24.3 Alkenes, Alkynes, and Aromatic Hydrocarbons

Hydrogen Chloride — 24.3 Alkenes, Alkynes, and Aromatic Hydrocarbons

Methanol — 24.4 Organic Functional Groups
Ethanamine (ethylamine) — 24.4 Organic Functional Groups
Ethanal (acetaldehyde) — 24.4 Organic Functional Groups
Propanone (acetone) — 24.4 Organic Functional Groups
Ethanoic Acid (acetic acid) — 24.4 Organic Functional Groups
Ethyl Ethanoate (ethyl acetate) — 24.4 Organic Functional Groups
Ethanamide (acetamide) — 24.4 Organic Functional Groups
2-chlorobutane — 24.5 Chirality in Organic Chemistry
2-bromopentane — 24.5 Chirality in Organic Chemistry
Albuterol — 24.5 Chirality in Organic Chemistry
Ibuprofen — 24.5 Chirality in Organic Chemistry
Phenylalanine — 24.7 Proteins
Lactose — 24.8 Carbohydrates
Glycerophospholipid (lecithin) — 24.10 Nucleic Acids
Guanine — 24.10 Nucleic Acids

Other Resources

Further Readings:

Section:

Alkanes: Abundant, Pervasive, Important, and Essential — 24.2 Introduction to Hydrocarbons

The IUPAC Rules for Naming Organic Molecules — 24.2 Introduction to Hydrocarbons
Why Is 'R' Used to Symbolize Hydrocarbon Substituents? — 24.2 Introduction to Hydrocarbons

A Simple Method of Drawing Stereoisomers from Complicated Symmetrical Structures — 24.2 Introduction to Hydrocarbons

The Origins of Ortho-, Meta-, and Para- Prefixes in Chemical Nomenclature — 24.3 Alkenes, Alkynes and Aromatic Hydrocarbons
Ester, What's in My Food? — 24.4 Organic Functional Groups
A Miracle Drug — 24.4 Organic Functional Groups
Trans Fatty Acids — 24.4 Organic Functional Groups

Icie Macy Hoobler: Pioneer Woman Biochemist — 24.6 Introduction to Biochemistry
Why Teach Biochemistry? — 24.6 Introduction to Biochemistry
Chemistry of Dyeing of Eggs — 24.7 Proteins
Reversible Oxygenation of Oxygen Transport Proteins — 24.7 Proteins
How Life Lost Its Symmetry — 24.7 Proteins
An Easy Way to Convert a Fischer Projection into a Zigzag Representation — 24.8 Carbohydrates
The Use of Stick Figures to Visualize Fischer Projections — 24.8 Carbohydrates
A New Method to Convert the Fischer Projection of Monosaccharide to the Haworth Projection — 24.8 Carbohydrates
Carbohydrate Stereochemistry — 24.8 Carbohydrates
'Absolutely' Simple Stereochemistry — 24.8 Carbohydrates
The Biochemistry of Brewing — 24.8 Carbohydrates
βrαnd the Name with the Linkage of the Same — 24.8 Carbohydrates
Rosalind Franklin: From Coal to DNA to Plant Viruses — 24.10 Nucleic Acids
DNAmonic — 24.10 Nucleic Acids
A Simple Demonstration of How Intermolecular Forces Make DNA Helical — 24.10 Nucleic Acids
The DNA Story — 24.10 Nucleic Acids
Meeting the Matchmaker — 24.10 Nucleic Acids

Live Demonstrations: — **Section:**

Oxidation of Alcohol by Mn_2O_7 — 24.4 Organic Functional Groups
The Disappearing Coffee Cup — 24.4 Organic Functional Groups
Making Canned Heat — 24.4 Organic Functional Groups
The World's First 'Pastarimeter': An Analogous Demonstration of Polarimetry Using Pasta *Fusilli* — 24.5 Chirality in Organic Chemistry
Demonstration of Enantiomer Specificity of Proteins and Drugs — 24.5 Chirality in Organic Chemistry
A Variation of the Starch-Iodine Clock Reaction — 24.8 Carbohydrates

Chapter 24. The Chemistry of Life: Organic and Biological Chemistry

Common Student Misconceptions
- Students will often find the distinction between organic and inorganic molecules as somewhat vague. As a rule of thumb, inorganic carbon is carbon that is *not* bound to hydrogen, for example, H_2CO_3.
- Students interpret straight chain to mean geometrically linear. They need to be reminded of the tetrahedral C atom from VSEPR theory.
- Students often think that chirality is only possible for organic compounds, and that chiral centers are limited to C atoms.
- Many students think that one cannot have aqueous reactions involving organic compounds.
- Students are surprised that, in organic chemistry, acid-base reactions are more often viewed as an electron pair transfer from a Lewis base to a Lewis acid instead of a proton transfer from a B-L acid to a B-L base.
- Students are surprised that the –OH (hydroxyl) group in organic chemistry is not the same as the OH^- ion in ionic compounds, such as metal hydroxides.

Teaching Tips
- Students should be encouraged to follow the chapter links to review earlier material as they progress through this chapter.
- In particular, students should review Lewis structures as well as Lewis acids and bases.
- Students should be encouraged to draw and re-draw structures of organic compounds.

Lecture Outline

24.1 General Characteristics of Organic Molecules
- **Organic chemistry** is the branch of chemistry that studies carbon compounds.
- **Biochemistry**, *biological chemistry, or chemical biology* is the study of the chemistry of living things.

The Structures of Organic Molecules[1,2,3]
- The shapes of organic and biochemical molecules are important in determining their physical and chemical properties.
- Consider the element carbon:
  - Using the VSEPR model we find that the bonds to carbon involve four electron pairs.
    - The electron pairs are in a tetrahedral arrangement when all four bonds are single bonds.
      - The carbon is sp^3 hybridized.
    - A carbon with one double bond shows a trigonal arrangement.
      - The carbon is sp^2 hybridized.
    - If the carbon has a triple bond, the arrangement is linear.
      - The carbon is sp hybridized.
- C–H bonds occur in almost every organic molecule.

---

[1] "Methane" 3-D Model from Instructor's Resource CD/DVD
[2] "Acetonitrile" 3-D Model from Instructor's Resource CD/DVD
[3] Figure 24.1 from Transparency Pack

- Carbon-carbon bonds for the *backbone* or *skeleton* of the molecule and the H atoms are on the *surface* of the molecule.

The Stabilities of Organic Substances

- The stability of organic substances varies.
- Substances such as benzene have a special stability due to the delocalization of π electrons.
- A group of atoms that determines how an organic molecule functions or reacts is a **functional group**.
  - Functional groups are the center of reactivity in organic molecules.
    - This group of atoms determines how an organic molecule reacts or *functions*.

Solubility and Acid-Base Properties of Organic Substances[4,5]

- The most common bonds in organic substances are carbon-carbon bonds.
  - This results in a low overall polarity of many organic molecules.
    - Such molecules are soluble in nonpolar solvents.
- Organic substances that are soluble in water and other polar solvents have polar groups.
  - Examples: glucose and ascorbic acid (vitamin C).
- Soaps and detergents are examples of molecules that have both a polar part (which is water soluble) and a nonpolar part (which is soluble in nonpolar substances such as fat).
  - They function as *surfactants*.
- Many organic molecules contain acidic or basic groups.
  - Carboxylic acids contain the functional group –COOH.
  - Amines are important organic bases.
    - They contain the functional groups $-NH_2$, –NHR, or $-NR_2$.
    - "R" groups are groups consisting of carbon-carbon and carbon-hydrogen bonds.
- Some molecules contain both an acidic and a basic group.

24.2 Introduction to Hydrocarbons[6,7,8,9,10,11,12,13]

- The simplest class of organic molecules is the *hydrocarbons*.
  - Hydrocarbons consist only of carbon and hydrogen.
  - There are four major classes of hydrocarbons: alkanes, alkenes, alkynes, and aromatics.
- **Alkanes** contain only single bonds.
  - These compounds are also called *saturated hydrocarbons* because they have the largest possible number of hydrogen atoms per carbon.
  - An example is ethane (C_2H_6).
- **Alkenes** contain at least one carbon-carbon double bond.
  - They are also called *olefins*.
  - An example is ethylene (C_2H_4).
- **Alkynes** contain a carbon-carbon triple bond.
  - An example is acetylene (C_2H_2).

---

[4] "Glucose" 3-D Model from Instructor's Resource CD/DVD
[5] "Sodium Stearate" 3-D Model from Instructor's Resource CD/DVD
[6] Table 24.1 from Transparency Pack
[7] "Ethane" 3-D Model from Instructor's Resource CD/DVD
[8] "Propane" 3-D Model from Instructor's Resource CD/DVD
[9] "Ethene (ethylene)" 3-D Model from Instructor's Resource CD/DVD
[10] "Ethyne (acetylene)" 3-D Model from Instructor's Resource CD/DVD
[11] "Benzene" 3-D Model from Instructor's Resource CD/DVD
[12] "Boiling Point" Activity from Instructor's Resource CD/DVD
[13] "Alkanes: Abundant, Pervasive, Important, and Essential" from Further Readings

- **Aromatic hydrocarbons** have carbon atoms connected in a planar ring structure.
  - The carbons are linked by both σ and π bonds.
  - The best known example is benzene (C_6H_6).
- Alkenes, alkynes, and aromatic hydrocarbons are all examples of *unsaturated hydrocarbons*.
- The name of the alkane varies according to the number of C atoms present in the chain.
- We can make a table of members of a homologous series of straight-chain alkanes.
  - In this table, each member differs by one CH_2 unit.
  - The names each end in -ane.
  - The prefix assigned indicates the number of carbon atoms.
    - Example: CH_4 is the alkane with a single carbon atom; it is called *meth*ane.
    - The next member of the series is C_2H_6, with two carbon atoms; it is called *eth*ane.
- The formulas for alkanes may be written in a notation called *condensed structural formulas*.
  - This notation shows which atoms are bonded to one another, but does not require that we draw in all of the bonds.
  - Notice that each carbon in an alkane has four single bonds.

Structures of Alkanes[14]

- VSEPR theory predicts each C atom is tetrahedral.
  - Therefore, each C atom has sp^3-hybridized orbitals.
  - Rotation about the C–C bond in alkanes is relatively easy.

Structural Isomers[15,16,17,18,19]

- In *straight-chain hydrocarbons,* the C atoms are joined in a continuous chain.
  - In a straight-chain hydrocarbon, no one C atom may be attached to more than two other C atoms.
  - Straight chain hydrocarbons are not linear.
    - Each C atom is tetrahedral, so the chains are bent.
- *Branched-chain hydrocarbons* are possible for alkanes with four or more C atoms.
  - Structures with different branches can be written for the same formula.
    - **Structural isomers** are compounds with the same molecular formula but different bonding arrangements.
    - Structural isomers have somewhat different physical and chemical properties.

Nomenclature of Alkanes[20,21,22,23,24,25]

- Organic compounds are named according to rules established by the International Union for Pure and Applied Chemistry (IUPAC).
- To name alkanes:
  - Find the longest chain and use it as the base name of the compound.

---

[14] Figure 24.3 from Transparency Pack
[15] Figure 24.4 from Transparency Pack
[16] "Butane" 3-D Model from Instructor's Resource CD/DVD
[17] "Methylpropane (isobutane)" 3-D Model from Instructor's Resource CD/DVD
[18] "Pentane" 3-D Model from Instructor's Resource CD/DVD
[19] "Neopentane (dimethylpropane)" 3-D Model from Instructor's Resource CD/DVD
[20] "Nomenclature of Alkanes" Activity from Instructor's Resource CD/DVD
[21] Table 24.4 from Transparency Pack
[22] "The IUPAC Rules for Naming Organic Molecules" from Further Readings
[23] "Why is 'R' Used to Symbolize Hydrocarbon Substituents?" from Further Readings
[24] "A Simple Method of Drawing Stereoisomers from Complicated Symmetrical Structures" from Further Readings
[25] "Condensed Structural Formula" Activity from Instructor's Resource CD/DVD

- Groups attached to the main chain are called *substituents*.
- Number the carbon atoms in the longest chain starting with the end closest to a substituent.
  - The preferred numbering will give substituents the lowest numbers.
- Name and give the location of each substituent.
  - A substituent group formed by removing an H atom from an alkane is called an **alkyl group**.
  - Alkyl groups are named by replacing the *–ane* ending with *-yl*.
    - Example: CH_4 is meth*ane* and a $–CH_3$ group is a meth*yl* group.
- When two or more substituents are present, list them in alphabetical order.
  - When there are two or more of the same substituent, the number of that type of substituent is indicated by a prefix: (i.e., "dimethyl" indicates two methyl group substituents).

Cycloalkanes

- Alkanes that form rings are called **cycloalkanes**.
- Cyclopropane and cyclobutane are strained because the C–C–C bond angles in the ring are less than the 109.5° required for a tetrahedral geometry.
  - Because of the strain in the ring, cyclopropane is very reactive.

Reactions with Alkanes[26]

- The C–C and C–H bonds are very strong.
  - Therefore, alkanes are very unreactive.
- At room temperature alkanes, do not react with acids, bases, or strong oxidizing agents.
- Alkanes do undergo *combustion* in air (making them good fuels):
$$2C_2H_6(g) + 7O_2(g) \rightarrow 4CO_2(g) + 6H_2O(l) \qquad \Delta H = -2855 \text{ kJ}$$

24.3 Alkenes, Alkynes, and Aromatic Hydrocarbons

- Alkanes contain the largest possible number of hydrogen atoms per carbon atom; they are called *saturated hydrocarbons*.
- Alkenes, alkynes, and aromatic hydrocarbons contain less hydrogens than an alkane with the same number of carbon atoms.
  - They are called *unsaturated hydrocarbons*.
  - They tend to be more reactive than unsaturated hydrocarbons.

Alkenes[27]

- Alkenes are unsaturated hydrocarbons that contain C and H atoms and at least one C-C double bond.
- The simplest alkenes are $H_2C=CH_2$ (ethene) and $CH_3CH=CH_2$ (propene).
  - Their common names are ethylene and propylene.
- Alkenes are named in the same way as alkanes with the suffix *-ene* replacing the *-ane* in alkanes.
  - The location of the double bond is indicated by a number.
  - If a substance has two or more double bonds, the number of double bonds is indicated with a prefix .
- **Geometric isomers** are possible in alkenes since there is no rotation about a C=C π bond.
  - Note that the overlap between orbitals is above and below the plane of the σ bonds.
  - As the C–C bond begins to rotate (moving from *cis* to *trans*) the overlap decreases.
  - At 90°, the π bond breaks completely.
    - Therefore, there is no "free" rotation about a π bond.
  - Therefore, *cis* and *trans* isomers do not readily interconvert.

Alkynes

- Alkynes are hydrocarbons with one or more C≡C bond.

---

[26] "Chloromethane" 3-D Model from Instructor's Resource CD/DVD
[27] "*Trans*-2-butene" 3-D Model from Instructor's Resource CD/DVD

- The triple bond has one σ and two π bonds between two C atoms.
- Ethyne (acetylene) is the simplest alkyne: HC≡CH.
- Alkynes are named in the same way as alkenes with the suffix *-yne* replacing the *-ene* for alkenes.

Addition Reactions of Alkenes and Alkynes[28,29,30,31,32]

- The dominant reactions for alkenes and alkynes are **addition reactions**.
  - They involve the addition of something to the two atoms that form the double or triple bond.
    - Example: The addition of a halogen (bromine) to ethylene:
      $$H_2C{=}CH_2 + Br_2 \rightarrow H_2BrC{-}CBrH_2$$
    - Note that the C–C π bond has been replaced by two C–Br σ bonds.
  - A common addition reaction is *hydrogenation*:
    $$CH_3CH{=}CHCH_3 + H_2 \rightarrow CH_3CH_2CH_2CH_3$$
    - Hydrogenation requires high temperatures and pressures as well as the presence of a catalyst (e.g., finely divided metals such as Ni, Pt, Pd).
    - Note that the alkene is converted to an alkane.
  - Another common addition reaction involves the addition of hydrogen halides or water across the π bond:
    $$CH_2{=}CH_2 + HBr \rightarrow CH_3CH_2Br$$
    $$CH_2{=}CH_2 + H_2O \rightarrow CH_3CH_2OH$$
- Alkynes are also capable of addition reactions.

Aromatic Hydrocarbons[33]

- Aromatic structures are formally related to benzene (C_6H_6).
  - Many aromatic compounds are given common names (e.g., naphthalene, toluene, anthracene).

Stabilization of π Electrons by Delocalization

- Benzene is a planar symmetrical molecule.
- The delocalized π electrons are usually represented as a circle in the center of the ring.

Substitution Reactions

- Benzene is not reactive because of the stability associated with the delocalized π electrons.
- Even though they contain π bonds, aromatic hydrocarbons undergo **substitution reactions** more readily than addition reactions.
  - In a substitution reaction, one atom of a molecule is removed and replaced or substituted by another atom or group of atoms.
  - Example: If benzene is treated with nitric acid in the presence of sulfuric acid (catalyst), nitrobenzene is produced.
    - Under some conditions, more than one nitro group may be added to the benzene.
    - If two nitro groups are added, three possible isomers may be formed: *-ortho*, *-meta*, and *–para*-dinitrobenzene.
  - Another type of substitution reaction is a *Friedel-Crafts reaction* in which alkyl groups can be substituted onto an aromatic ring by reaction with an alkyl halide in the presence of aluminum chloride (catalyst).

---

[28] "Addition Reactions of Alkenes" Activity from Instructor's Resource CD/DVD
[29] "Surface Reaction-Hydrogenation" Animation from Instructor's Resource CD/DVD
[30] "Testing for Unsaturated Hydrocarbons with Bromine" Movie from Instructor's Resource CD/DVD
[31] Figure 24.8 from Transparency Pack
[32] "Hydrogen Chloride" 3-D Model from Instructor's Resource CD/DVD
[33] "The Origins of the Ortho-, Meta-, and Para- Prefixes in Chemical Nomenclature" from Further Readings

24.4 Organic Functional Groups

- Hydrocarbons are relatively unreactive.
- For an organic molecule to be reactive it needs something additional.
- A site of reactivity in an organic molecule is called a *functional group*. Functional groups determine the chemistry of a molecule.
- The simplest functional groups are π electrons.
  - C=C double bonds and C≡C triple bonds are functional groups.
- Other functional groups contain elements other than C or H.
- Chemists usually use R, R', R", etc., to represent alkyl groups.

Alcohols[34,35]

- **Alcohols** are derived from hydrocarbons and contain –OH (*hydroxyl* or *alcohol*) groups.
- The names are derived from the hydrocarbon name with *-ol* replacing the *-ane* suffix.
  - Example: eth*ane* becomes ethan*ol*.
- Because the O–H bond is polar and can participate in hydrogen bonding, alcohols are more water soluble than alkanes.
- Consider the properties of some representative alcohols:
  - CH_3OH, methanol, is used as a gasoline additive and a fuel.
    - Methanol is produced by the reaction of CO with hydrogen under high pressure and high temperature:
$$CO(g) + 2H_2(g) \rightarrow CH_3OH(g)$$
  - Ethanol is produced by the fermentation of carbohydrates.
    - Ethanol is the alcohol found in alcoholic beverages.
  - Polyhydroxy alcohols (polyols) contain more than one –OH group per molecule (e.g., ethylene glycol used as antifreeze).
  - Aromatic alcohols can also be formed (e.g., phenol).
    - Note that aromatic alcohols are weak acids.
  - Cholesterol is a physiologically important alcohol.

Ethers

- Compounds in which two hydrocarbons are linked by an oxygen are called **ethers**.
- Ethers can be formed by a dehydration reaction:
$$CH_3CH_2-OH + H-OCH_2CH_3 \rightarrow CH_3CH_2-O-CH_2CH_3 + H_2O$$
  - This *condensation reaction* involves the removal of a water molecule from two molecules of alcohol.
- Ethers are commonly used as solvents.
  - Common examples are diethyl ether and tetrahydrofuran (a cyclic ether).

Aldehydes and Ketones[36,37,38]

- The **carbonyl group** is C=O.
- The carbonyl group plus the type of atoms attached to the carbonyl carbon defines the particular kind of compound.
- **Aldehydes** must have at least one H atom attached to the carbonyl C:
  R–CHO
- **Ketones** must have two C atoms attached to the carbonyl C:

---

[34] "Oxidation of Alcohol by Mn_2O_7" from Live Demonstrations
[35] "Methanol" 3-D Model from Instructor's Resource CD/DVD
[36] "The Disappearing Coffee Cup" from Live Demonstrations
[37] "Ethanal (acetaldehyde)" 3-D Model from Instructor's Resource CD/DVD
[38] "Propanone (acetone)" 3-D Model from Instructor's Resource CD/DVD

R–COR'
- Aldehydes and ketones are prepared by the oxidation of alcohols.
- Ketones are less reactive than aldehydes and are used as solvents.
  - Two common examples of ketones are acetone and methyl ethyl ketone (MEK).
- Other examples of molecules that contain aldehydes or ketones are vanilla and cinnamon flavorings. The ketones carvone and camphor are responsible for the flavors of spearmint and caraway, respectively.

Carboxylic Acids and Esters[39,40,41,42,43,44]
- **Carboxylic acids** contain a carbonyl group with an –OH attached.
- The *carboxyl* functional group is –COOH:

R–COOH
- Common names of carboxylic acids reflect their origins (e.g., formic acid was first extracted from ants, the Latin *formica* means "ant").
- Carboxylic acids are generally weak acids.
  - Typical carboxylic acids are found in spinach (oxalic acid), vinegar (acetic acid), vitamin C (ascorbic acid), aspirin (acetylsalicylic acid), and citrus fruits (citric acid).
- Carboxylic acids can be prepared by oxidizing alcohols that contain a –CH_2OH group.
  - Example: Oxidation of ethanol (CH_3CH_2OH) to acetic acid (CH_3COOH) is responsible for the souring of wines.
- Acetic acid can be prepared by reacting methanol with CO in the presence of a catalyst.
  - This kind of reaction is called *carbonylation*.
- **Esters** can be prepared by condensation reactions involving a carboxylic acid and an alcohol; the products are the ester and water.
- Esters contain –COOR groups:

R–COOR'
- Esters are named using the alcohol part first and then the acid part.
  - Example: The ester formed from ethanol and acetic acid is ethyl acetate.
- Esters tend to have very pleasant characteristic odors and are often used as food flavorings and scents.
  - Some common esters are benzocaine (used in some sunburn lotions), ethyl acetate (a component of some nail polish removers), vegetable oils, polyester thread, and aspirin.
- In the presence of a base, esters hydrolyze (the molecule splits into acid and alcohol).
  - **Saponification** is the **hydrolysis** of an ester in the presence of a base.
  - This process is used in the production of soaps from animal fats or vegetable oils.
    - Soap is made by heating fats or oils in a strong base (NaOH).
      - The long-chain carboxylic acid and alcohol components of the fats are released.
      - The soap made from this process consists of sodium salts of the long-chain carboxylic acids called fatty acids.
      - Using potassium hydroxide produces soft or liquid soaps.

Amines and Amides[45,46]
- *Amines* are organic bases.

---

[39] "A Miracle Drug" from Further Readings
[40] "Ester, What's in My Food?" from Further Readings
[41] "Making Canned Heat" from Live Demonstrations
[42] "Trans Fatty Acids" from Further Readings
[43] "Ethanoic Acid (acetic acid)" 3-D Model from Instructor's Resource CD/DVD
[44] "Ethyl Ethanoate (ethyl acetate)" 3-D Model from Instructor's Resource CD/DVD
[45] "Ethanamine (ethylamine)" 3-D Model from Instructor's Resource CD/DVD
[46] "Ethanamide" 3-D Model from Instructor's Resource CD/DVD

- Just as alcohols can be thought of as organic forms of water, amines can be thought of organic forms of ammonia.
  - They have the general formula R_3N where R may be either H or a hydrocarbon group.
    - Examples of organic amines are ethylamine ($CH_3CH_2NH_2$), triethylamine [$(CH_3)_3N$], and aniline ($C_6H_5–NH_2$).
- Amides are composites of carbonyl and amine functionalities.

24.5 Chirality in Organic Chemistry[47,48,49,50,51,52,53,54,55]

- Recall that molecules whose mirror images are nonsuperimposable are **chiral.**
  - Compounds containing carbon atoms with four different attached groups are inherently chiral.
- Chemists use the labels *R*– and *S*– to distinguish between these *enantiomers*.
  - The physical properties of enantiomers are generally identical.
  - Enantiomers have identical chemical properties if the molecules are reacting with reagents that are nonchiral.
    - Enantiomers exhibit different chemical properties in a chiral environment.
- A mixture of two enantiomers present in the same quantity is called a *racemic* mixture.
- Some molecules have more than one chiral center.
  - Examples include tartaric acid (found as crystalline deposits in wine) and some of the amino acids found in proteins.

24.6 Introduction of Biochemistry[56,57]

- The biosphere is the part of the Earth containing living organisms.
- Biochemical molecules tend to be very large and difficult to synthesize.
- Organisms build biochemical molecules from the smaller molecules available in the biosphere.
- Living organisms are highly ordered.
  - Therefore, living organisms have very low entropy.
  - Living systems must continually resist the tendency to become less ordered!
- Many biologically important molecules are polymers, called **biopolymers.**
- Biopolymers fall into three broad classes:
  - proteins,
  - polysaccharides (carbohydrates), and
  - nucleic acids.

24.7 Proteins

Amino Acids[58,59]

---

[47] "The World's First 'Pastarimeter': An Analogous Demonstration of Polarimetry Using Pasta *Fusilli*" from Live Demonstrations

[48] "Chirality" Animation from Instructor's Resource CD/DVD

[49] Figure 24.15 from Transparency Pack

[50] "Optical Activity" Animation from Instructor's Resource CD/DVD

[51] "Demonstration of Enantiomer Specificity of Proteins and Drugs" from Live Demonstrations

[52] "2-chlorobutane" 3-D Model from Instructor's Resource CD/DVD

[53] "2-bromopentane" 3-D Model from Instructor's Resource CD/DVD

[54] "Albuterol" 3-D Model from Instructor's Resource CD/DVD

[55] "Ibuprofen" 3-D Model from Instructor's Resource CD/DVD

[56] "Icie Macy Hoobler: Pioneer Woman Biochemist" from Further Readings

[57] "Why Teach Biochemistry?" from Further Readings

[58] "Proteins and Amino Acids" Animation from Instructor's Resource CD/DVD

- **Proteins** are macromolecules present in all cells.
- They are made up of building blocks called α-**amino acids**.
- At normal physiological pH, amino acids are present in aqueous solution as the doubly ionized forms called *zwitterions*.
  - A zwitterion has both positive and negative charges in one molecule.
    - The carboxyl group is deprotonated ($-COO^-$) and the amino group is protonated ($-NH_3^+$).
- There are 20 different amino acids that are used to synthesize proteins in biological systems.
  - These amino acids differ with respect to the nature of the R-group attached to their α-carbon.
  - Our bodies can synthesize ten of these amino acids in quantities sufficient to meet our needs.
  - The other ten amino acids must be ingested; these are called *essential amino acids*.
- The α-carbon in all amino acids, except glycine, is chiral (has four different groups attached to it).
- The two enantiomeric forms of amino acids are often called *D*- and *L*-amino acids.
  - *L*-amino acids are used to synthesize proteins in living organisms.

Polypeptides and Proteins[60,61]

- Proteins are polyamides.
- When formed from amino acids, each amide group is called a **peptide bond**.
- Peptides are formed by condensation of the –COOH group of one amino acid with the $-NH_2$ group of another amino acid.
- The acid involved in the peptide bond is named first.
  - Example: If a dipeptide is formed from alanine and glycine so that the –COOH group of glycine reacts with the $-NH_2$ group of alanine, then the dipeptide is called *glycylalanine*.
  - Glycylalanine is abbreviated using a standard three-letter abbreviation for each amino acid, starting with the amino acid with the unreacted amino group.
    - Thus glycylalanine is abbreviated as gly-ala.
- **Polypeptides** are formed when a large number of amino acids are linked together by peptide bonds.
  - Proteins are polypeptides with molecular weights between 6000 and 50 million amu.

Protein Structure[62,63,64]

- The arrangement or sequence of amino acids along a protein chain is called the protein's **primary structure** or primary sequence.
  - A change in one amino acid can alter the biochemical behavior of the protein.
    - An example of such a change is found in the disease sickle-cell anemia.
    - This disease results from a single amino acid substitution on two of the subunits of hemoglobin.
- **Secondary structure** refers to the regular arrangement of segments of the protein chain.
  - One common secondary structure is the α-**helix**.
    - In an α-helix, hydrogen bonds between N–H groups and carbonyl groups hold the helix in place.
    - The pitch (distance between coils) and diameter ensure that no bond angles are strained and the N–H and carbonyl functional groups are optimized for H–bonding.
  - Another common secondary structure is the β-pleated sheet.
- Proteins are not biologically active until they are in a particular shape.
  - The process by which the protein adopts its biologically active shape is called **folding**.

---

[59] Figure 24.18 from Transparency Pack
[60] "Chemistry in the Dyeing of Eggs: from Further Readings
[61] "Phenylalanine" 3-D Model from Instructor's Resource CD/DVD
[62] Figure 24.20 from Transparency Pack
[63] "Reversible Oxygenation of Oxygen Transport Proteins" from Further Readings
[64] "How Life Lost Its Symmetry" from Further Readings

- **Tertiary structure** is the three-dimensional structure of the protein.
- There are two broad categories of tertiary structure:
  - *Globular proteins*: proteins that fold into a compact, roughly spherical shape, are soluble in water and mobile in cells.
    - Globular proteins generally have nonstructural functions (e.g., enzymes).
  - *Fibrous proteins*: proteins that often feature long coils that align themselves in a fairly parallel fashion to give rise to water-insoluble fibers.
    - Fibrous proteins often play structural roles (e.g., components of hair, muscle, tendons).
- The tertiary structure is stabilized by a variety of interactions.
  - In general, polar groups on the protein tend to be found on the surface of the protein while nonpolar groups tend to be tucked away within the molecule, away from the aqueous environment.
  - The polar groups interact with solvent and other polar molecules through ion-dipole, dipole-dipole or hydrogen bonding interactions.
- Some proteins are assemblies of more than one polypeptide chain.
  - Each chain or subunit has its own tertiary structure.
  - **Quaternary structure** refers to the arrangement of the subunits.

24.8 Carbohydrates[65,66,67,68,69,70,71]

- **Carbohydrates** have the empirical formula $C_x(H_2O)_y$.
  - Carbohydrate means "hydrate of carbon."
  - The most abundant carbohydrate is **glucose**, $C_6H_{12}O_6$.
- Carbohydrates are polyhydroxy aldehydes and ketones.
  - Glucose is a six-carbon aldehyde sugar (aldose); *fructose* is a six-carbon ketone sugar (ketose).
  - One of the alcohol groups of glucose can react with the aldehyde group to form a six-membered ring.
  - Most glucose molecules are present in the ring form.
    - Note that the six-membered rings are not planar.
  - Depending on how the ring forms, we can have one of two different isomers.
    - Consider the groups on carbons 1 and 5:
      - If the –CH$_2$OH group on carbon 5 and the –OH group on carbon 1 are on opposite sides of the ring, then we have the α form of glucose (α-anomer).
      - If they are on the same side of the ring, then we have β form of glucose (β-anomer).
  - The α- and β- forms of glucose are very different compounds.
    - Although these differences may seem trivial, they are not.
    - For example, the difference between these two forms is the key to the difference in the structures of starch and cellulose.

[65] Figure 24.21 from Transparency Pack
[66] "An Easy Way to Convert a Fischer Projection into a Zigzag Representation" from Further Readings
[67] Figure 24.22 from Transparency Pack
[68] "The Use of Stick Figures to Visualize Fischer Projections" from Further Readings
[69] "Carbohydrate Stereochemistry" from Further Readings
[70] "A New Method to Convert the Fischer Projection of Monosaccharide to the Haworth Projection" from Further Readings
[71] "'Absolutely' Simple Stereochemistry" from Further Readings

Disaccharides[72,73]

- Glucose and fructose are **monosaccharides,** simple sugars that cannot be broken down by hydrolysis with aqueous acids.
- **Disaccharides** are sugars formed by the condensation of two monosaccharides.
  - Examples are:
    - sucrose (table sugar), which is formed by the condensation of glucose and fructose.
    - lactose (milk sugar), which is formed by the condensation of galactose and glucose.
  - Sucrose is about six times sweeter than lactose, a little sweeter than glucose, and about half as sweet as fructose.
- Disaccharides can be converted into monosaccharides by treatment with acid in aqueous solution.
  - For example, when sucrose is hydrolyzed, it gives rise to a mixture of fructose and glucose, called *invert sugar*.

Polysaccharides[74,75,76]

- **Polysaccharides** are formed by condensation of several monosaccharide units.
- There are many different types.
  - Examples of polysaccharides based on glucose are starch, glycogen, and cellulose.
- The term **starch** refers to a group of polysaccharides found in plants (e.g., corn, potatoes, wheat, rice).
  - Starch consists of many glucose units joined by linkages of the α form.
  - Humans are capable of digesting starch; it is enzymatically hydrolyzed to glucose during digestion.
- **Glycogen** is a starch-like polysaccharide synthesized by muscle and liver tissues.
  - In the muscle, glycogen is an important source of quick energy.
  - In the liver, glycogen represents a storage form of glucose for the body.
    - The liver is also maintains the body's blood glucose concentration.
- **Cellulose** is a polysaccharide that is the major structural unit of plants.
  - For example, wood is approximately 50% cellulose.
  - Cellulose consists of glucose units, however, unlike starch, the glucose units present are linked in the β form.
    - Humans lack the enzymes required to hydrolyze cellulose.
    - Grazing animals such as cattle harbor bacteria in their digestive tract.
      - These bacteria have enzymes (cellulases) that hydrolyze cellulose.
      - The cattle are thus able to utilize the digested cellulose for food.

24.9 Lipids

- **Lipids** are another important class of biomolecule.
  - Lipids are used for energy storage (fats, oils) and as elements of biological structures such as cell membranes (phospholipids, cholesterol).
- Fats and oils are derived from glycerol and long-chain carboxylic acids called *fatty acids*.
  - Fats tend to be solid at room temperature and are enriched in saturated fatty acids.
    - Saturated fatty acids have R groups that are alkanes (no double bonds).
  - Oils tend to be liquid at room temperature and are enriched in unsaturated fatty acids.
    - Unsaturated fatty acids have R groups that are alkenes (at least one double bond).

[72] "The Biochemistry of Brewing" from Further Readings
[73] "Lactose" 3-D Model from Instructor's Resource CD/DVD
[74] "A Variation of the Starch-Iodine Clock Reaction" from Live Demonstrations
[75] Figure 24.24 from Transparency Pack
[76] "βrand the Name with the Linkage of the Same" from Further Readings

- *Trans* fatty acids have hydrogen atoms on the opposite side of the C=C double bond.
- *Cis* fatty acids have hydrogen atoms on the same side of the C=C double bond.
- Unsaturated fatty acids may have one or more C=C double bond.
  - For example, oleic acid has one C=C double bond in the chain.
    - It is a *monounsaturated* fatty acid.
  - *Polyunsaturated* fatty acids have more than one C=C double bond in the chain.
- Some fatty acids are essential nutrients.
  - Examples include omega-3 and omega-6 fatty acids.
    - The "omega" term refers to the last carbon in the chain (the carboxylic acid carbon is the first, or alpha, one).
- Glycerol **phospholipids** also contain glycerol and fatty acid components.
  - Their structure, however, also includes a charged phosphate-containing group linked to the glycerol.
  - In an aqueous environment, phospholipids cluster together with their charged polar head groups facing the water and their nonpolar tails facing inward.
    - Thus, phospholipids form bilayers that are key components of cellular membranes.

24.10 Nucleic Acids[77,78,79,80,81,82,83,84,85]

- **Nucleic acids** carry genetic information.
  - **DNA (deoxyribonucleic acids)** have molecular weights around $6 - 16 \times 10^6$ amu.
  - **RNA (ribonucleic acids)** have molecular weights around 20,000 to 40,000 amu.
- Nucleic acids are made up of monomers called **nucleotides**.
  - A nucleotides consist of three parts:
    - a five-carbon sugar
      - DNA and RNA have different sugars (*deoxy*ribose vs. ribose).
    - a nitrogen-containing organic base
      - Five bases are found in DNA and RNA:
        - adenine (A),
        - guanine (G),
        - cytosine (C),
        - thymine (T found in DNA only), and
        - uracil (U found in RNA only).
    - a phosphoric acid unit
- Nucleic acids form by the condensation of nucleotides (the phosphoric acid condenses with the O–H group of the sugar).
- DNA consists of two deoxyribonucleic acid strands wound together in a **double helix**.
  - The sugar-phosphate chains are wrapped around the outside of the DNA molecule.
  - Complementary base pairs are formed between bases on each chain.
    - The complementary base pairs are held together by London-dispersion forces and hydrogen bonding.

---

[77] "Rosalind Franklin: From Coal to DNA to Plant Viruses" from Further Readings
[78] Figure 24.28 from Transparency Pack
[79] Figure 24.31 from Transparency Pack
[80] "DNAmonic" from Further Readings
[81] "A Simple Demonstration of How Intermolecular Forces Make DNA Helical" from Further Readings
[82] "The DNA Story" from Further Readings
[83] "Meeting the Matchmaker" from Further Readings
[84] "Glycerophospholipid (lecithin)" 3-D Model from Instructor's Resource CD/DVD
[85] "Guanine" 3-D Model from Instructor's Resource CD/DVD

- The structures of T and A make them ideal hydrogen-bonding partners.
    - Two hydrogen bonds form between T and A.
  - The same is true for C and G.
    - Three hydrogen bonds form between C and G.
- During cell division, the DNA double helix unwinds.
  - Each strand serves as a template for the replication of a new strand.
  - Optimized hydrogen bonding helps to ensure that the correct bases are used along the new strand.
  - The newly synthesized DNA contains a sequence identical to that of the original molecule.
  - This allows genetic information to be preserved during cell division.

Further Readings:

1. Raymond B. Seymour, "Alkanes: Abundant, Pervasive, Important, and Essential," *J. Chem. Educ.*, Vol. 66, **1989**, 59–63.

2. Stanislaw Skonieczny, "The IUPAC Rules for Naming Organic Molecules," *J. Chem. Educ.*, Vol. 83, **2006**, 1633–1637.

3. William B. Jensen, "Why is 'R' Used to Symbolize Hydrocarbon Substituents?," *J. Chem. Educ.*, Vol. 87, **2010**, 360–361.

4. Arnaud Haudrechy, "A Simple Method of Drawing Stereoisomers from Complicated Symmetrical Structures," *J. Chem. Educ.*, Vol. 77, **2000**, 864–866.

5. William B. Jensen, "The Origins of the Ortho-, Meta-, and Para- Prefixes in Chemical Nomenclature," *J. Chem. Educ.*, Vol. 83, **2006**, 356.

6. Michele Clarke, Ann Brown, Dianne N. Epp, Mary Gallup, Jeffrey R. Wilson, and Judith A. Wuerthele, "Ester, What's in My Food?" *J. Chem. Educ.*, Vol. 63, **1986**, 1050–1051.

7. Sophie Jourdier, "A Miracle Drug," *Chemistry in Britain*, **February 1999**, 33–35. An article about the history of aspirin.

8. Ellin Doyle, "Trans Fatty Acids," *J. Chem. Educ.*, Vol. 74, **1997**, 1030–1032.

9. Sheldon J. Kopperl, "Icie Macy Hoobler: Pioneer Woman Biochemist," *J. Chem. Educ.*, Vol. 65, **1988**, 97–98.

10. Gil Downs, "Why Teach Biochemistry?" *J. Chem. Educ.*, Vol. 64, **1987**, 339.

11. Robert C. Mebane and Thomas R. Rybolt, "Chemistry in the Dyeing of Eggs," *J. Chem. Educ.*, Vol. 64, **1987**, 291–293.

12. C. M. Drain and Barry B. Corden, "Reversible Oxygenation of Oxygen Transport Proteins," *J. Chem. Educ.*, Vol. 64, **1987**, 441–443.

13. Sandra Signorella and Luis F. Sala, "An Easy Way to Convert a Fischer Projection into a Zigzag Representation," *J. Chem. Educ.*, Vol. 68, **1991**, 105–106.

14. Jon Evans, "How Life Lost Its Symmetry," *Chemistry World*, **April 2004**, 11.

15. Laurie S. Starkey, "The Use of Stick Figures to Visualize Fischer Projections," *J. Chem. Educ.*, Vol. 78, **2001**, 1486.

16. Qing-zhi Zhang and Shen-song Zhang, "A New Method to Convert the Fischer Projection of Monosaccharide to the Haworth Projection," *J. Chem. Educ.*, Vol. 76, **1999**, 799–801.

17. Robert S. Shallenberger and Wanda J. Wienen, "Carbohydrate Stereochemistry," *J. Chem. Educ.*, Vol. 66, **1989**, 67–73.

18. Philip S. Beauchamp, "'Absolutely' Simple Stereochemistry," *J. Chem. Educ.*, Vol. 61, **1984**, 666–667.

19. Charles L. Bering, "The Biochemistry of Brewing," *J. Chem. Educ.*, Vol. 65, **1988**, 519–521.

20. James M. Garrett, "βrand the Name with the Linkage of the Same," *J. Chem. Educ.*, Vol. 61, **1984**, 665. A mnemonic for remembering the configuration of the glucosidic linkage in disaccharides.

21. Maureen M. Julian, "Rosalind Franklin: From Coal to DNA to Plant Viruses," *J. Chem. Educ.*, Vol. 60, **1983**, 660–662.

22. A. B. Wolbarst, "DNAmonic," *J. Chem. Educ.*, Vol. 56, **1979**, 733. A mnemonic device for base-pairing in DNA is suggested: Pure Silver Taxi (purine: Ag; T=A, G=C).

23. Michael F. Bruist, Wayne L. Smith, and Galen Mell, "A Simple Demonstration of How Intermolecular Forces Make DNA Helical," *J. Chem. Educ.*, Vol. 75, **1998**, 53–55.

24. Susan Aldridge, "The DNA Story," *Chemistry in Britain*, **April 2003**, 28–30.

25. Jonathan Cox, "Meeting the Matchmaker," *Chemistry World*, **June 2004**, 50–55. An article about DNA fingerprinting.

Live Demonstrations:

1. Lee R. Summerlin and James L. Ealy, Jr., "Oxidation of Alcohol by Mn_2O_7," *Chemical Demonstrations, A Sourcebook for Teachers* (Washington: American Chemical Society, **1985**), pp. 103–104.

2. Lee. R. Summerlin,, Christie L. Borgford, and Julie B. Ealy, "The Disappearing Coffee Cup," *Chemical Demonstrations, A Sourcebook for Teachers, Volume 2* (Washington: American Chemical Society, **1988**), p. 96. A polystyrene coffee cup is "melted" in a pool of acetone.

3. Lee. R. Summerlin,, Christie L. Borgford, and Julie B. Ealy, "Making Canned Heat," *Chemical Demonstrations, A Sourcebook for Teachers, Volume 2* (Washington: American Chemical Society, **1988**), pp. 111–112. Saponification of stearic acid in the presence of alcohol is used to prepare a solid fuel--canned heat.

4. Claire Saxon, Scot Brindley, Nic Jervis, Graeme R. Jones, E. David Morgan, and Christopher A. Ramsden, "The World's First 'Pastarimeter': An Analogous Demonstration of Polarimetry using *Pasta Fusilli*," *J. Chem. Educ.*, Vol. 79, **2002**, 1214–1216.

5. Gretchen L. Anderson, "Demonstration of Enantiomer Specificity of Proteins and Drugs," *J. Chem. Educ.*, Vol. 81, **2004**, 971–974. A classroom exercise to illustrate the properties of enantiomers.

6. Lee R. Summerlin, Christie L. Borgford, and Julie B. Ealy, "A Variation of the Starch-Iodine Clock Reaction," *Chemical Demonstrations, A Sourcebook for Teachers, Volume 2* (Washington: American Chemical Society, **1987**), pp. 147–148.